W9-ADY-948

L.R. COLLE

DISCARDED

PROCEDURES
IN
NUCLEIC ACID
RESEARCH

PROCEDURES
IN
NUCLEIC ACID
RESEARCH

EDITED BY

G. L. Cantoni & David R. Davies

NATIONAL INSTITUTES OF HEALTH

Harper & Row, Publishers

NEW YORK AND LONDON

CARL A. RUDISILL LIBRARY
LENOIR RHYNE COLLEGE

QP
551
.P692
v 1

64190

December, 1968

Procedures in Nucleic Acid Research / Copyright © 1966
by G. L. Cantoni and David R. Davies. Printed in the
United States of America. All rights reserved. No part of
this book may be used or reproduced in any manner
whatsoever without written permission except in the case
of brief quotations embodied in critical articles and reviews. For information address Harper & Row, Publishers,
Incorporated, 49 East 33rd Street, New York, N.Y. 10016.

D-Q

LIBRARY OF CONGRESS CATALOG CARD NUMBER: 66–14165

Contributors

Numbers in brackets denote pages on which articles begin.

JOHN ABELSON. Department of Biophysics, The Johns Hopkins University, Baltimore, Md. [553]

CHRISTIAN B. ANFINSEN. National Institute of Arthritis and Metabolic Diseases, National Institutes of Health, Bethesda, Md. [79]

YASUHIRO ANRAKU. National Institute of Arthritis and Metabolic Diseases, National Institutes of Health, Bethesda, Md. [130]

H. VASKEN APOSHIAN. Department of Microbiology. Tufts University School of Medicine, Boston, Mass. [277]

S. AURISICCHIO. International Laboratory of Genetics and Biophysics, Naples, Italy. [562]

ANNE NORRIS BALDWIN. Department of Biochemistry, Stanford University School of Medicine, Stanford, Calif. [400]

J. BARLOW. Department of Biochemistry, University College London, London, England. [444]

PAUL BERG. Department of Biochemistry, Stanford University School of Medicine, Stanford, Calif. [375, 384, 400]

ALBERTO BERNARDI. Center for Research in Macromolecules, Strasbourg, France. [144]

GIORGIO BERNARDI. Center for Research in Macromolecules, Strasbourg, France. [37, 102, 144, 236]

K. I. BERNS. Department of Biophysics, The Johns Hopkins University, Baltimore, Md. [535]

MARTIN A. BILLETER. Department of Biochemistry, New York University School of Medicine, New York, N.Y. [498]

F. J. BOLLUM. Biology Division, Oak Ridge National Laboratory, Oak Ridge, Tenn. [284, 296, 577, 592]

ELLIS T. BOLTON. Department of Terrestrial Magnetism, Carnegie Institution of Washington, Washington, D.C. [437]

ERNEST BOREK. College of Physicians and Surgeons, Columbia University, New York, N.Y. [461]

PIET BORST. Department of Biochemistry, New York University School of Medicine, New York, N.Y. [340]

R. CALENDAR. Department of Biochemistry, Stanford University School of Medicine, Stanford, Calif. [384]

G. L. CANTONI. National Institute of Mental Health, National Institutes of Health, Bethesda, Md. [617, 624]

LIEBE F. CAVALIERI. Division of Biological Chemistry, Sloan-Kettering Institute, New York, N.Y. [584]

MICHAEL J. CHAMBERLIN. Virus Laboratory, University of California, Berkeley, Calif. [513]

VIOLET DANIEL. Biochemistry Section, Weizmann Institute of Science, Rehovoth, Israel. [353]

A. DE WAARD. Department of Biochemistry, Stanford University School of Medicine, Stanford, Calif. [122]

FUJIO EGAMI. Department of Biophysics and Biochemistry, The University of Tokyo, Tokyo, Japan. [3, 46]

ERWIN FLEISSNER. The Rockefeller University, New York, N.Y. [461]

H. FRAENKEL-CONRAT. Virus Laboratory, University of California, Berkeley, Calif. [480]

ECKART FUCHS. Max Planck Institute for Biochemistry, Munich, West Germany. [323]

J. J. FURTH. Department of Pathology, University of Pennsylvania School of Medicine, Philadelphia, Penna. [347]

MARVIN GOLD. Albert Einstein College of Medicine, Yeshiva University, Bronx, N.Y. [301, 362]

PETER JOHN GOMATOS. Sloan-Kettering Institute, New York, N.Y. [493]

J. W. HEALY. Graduate Department of Biochemistry, Brandeis University, Waltham, Mass. [188]

JAMES N. HEINS. National Institute of Arthritis and Metabolic Diseases, National Institutes of Health, Bethesda, Md. [79]

LEON A. HEPPEL. National Institute of Arthritis and Metabolic Diseases, National Institutes of Health, Bethesda, Md. [31]

ROLLIN D. HOTCHKISS. The Rockefeller University, New York, N.Y. [541]

JERARD HURWITZ. Albert Einstein College of Medicine, Yeshiva University, Bronx, N.Y. [301, 347, 362]

CELIA JESENSKY. National Institutes of Health, Bethesda, Md. [420]

T. J. KELLY, JR. Department of Biophysics, The Johns Hopkins University, Baltimore, Md. [535]

WERNER A. KLEE. National Institute of Mental Health, National Institutes of Health, Bethesda, Md. [20]

M. LASKOWSKI, SR. Roswell Park Memorial Institute, Buffalo, N.Y. [85, 154]

ROBERT A. LAZZARINI. National Institutes of Health, Bethesda, Md. [409]

SYLVIA LEE-HUANG. Division of Biological Chemistry, Sloan-Kettering Institute, New York, N.Y. [584]

I. R. LEHMAN. Department of Biochemistry, Stanford University School of Medicine, Stanford, Calif. [122, 203]

L. LEVINE. Graduate Department of Biochemistry, Brandeis University, Waltham, Mass. [188]

URIEL Z. LITTAUER. Biochemistry Section, Weizmann Institute of Science, Rehovoth, Israel. [353]

MAYNARD H. MAKMAN. Albert Einstein College of Medicine, Yeshiva University, Bronz, N.Y. [424]

A. P. MATHIAS. Department of Biochemistry, University College London, London, England. [444]

ALAN H. MEHLER. Marquette University School of Medicine, Milwaukee, Wis. [409, 414, 420]

ROBERT MILLETTE. Max Planck Institute for Biochemistry, Munich, West Germany. [323]

KARL H. MUENCH. Department of Medicine, University of Miami, Miami, Fla. [375]

SUSUMU NISHIMURA. National Cancer Center Research Institute, Tokyo, Japan. [56]

SEVERO OCHOA. Department of Biochemistry, New York University School of Medicine, New York, N.Y. [340]

K. K. REDDI. The Rockefeller University, New York, N.Y. [71]

H. H. RICHARDS. National Institute of Mental Health, National Institutes of Health, Bethesda, Md. [617, 624]

CHARLES C. RICHARDSON. Department of Biological Chemistry, Harvard Medical School, Boston, Mass. [212, 263]

MAXINE F. SINGER. National Institute of Arthritis and Metabolic Diseases, National Institutes of Health, Bethesda, Md. [192, 245]

ROBERT L. SINSHEIMER. Division of Biology, California Institute of Technology, Pasadena, Calif. [569]

BETH P. SONNENBERG. Department of Zoology, Columbia University, New York, N.Y. [600]

PIERRE F. SPAHR. Institute of Molecular Biology, Laboratory of Genetic Biochemistry, University of Geneva, Switzerland. [64]

ROBERT STERN. Weizmann Institute of Science, Rehovoth, Israel. [414]

D. STOLLAR. Graduate Department of Biochemistry, Brandeis University, Waltham, Mass. [188]

DONALD F. SUMMERS. Albert Einstein College of Medicine, Yeshiva University, Bronx, N.Y. [488]

KENTARO TANAKA. Shionogi Research Laboratory, Shionogi & Co., Ltd., Osaka, Japan. [14, 466]

HIROSHI TANIUCHI. National Institute of Arthritis and Metabolic Diseases, National Institutes of Health, Bethesda, Md. [79]

ROBERT E. THACH. Harvard University, Cambridge, Mass. [520]

C. A. THOMAS, JR. Department of Biophysics, The Johns Hopkins University, Baltimore, Md. [535, 553]

A. TORRIANI. Department of Biology, Massachusetts Institute of Technology, Cambridge, Mass. [224]

TSUNEKO UCHIDA. Department of Biophysics and Biochemistry, The University of Tokyo, Tokyo, Japan. [3, 46]

CHARLES WEISSMANN. Department of Biochemistry, New York University School of Medicine, New York, N.Y. [340, 498]

WOLFRAM ZILLIG. Max Planck Institute for Biochemistry, Munich, West Germany. [323]

STEVEN B. ZIMMERMAN. National Institute of Arthritis and Metabolic Diseases, National Institutes of Health, Bethesda, Md. [307]

GEOFFREY ZUBAY. Department of Zoology, Columbia University, New York, N.Y. [455, 600]

Contents

ix

Section C. Enzymes of tRNA Metabolism

II. ISOLATION, PREPARATION, AND CHARACTERIZATION OF NATURAL AND SYNTHETIC NUCLEIC ACIDS

Section A. Ribonucleic Acid

1. rRNA

Section B. Deoxyribonucleic Acid

† For two additional articles on this subject, one on rabbit liver and one on yeast, see Appendix.

Preface

Nucleic acids have emerged in the last 15 years as one of the focal points of research in molecular biology, genetics, biochemistry, microbiology, and physical chemistry. As a consequence of this concentration of effort, new techniques have developed and new applications of well-established techniques have become of particular interest to workers in the field of nucleic acid research. Because of the multidisciplinary nature of this research, we felt it would be valuable to bring together in a multivolume work the wide variety of methods and techniques which are currently employed. We realize that in an area of such rapid change, a single comprehensive work is probably an almost impossible undertaking. Nevertheless, we have been encouraged to attempt the task, and to believe that a publication of this kind would fill a real need among active workers in the field of nucleic acid research, by the favorable and enthusiastic response of those colleagues whom we asked to contribute to this first volume. We hope that this publication will be useful not only to those working directly in the field of nucleic acids but also to those who only occasionally need to use procedures and techniques which are special to this field.

This first volume contains descriptions of methods for the isolation and characterization of enzymes of nucleic acid metabolism and degradation. In addition, techniques are described for the isolation and preparation of a variety of representative nucleic acids. With some exceptions, we have included only those enzyme preparations which have been obtained in highly purified form. Some enzymes, however, are of such importance to a rapidly evolving field that they merit description now, even while work on their more complete purification and characterization may be proceeding. Moreover, in certain cases, it may be necessary to study these enzymes in crude extracts in order to explore the significance of certain physiological variables and/or control mechanisms. For the nucleic acid preparations the same criteria have been used.

In this volume, we have not included enzymes involved in the metabolism of nucleic acid precursors, such as purines and pyrimidines and their phosphorylated derivatives, since these enzyme preparations have been adequately described elsewhere.

Although, within this framework, we have attempted to be comprehensive, we are aware of certain serious omissions which we shall attempt to remedy in future volumes. The usefulness of a work of this nature, in a rapidly changing area of science, depends on the extent to which it is current and to which it is kept up-to-date. It is our intention to provide extensive revisions and additions with each additional volume.

In future volumes, we also plan to cover physical, physicochemical, and chemical techniques of analysis, characterization, and degradation of nucleic acids, as well as techniques for the preparation of defined species of nucleic acids such as amino acid-specific transfer RNA. Techniques for sequence determination of DNA and RNA and for the study of the role of nucleic acid in protein synthesis will also be included.

Our contributors are all pre-eminent in their special fields of research; consequently we have deferred in general to their preferences in matters of nomenclature, and have not attempted to impose such restrictions as would have been necessary to insure complete uniformity. For instance, sRNA is referred to in some places as soluble RNA (sRNA) and elsewhere as transfer RNA (tRNA). Generally, but not always, these two terms are synonymous, and we have felt that the author would be the best judge of the correct usage.

We have made use of the AIBS *Style Manual* for guidance in matters of format and abbreviations. This choice has resulted in a few departures from conventional usage, one notable example being the use of C to denote temperature in degrees centigrade. We are confident that these differences will not cause any confusion.

We are grateful to all contributors and to our publisher for their excellent cooperation. Without their combined efforts the expeditious publication of this book would have been impossible. We are very much indebted to a number of our colleagues at the National Institutes of Health who have helped generously and formed a sort of unofficial advisory board. In particular, we wish to thank Drs. G. Felsenfeld, M. Gellert, L. Heppel, W. Klee, M. Singer, and S. Zimmerman for their useful advice and discussions. Our appreciation is also extended to Mr. Andrew Sinauer for his enthusiastic support and to his colleagues at Harper & Row for their valuable assistance; they frequently supplied a needed stimulus to two wayward editors. Above all, we wish to thank our contributors for their uniformly excellent contributions and for the speed and punctuality of their response.

G. L. C.
D. R. D.

I.

ENZYMES OF

NUCLEIC ACID

METABOLISM

Section A. Enzymes of Nucleic Acid Degradation

1. Specific Ribonucleases (Endonucleases)

Ribonuclease T_1 from Taka-Diastase

TSUNEKO UCHIDA AND FUJIO EGAMI
DEPARTMENT OF BIOPHYSICS AND BIOCHEMISTRY
THE UNIVERSITY OF TOKYO
TOKYO, JAPAN

ASSAY

I. General Method

Reagents

1. The reaction mixture (total volume 0.75 ml) contains

0.2 M Tris-HCl buffer, pH 7.5	0.25 ml
20 mM EDTA aqueous solution	0.1 ml
Enzyme (properly diluted with distilled water)	0.1 ml

2. RNA (sodium salt) solution 12 mg/ml 0.25 ml
3. Uranyl reagent (0.75% uranyl acetate in 25% perchloric acid)

Procedure I

This assay measures the absorption at 260 mμ of the acid-soluble digestion products from commercial yeast RNA† and is used to follow enzymatic activity during the purification procedure.

The reaction is started by addition of RNA solution to the rest of the reaction mixture and, after 15 min of incubation at 37 C, it is stopped with 0.25 ml of the uranyl reagent. The precipitate is immediately removed by centrifugation, 0.2 ml of the supernatant solution is diluted with 5.0 ml of distilled water, and the optical density at 260 mμ is read against a blank incubated without enzyme. The dilution procedure should be performed as fast as possible, because the blank value for the RNA solution increases somewhat with time.

This assay is linear up to absorption values of approximately 0.4. Within the range of linearity an increase in absorption value of 0.1 is defined as 0.1 unit of enzyme activity. Protein concentration is determined by measuring the absorption of the enzyme solution at 280 mμ. Specific activity is defined as the ratio of the enzyme units in 0.1 ml of the enzyme solution and the absorption values at 280 mμ of the same solution.

II. Alternate Method

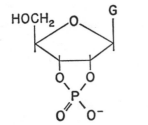 + H_2O $\longrightarrow$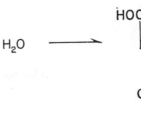

Reagents

1. The reaction mixture (total volume 2.5 ml) contains

0.025 M imidazole-HCl buffer, pH 7.0	0.1 ml
0.25 M NaCl	0.5 ml
Guanosine 2′,3′-cyclic phosphate (Sodium salt) 4 mg/ml	1.0 ml

† The blank value for the absorption of the RNA solution is approximately 0.1 at 260 mμ. When the commercial RNA used for assay contains larger amounts of acid-soluble fraction, it should be applied to a Sephadex G-25 column and only the excluded fraction is used for the assay.

2. Enzyme (properly diluted with distilled water)   50 μl
3. 0.01 N NaOH solution

Procedure II

This assay measures the hydrolase activity of ribonuclease T_1, that is, the amount of titratable hydroxyl group produced from guanosine 2′,3′-cyclic phosphate is titrated with alkali solution in a pH stat.

After the pH stat is set at pH 7.0, the reaction is started by addition of enzyme at 25 C and the relation of alkali consumption to reaction time is recorded. The volume change of reaction mixture resulting from the titration with alkaline solution is negligible since it is below 0.1 ml. The amount of guanosine 3′-phosphate produced from guanosine 2′,3′-cyclic phosphate by ribonuclease T_1 is calculated from the slope of this relation within the range of linearity.

ISOLATION PROCEDURE (3,4)

Crude Extract

Five hundred grams of Taka-Diastase powder are added to 3 liters of distilled water and well dispersed. The suspension is centrifuged at 3000 rev/min for 10 min. During centrifugation the powder dissolves almost completely without any special treatment. If a brown gum-like residue remains under the black and muddy residue in the bottom of the centrifuge tube, the whole residue is re-extracted with 2 liters of distilled water as above. The muddy precipitate is centrifuged off at 3000 rev/min for 10 min. The clear reddish-brown supernatant fluid (5 liters) is diluted with 15 liters of distilled water and then adjusted to pH 7.0 with 2 N NaOH.

Batchwise Treatment with DEAE-Cellulose

300 g of DEAE-cellulose are washed with 0.5 N NaOH and then with water until the pH of the suspension is below 9; finally they are washed 2 or 3 times to be equilibrated with 0.005 M Na_2HPO_4. About 2/3 portions of the filter cake (corresponding to 1/2 weight of the total protein in the crude extract) are added to the crude extract and the suspension is filtered after occasional stirring and standing for 20 min at room temperature. Preliminary experiments have verified that the adsorption equilibrium between the solution and DEAE-cellulose is accomplished in 10 min. The activity remaining in the filtrate is further adsorbed on DEAE-cellulose (1/3 portions of the above-mentioned filter cake). 90 or 95% of the total activity can thus be adsorbed on DEAE-cellulose.

The elution from the exchanger is carried out as follows: DEAE-cellulose carrying adsorbed ribonuclease T_1 and T_2 is suspended in 0.1 M NaCl in 0.01 M Na_2HPO_4 (1.5 liters) and filtered after 15 min. This elution procedure is repeated 4 or 5 times to elute ribonuclease T_2 activity completely. Next, ribonuclease T_1 is eluted from the exchanger with 0.35 M NaCl in 0.01 M Na_2HPO_4 (1.5 liters $\times$ 5) as above.

The ribonuclease activity in the crude extract is separated into two fractions by this procedure: The first fraction eluted below 0.1 M NaCl contains mainly ribonuclease T_2 activity and the second one eluted between 0.1 M and 0.35 M NaCl contains ribonuclease T_1 activity. The recovery of activity at pH 7.5 in the ribonuclease T_1 fraction is 65–85% of the total activity in the crude extract.

After use the DEAE-cellulose is regenerated by washing, in turn, with 2 M NaCl, 0.5 N NaOH, and water; it may be reused quite well for this batchwise treatment until the regeneration procedure has been carried out 5 times, but the yield of ribonuclease activity decreases somewhat with the repetition of regeneration. All procedures described above can be also carried out with tap water instead of distilled water.

Heat Treatment

The ribonuclease T_1 fraction is adjusted to pH 1.5–1.8 with 2 N HCl; this pH is relatively critical because ribonuclease T_1 activity in crude preparations disappears rapidly at higher temperatures above pH 2. After the white and solid precipitates formed were removed by centrifugation at 3000 rev/min for 10 min, the clear, yellowish-brown supernatant fluid is poured in a stew pan (1.5 liters), heated with stirring at 80 C in a boiling water bath for 2 min, and quickly cooled to room temperature in an ice bath. No additional precipitate of the denatured protein is produced during the heating. The recovery of enzymatic activity is 85–95%. This procedure serves to inactivate other contaminating enzymes, such as deoxyribonuclease, nucleotidase, and protease.

Acid Clay Treatment

Japanese acid clay† (corresponding to threefold the weight of the protein in solution calculated from the absorption value at 280 nμ, assuming that 1 mg of protein in 1 ml shows OD_{280} of 1.00) is added to the heat-treated ribonuclease T_1 fraction (pH 1.5). The mixture is

---

† Acid clay (100 mesh), which is dug out from Okayama region, is the product of the Kukita Yakuhin Kogyo Company, Tokyo. Its composition is as follows: 70.40% SiO_2, 15.71% Al_2O_3, 3.15% Fe_2O_3, 1.17% CaO, 2.13% MgO, 1.43% Na_2O and K_2O, and 6.89% H_2O.

allowed to stand with occasional stirring for 20 min and is then filtered. The faint yellow filtrate does not contain any enzymatic activity. The cake of acid clay is suspended in a small amount of 0.1 M citrate buffer at pH 6.3. The suspension is allowed to stand overnight and then centrifuged to remove the acid clay at 3000 rev/min for 10 min. The acid clay is resuspended in the same buffer and after 10 min is centrifuged off at 8000 rev/min for 20 min. This extraction is repeated four times to elute ribonuclease T_1 completely and all extracts are combined (less than 750 ml). The recovery of enzymatic activity is over 95% and specific activity is raised threefold. Ribonuclease T_1 is usually concentrated about tenfold by this treatment.

The adsorption of ribonuclease T_1 to acid clay and the desorption of ribonuclease T_1 from acid clay are dependent on the pH of the solution, but quite independent of the concentrations of the enzyme and the salt. Therefore this procedure is more effective for the separation of ribonuclease T_1 from a dilute solution or a solution with high salt concentrations.

Ammonium Sulfate Fractionation

The extract from acid clay (pH maintained around 6.0) is brought to 70% $(NH_4)_2SO_4$ saturation by the addition of 530 g of solid salt/liter. After 20 min with occasional stirring, the suspension is centrifuged at 3000 rev/min for 15 min and the precipitate containing contaminating inactive proteins and a small amount of acid clay is discarded. The supernatant fluid is adjusted to pH 4.2 with 2 N H_2SO_4 and then brought to 100% $(NH_4)_2SO_4$ saturation by the addition of 175 g of solid salt/liter. The precipitate is collected as above, dissolved in a small amount of 0.1 M citrate buffer, pH 6.3, and dialyzed against running tap water overnight.

Column Chromatography on DEAE-Cellulose

The dialyzed ribonuclease T_1 solution is adjusted to pH 7.0–7.5 by adding 0.5 M Na_2HPO_4 to a final concentration of 0.005 M. The chromatography on DEAE-cellulose is carried out according to the procedure of Takahashi (1,5).

The enzyme solution (containing about 2 g of protein) is loaded on a column of DEAE-cellulose (1.8 cm $\times$ 20 cm) that has previously been equilibrated with 0.005 M Na_2HPO_4. Then two 5-ml portions of 0.005 M Na_2HPO_4 are used to wash the last bit of the enzyme solution onto the column. A 5-ml head of 0.005 M Na_2HPO_4 solution is applied and nonlinear elution gradient is started. The mixer flask contains 600 ml of 0.005 M Na_2HPO_4 and the reservoir contains 1 liter of 0.25 M NaCl containing 0.25 M NaH_2PO_4. Fractions of approximately 10 ml are collected, and the flow rate is approximately 2 ml/min. Ribonuclease T_1 is eluted with a brown band as a single homogeneous peak with respect to the enzyme activity as well as the protein concentration. The ribonuclease T_1 fractions of specific activity above 500 are obtained by this procedure in a yield above 50%.

Crystallization

The fractions of specific activity above 500 are combined and precipitated at 0.7 saturation with ammonium sulfate at pH 4.0. The brown contaminants remain in the supernatant fluid. The faint yellow precipitates are collected by centrifugation and dissolved in a small amount of 0.1 M citrate buffer at pH 6.3. This enzyme solution (protein concentration about 0.2%) is poured into a cellophane dialysis tubing and dialyzed overnight in the cold room against 50 volumes of aqueous ammonium sulfate solution of 0.6 saturation, at pH 4.0. The enzyme gradually precipitates out at the wall of cellophane tubing in colorless and spherulite-like crystals (5). When the supernatant solution and the faint yellow mother liquid are allowed to stand for a few days in the cold room, a small second crop of the colorless and spherulite-like crystals precipitates out. The enzyme crystals are dissolved in a small amount of 0.1 M citrate buffer at pH 6.3 and stored in a deep-freeze after dialysis against several changes of the cold distilled water.

Comments

By this procedure, ribonuclease T_1 is purified in five days from 500 g of Taka-Diastase powder. In large-scale preparations, the procedures before adsorption on acid clay are repeated once more and the two samples are treated together after desorption from acid clay. Consequently, ribonuclease T_1 is purified in a week from 1 kg of Taka-Diastase (4). In the course of preparation samples may be stored frozen without appreciable loss of activity at any step after the heat treatment.

A typical preparation is shown in Table I. The ribonuclease T_1 thus obtained is purified about 1000-fold in good yield, and is colorless and quite homogeneous in chromatography, electrophoresis, and sedimentation analysis.

Another method for the purification of ribonuclease T_1, in which acid clay is not used, is presented by Rushizky et al. (6). The method consists of water extraction, acid treatment, acetone fractionation, and DEAE-cellulose chromatography (four times). The purity and recovery of the product are nearly the same as those of the above-mentioned procedure.

TABLE 1.   *Purification of Ribonuclease T_1 from Taka-Diastase*

Fraction	Total Protein (g)	Total Activity ($\times 10^3$ units)	Specific Activity
I. Crude extract	382	4425	1.1
II. Batchwise treatment with DEAE-cellulose	134	3800	2.8
III. Heat treatment	20.8	3485	16
IV. Acid clay treatment	8.50	3093	36
V. $(NH_4)_2SO_4$(0.7-sat)	1.90	3008	158
VI. DEAE-cellulose peak fractions	0.28	1582	500–700

Highly purified ribonuclease T_1 and Taka-Diastase powder may be purchased from Sankyo Co. Ltd., Ginza, Tokyo.

PROPERTIES OF ENZYME (3)

Contamination with Other Enzymes

The purest ribonuclease T_1 contains no other enzymatic activity, such as phosphomonoesterase, phosphodiesterase, deoxyribonuclease, and ribonuclease T_2.

These enzymatic activities are tested as follows: Phosphomono-esterase activity and phosphodiesterase activity are determined by meas-uring the increase in absorption values at 405 mμ of p-nitrophenol liberated from p-nitrophenyl phosphate and from bis, p-nitrophenyl phosphate, respectively (7). Deoxyribonuclease activity is determined by measuring the absorption at 260 mμ of acid-soluble products formed from heat-denatured DNA (8). Ribonuclease T_2 is determined by meas-uring spectrophotometrically uridine 3'-phosphate produced from uri-dine 2',3'-cyclic phosphate (9).

Stability (3)

Ribonuclease T_1 is a stable enzyme. Around pH 6.0, it can be stored frozen for several months or in solution in cold for several weeks with-out appreciable loss in the activity. At acidic pH values it is fairly stable: It retained almost full activity for more than 24 hr in 0.1 N HCl at room temperature and for more than 48 hr in 0.4 N HCl at 4 C (6). However, it is somewhat unstable at alkaline pH values: It is irrevers-ibly inactivated fairly rapidly above pH 9. Ribonuclease T_1 possesses full activity after heating at 100 C for 10 min in solution (about 5 μg of protein/ml of 0.01 M citrate buffer, pH 6.0) (10) and after exposure to 8 M urea at room temperature for 28 hr. It suffers little inactivation on phenol treatment (11) or on precipitation with cold acetone (6), ethanol (12), Rivanol, or Trypaflavin. Lyophilization of ribonuclease T_1 is attended with a slight inactivation owing to the production of a small amount of insoluble materials.

Activators and Inhibitors

The influences of various substances on ribonuclease T_1 are summarized in Table 2. Ribonuclease T_1 is inhibited by Zn^{2+} and heavy metal ions, and slightly affected by Mg^{2+} and Ca^{2+}. EDTA apparently stimulates ribonuclease T_1 eliminating inhibiting metallic ions.

Unlike ribonuclease I-A, ribonuclease T_1 is insensitive to heparin and natural ribonuclease inhibitor (13).

TABLE 2. *Activators and Inhibitors*

Reagents	Final Concentration $(- \log M)$	Activity Remaining (%)
NaCl	0	75
	1	100–115
NaF	1	93–100
NaN$_3$	2	95–100
Na$_2$S	2	10
AgNO$_3$	3	0
MgCl$_2$	1	60
CaCl$_2$	2	70–75
HgCl$_2$	3	10
MnSO$_4$	2	45
ZnSO$_4$	3	0
CuSO$_4$	3	20–50
FeSO$_4$	2	20
ICH$_2$COOH	2	100
BrCH$_2$COOH	4	100
DFP	6	100

Specificity

The studies on the specificity of ribonuclease T_1 have been carried out near the optimum pH (pH 7.5) for the cleavage of 3'-guanylic acid phosphodiester bonds.

Ribonuclease T_1 splits internucleotide bonds between the 3'-guanylic acid group and the 5'-hydroxyl group of the adjacent nucleotides in RNA with the intermediate formation of guanosine 2',3'-cyclic phosphate, and does not split the secondary phosphate ester bonds of other nucleotides in RNA (14). Hence it is regarded as a guanylic acid-specific endoribonuclease [EC. 2.7.7.26, Ribonucleate guanine-nucleotide-2'-transferase (cyclizing)].

Studies on the action of the enzyme on modified RNA and related nucleotides may be summarized as follows: Ribonuclease T_1 can digest deaminated RNA, hydrolyzing the secondary phosphate ester bonds of both inosine 3'-phosphate and xanthosine 3'-phosphate, the latter far more slowly (15,16). In both cases, nucleoside 2',3'-cyclic phosphates are formed as intermediates. A 6-oxo group thus seems to be required for the susceptibility to ribonuclease T_1. Phosphodiester bonds of 1-methylguanylic acid in sRNA cannot be attacked by the enzyme (17,18). These results, together with the observations on the action on small substrates, suggest that the reaction of ribonuclease T_1 requires the protonated form at N-1 (or at the oxygen in position 6) of the purine base (19).†
The resistance of RNA methylated with dimethylsulfate, in which the 7-position of most of the guanylic residues is methylated, might be explained by the same consideration (20). Ribonuclease T_1 splits the RNA chain next to N^2-dimethylguanylic acid, forming the cyclic phosphate of dimethylguanosine (17,18). This is not hydrolyzed or very slowly hydrolyzed further by the enzyme to 3'-nucleotides. Neither guanosine 3',5'-cyclic phosphate (21) nor 2',5'-phosphodiester bonds in chemically synthesized poly G (22) can be hydrolyzed by the enzyme.

Other Properties

Physical and chemical properties of ribonuclease T_1 are listed in Table 3. The molecular weight of ribonuclease T_1 is 11,000; ribonuclease T_1 is a very acidic, simple protein consisting of a single polypeptide chain. From the results of amino acid composition ribonuclease T_1 is characterized as follows (23): (a) It contains 104 amino acid residues per molecule. (b) It contains three histidine residues per molecule, comparable to ribonuclease I-A, despite the lower lysine and arginine content (one residue, respectively). (c) It has one residue of tryptophan and no methionine residue, in contrast to ribonuclease I-A. (d) It possesses two disulfide bonds in a molecule, but no cysteine residue. Recently, the primary structure of ribonuclease T_1 has been investigated and elucidated (25).

† However, Holley et al. recently detected Up 1-MeG 2',3' cyclic-p in the digests by ribonuclease T_1 (26).

TABLE 3. *Physical and Chemical Properties of Ribonuclease T_1*

Molecular weight	11,000
$S_{20, w}$	1.62 S
$D_{20, w}$	12.0×10^{-7} cm^{2}sec^{-1}
Isoelectric point	pH 2.9
Absorption maximum	278 mμ
Absorption minimum	251 mμ
OD_{max}/OD_{min}	3.9_2
$OD_{max\ 1\ cm}^{0.\ 1\%}$	1.9
$[\alpha]_D^{20}$	$- 15.7°$
Nitrogen content	16.5%
Sugar content	$<0.5\%$
Amino terminal	Alanine
Carboxyl terminal	Threonine
Specific enzyme activity	14×10^3 units/mg of enzyme

Specific enzyme activity is presented by arbitrary units in Table 3. Although molecular activity may be calculated using guanosine 2',3'-cyclic phosphate as a substrate, this has not yet been carried out.

Ribonuclease T_1 can produce the antibody to itself in rabbits and the enzymatic activity on RNA is inhibited by the antibody (3,24).

REFERENCES

1. TAKAHASHI, K. 1961. J. Biochem. (Tokyo). *49:* 1.
2. SATO, S., and F. EGAMI. Unpublished data.
3. EGAMI, F., K. TAKAHASHI, and T. UCHIDA. 1964. In J. N. Davidson and W. E. Cohn, editors, Progress in nucleic acid research and molecular biology. Academic Press: New York. Vol. III, p. 59.
4. UCHIDA, T. 1965. J. Biochem. (Tokyo). *57:* 547.
5. TAKAHASHI, K. 1962. J. Biochem. (Tokyo). *51:* 95.
6. RUSHIZKY, G. W., and H. A. SOBER. 1962. J. Biol. Chem. *237:* 834.
7. KOERNER, J. F., and R. L. SINSHEIMER. 1957. J. Biol. Chem. *228:* 1039.
8. ANDO, T. Biochim. Biophys. Acta. In press.
9. UCHIDA, T., and F. EGAMI. This volume, p. 46.
10. SATO, K., and F. EGAMI. 1957. J. Biochem. (Tokyo). *44:* 753.
11. RUSHIZKY, G. W., C. A. KNIGHT, and H. A. SOBER. 1961. J. Biol. Chem. *236:* 2732.
12. UCHIDA, T. J. Biochem. (Tokyo). 1966. To be published.
13. SHORTMAN, K. 1962. Biochim. Biophys. Acta. *55:* 88.
14. SATO-ASANO, K. 1959. J. Biochem. (Tokyo). *46:* 31.
15. SATO-ASANO, K., and Y. FUJII. 1960. J. Biochem. (Tokyo). *47:* 608.

16. UCHIDA, T., and F. EGAMI. 1965. J. Biochem. (Tokyo). 57: 742.
17. STAEHELIN, M. 1964. Biochim. Biophys. Acta. 87: 493.
18. DÜTTING, D., and H. G. ZACHAU. 1964. Z. Physiol. Chem. 336: 132.
19. WHITFELD, P. R., and H. WITZEL. 1963. Biochim. Biophys. Acta. 72: 338.
20. NAGAMATSU, T., T. UCHIDA, and F. EGAMI. Unpublished data.
21. SATO, S., T. UCHIDA, and F. EGAMI. Unpublished data.
22. KURIYAMA, T., J. KOYAMA, and F. EGAMI. 1964. J. Japan. Biochem. Soc. 36: 135.
23. TAKAHASHI, K. 1962. J. Biochem. (Tokyo). 52: 72.
24. UCHIDA, T. J. Biochem. (Tokyo). 1966. To be published.
25. TAKAHASHI, K. 1965. J. Biol. Chem., 240: 10.
26. HOLLEY, R. W., G. A. EVERETT, J. T. MADISON, and A. ZAMIR. 1965. J. Biol. Chem. 240: 2122.

Ribonuclease from
Streptomyces erythreus

KENTARO TANAKA
SHIONOGI RESEARCH LABORATORY
SHIONOGI & CO., LTD.
OSAKA, JAPAN

ASSAY

$$\text{RNA} \longrightarrow \text{Oligonucleotides} + \text{Mononucleotides}$$

Reagents

1. Yeast RNA (deproteinized, thoroughly dialyzed) dissolved in 0.2 M phosphate buffer, pH 7.4 (6 mg/ml)
2. 0.75% uranyl acetate in 25% perchloric acid

Procedure

The assay depends on measuring the formation of oligonucleotides that are soluble in uranyl acetate–perchloric acid solution.

To 0.5 ml of yeast RNA solution, 0.5 ml of enzyme solution is added. The mixture is incubated at 37 C for 15 min, then 0.2 ml of uranyl acetate reagent is added with thorough mixing. Twenty minutes later, the formed precipitate is centrifuged off. The supernatant fluid is diluted 20-fold with water and the absorbancy at 260 mμ is read. With each set of assays a control is carried out in which the enzyme solution is added after the addition of the precipitating reagent. The reading of the control is subtracted from the experimental readings. To obtain satisfactory proportionality between activity and enzyme

14

concentration, the amount of enzyme should be restricted so that the net absorbancy at 260 mμ of the final diluted sample does not exceed 0.2.

Unit of Ribonuclease

One unit of ribonuclease is defined as the amount that causes a change of absorbancy ($\Delta A_{260 m\mu}$) of 1.0 in the assay mixture. Thus the units of the 1.0 ml solution used in the assay are: $\Delta A_{260 m\mu} \times 1.2$ (volume correction for precipitating reagent) $\times$ 20 (correction for dilution) $\times$ 2 (correction for the volume of enzyme solution).

Specific activity is defined as units of activity per unit absorbancy of the enzyme solution at 280 mμ with 1-cm light path.

PURIFICATION PROCEDURE (1)

Growth of Cells

Streptomyces erythreus (American Type Culture Collection no. 11635 or Northern Regional Research Laboratory no. 2338) is grown on slightly modified Bennett's agar slant (2) composed of 10 g of glucose, 2 g of Difco Bacto-yeast extract, 1 g of Difco Bacto-beef extract, 2 g of Difco Bacto-casamino acids, 15 g of agar, and 1000 ml of water (pH 7.3). The slant is incubated at 37 C for 10–12 days.

The same medium (with the omission of agar) as that used for the slant culture is employed for the vegetative culture. A spore suspension is inoculated to 130 ml of the medium in a 1-liter Sakaguchi long-neck flask. After shaking the culture for 48 hr at 32 C, the vegetative culture is used in 6.5-ml portions to inoculate 130 ml of fermentation medium in a number of 1-liter Sakaguchi long-neck flasks and the inoculated medium is cultured on a shaker at 32 C. The fermentation medium is composed of 10 g of soybean meal, 10 g of potato starch, 5 g of glycerol, 5 g of cornsteep liquor, 1 g of yeast extract, 3 g of NaCl, 3.5 g of $CaCO_3$, and 1000 ml of tap water (pH 7.0). Because ribonuclease production depends on the incubation period and on the conditions of incubation, an increase of ribonuclease activity of the culture fluid is followed during the course of the incubation. Usually the activity reaches its maximum value after 5 days and no significant change is observed during further incubation for 2 to 3 days.

Acrinol Precipitation

The incubation is terminated after maximum enzyme production has been reached. The broth (pH 7.3) is separated from the mycelium by centrifugation and diluted with two volumes of water.† 1% aqueous acrinol (2-ethoxy-6,9-diaminoacridinium lactate) solution is added with stirring to bring the final concentration to 0.1% and the mixture is allowed to stand for 2 days in the cold room. The yellow precipitate is collected by centrifugation, and extracted repeatedly by stirring with 1 M Na acetate (pH 6.0) (a total of about 500 ml of 1 M acetate is used for the extraction of the precipitate obtained from 7.5 liters of culture broth). Cold acetone is added to the combined extracts to a final concentration of 67%. After standing 2 hr, the precipitate of crude ribonuclease is collected by centrifugation, thoroughly washed with acetone, and then dried under reduced pressure. These operations are carried out in a cold room kept at 4 C. The acetone precipitate can be stored without significant loss of activity in a desiccator at low temperature for at least a few years.

Batchwise Treatment with DEAE-Cellulose

For further purification steps, it is best to use several grams of the acetone precipitate so that the protein peaks may be easily determined by measuring absorbancy at 280 mμ and thereby the purity of the fractions may be readily estimated.

Ten grams of DEAE-cellulose is equilibrated with 0.1 M Na acetate buffer, pH 4.0, on a sintered glass funnel (5.4 cm in diameter). Four grams of the acetone precipitate are dissolved in 100 ml of the same buffer and adsorbed on DEAE-cellulose. The DEAE-cellulose is then washed with 300 ml of the same buffer and with 200 ml of a solution of 0.02 M NaCl in 0.1 M acetate buffer at pH 4.0. Five successive elutions are carried out, each with 100 ml of 0.06 M NaCl in 0.1 M acetate buffer, pH 4.0.

Each of these fractions is assayed for its ribonuclease activity. The active effluents obtained from 8 g of acetone precipitate are pooled, concentrated to 10–15 ml under reduced pressure at low temperature or lyophilization, and dialyzed against distilled water.

Column Chromatography on DEAE-Cellulose

The dialyzed solution is mixed with an equal volume of 0.2 M acetate buffer, pH 4.0, then charged on a DEAE-cellulose column (14 cm $\times$ 3.1 cm²), which has been pre-equilibrated with 0.1 M acetate, pH 4.0. The column is first washed with 300 ml of 0.03 M NaCl in 0.1 M acetate, pH 4.0. Elution of the enzyme is then carried out with 0.06 M NaCl in the same buffer. A sharp main peak of enzyme activity

† High concentrations of inorganic salts and other organic materials interfere with the precipitation of ribonuclease by the addition of acrinol solution.

is found just before the main peak of the protein.† The fractions corresponding to the main peak of ribonuclease activity are pooled, concentrated to about 10 ml, as described above, then dialyzed against 2 liters of distilled water with stirring.

Rechromatography on DEAE-Cellulose Column

The final purification is carried out by rechromatography on a DEAE-cellulose column and application of salt elution gradient.

The dialyzed enzyme solution is mixed with an equal volume of 0.2 M acetate buffer, pH 4.0, then applied on the DEAE-cellulose column (14 cm × 3.1 cm²), which has previously been equilibrated with 0.1 M acetate buffer, pH 4.0. The column is initially washed with 150 ml of 0.03 M NaCl in the same buffer. A convex elution gradient is established by use of 420 ml of 0.03 M NaCl in 0.1 M acetate buffer, pH 4.0, in the mixing vessel and 500 ml of 0.09 M NaCl in the same

TABLE 1. *Purification of Ribonuclease from* Streptomyces erythreus (1)

Purification Step	Total Activity (unit)		Specific Activity (unit/$A_{280\ m\mu}$)		Yield (%)	
	Exp. 1	Exp. 2	Exp. 1	Exp. 2	Exp. 1	Exp. 2
I. Starting broth	(7.5 liters) 9,360,000	(1.64 liters) 624,000	31	38	100	100
II. Acrinol precipitate	(8 g) 3,168,000	(1.07 g) 291,000	552	332	34	47
III. Batchwise treatment with DEAE-cellulose	1,872,000	211,000	5,750	530	20	34
IV. First chromatography on DEAE-cellulose		163,000		11,600		26
V. Rechromatography	611,500	133,000	53,800	22,700	6.5	21

buffer, in the reservoir bottle.† Elution proceeds at a flow rate of about 0.2 ml/cm²/min, and fractions of approximately 9 ml are collected. The activity of the fractions is assayed after 1000-fold dilution with 0.2 M phosphate buffer, pH 7.4, containing 20 μg of bovine serum

† The enzyme may be eluted with lower concentration of salt (0.08 M NaCl), if the active fraction has not been thoroughly dialyzed in the previous step.

albumine/ml. The ribonuclease activity is found in the fractions that correspond with the first protein peak.

The active fractions are pooled and stored in a deep freeze. Alternatively and more conveniently the pooled fractions are lyophilized and stored in a desiccator at a low temperature (4 C). Although this preparation contains a large amount of inorganic salts, the enzyme activity is so high that the effect of the inorganic salts may be ignored in most cases. A typical preparation is shown in Table 1.

PROPERTIES OF ENZYME

Optimum pH

The pH optimum of this enzyme is from 7.3 to 7.4 in 0.2 M phosphate (1).

Stability

The enzyme preparation obtained by rechromatography on DEAE-cellulose shows remarkable stability. The enzyme solution in 0.1 M acetate buffer, pH 4.0, can be stored at 2 C for over a month without any decrease of its activity. The enzyme preparation is also remarkably resistant to heat treatment (Table 2).

TABLE 2. *Stability of* Streptomyces erythreus *Ribonuclease*(1)[a]

Temperature	Time (min)	pH	Relative Activity
Nonheated (control)			100
100	10	7.4	85
100	10	5.6	90
100	10	2.0	51
80	5	7.4	95
80	5	5.6	103
80	5	2.0	85

[a] Rechromatographed enzyme preparation was diluted with buffers (0.1 M phosphate, pH 7.4; 0.1 M acetate, pH 5.6; 0.1 M glycine, pH 2.0). After heating, the samples were diluted 50-fold with 0.2 M phosphate (pH 7.4) and activity was assayed.

Specificity

The specificity of this enzyme is very similar to ribonuclease T_1, which was found by Sato and Egami in an extract of *Aspergillus oryzae*

(3). The digestion of yeast RNA with this enzyme preparation yields 3'-GMP and oligonucleotides terminated 3'-GMP, through the formation of 2',3'-cyclic phosphate of terminal GMP (1). Among 2',3'-cyclic phosphates of adenosine, guanosine, cytidine, and uridine, only the 2',3'-cyclic phosphate of guanosine is hydrolyzed, its cyclic phosphate bond yielding 3'-GMP.

Digestion of deaminated yeast RNA with a small amount of this enzyme preparation resulted in the formation of 2',3'-cyclic phosphates of inosine and xanthosine, in addition to the 2',3'-cyclic phosphate of guanosine, which may be due to undeaminated guanylic acid residues in the substrate. Terminal nucleotide analysis of the enzyme digest of deaminated yeast RNA shows that cleavage of the secondary phosphate ester bonds of inosine-3'-phosphate and guanosine-3'-phosphate requires milder conditions of enzyme digestion than those needed for cleavage of the secondary phosphate ester bonds of xanthosine-3'-phosphate (4).

Study of yeast sRNA digestion by this enzyme reveals that the enzyme can cleave the secondary phosphate ester bonds of 1-methylguanine riboside 3'-phosphate, 2-methylamino-6-hydroxypurine riboside 3'-phosphate, and 2-dimethylamino-6-hydroxypurine riboside 3'-phosphate, in addition to those of guanosine 3'-phosphate (5). Staehelin demonstrated that the secondary ester bond of 1-methylguanine ribotide in 1-methylGp-2-methylGpCp is resistant to ribonuclease T_1 digestion (6). These facts suggest a difference in the specificities between these two enzymes, although a definite conclusion may not yet be drawn as the differences in experimental conditions may also play a role in the observed results.

REFERENCES

1. TANAKA, K. 1961. J. Biochem. (Tokyo) . *50:* 62.
2. WAKSMAN, S. A. 1961. *In* The Actinomycetes. The Williams & Wilkins Co.: Baltimore. Vol. 2, p. 331.
3. UCHIDA, T., and F. EGAMI. This volume, page 3.
4. TANAKA, K. Unpublished data.
5. TANAKA, K., and G. L. CANTONI. 1963. Biochim. Biophys. Acta. *72:* 641.
6. STAEHELIN, M. 1964. Biochim. Biophys. Acta. *87:* 493.

Bovine Pancreatic

Ribonuclease A,

Ribonuclease S,

and Ribonuclease E

WERNER A. KLEE

NATIONAL INSTITUTE OF MENTAL HEALTH

NATIONAL INSTITUTES OF HEALTH

BETHESDA, MARYLAND

Bovine pancreatic ribonuclease is the subject of a vast literature, which has been extensively reviewed (1–4). The purpose of this article is not to add to this list of general reviews, but rather to describe the preparation of homogeneous ribonuclease and some derivatives, which may be useful to workers interested primarily in nucleic acids. Ribonuclease has proven useful in the study of RNA structure (5), the biological activity of RNAs (6), ribonucleoprotein complexes and particles (7), DNA-RNA hybrids (8), and also in the preparation of oligo-ribonucleotides both by degradation of polymeric materials (9) and synthetically by transesterification reactions (10).

For many of the applications of this enzyme, all that is required of the preparation is that it hydrolyze RNA and nothing else. In these cases the crystalline enzyme of commerce is quite satisfactory. However, it is well known that crystalline ribonuclease contains a number of components with ribonuclease activity (11). Only the major component of these preparations, ribonuclease A, has been thoroughly studied. Prudence therefore demands that in the more exacting applications of this enzyme chromatographically homogeneous preparations be employed. In view of recent reports to the effect that some derivatives of ribonuclease A have a significantly higher ratio of transfer to hydrolytic activity (12), a description of the preparation of some readily prepared derivatives of ribonuclease A is included. These are ribonuclease S (13) (including also S-peptide and S-protein) and the closely related ribonuclease E (14).

ASSAY METHODS

There are three general types of assay methods for ribonuclease in current use and an example will be given of each of these. Each method depends on a different property of the enzyme, namely: A, the depolymerization of RNA, B, the production of acid soluble fragments from RNA, and C, the hydrolysis of pyrimidine nucleoside cyclic phosphates. The choice of the most advantageous procedure will depend on the particular experimental situation. Method A is a rapid, but only moderately accurate assay useful for many routine applications. Method B lends itself well to the assay of a large number of samples, for example in analyzing chromatographic eluates. Method C is the most precise of the assay procedures described and is the method of choice for kinetic studies; it is however relatively slow and the substrate is expensive so that it is generally not to be recommended for routine assays.

Method A.   Kunitz Spectrophotometric Assay (15)

Substrate

Yeast ribonucleic acid (a good commercial grade is adequate) dissolved in 0.1 M sodium acetate buffer, pH 5.0, at a concentration sufficient to yield an absorbancy at 300 mμ of about 1.0.

Procedure

The enzyme to be assayed (1–20 μg) is dissolved in 2 ml of 0.1 M sodium acetate buffer, pH 5. This solution is mixed with an equal volume of substrate solution and the optical density at 300 mμ is recorded at 30-sec intervals over the course of 5 min. The curves so obtained are compared with standard curves obtained with known amounts of enzyme.

Method B.   Precipitation Assay (16)

Substrate

0.5% RNA in 0.1 M sodium acetate buffer, pH 5. A good grade of commercial RNA may be used without purification. Alternately, a

1% solution of RNA in the acetate buffer may be treated with 3 volumes of ethanol and ⅕ volume of glacial acetic acid. The precipitate after two such treatments is sufficiently free of low molecular weight nucleotides.

Precipitating Reagent

0.25% uranyl acetate in 2.5% trichloroacetic acid.

Procedure

1 ml of the RNA substrate is incubated with 10–100 μliters of enzyme solution for 15 min at 25 C. The reaction is stopped by the addition of 1 ml of the precipitant. After 5 min, the suspension is centrifuged at 1500 rev/min for 5 min and a sample of the clear supernatant fluid is diluted with 10 volumes of water. The optical density of this solution is measured at 260 mμ and compared to a standard curve, which must be established for each batch of substrate solution. This procedure gives a linear response between 1 and 10 μg of ribonuclease.

Method C.   Pyrimidine Cyclic Phosphate Hydrolase Assay (17)

Substrate

A solution of the barium salt of cytidine 2′:3′-cyclic phosphate, 3 mg/ml in 0.3 M NaCl. The pH of the solution is carefully adjusted to 7.0. This solution must be freshly prepared because of the instability of the cyclic phosphate.

Procedure

3 ml of the substrate solution is introduced into a pH-stat cell, which is maintained at 25 C by circulating water from a constant temperature bath. The pH is maintained at 7.0 by the automatic addition of 0.02 N NaOH. There should be a negligible blank reaction under these conditions. The enzyme solution to be assayed is added and the base consumption necessary to maintain pH 7 is recorded as a function of time for 10 min. The initial slope of this curve is proportional to enzyme concentration in the range of 1–10 μg.

PREPARATION OF RIBONUCLEASE A

Ribonuclease A is the major chromatographic component of crystalline ribonuclease (18). This material may be considered as the standard preparation of the enzyme and has been well characterized with respect to its chemical, physical, and enzymatic properties. The amounts and nature of the other components of the crystalline enzyme may vary widely from preparation to preparation. In view of reports of specificity differences between ribonuclease A and some of the other components of the crystalline preparation (19), the chromatographically purified material should be employed in all careful work. The procedure described is that of Hirs, Moore, and Stein (18) with only minor modifications.

Materials

The *Ion Exchange Resin* used is Amberlite IRC-50 (XE-64), a finely ground carboxyl substituted polyacrylic resin. The resin should be in the form of 200–400 mesh particles with the fines removed by decantation after settling of the bulk of the material in water. The air-dried resin should be washed with acetone until the washings are clear and is then converted to the sodium salt by the slow addition of 40% NaOH. The resin is washed with water on a Büchner funnel (until the pH of the filtrate is about 10) and reconverted to the acid form with 3 N HCl. The resin is finally washed with water to remove excess acid.

BUFFER. The buffer used is 0.2 M sodium phosphate, pH 6.47. It is prepared by dissolving 165.6 g of $NaH_2PO_4 \cdot H_2O$ and 113.6 g of anhydrous Na_2HPO_4 in water and diluting to 10 liters. Thymol may be added as a preservative or alternately all operations may be performed at 2 C.

THE COLUMN. For preparative purposes a column 7.5 cm in diameter and 60 cm long is a useful size. Approximately 800 g of resin should be worked up in order to pour such a column. The water-washed resin is suspended in 2.5 liters of buffer and the pH of the suspension is brought to 6.5 by the addition of 15-ml portions of 40% NaOH at 15-min intervals. After stirring overnight, the pH of the suspension is readjusted with NaOH until it remains constant between 6.45 and 6.50. At this point the resin is washed with buffer on a Büchner funnel until the pH of the filtrate is the same as that of the starting buffer. 15 liters of buffer should suffice for this operation. The resin is now suspended as a freely flowing slurry in buffer and the column is poured in four equal sections. The column should be closed at the bottom by a stopcock or pinch-clamp during the addition of the suspension. Buffer should be allowed to flow only after the suspension has been stirred into the column and allowed to settle. A 7-cm circle of filter paper is placed on top of the column in order to protect its surface during the addition of sample. Before use the column should be washed with a few liters of buffer.

Column Operation. This column can be used to chromatograph up to about 1 g of ribonuclease (or any of a number of chemically or enzymically modified ribonucleases). The sample may be dissolved in 20 to 30 ml of buffer or neutral salt and should be washed into the column with two 10-ml portions of buffer before starting the elution. Chromatography can conveniently be carried out under gravity flow, however, the flow rate should not be allowed to exceed 100 ml/hr. Ribonuclease A, which represents 80–90% of ordinary crystalline ribonuclease will be eluted after 2.5–3 liters of buffer have passed through the column. The column is conveniently monitored by following the optical density of the effluent at 280 mμ, together with ribonuclease assays on the appropriate fractions. The column may be used repeatedly without repouring, but should be protected from microbial action by the addition of thymol or toluene to the buffer. It is good practice to wash the column with several liters of buffer prior to subsequent use.

Desalting and Concentration

The ribonuclease A obtained as described above is in the form of a rather dilute solution in phosphate buffer. For many purposes it is convenient to have this material in the form of a salt-free lyophilized powder. Because of its small size and basic character, ribonuclease readily diffuses through most commercial dialysis membranes. Desalting by dialysis can therefore result in large losses of material and is generally avoided. Furthermore, it is very difficult to remove the last traces of phosphate from ribonuclease solution by dialysis procedures.

A useful desalting procedure is as follows (**13,14**): The ribonuclease solution is diluted with three volumes of water and the pH is adjusted to 5.0 with glacial acetic acid. The solution is poured through a 2.5- × 30-cm column of carboxymethyl cellulose (adjusted to pH 5 and washed with water). After all of the ribonuclease has been applied to the column, it is washed with 250 ml of water. The ribonuclease is eluted with 0.4 M ammonium bicarbonate (pH 7.8–8.0). It is convenient to collect 10-ml fractions and to pool those containing the bulk of the ribonuclease. The bulk of the ammonium bicarbonate is removed by lyophilization after which last traces of salt may be removed by dissolving the lyophilized material in water and passage through a 1- × 10-cm column of a mixed-bed ion-exchange resin. Lyophilization has sometimes been found to lead to some aggregation of ribonuclease (**20**), although the procedure outlined above has generally been found to largely avoid this difficulty.

SPECIFICITY AND SOME PROPERTIES
OF RIBONUCLEASE A

Ribonuclease breaks down RNA in a two stage process. In the first step, the substrate is depolymerized by a transesterification reaction in which internucleotide phosphodiester bonds are converted to intranucleotide cyclic 2′:3′-phosphodiesters. These latter are subsequently hydrolyzed to 3′-phosphates. Ribonuclease classically is considered to hydrolyze only those phosphodiester bonds of RNA that involve phosphate esterified to the 3′-hydroxyl of a pyrimidine nucleoside (21). This specificity seems to be strictly obeyed with RNA substrates, but polyadenylic acid (22) and polyribose phosphate (23) have also been found to be degraded by apparently pure ribonuclease A. The significance of these interesting anomalies is still obscure.

The enzyme catalyzes also the formation of internucleotide bonds by transesterification reactions (24) between pyrimidine nucleoside cyclic phosphates and suitable acceptor alcohols. Only primary alcohols have been found to be utilized, assuring that only 3′-5′ internucleotide bonds may be formed in such reactions.

Ribonuclease is a small protein containing 124 amino acids in a single polypeptide chain, which is folded and held in a highly compact, almost spherical, shape by four disulfide bridges and a large but undetermined number of noncovalent interactions. A summary of some of the important properties of the enzyme is shown in Table 1. The complete amino acid sequence of the protein is known as the

TABLE 1. *Properties of Ribonuclease A*

Molecular weight	13,683	(25)[a]
Isoionic point	9.6	(26)
Sedimentation coefficient ($S_{20, w}$)	1.90	(27)
Molar extinction coefficient (2775 Å)	9800	(4)
Intrinsic viscosity (cc/g)	3.3	(28)
Amino acid residues believed to be in the "active center"		
Histidine *12*		(29)
Histidine *119*		(30)
Lysine *41*		(31)
pH optimum	7.7	(32)

[a] Numbers in parentheses refer to bibliography at end of chapter.

result of the early studies of Anfinsen, and of the work of Hirs, Stein, and Moore and their colleagues (33). As indicated in Table 1, there is a considerable body of evidence that implicates histidine residues 12 and 119 together with lysine 41 as direct participants in the catalytic process. The manner in which these amino acid residues interact to form a catalytic site remains to be clarified as does the probable involvement of other amino acid residues.

One of the most important properties of ribonuclease is its remarkable stability. The enzyme is quite stable to the action of dilute acid, heat, and many proteolytic enzymes. This stability is generally enhanced by the presence of RNA or its degradation products so that the problem of inactivating the enzyme in the presence of its substrate can be difficult. Perhaps the surest way of irreversibly destroying ribonuclease activity is by treatment with alkali at room temperature. A few minutes of exposure at pH 13 or higher generally suffices to completely destroy ribonuclease activity. It is a good idea to rinse all glassware with 0.1 N NaOH after exposure to ribonuclease if accidental contamination of RNA preparations is to be avoided. For some purposes it is not feasible to treat the sample with alkali to remove ribonuclease. In these cases the enzyme can often be removed completely by adsorption on bentonite particles (35). Ribonuclease is denatured by 8 M urea, but the effects of urea are readily reversed on dilution or simply on the addition of RNA (36). Denaturation by high concentrations of guanidinium chloride is also reversible by dilution, but not by RNA (36), so that this reagent may provide an alternate way of inactivating ribonuclease in the presence of substrate.

Ribonuclease S is clearly the most interesting of all of the derivatives of ribonuclease prepared to date. This material is the product of the limited hydrolysis of ribonuclease by the bacterial protease subtilisin and was isolated and characterized by Richards and his colleagues (13,34). Ribonuclease S results from the scission of the peptide bond between residues 20 and 21. The two parts (which are known as S peptide and S protein for the short and long piece, respectively) may be separated and recombined with accompanying loss and regain of enzymatic activity. The very strong attachment of the two parts in neutral solution is a dramatic demonstration of the importance and specificity of noncovalent interactions in macromolecular structures. The system provides a highly instructive model with which to consider such phenomena as hormone action, interallelic complementation, and perhaps even gene repression.

A very closely related derivative, ribonuclease E, is the result of the hydrolysis of two adjacent peptide bonds (19–20, and 20–21) in the ribonuclease molecule as catalyzed by porcine pancreatic elastase (14).

Aside from the fact that a carboxyl terminal alanine residue is removed from the peptide portion, ribonuclease E and its two parts are identical with ribonuclease S. It is likely that some structural feature of the ribonuclease molecule is responsible for the unusual susceptibility to proteolysis of peptide bonds near residues 19 and 20. It has been proposed that a cross β type of structure in this region of the ribonuclease molecule could account for this interesting property.

Interest in ribonuclease S (and in a number of other modified ribonucleases) has recently received an additional stimulus through the work of Bernfield and Nirenberg (12), who have found that S-protein (which is identical with E-protein) has a small amount of residual ribonuclease activity and a *relatively* high synthetic activity. In making use of this observation, they have prepared a number of oligonucleotides. It is still too early to assess the significance of this observation with regards to the question of the nature of the active center of the enzyme.

PREPARATION OF RIBONUCLEASE S (13)

Subtilisin (subtilopeptidase A) may be obtained commercially from a number of sources. Because of strain differences in the *Bacillus Subtilis* used by the various manufacturers, the preparations may not all be identical in their properties, but they can in general be used to prepare ribonuclease S in reasonable yield.

Diisopropylfluorophosphate is a convenient reagent for inactivating subtilisin. It should be handled with care in a good hood.

A *pH stat* is desirable, but it is not essential. In its absence, the pH of the reaction mixture should be maintained by the manual addition of NaOH with a microburette. The reaction vessel should be maintained at 3 C by immersion in a constant temperature bath or by circulating ice water through a water jacket surrounding the vessel.

Procedure

Ribonuclease A, 700 mg (50 μmoles) is dissolved in 5 ml of 0.1 M NaCl and placed in a titration vessel of the pH stat. The temperature should be lowered to about 3 C by circulating cold water through the walls of the vessel. The pH of the reaction mixture should be adjusted to 8.0 and automatically maintained at this value with 0.1 N NaOH. 1 mg of subtilisin is added in 200 μliters of water. After about 3 hr the rate of the reaction becomes very slow and approximately 450 μliters of base (0.9 moles/mole of ribonuclease) have been consumed. The reaction is terminated by the addition of 2 μliters of diisopropylfluoro-phosphate. The entire reaction mixture is chromatographed on an IRC-50 (XE-64) column. The procedure used is as described above for ribonuclease A with the exception that the pH at which the column is run is lowered slightly to 6.35. Ribonuclease S is eluted after ribo-nuclease A and should represent the major component (up to 90%) of the reaction mixture. Desalting and concentration are effected ex-actly as described for ribonuclease A.

Resolution into S-Peptide and S-Protein

Desalted and lyophilized ribonuclease S is dissolved in water at a concentration of 10 mg/ml. The solution is chilled to 0 C and 0.2 volumes of cold, freshly prepared, 20% trichloroacetic acid are added. The mixture is allowed to warm to 25 C over the course of an hour, during which time a copious precipitate forms. The mixture is cen-trifuged and the supernatant solution is removed with a Pasteur pipette. The residue is dissolved in the original volume of water and the precipitation is repeated exactly as before. The combined super-natant solutions are freed of trichloroacetic acid by exhaustive extrac-tion with ether (acidification with a little acetic acid is helpful after the bulk of the trichloroacetic acid has been removed) and lyophilized. This material is S-peptide and is free of ribonuclease activity. The precipitate, which is S-protein in an almost pure state (it is difficult to remove the last traces of ribonuclease A from ribonuclease S), is conveniently desalted by passage over a small mixed bed resin deioniz-ing column and lyophilized.

PREPARATION OF RIBONUCLEASE E (14)

Ribonuclease E is prepared by procedures similar to those used in the preparation of ribonuclease S. Ribonuclease A is prepared as a 2% solution in 0.1 M NaCl, which is also 11 mM in uridylic acid (the commercial mixture of 2' and 3' isomers). The uridylic acid improves the yield of ribonuclease E by inhibiting its degradation. The reaction is performed in the pH stat at 25 C and the pH is maintained at 8.0 with 0.1 N NaOH. Porcine pancreatic elastase is added to initiate the reaction (4 mg of the crystalline enzyme/of ribonuclease). The reaction is allowed to proceed until approximately two bonds have been hy-drolyzed per ribonuclease molecule (1.3 ml of 0.1 N NaOH/g of ribo-nuclease). The reaction is terminated by the addition of 2 μliters of diisopropylfluorophosphate and the entire reaction mixture is chromatographed on the XE-64 column as described for ribonuclease A. Ribonuclease E migrates more slowly than ribonuclease A and is obtained in approximately 50% yield. The remaining 50% will chromatograph at the position of ribonuclease A, but represents a mixture of species (14). Concentration and desalting are effected as for ribonuclease A. The material may be resolved into E-peptide and E-protein exactly as described for ribonuclease S. E-protein is identical with S-protein, whereas E-peptide differs from S-peptide in that it is lacking an alanine residue from its COOH terminus. This deletion does not have any detectable effect on the ability of E-peptide to activate E-protein.

REFERENCES

1. LINDERSTRØM-LANG, K. U., and J. A. SCHELLMAN. 1959. *In* P. D. Boyer, H. Lardy, and K. Myrbäck, eds., The enzymes. Academic Press, New York. Vol. I, p. 443.
2. HUMMEL, J. P., and G. KALNITSKY. 1964. Ann. Rev. Biochem. *33:* 15.
3. RICHARDS, F. M. 1964. *In* T. W. Goodwin, J. I. Harris, and B. S. Hartley, eds., Structure and activity of enzymes. Academic Press, New York. P. 5.
4. SCHERAGA, H. A., and J. A. RUPLEY. 1962. Advan. Enzymol. *24:* 161.
5. MCCULLY, K. S., and G. L. CANTONI. 1962. J. Biol. Chem. *237:* 3760.
6. ZAMECNIK, P. C., and E. B. KELLER. 1957. J. Biol. Chem. *224:* 1065.
7. WETTSTEIN, F. O., T. STAEHLIN, and H. NOLL. 1963. Nature. *197:* 430.
8. HAYASHI, M., and S. SPIEGELMAN. 1961. Proc. Natl. Acad. Sci., U.S. *47:* 1564.
9. HEPPEL, L. A., P. J. ORTIZ, and S. OCHOA. 1957. J. Biol. Chem. *229:* 679.
10. HEPPEL, L. A., P. R. WHITFIELD, and R. MARKHAM. 1955. Biochem. J. *60:* 8.
11. MARTIN, A. J. P., and R. R. PORTER. 1951. Biochem. J. *49:* 215.
12. BERNFIELD, M. R. 1965. J. Biol. Chem. In press.
13. RICHARDS, F. M., and P. J. VITHAYATHIL. 1959. J. Biol. Chem. *234:* 1459.
14. KLEE, W. A. 1965. J. Biol. Chem. *240:* 2900.
15. KUNITZ, M. 1946. J. Biol. Chem. *164:* 563.
16. KLEE, W. A., and F. M. RICHARDS. 1957. J. Biol. Chem. *229:* 489.
17. STARK, G. R., and W. H. STEIN. 1964. J. Biol. Chem. *239:* 3755.
18. HIRS, C. H. W., S. MOORE, and W. H. STEIN. 1953. J. Biol. Chem. *200:* 493.
19. HAKIM, A. A. 1952. Arch. Biochem. Biophys. *70:* 591.
20. CRESTFIELD, A. M., W. H. STEIN, and S. MOORE. 1962. Arch. Biochem. Biophys. Suppl. *1:* 217.
21. MARKHAM, R., and J. D. SMITH. 1952. Biochem. J. *52:* 552.
22. BEERS, R. F., JR. 1960. J. Biol. Chem. *235:* 2393.
23. ROSENBERG, E., and S. ZAMENHOF. 1961. J. Biol. Chem. *236:* 2845.
24. HEPPEL, L. A., and P. R. WHITFIELD. 1955. Biochem. J. *60:* 1.
25. HIRS, C. H. W., S. MOORE, and W. H. STEIN. 1956. J. Biol. Chem. *219:* 623.
26. TANFORD, C., and J. D. HAUENSTEIN. 1956. J. Am. Chem. Soc. *78:* 5287.

27. HARRINGTON, W. F., and J. A. SCHELLMAN. 1956. Compt. rend. trav. Lab. Carlsberg Sér. chim., *30:* 21.
28. BUZZELL, J. G., and C. TANFORD. 1956. Phys. Chem. *60:* 1204.
29. CRESTFIELD, A. M., W. H. STEIN, and S. MOORE. 1963. J. Biol. Chem. *238:* 2413.
30. STEIN, W. D., and E. A. BARNARD. 1959. J. Mol. Biol. *1:* 350.
31. HIRS, C. H. W. 1962. Brookhaven Symp. Biol. *15:* 154.
32. KUNITZ, M. 1940. J. Gen. Physiol. *24:* 15.
33. SMYTH, D. G., W. H. STEIN, and S. MOORE. 1963. J. Biol. Chem. *238:* 227.
34. RICHARDS, F. M. 1958. Proc. Natl. Acad. Sci., U.S. *44:* 162.
35. LITT, M., and V. M. INGRAM. 1964. Biochemistry. *3:* 560.
36. SELA, M., and C. B. ANFINSEN. 1957. Biochim. Biophys. Acta. *24:* 229.

2. Nonspecific Ribonucleases (Endonucleases)

Pig Liver Nuclei Ribonuclease (1)

LEON A. HEPPEL
NATIONAL INSTITUTE OF ARTHRITIS
AND METABOLIC DISEASES
NATIONAL INSTITUTES OF HEALTH
BETHESDA, MARYLAND

ASSAY

Poly A → oligonucleotides bearing a 5'-phosphate end group

Reagents

1. The reaction mixture (total volume 0.15 ml) contains

   Poly A (3.3 mg/ml)
   0.013 M $MgCl_2$
   0.066 M potassium phosphate, pH 7

   Enzyme

2. 3% perchloric acid

Procedure

This assay measures the formation of acid soluble products from poly A. It is not entirely specific for the ribonuclease; it also measures

31

a phosphodiesterase present in the initial fractions, which forms
5'-AMP from poly A. However, this introduces only a small error for
the bulk of the acid-soluble products arise from the activity of the
ribonuclease.

Fractions of 0.04 ml are removed after 30 and 60 min at 37 C and
introduced into a small centrifuge tube containing 0.46 ml of 3%
perchloric acid. The mixture is kept in ice for 10 min and centrifuged,
after which 0.1 ml of the supernatant fluid is mixed with 0.9 ml of
water and the absorbance is measured at 257 mμ. When necessary,
corrections are applied due to acid-soluble material in the enzyme
fraction. In 30 min, 50 μliters of crude liver homogenate produces an
increase in absorbance of 0.1. The units of activity are expressed as
micromoles of adenylic acid residues liberated per hour.

Purification Procedure (all steps below 4 C)

STEP 1. PREPARATION OF NUCLEI.   Two pig livers (yielding
2190 g of minced tissue) are obtained fresh at the slaughterhouse, cut
into 1-in. cubes and immersed in 3–4 liters of 0.25 M sucrose–0.0018 M
CaCl$_2$ contained in a large glass cylinder. The cylinder is surrounded
by ice during transportation to the laboratory. The pieces of liver are
now removed, blotted on filter paper, cut with scissors to $\frac{1}{4}$-in. cubes
and blotted once more. A 330-g portion of minced liver is blended
with 2550 ml of the sucrose–CaCl$_2$ mixture for 3 min in the large
5-speed Waring Blendor, using position 2 (40 v). The homogenate is
strained through 3 layers of cheesecloth and centrifuged for 10 min at
2500 rev/min in 250-ml glass bottles in the International no. 2 centrifuge or at 3500 rev/min in the large-angle head of the refrigerated
Lourdes centrifuge. At least 4 min are taken for acceleration and de-
celeration of the centrifuge. The supernatant fluid is removed by suction and the packed nuclei (about 1800 cc from 2190 g of liver) are
stored at −10 C. Preparations have been stable at this stage for several
years.

STEP 2. RUPTURE OF NUCLEI AND SOLUBILIZATION OF
ENZYME.   About 200 ml of packed nuclei are mixed with 300 ml of
0.02 M potassium phosphate buffer, pH 8, containing 0.01 M 2-mer-
captoethanol. The mixture is stirred in an ice bath during the addition
of one-quarter volume of n-butanol over a period of 11 min; stirring is
then continued for 5 min. Mixing is rapid enough to form a small
crater, but foaming is avoided. The mixture is centrifuged at 6000 × g
for 15 min. With a long-tip pipette the clear, yellow aqueous layer is
separated both from the butanol layer and from a protein gel floating

on top. This butanol-extracted solution is extracted three times with $\frac{1}{2}$ volume of cold ether in a cylinder. Mixing is gentle in order to avoid forming an emulsion. The final solution is centrifuged for 10 min at $5000 \times g$ and the ether layer is removed. Dissolved ether is removed by evaporation under vacuum over a period of 2–3 min. This does not seem to injure the enzyme.

STEP 3. The treated solution (488 ml) is mixed with 94.6 g of ammonium sulfate (19.4 g per 100 ml, 0–0.35 saturation). After 15 min the mixture is centrifuged at $5000 \times g$ for 10 min and the precipitate discarded. To the supernatant fluid (513 ml) is added 60.5 g of ammonium sulfate (11.8 g per 100 ml solution, 0.35–0.55 saturation). The precipitate is collected by centrifugation and dissolved in 0.02 M potassium phosphate, pH 7–0.001 M mercaptoethanol–0.001 M EDTA (45 ml). This material can be stored for at least several weeks at -10 C before going to the next step.

STEP 4. PROTAMINE PRECIPITATION OF NUCLEIC ACIDS. The preparation from Step 3 is thawed, at which time an inert precipitate is seen. This is removed by centrifugation. The supernatant solution (41 ml) is diluted with an equal volume of water, and 1% protamine sulfate is added until a precipitate no longer forms (about 2 ml). The mixture is allowed to stand for 10 min in an ice bath, after which it is centrifuged for 2 min at $10,000 \times g$ and the precipitate discarded.

STEP 5. ALKALINE AMMONIUM SULFATE PRECIPITATION. Ammonium hydroxide (0.3 N) is added to the supernatant solution with stirring until the pH (measured at 11 C) reaches 8; then 0.67 volume of saturated ammonium sulfate is added and stirring is continued for 10 min. The saturated ammonium sulfate was adjusted to pH 8.0 with concentrated NH_4OH, the pH being measured at 11 C on a fivefold dilution in water. The precipitate obtained by centrifugation is dissolved in the phosphate–mercaptoethanol–EDTA solution (15 ml).

STEP 6. PRECIPITATION BY DIALYSIS AND EXTRACTION OF ENZYME. The preparation is dialyzed against 0.002 M potassium phosphate–0.001 M mercaptoethanol–0.001 M EDTA, pH 7, for 5–6 hr. A precipitate develops, which is centrifuged down at $5000 \times g$ for 5 min and extracted with 6 ml of 0.2 M phosphate–0.001 M mercaptoethanol, pH 7.0. On freezing the supernatant solution a second precipitate often develops, which is collected and treated in the same manner.

As an alternative, potassium phosphate may be omitted from the dialysis medium or the pH may be changed to 7.8.

Comments

A summary of a typical preparation is shown in Table 1. The procedure has been carried out many times and the experience of six different laboratories is known. A considerable variation in yield and extent of purification is recorded, but a satisfactory fraction for preparation of oligonucleotides has been consistently obtained.

TABLE 1. *Purification of Ribonuclease from Pig Liver*

Step	Specific Activity	Percent of Total Units
2. Treatment with *n*-butanol	0.6	100
3. Ammonium sulfate	0.9	33[a]
4. Protamine supernatant	1.1	46
5. Ammonium sulfate	4.4	65
6. Dialysis		
a. Supernatant	1.9	25
b. Extract of precipitate	49.0	16

[a] An inhibitor is concentrated in this fraction and is removed on further purification.

PROPERTIES OF ENZYME

Contamination with Other Enzymes

Oligonucleotides can be formed from poly A and poly I even with the crude extract, if the incubation is carried out in the presence of 0.1 M phosphate to inhibit phosphomonoesterase activity. However, due to a phosphodiesterase, substantial amounts of 5′-mononucleotide are produced. Incubations with poly U and poly C show evidence of contamination with an enzyme similar to pancreatic ribonuclease. These contaminating activities are removed in the course of purification, except that traces of 5′-mononucleotides are found after exhaustive digestion with the purified enzyme. Only traces of deoxyribonuclease activity can be detected.

Specificity

All of the ribonucleotide homopolymers except poly G (average chain length 12 or 120) are hydrolyzed; however, the splitting of poly I requires a several-fold increase in the concentration of Mg^{2+}. Ribosomal RNA is also hydrolyzed. Polymers are hydrolyzed at a relatively rapid rate to oligonucleotides with a 5′-terminal phosphate, varying in chain length from about 8 to 12. These are further hydrolyzed at a slower rate to a mixture ranging from the dinucleotide to the hexanucleotide. The trinucleotide is almost totally resistant, whereas the tetranucleotide is hydrolyzed to the dinucleotide at an extremely slow rate.

Metal Requirements (2)

The enzyme shows activity only in the presence of Mg^{2+}, Mn^{2+}, or Co^{2+}; these cannot be replaced by Ca^{2-}, Zn^{2+}, Cu^{2+}, Ba^{2+}, Fe^{2+}, or Sr^{2+}. Also, they could not be replaced by spermidine, spermine, putrescine, or cadaverine. The optimal concentration of metal varies with the concentration of substrate. If 0.1 M Tris is substituted for phosphate in the standard assay, about 5×10^{-4} M Mg^{2+} is required for the hydrolysis of poly A that had been dialyzed against EDTA. Undialyzed polymers contain sufficient bound metals so that no stimulation by added Mg^{2+} is observed.

Stability (2)

The final preparation of enzyme can be stored for a year with less than 20% loss of activity if kept at −15 C in the presence of 20% sucrose. The enzyme can be lyophilized from a solution containing 20% sucrose, 5×10^{-3} M mercaptoethanol, and 1% KCl. After storage for 2 weeks at 2 C the reconstituted preparation shows no loss of activity. At 2 C there is no loss of activity after 24 hr at pH 7.6 or 8.6, but a 20% loss occurs after 3 hr at pH 6.5 and no activity remains after 3 hr at pH 5.3.

Other Properties

Activity of purified fractions was not linear as the concentration of enzyme was decreased. This could be corrected by the addition of 75–200 μg of bovine serum albumin to the test system. When dilution of the enzyme is necessary before assay, it is desirable to dilute with 0.5% bovine serum albumin–0.01 M phosphate, pH 7.

In some respects the pig liver ribonuclease resembles a nuclease from *Azotobacter agilis* (3). However, the latter enzyme hydrolyzes poly U and poly C very slowly. For this reason the pig liver fraction is more generally useful in the preparation of oligonucleotides bearing a 5′-phosphomonoester end group.

REFERENCES

1. HEPPEL, L. A., W. E. RAZZELL, and M. N. LIPSETT. 1961. Unpublished observations.
2. LIPSETT, M. N. 1962. Unpublished observations.
3. STEVENS, A., and R. J. HILMOE. 1960. J. Biol. Chem. *235:* 3016.

Spleen Acid Ribonuclease (1)

GIORGIO BERNARDI

CENTER FOR RESEARCH IN MACROMOLECULES

STRASBOURG, FRANCE

The preparation of a purified spleen acid ribonuclease has been described by Maver and Greco (2). A very highly purified preparation has been obtained by Bernardi and Bernardi (1) as a by-product of acid deoxyribonuclease during the purification of this latter enzyme.

ASSAY

Reaction

$$RNA \longrightarrow Oligonucleotides$$

The ribonuclease activity is assayed by measuring the liberation of acid-soluble oligonucleotides from soluble RNA, which is an excellent substrate for acid ribonuclease.

Reagents for the Acid Ribonuclease Assay

1. The reaction mixture (total volume 1.25 ml) contains

    a. 0.8 μmoles of sRNA-P†
       187.5 μmoles of acetate buffer, pH 5.0
       12.5 μmoles of EDTA
    b. Enzyme—if necessary this is diluted with 0.15 M acetate buffer +

---

† Yeast-soluble RNA from General Biochemicals, Chagrin Falls, Ohio, was used in the original work.

0.01 M EDTA, pH 5.0, containing 0.05% Armour bovine serum albumin

2. 12% Perchloric acid

Reagents for the Basic Ribonuclease Assay

1. The reaction mixture (total volume 1.25 ml) contains

   a. 0.8 μmoles of sRNA-P†
      125 μmoles of phosphate buffer, pH 7.2
      12.5 μmoles of $MgCl_2$
   b. Enzyme—if necessary this is diluted with 0.1 M phosphate buffer, pH 7.2 + 0.01 M $MgCl_2$, containing 0.05% Armour bovine serum albumin

2. 12% Perchloric acid

Procedure

The procedure described for acid deoxyribonuclease (p. 103) is used, except that all volumes are halved. Activity units are defined as for acid deoxyribonuclease (p. 103), except that the activity is not divided by two.

CHROMATOGRAPHIC PURIFICATION

The starting material is crude spleen nuclease II (see p. 105). The chromatographic purification is patterned on Procedure C for spleen acid deoxyribonuclease and summarized in Table 1.

STEP 1. DEAE-SEPHADEX A-50 (FIG. 1). This step has been described on p. 113. Two ribonuclease activities are not retained by the column equilibrated with 0.05 M phosphate buffer, pH 6.8. The first peak shows a ratio of acid to basic activity equal to about 40. The second peak shows a ratio equal to about 10. These ribonuclease activities were not studied further.‡

A third ribonuclease activity peak is retained by the column and eluted by 0.5 M phosphate buffer, pH 6.8; the ratio of acid to basic activity is over 500. This fraction is processed further. For the sake of convenience, acid ribonuclease-rich fractions from several chromato-

† Yeast-soluble RNA from General Biochemicals, Chagrin Falls, Ohio, was used in the original work.

‡ Their behavior on hydroxyapatite is shown in Fig. 4 (Spleen acid deoxyribonuclease, p. 114).

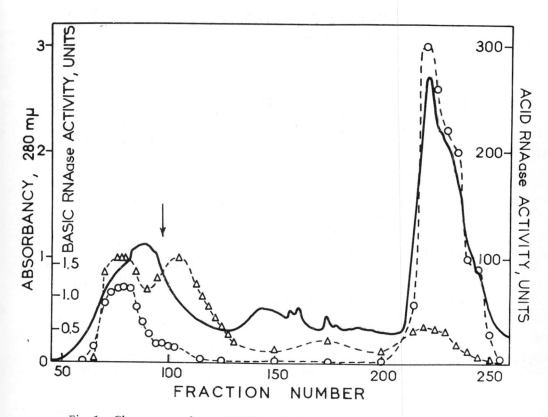

Fig. 1. Chromatography on DEAE-Sephadex A-50 of crude spleen nuclease II (see also p. 112) (Step 1). 330 ml of preparation HS 9 ($OD_{280} = 10.3$; $OD_{260} = 6.9$) were loaded on a 8- × 80-cm column of DEAE-Sephadex A-50 equilibrated with 0.05 M phosphate buffer, pH 6.8. This buffer was also used to elute the first protein peak. 0.5 M phosphate buffer, pH 6.8, was loaded at the fraction indicated by the arrow. 24-ml fractions were collected. The continuous line indicates the absorption at 280 mμ. Circles indicate the acid ribonuclease activity (right-hand scale). Triangles indicate the basic ribonuclease activity (left-hand inner scale). Acid deoxyribonuclease, cytochrome c, acid phosphomonoesterase, and phosphodiesterase were also assayed; the results are shown on pp. 112 and 238.

TABLE 1.   *Chromatographic Purification of Spleen Acid Ribonuclease[a]*

	Volume (ml)	Total OD_{280}	Total Units	Specific Activity
Crude spleen nuclease II				12.5[b]
Step 1. DEAE-S	70	1820	87,000	48
Step 2. Sephadex G-100	200	680	74,000	109
Step 3. Hydroxyapatite	120	80.5	43,300	538
Step 4. CM-Sephadex	183	19	41,000	2160
Step 5. Hydroxyapatite	5.1	6.2	15,000	2410

[a] All values reported refer to the fractions that were processed further or to the final product. The side fractions of the activity peaks were processed separately.

[b] This is the value obtained for preparation HS 11.

graphic purifications of crude spleen nuclease II preparations are precipitated with $(NH_4)_2SO_4$ (0.8 saturation at 20 C; the solutions are made 0.001 M with EDTA). The precipitate is collected by centrifugation and dissolved in a small volume of water.

STEP 2. SEPHADEX G-100 (FIG. 2).   The acid ribonuclease solution from the previous step is loaded on a Sephadex G-100 column equilibrated with 0.05 M phosphate buffer, pH 6.8. A complete separation of an acid phosphomonoesterase and acid ribonuclease is obtained by eluting with 0.05 M phosphate buffer, pH 6.8.

STEP 3. HYDROXYAPATITE (FIG. 3).   The active fraction from Sephadex G-100 is loaded on a hydroxyapatite column equilibrated with 0.1 M phosphate buffer, pH 6.8, which is also used to wash the column to elute some inactive material. A molarity gradient (0.05 to 0.5) of phosphate buffer, pH 6.8, elutes the ribonuclease activity at a molarity of about 0.12. The active fractions are concentrated to a small volume by freeze-drying and loaded on a Sephadex G-25 column equilibrated with 0.05 M phosphate buffer, pH 6.0.

STEP 4. CM-SEPHADEX C-50 (FIG. 4).   The ribonuclease fraction from Sephadex G-25 is loaded on a CM-Sephadex C-50 column, equilibrated with 0.05 M phosphate buffer, pH 6.0. Elution is carried out with a 0.05–0.4 M phosphate buffer gradient, pH 6.0. Acid ribonuclease is eluted after an inactive peak at a molarity of 0.15.

STEP 5. HYDROXYAPATITE (FIG. 5).   The central fractions from the activity-rich peak are pooled and run on a Sephadex G-25 column equilibrated with 0.05 M phosphate buffer.

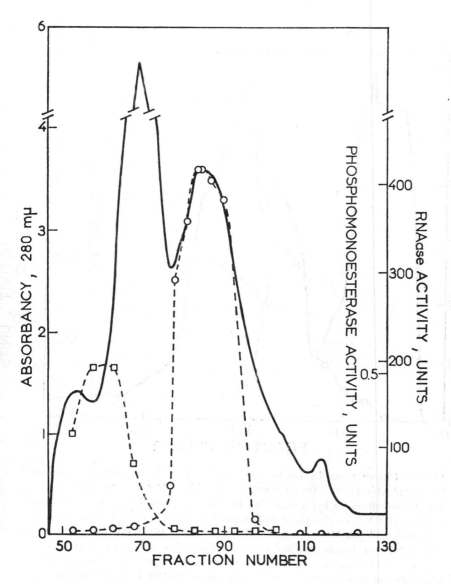

Fig. 2. Gel filtration on Sephadex G-100 of an acid ribonuclease–rich fraction obtained from DEAE-Sephadex. 70 ml ($OD_{280} = 26.00$; $OD_{260} = 15.80$) were loaded on a 4- × 90-cm column of Sephadex G-100 equilibrated with 0.05 M phosphate buffer, pH 6.8. The same buffer was used for the elution. 10-ml fractions were collected. The continuous line indicates the absorption at 280 mμ. Circles indicate the acid ribonuclease activity (right-hand scale). Squares indicate the phosphomonoesterase activity (right-hand inner scale). Fractions 77–96 were processed further.

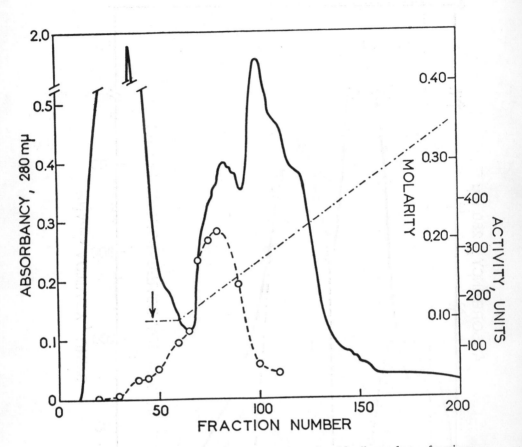

Fig. 3. Chromatography on hydroxyapatite of acid ribonuclease fractions from Sephadex G-100. 200 ml (OD_{280} = 3.40; OD_{260} = 2.78) were loaded on a 2- × 40-ml column of hydroxyapatite. Elution was carried out with a molarity gradient (0.1–0.5) of phosphate buffer, pH 6.8; this was started at the fraction indicated with an arrow (right-hand inner scale). 10-ml fractions were collected. The continuous line indicates the absorption at 280 mμ. Circles indicate the acid ribonuclease activity (right-hand outer scale). No phosphomonoesterase activity was detected in fractions 20–120. Fractions 60–90 were processed further.

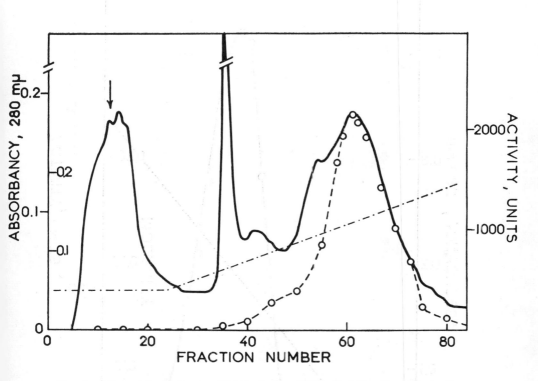

Fig. 4. Chromatography on CM-Sephadex C-50 of acid ribonuclease fractions from hydroxyapatite. 120 ml ($OD_{280} = 0.67$; $OD_{260} = 0.40$) are loaded on a 2- × 40-cm column of CM-Sephadex C-50 equilibrated with 0.05 M phosphate buffer, pH 6.0. Elution is carried out with a molarity gradient (0.05–0.4 M) of phosphate buffer. This was started at the fraction indicated by the arrow (left-hand inner scale). 10-ml fractions were collected. The continuous line indicates the absorption at 280 mμ. Circles indicate the acid ribonuclease activity (right-hand scale). Fractions 58–72 were processed further.

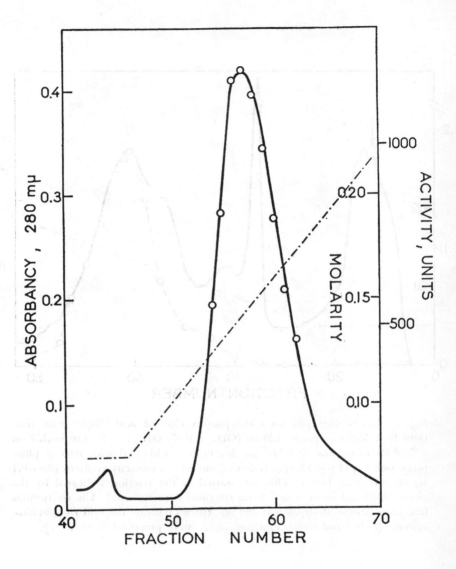

Fig. 5. Chromatography on hydroxyapatite of acid ribonuclease fractions from CM-Sephadex. 183 ml (OD_{280} = 0.104; OD_{260} = 0.064) are loaded on a 1- × 13-cm hydroxyapatite column equilibrated with 0.05 M phosphate buffer, pH 6.8. A molarity gradient (0.005–0.3) of phosphate buffer was used to elute acid ribonuclease (right-hand inner scale). 4.6-ml fractions were collected. The continuous line indicates the absorption at 280 mμ. Circles indicate the acid ribonuclease activity (right-hand outer scale). Fractions 53–60 were processed further.

The ribonuclease activity is then loaded on a hydroxyapatite column equilibrated with 0.05 M phosphate buffer and eluted with a 0.05–0.3 M molarity gradient. The ribonuclease activity is eluted at 0.12 M phosphate; the central fractions of the peak show a constant specific activity. They are run through a Sephadex G-25 column equilibrated with 0.004 M acetate buffer, pH 5.0, and then they are concentrated by freeze-drying to an $OD_{280} = 1.2$. The concentrated enzyme solution referred to as the final product in Table 1 is then frozen and stored at −60 C. Alternatively, the enzyme may be freeze-dried and stored at 60 C without any loss in activity.

Properties of the Enzyme

Spleen acid ribonuclease as obtained by this method is completely free of the following activities: phosphodiesterase as assayed on bis(*p*-nitrophenyl) phosphate, basic ribonuclease, and acid deoxyribonuclease. Its pH optimum is close to 5.3.

It is highly active on yeast-soluble RNA and on RNA "core," the water undialyzable RNA oligonucleotides resistant to pancreatic ribonuclease. Among synthetic polyribonucleotides, polyadenylic and polyuridylic acid are attacked, whereas polycytidylic acid is highly resistant.

The enzyme is heat labile; incubation at 55 C for 20 min causes a 50% loss in activity.

REFERENCES

1. BERNARDI, A., and G. BERNARDI. In preparation.
2. MAVER, M. E., and A. E. GRECO. 1962. J. Biol. Chem. *211:* 907.

Ribonuclease T₂ from Taka-Diastase

TSUNEKO UCHIDA AND FUJIO EGAMI
DEPARTMENT OF BIOPHYSICS AND BIOCHEMISTRY
THE UNIVERSITY OF TOKYO
TOKYO, JAPAN

ASSAY

I. General Method

Reagents

1. The reaction mixture (total volume 0.75 ml) contains

0.2 M Acetate buffer, pH 4.5	0.25 ml
20 mM EDTA aqueous solution	0.1 ml
Enzyme solution	0.1 ml

2. RNA (sodium salt) solution 12 mg/ml   0.25 ml
3. Uranyl reagent (0.75% uranyl acetate in 25% perchloric acid)

Procedure I

This assay measures the absorption at 260 mμ of the acid-soluble digestion products from commercial yeast RNA† and is used to follow enzymatic activity during the purification procedure.

---

† The blank value for the absorption by the RNA solution is approximately 0.1 at 260 mμ. When the commercial RNA used for assay contains larger amounts of acid-soluble fraction, it should be applied to a Sephadex G-25 column and the excluded fraction is used for the assay.

The reaction is started by addition of RNA solution to the rest of the reaction mixture and, after 15 min of incubation at 37 C, it is stopped with 0.25 ml of the uranyl reagent. The precipitate is immediately removed by centrifugation, 0.2 ml of the supernatant solution is diluted with 5.0 ml of distilled water, and the optical density at 260 mμ is read against a blank incubated without enzyme. The dilution procedure should be performed as fast as possible, because the blank value for the RNA solution increases somewhat with time. Enzyme solutions used for assay are diluted with 0.1% gelatin for avoiding the denaturation of ribonuclease T_2 due to dilution.

This assay is linear up to absorption values at 260 mμ of approximately 0.6. Within the range of linearity an increase in absorption values at 260 mμ of 0.1 is defined as 0.1 unit of enzyme activity. Protein concentration is determined by measuring the absorption of the enzyme solution at 280 mμ. Specific activity is defined as the ratio of the enzyme units in 0.1 ml of the enzyme solution and the absorption values at 280 mμ of the same solution.

II. Alternate Method

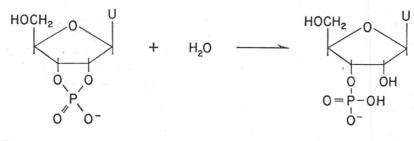

Reagents

1. The reaction mixture (total volume 2.5 ml) contains

0.25 M Citrate-NaOH buffer, pH 6.0	0.25 ml
Uridine 2',3'-cyclic phosphate (sodium salt) 4 mg/ml	0.25 ml

2. Enzyme (properly diluted with distilled water)   10 μl

Procedure

This assay measures the hydrolase activity of ribonuclease T_2, that is, the difference of absorption around 275–285 mμ between pyrimidine 2',3'-cyclic nucleotide as substrate and 3'-nucleotide as product is measured.

A recording spectrophotometer is set at an arbitrary wavelength within the range from 275 to 285 mμ, and both the "reference" and "sample" cells are filled up with the reaction mixture. The reaction is started by addition of enzyme to the "sample" cell at 25 C, and the relation of the increase in absorption to reaction time is recorded. The amount of uridine 3'-phosphate produced from uridine 2',3'-cyclic phosphate by ribonuclease T_2 is calculated from the slope of this relation within the range of linearity.

According to the recommendation of the International Union of Biochemistry, one unit (standard unit) of ribonuclease T_2 is the amount that will catalyze the transformation of 1 μmole of uridine 2',3'-cyclic phosphate to 3'-uridylic acid per minute in the above-mentioned condition. One unit as defined in Procedure I using RNA as substrate corresponds to ca. 0.30 standard unit (2).

ISOLATION PROCEDURE (1,3)

Crude Extract

Five hundred grams of Taka-Diastase powder are added to 3 liters of distilled water and well dispersed. The suspension is centrifuged at 3000 rev/min for 10 min. During centrifugation the powder dissolves almost completely without any special treatment. If a brown gum-like residue remains under the black and muddy residue in the bottom of the centrifuge tube, the whole residue is re-extracted with 2 liters of distilled water. The muddy precipitate is centrifuged off at 3000 rev/min for 10 min. The clear, reddish-brown supernatant solution (5 liters) has a conductivity corresponding to about a 0.1 M salt solution. It is adjusted to pH 7.0 with 2 N NaOH.

Batchwise Treatment with DEAE-Cellulose

300 g of DEAE-cellulose are washed with 0.5 N NaOH and then with water until the pH of the suspension is below 9. Finally they are washed 2 or 3 times to be equilibrated with 0.005 M Na_2HPO_4. About $\frac{2}{3}$ portions of the filter cake (corresponding to $\frac{1}{2}$ weight of the total protein in the crude extract) are added to the crude extract and the suspension is filtered after occasional stirring and standing for 20 min at room temperature. Preliminary experiments have verified that the adsorption equilibrium between the solution and DEAE-cellulose is accomplished in 10 min. The activity remaining in the filtrate is further adsorbed on DEAE-cellulose ($\frac{1}{3}$ portions of the above-mentioned filter cake). Most of the ribonuclease T_1 and colored impurities are adsorbed on DEAE-cellulose by this treatment. The filtrate, or ribonuclease T_2 rich fraction, contains 25–30% of the total activity at pH 4.5 in the crude extract. 50 or 60% of the total activity at pH 7.5 is recovered from DEAE-cellulose by elution with 0.35 M NaCl.

After use the DEAE-cellulose is regenerated by washing, in turn, with 2 N NaCl, 0.5 N NaOH, and water; it may be reused quite well for this batchwise treatment until the regeneration procedure has been carried out 5 times.

Heat Treatment

The ribonuclease T_2 rich fraction is adjusted to pH 1.5–1.8 with 2 N HCl. A small fine precipitate is removed by centrifugation at 3000 rev/min for 15 min. The turbid supernatant fluid is poured in a stew pan (1.5 liters), heated with stirring in a boiling water bath until the temperature of the solution reaches 78 C, kept at 78–81 C for 2 min, and quickly cooled to room temperature in an ice bath. The fine precipitate in the turbid supernatant fluid becomes larger during the heating. The recovery of enzymatic activity at pH 4.5 is 80–95%. This procedure serves to inactivate contaminating enzymes, such as deoxyribonuclease, nucleotidase, and protease.

Concentration by Ammonium Sulfate

The suspension obtained in the heat treatment is adjusted to pH 6.0 with 2 N NaOH, and brought to 0.4 $(NH_4)_2SO_4$ saturation by the addition of 300 g of solid salt/liter. After 30 min at room temperature, the flocculent precipitate is separated by centrifugation at 3000 rev/min for 20 min. The supernatant fluid is adjusted to pH 4.0 with 2 N HCl and brought to 1.0 saturation by the addition of 390 g of solid ammonium sulfate/liter. The turbid suspension is placed in the cold room overnight. The brown precipitate (containing ribonuclease T_2 and a part of ribonuclease T_1) is collected by centrifugation at 8000 rev/min for 20 min, dissolved in a small amount of 0.1 M citrate buffer at pH 6.0, and then dialyzed against tap water overnight.

DEAE-Cellulose Column Chromatography I

The dialyzed ribonuclease T_2 rich solution is adjusted to pH 7.0–7.5 by addition of 0.5 M Na_2HPO_4 to a final concentration of 0.005 N.

The enzyme solution (about 750 ml, containing about 8–10 g of protein) is loaded on a column of DEAE-cellulose (2.8 cm × 50 cm) that has previously been equilibrated with 0.005 M Na_2HPO_4. Then, two 20-ml portions of 0.005 M Na_2HPO_4 are used to wash the last bit of enzyme solution on the column. A 20-ml head of 0.005 M Na_2HPO_4 solution is applied and a nonlinear elution gradient is started. The mixer flask contains 1 liter of 0.005 M Na_2HPO_4 and the reservoir contains 2 liters of 0.25 M NaCl containing 0.25 M NaH_2PO_4. Fractions of approximately 10 ml are collected, and the flow rate is approximately 3.5 ml/min. Enzymatic activity is separated into three fractions; the first two peaks contain ribonuclease T_2 activity and are designated ribonuclease T_2–B and ribonuclease T_2–A in order of elution, whereas the last peak is ribonuclease T_1, which is obtained as by-product. Usually the amount of ribonuclease T_2–A exceeds that of ribonuclease T_2–B. The total activities at pH 4.5 of ribonuclease T_1 and ribonuclease T_2 are almost equal.

Alcohol Fractionation

The fractions containing ribonuclease T_2–A are combined and brought to 35% ethanol solution (v/v) with 99.5% ethanol, the temperature being maintained below 5 C in an ice bath. After standing for 20 min at 0 to -2 C, the solution is centrifuged at 12,000 rev/min for 20 min at -2 C. The supernatant fluid is brought to 52% ethanol solution (v/v) with 99.5% ethanol at temperatures below 5 C as above. A large amount of crystals of NaH_2PO_4 precipitates out together with the precipitate of ribonuclease T_2. They are collected by centrifugation at 12,000 rev/min for 20 min, dissolved in a small amount of 0.1 N citrate buffer (pH 6.3), and dialyzed against cold distilled water in a cold room overnight. The recovery of enzymatic activity is about 80%. (About 10% of enzymatic activity is further recovered from the 52–60% fraction.) The specific activity is raised to 30. This value is fairly variable within the range of 15–30 depending on the lot of Taka-Diastase powder. If the specific activity is below 25, further refractionation with ethanol must be carried out as above to obtain ribonuclease T_2 of high specific activity in the next step. Ribonuclease T_1 and colored impurities are precipitated above 52% by ethanol. Therefore, ribonuclease T_1 is separable from ribonuclease T_2, even if it is contained in the ribonuclease T_2 fraction.

Ribonuclease T_2–B fractions are fractionated as well as ribonuclease T_2–A fractions.

DEAE-Cellulose Column Chromatography II

The faintly yellow dialyzed solution of ribonuclease T_2–A is adjusted to pH 7.0–7.5 by the addition of 0.5 M Na_2HPO_4 to a final concentration of 0.005 M.

The enzyme solution (about 15 ml, containing about 50–100 mg of protein) is applied on a column of DEAE-cellulose (1.2 cm × 18 cm) previously equilibrated with 0.005 M Na_2HPO_4. Then two 5-ml portions of 0.005 M Na_2HPO_4 are used to wash the last bit of enzyme solution onto the column. A 5-ml head of 0.005 M Na_2HPO_4 solution is applied and a nonlinear elution gradient is started. The mixer flask contains 280 ml of 0.005 M Na_2HPO_4 and the reservoir contains 600 ml of 0.15 M NaCl containing 0.15 M NaH_2PO_4. Fractions of approximately 5 ml are collected, and the flow rate is approximately 1 ml/min. Ribonuclease T_2–A is eluted as a single peak with respect to the enzymatic activity as well as to the protein concentration. But in some cases, a small peak of ribonuclease T_2–B is eluted before the ribonuclease T_2–A peak. The ribonuclease T_2–A fractions of specific activity above 50 are collected and pooled; the recovery is 50–60%.

Ribonuclease T_2–B, as well as ribonuclease T_2–A, is also purified by this procedure.

Comments

A typical preparation is shown in Table 1.

TABLE 1. *Purification of Ribonuclease T_2 from Taka-Diastase*

Fraction	Total Protein (g)	Total Activity ($\times 10^3$ units)	Specific Activity	Activity pH 7.5/pH 4.5
I. Crude Extract	362	1344	0.37	2.3_3
II. Batchwise treatment with DEAE-cellulose	276	427	0.15	1.6
III. Heat treatment	212	422	0.20	1.4_4
IV. $(NH_4)_2SO_4$ (0.4–sat)	8.9_5	160	1.7_2	1.1_7
V. DEAE-cellulose I peak fractions	1.3_7	40	2.9_4	0.62
VI. Alcohol (35–52%)				
1st	0.18_6	25	13.5	0.49
2nd	0.05_8	18	30.2	—
VII. DEAE-cellulose II peak fractions	0.01_0	6	53–66	0.20

Note: After Step V, only the result of ribonuclease T_2–A is shown.

The ratio of ribonucleases T_2 and T_1 in the crude preparation is reflected in the ratio of enzymatic activity at pH 4.5 and 7.5. Ribonuclease T_2 exhibits some activity at pH 7.5–pH 7.5 activity/pH 4.5 activity = 1/15(1)–but ribonuclease T_1 shows considerable activity at pH 4.5–pH 7.5 activity/pH 4.5 activity = 5(3). Although the amount of ribonuclease T_2 contained in Taka-Diastase is variable depending on the lot, it appears from DEAE-cellulose column chromatography of a water extract of Taka-Diastase (pH 7.5 activity/pH 4.5 activity = 2.3) that less than about 20% of the total activity at pH 4.5 in the crude extract is due to ribonucleases T_2–A and T_2–B (1).

Ribonuclease T_2 thus obtained is purified about 800-fold, and is colorless and homogeneous in chromatography, paper electrophoresis, and sedimentation analysis. But in some cases where no increase of the specific activity above 50 can be revealed, even though the purification procedures are repeated several times, about 10% of a high-molecular contaminant is observed on gel filtration on a Sephadex G-75 column (1.5 cm × 70 cm), eluting with 0.03 M citrate buffer, pH 6.3.

Another method for the purification of ribonuclease T_2 is presented by Rushizky et al (4). The method consists of water extraction, acid treatment, acetone fractionation, and column chromatography on DEAE-cellulose (twice) and CM-cellulose (twice). The purity and specificity of their preparation may be nearly the same as those of the previously mentioned preparation, although an exact comparison is difficult because of the different method of enzyme assay used by these authors.

PROPERTIES OF ENZYME

Contamination with Other Enzymes

The purest ribonuclease T_2 fraction contains no other enzymatic activity such as phosphomonoesterase, phosphodiesterase, deoxyribonuclease, and ribonuclease T_1.

These enzymatic activities are tested as follows: Phosphomonoesterase activity and phosphodiesterase activity are determined by measuring the increase in absorption values at 405 mμ of p-nitrophenol liberated from p-nitrophenyl phosphate and from bis, p-nitrophenyl phosphate, respectively (5). Deoxyribonuclease activity is determined by measuring the absorption at 260 mμ of acid-soluble products formed from heat-denatured DNA (6). The contamination of ribonuclease T_1 is roughly checked by measuring the ratio of enzymatic activity at pH 4.5 and 7.5 (7). However, there is no method for the determination of a small amount of ribonuclease T_1 in ribonuclease T_2. Ribonuclease T_2 can be completely separated from ribonuclease T_1 by DEAE-cellulose column chromatography or gel filtration of Sephadex G-75 (1).

Stability

As shown in Table 2, ribonuclease T_2 is somewhat less stable than ribonuclease T_1, but is fairly stable as compared with most enzymes (1). It is most stable around neutral pH to room temperature and also to heating. It may be heated at 90 C for 5 min at pH 6.0 without loss of activity, but it loses activity fairly rapidly above 90 C. At weak alkaline pH it suffers little inactivation at room temperature, in contrast to the

TABLE 2. *Stability of Ribonuclease T₂*

Condition	pH									
	1.0[a]	2.2[b]	3.0[b]	4.0[b]	5.0[b]	6.0[b]	7.0[b]	8.1[b]	9.5[c]	11.3[c]
Room temp. % (25 C), 23 hr	24	58	74	80	92	93	95	98	92	78–70
80 C, 5 min %		76		80		100		66		0
Lyophilization %					84					

[a] 0.01 N HCl.
[b] 0.05 M Citrate–phosphate buffer.
[c] 0.05 M Na₂CO₃–NaOH buffer.

instability of ribonuclease T_1 at alkaline pH. However, in the acidic pH region ribonuclease T_2 is rather less stable than ribonuclease T_1.

About 80% of ribonuclease T_2 activity is recovered after frozen storage for several months at neutrality. Repeated freezing and thawing of the enzyme solution lead to some loss of activity. On lyophilization only about 15% inactivation at pH 6.0 is observed.

Activators and Inhibitors

The effects of various substances on ribonuclease T_2 are summarized in Table 3 (1).

TABLE 3. *Activators and Inhibitors*

Reagents	Final Concentration (−log M)	Activity Remaining (%)
NaCl	0	44
	1	91
NaF	1	104
NaH₃	2	92
Na₂S	2	36
AgNo₃	3	53
MgCl₂	1	78
CaCl₂	2	91
HgCl₂	3	40
MnSO₄	2	66
ZnSO₄	3	50
CuSO₄	3	0
FeSO₄	2	58
ICH₂COOH	2	120
BrCH₂COOH	4	100
DFP	6	104

Ribonuclease T_2 is inhibited by heavy metal ions, particularly by Cu^{2+} and slightly by Mg^{+2} and Ca^{2+}. The highly purified preparations of ribonuclease T_2 are not so clearly activated by EDTA as the partially purified enzyme.

Specificity

The studies on the specificity of ribonuclease T_2 have been carried out near the optimum pH (pH 4.5) for the cleavage of 3'-nucleotide phosphodiester bonds in high molecular weight substrates (8), such as RNA, or poly A, poly U, and poly C synthesized by polynucleotide phosphorylase, and at pH 6.0, in low molecular weight substrates (2), such as nucleotide 2',3'-cyclic phosphates or nucleotide benzyl esters.

Ribonuclease T_2 splits preferentially internucleotide bonds between the 3'-adenylic acid group and the 5'-hydroxyl groups of the adjacent nucleotide in RNA with the intermediate formation of adenosine 2', 3'-cyclic phosphate. It also splits the secondary phosphate ester bonds of other nucleotide in RNA via each nucleoside 2',3'-cyclic phosphate (4)(8) at a slower rate. Hence it is regarded as a nonspecific endo-ribonuclease [EC. 2.7.7.17, Ribonucleate nucleotido-2'-transferase (cyclizing)].

Other Properties (3)

Some physical and chemical properties of ribonuclease T_2 are listed in Table 4. Ribonuclease T_2 is a neutral protein. Ribonuclease T_2 contains some neutral sugars. Although ribonuclease T_2–A and ribonuclease T_2–B are quite identical as proteins, their carbohydrate components may be somewhat different (1). From the results of amino acid composition ribonuclease T_2 is characterized as follows (1,3): (a) It is

TABLE 4.   *Physical and Chemical Properties of Ribonuclease T_2*

Molecular weight	36,000
$s_{20,\,w}$	3.6_1 S
Isoelectric point	Ca. 5
Absorption maximum	281 mμ
Absorption minimum	252 mμ
OD_{max}/OD_{min}	2.5_2
$OD^{0.1\%}_{max\ 1\ cm}$	1.9_9
Carbohydrate content	12–15%
Amino terminal	Glutamic acid (or glutamine)
Specific enzyme activity	1.4×10^3 units/mg of enzyme
	4.2×10^2 standard units/mg of enzyme
Molecular activity	15×10^3

composed of 325 amino acid residues per molecule. (b) It contains six histidine residues per molecule, that is, twice as many as ribonuclease T_1. Like ribonuclease I-A it is rich in lysine residues (23 residues), in spite of the lower content of histidine and arginine. (c) It has both tryptophan (7 residues) and methionine (One residue). (d) It possesses 11 residues of half-cystine. It has not yet been determined if there are free SH-groups.

Specific enzyme activity of ribonuclease T_2 is one-tenth of that of ribonuclease T_1 in arbitrary units (1). Molecular activity was calculated using uridine 2′,3′-cyclic phosphate as a substrate (2).

REFERENCES

1. UCHIDA, T. J. Biochem. (Tokyo). 1966. To be published.
2. SATO, S., T. UCHIDA, and F. EGAMI. Unpublished data.
3. EGAMI, F., K. TAKAHASHI, and T. UCHIDA. 1964. *In* J. N. Davidson and W. E. Cohn, editors, Progress in nucleic acid research and molecular biology. Academic Press: New York. Vol. III, p. 59.
4. RUSHIZKY, G. W., and H. A. SOBER. 1963. J. Biol. Chem. *238:* 371.
5. KOERNER, J. F., and R. L. SINSHEIMER. 1957. J. Biol. Chem. *228:* 1039.
6. ANDO, T. Biochim. Biophys. Acta. In press.
7. NAOI-TADA, M., K. SATO-ASANO, and F. EGAMI. 1959. J. Biochem. (Tokyo). *46:* 757.
8. UCHIDA, T., and F. EGAMI. J. Biochem. (Tokyo). 1966. To be published.

Bacillus subtilis Ribonuclease

SUSUMU NISHIMURA
NATIONAL CANCER CENTER RESEARCH
INSTITUTE
TOKYO, JAPAN

INTRODUCTION

Bacillus subtilis strain H produces three types of ribonucleases—two types of extracellular ribonucleases found in the culture medium (1,2) and an intracellular ribonuclease located inside the cells (3). The properties of the intracellular ribonuclease are quite different from those of the extracellular ribonucleases (3). The intracellular enzyme liberates all four constituent mononucleotides from the substrate RNA indicating that there is no base-specificity. The enzymatic activity is completely inhibited by 1.7×10^{-3} M EDTA. The pH optimum of this enzyme is 5.8 in contrast with that of the extracellular ribonucleases, which is 7.5.

Two forms of extracellular ribonucleases are isolated by column chromatography on IRC-50 or CM-cellulose. They do not differ from each other with respect to insensitivity to EDTA and metal ions, and enzymatic specificity on RNA (4–6). Since the extracellular ribonuclease 2 eluted later from the column is the predominant product from a culture medium and can be purified to yield crystalline enzyme, only the isolation and properties of this enzyme are described in this chapter.

ASSAY

Measurement of ultraviolet absorbance in
acid-soluble materials produced from RNA.

Reagent

1. The reaction mixture has essentially the same composition as described by Frisch-Niggemeyer and Reddi (7). In a total volume of 0.25 ml it contains

   0.067 M Sodium phosphate buffer, pH 7.3
   1.25 mg of Yeast high molecular weight RNA†
   0.01–0.1 Units of enzyme

2. 2 N HCl

Procedure

Just before the assay the ribonuclease is diluted to the appropriate concentration by use of chilled 0.067 M sodium phosphate buffer, pH 7.3. 0.125 ml of the diluted enzyme solution is mixed with an equal volume of the cooled RNA solution (10 mg/ml in 0.067 M sodium phosphate buffer, pH 7.3) in an ice bath. The reaction is started by bringing the reaction mixture to 37 C. After 15 min of incubation, the reaction is stopped by putting the tubes in an ice bath. Three minutes later, 0.1 ml of 2 N HCl are added. After 10 min at 0 C, the precipitate formed is removed by centrifugation at 2000 rev/min for 5 min. 0.05 ml of the supernatant fluid is taken and diluted to 2.5 ml by water. Ultraviolet absorbance of this solution is measured at 260 mμ. Usually the ultraviolet absorbance of the reaction mixture incubated without enzyme is taken as the blank. In order to standardize the relative amounts of the enzyme, 10 mg/ml of a stock solution of crystalline bovine pancreatic ribonuclease is used as a standard enzyme. Both enzymes, namely, *B. subtilis* ribonuclease and bovine pancreatic ribonuclease, must be diluted to the proper concentration *just* before assay, otherwise the activity is decreased. The assay is almost linear up to 0.35 of OD at 260 mμ. One unit of the *B. subtilis* ribonuclease is defined as the activity of the enzyme equivalent to 1 μg of bovine pancreatic ribonuclease measured under the above assay conditions.

ISOLATION PROCEDURE

Preparation of Culture Medium

The medium for growth of *B. subtilis* contains

8% Soluble starch
0.04 M Sodium citrate

---

† Yeast high molecular weight RNA is prepared as described by Crestfield *et al.* (14).

0.15 M $(NH_4)_2HPO_4$
0.02 M KCl
0.002 M $MgSO_4 \cdot 7H_2O$
0.001 M $CaCl_2$
1% Ethyl alcohol
Soybean extract†

The soybean extract is prepared as follows: 500 g of soybeans are suspended in 2.5 liters of 0.1% NaOH and boiled for 30 min the volume being kept constant by addition of water. After boiling, the swollen soybeans are homogenized together with the supernatant liquid by means of a Waring Blendor. The mushy material is then boiled again for 30 min with vigorous mixing.‡ The boiled material is filtered by using a Büchner funnel which has been covered with Hyflo Super Cel. The residue is washed with water. The combined filtrate is used for 10 liters of the medium.

After mixing all the components, the mixture (10 liters) is heated to boiling temperature with vigorous stirring. The hot medium is mixed with about 300 g of Hyflo Super Cel and immediately filtered

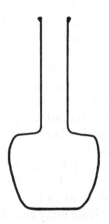

Fig. 1. The flask called a Sakaguchi bottle. Aeration can be done efficiently by a reciprocal shaking, due to the constricted shape of upper portion of a flask. (Reproduced from Biochim. Biophys. Acta., Ref. 5.)

† Soybean extract can be replaced by 1–2% of Soytone from Difco Laboratories in order to obtain the ribonuclease. However, in this case, the purification of the enzyme is unsuccessful since the materials from Soytone are eluted out in the same fraction with the enzyme from the CM-cellulose column. Hartley *et al.* (12) made a similar observation in the case of Neopeptone from Difco Laboratories.

‡ Baking the mushy material must be avoided. Baked extract does not have a good potency to stimulate the ribonuclease formation.

through a Büchner funnel, which has been coated with Hyflo Super Cel. 150-ml portions of this medium are added to 600-ml flasks as shown in Fig. 1. The medium is sterilized in an autoclave at 110 C for 15 min.

Growth of Cells

Bacillus subtilis strain H can be stored in a cold room on 2% agar slants containing 1% tryptone, 1% yeast extract, and 0.5% NaCl. Cells from the agar slants are transferred to a 600-ml flask containing 150 ml of the medium. The cells are grown for 24 hr at 30 C by shaking on a reciprocal shaker. One ml of this culture is then transferred to 600-ml flasks containing 150 ml of the medium. The flasks are shaken at about 130 rev/min at 30 C on a reciprocal shaker with a moving distance of about 6 cm. After shaking for 70 hr, maximum amounts of the extracellular ribonuclease are produced.†

Purification

ACID TREATMENT, ABSORPTION ON IRC-50 AND AMMO-NIUM SULFATE FRACTIONATION.   The 9 liters of the culture medium are pooled. The medium including the cells is acidified to pH 2 by the addition of 4 N H_2SO_4. After 10 min, 200 g of Hyflo Super Cel are added. The mixture is allowed to stand overnight at 4 C. First, the clear upper layer is filtered through a Büchner funnel, which is covered with Hyflo Super Cel, then the precipitates on the bottom are filtered. The filter cake is washed once with distilled water. The pH of the combined filtrate is adjusted to 4.2 by the addition of 4 N NaOH. 300 g of wet IRC-50 resin‡ are added to this filtrate. The pH of the suspension is again adjusted to 4.2 by the addition of 4 N H_2SO_4; next the suspension is filtered quickly with the aid of suction. The filtered resin thus obtained is washed with a small volume of distilled water. After the washing, the resin is dispersed in 400 ml of 0.2 M sodium phosphate buffer, pH 7.3, then 8% NH_3 solution is slowly added at 0 C until the pH reaches 7.3. The suspension is then filtered and the resin is washed with 300 ml of the same buffer. The combined filtrates

---

† The ribonuclease activity in the culture medium after 70-hr incubation varies from 5 to 20 units per ml. The cause of this variation is unknown. Overheating of the medium during sterilization must be avoided. Strong aeration is necessary for the production of the enzyme. Production of the enzyme using 10-liter fermenter with forced bubbled aeration instead of shaking was tried. However, it was not successful.

‡ The IRC-50 (XE-64) resin was obtained from the Rohm and Haas Co. and was treated before use by the procedure of Hirs (15). The resin can be reused after washing with 2 M NaOH and with water, respectively. The pH of the resin is adjusted to 7.3 by HCl and finally washed with water.

are then subjected to ammonium sulfate fractionation at pH 5.9 by addition at 0 C of 530 g of ammonium sulfate per liter of the filtrate. After 2 hr, the precipitate formed is collected by centrifugation at 5000 rev/min for 15 min and dissolved in 50 ml of distilled water. The over-all yield of the enzyme from the initial culture medium is usually about 50%. The enzyme can be kept frozen.

COLUMN CHROMATOGRAPHY BY CM-CELLULOSE.† The enzyme solution is dialyzed against 15 liters of deionized water for 15 hr at 4 C. The dialyzed enzyme solution is put on a CM-cellulose column (1.7 × 20 cm), which was equilibrated with 0.01 M sodium phosphate buffer, pH 6.0. The column is washed with 0.01 M phosphate buffer, pH 6.0, until the brown materials are almost washed

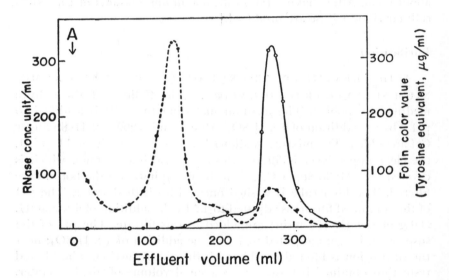

Fig. 2. Column chromatography of *B. subtilis* ribonuclease. The enzyme preparation loaded on a column (82 ml) contains 88 mg (tyrosine equivalent); the enzyme, 17,600 units. A, start elution with 0.1 M NaCl–0.01 M sodium phosphate. 63 mg (tyrosine equivalent) of contaminating protein in a volume of 110 ml is eluted out before the gradient elution is started. White circles indicate ribonuclease activity; black circles, protein content. The flow rate is about 30 ml/cm²hr. The protein content is assayed by the method of Lowry *et al.* (8), and is expressed as tyrosine equivalent by using a standard tyrosine solution.

† CM-cellulose, 0.58 meq/g is treated for use by washing with 0.1 M Na₂HPO₄, 0.1 M NaH₂PO₄, and deionized water, respectively, adjusting the pH of the CM-cellulose to 6.0 by the addition of NaOH, and finally washing with 0.01 M sodium phosphate buffer, pH 6.0.

through. Under these conditions, the enzyme is not eluted from the column. Convex elution gradient is then initiated with a 165-ml constant-volume mixing chamber filled with 0.01 M sodium phosphate buffer, pH 6.0, into which 0.1 M NaCl–0.01 M sodium phosphate, pH 6.0, is introduced. *B. subtilis* ribonuclease is eluted as shown in Fig. 2. The fractions corresponding to the last peak (250–330 ml) are collected, pooled, and dialyzed against 100 volumes of deionized water for 4 hr at 0 C with one change of water during the course of dialysis.† The dialyzed solution is then lyophilized to dryness and stored frozen at −20 C. Data in Fig. 2 show that the recovery of the enzyme from the column is almost 95%. Specific activity of the enzyme thus obtained is almost the same as that of crystalline bovine pancreatic ribonuclease when the protein content is assayed by Lowry's method (8). This enzyme preparation is considered pure in many respects (as mentioned later) and can be used for enzymatic purposes even though it contains small amounts of sodium chloride (which is used for the elution of the enzyme from the column).

Crystallization

The lyophilized enzyme is dissolved in distilled water with a concentration of 4 mg of tyrosine equivalent/ml. At 4 C saturated ammonium sulfate solution is slowly added with constant gentle stirring until a very faint turbidity appears. The solution is then left for 2 days at 4 C. Needle-shaped crystals of the enzyme are gradually formed. During the next two days, saturated ammonium sulfate solution is slowly added up to 0.7 saturation; two-thirds of the original enzyme can be crystallized as needles.

PROPERTIES OF ENZYME

Stability

The lyophilized enzyme is quite stable when kept frozen at −20 C. Activity decrease is not detected even after storage for 4 yr. The enzyme can be dissolved in distilled water at a concentration of 2–10 mg/ml, and also stored in a freezer at −20 C. Repeated freezing and thawing are not harmful to the enzyme.

Purity

No evidence for contamination of the lyophilized enzyme with deoxyribonuclease, phosphodiesterase, and phosphomonoesterase was

† The enzyme is lost by prolonged dialysis.

obtained (6,9,10). The enzyme shows a single N-terminal amino acid (serine) by the dinitrofluorobenzene or the trinitrofluorobenzene method (5). It is homogeneous as shown either by rechromatography using CM-cellulose or by ultracentrifugation.

Since no differences in enzymatic properties between the enzyme eluted from a CM-cellulose column and the crystallized enzyme are not observed, the former enzyme can be used for the enzymatic study.

Specificity

B. subtilis ribonuclease hydrolyzes preferentially the secondary phosphate esters of purine ribonucleoside 3′-phosphates of RNA. Cyclic nucleotides are formed as intermediates. After extensive hydrolysis of yeast high molecular weight RNA, 33% of guanylic acid, 9.6% of adenylic acid, and 1.2% of pyrimidine nucleotides are released as terminal nucleotides (4). It has been thought that the specificity of the enzyme is more complex than simple purine specific. The most extensive studies in this connection were carried out by Whitfeld and Witzel (11) and Rushizky *et al.* (6) using polynucleotides and oligonucleotides as substrates for the enzyme. The enzyme hydrolyzed GpGp and GpAp linkages in trinucleotides about 100 times faster than other phosphodiester bonds. ApApAp is hydrolyzed by the enzyme to form ApAp and cyclic adenylic acid. Similarly the products from ApApA are ApA and cyclic adenylic acid. GpCp and GpUp are split at an enzyme–substrate ratio at which CpGp, UpGp, ApGp, ApUp, and ApCp are resistant to cleavage. Dinucleoside monophosphates, such as GpA, GpC, GpG, GpU, IpC, and XpC, are hydrolyzed slowly, but faster than ApAp. ApA, CpA, and UpA are resistant to the enzyme. Experiments using polynucleotides showed that poly I is more rapidly hydrolyzed by the enzyme than poly A. Poly U and poly C are almost completely resistant when compared with poly A. However, poly U and poly C may be hydrolyzed if the enzyme is used in very great excess. Formation of pyrimidine nucleotides from RNA by excess amounts of the enzyme has also been reported (6,11).

Molecular Size and Amino Acid Composition

The sedimentation coefficient of the enzyme was found to be 1.4 compared with 1.6 for bovine pancreatic ribonuclease measured under the same condition (4). Hartley *et al.* also reported that the sedimentation coefficient, $s_{20,w}$ was 1.5 S. Molecular weight was determined to be $10,700 \pm 400$ (12).

Analysis of amino acid composition of the enzyme indicates that it differs from bovine pancreatic ribonuclease in many respects (5). The most remarkable difference is that *B. subtilis* ribonuclease does not contain cysteine and therefore has no disulfide bridges (5,12,13). The enzyme contains 3 moles of histidine residues and 4 moles of tryptophan residues per molecule. The enzymatic activity is inactivated either by photooxidation in the presence of methylene blue due to the specific degradation of histidine residue or by titration with N-bromosuccinimide due to the selective cleavage of C-tryptophyl peptide bonds (5).

Other Properties

The optimum pH value for the enzyme activity is 7.5 when 0.067 M phosphate is used as a buffer solution (2).† EDTA (0.01 M) has no inhibitory effect on the activity. Polyvinylsulfate known as a ribonuclease inhibitor also does not affect the enzymatic activity. Metal ions, such as Pb^{2+}, Mg^{2+}, Fe^{2+}, Fe^{3+}, Ca^{2+}, Mn^{2+}, Cu^{2+}, Co^{2+}, and Hg^{2+}, are not strongly inhibitory except for Hg^{2+} at the concentration of 0.01 M (4).

REFERENCES

1. NISHIMURA, S., and M. NOMURA. 1958. Biochim. Biophys. Acta. *30:* 430.
2. NISHIMURA, S., and M. NOMURA. 1959. J. Biochem. *46:* 161.
3. NISHIMURA, S., and B. MARUO. 1960. Biochim. Biophys. Acta. *40:* 355.
4. NISHIMURA, S. 1960. Biochim. Biophys. Acta. *45:* 15.
5. NISHIMURA, S., and H. OZAWA. 1962. Biochim. Biophys. Acta. *55:* 421.
6. RUSHIZKY, G. W., A. E. GRECO, R. W. HARTLEY, JR., and H. A. SOBER. 1963. Biochemistry. *2:* 787.
7. FRISCH-NIGGEMEYER, W., and K. K. REDDI. 1957. Biochim. Biophys. Acta. *26:* 40.
8. LOWRY, O. H., N. J. ROSEBROUGH, A. L. FARR, and R. J. RANDALL. 1951. J. Biol. Chem. *193:* 265.
9. NISHIMURA, S. Unpublished data.
10. WHITFELD, P. R. Personal communication.
11. WHITFELD, P. R., and H. WITZEL. 1963. Biochim. Biophys. Acta. *72:* 362.
12. HARTLEY, R. W., JR., G. W. RUSHIZKY, A. E. GRECO, and H. A. SOBER. 1963. Biochemistry. *2:* 794.
13. POLLOCK, M. R., and M. H. RICHMOND. 1962. Nature. *194:* 446.
14. CRESTFIELD, A. M., K. C. SMITH, and F. W. ALLEN. 1955. J. Biol. Chem. *216:* 185.
15. HIRS, C. W. H. 1955. In S. P. Colowick and N. O. Kaplan, editors, Methods in enzymology. Academic Press: New York. Vol. I, p. 113.

† Rushizky *et al.* reported that 8.5 is the pH optimum of the enzyme in Tris-Cl (6).

The Isolation, Assay,

and Properties of

Ribonuclease I from

Escherichia coli

PIERRE F. SPAHR
INSTITUTE OF MOLECULAR BIOLOGY
LABORATORY OF GENETIC BIOCHEMISTRY
UNIVERSITY OF GENEVA, SWITZERLAND

ASSAY

Procedure A (1)

This assay measures the production of acid-soluble nucleotides from yeast RNA by ribonuclease I and was used to determine the enzymic activity through the steps of the purification procedure.

The reaction mixture contains† 1 ml of a 1% solution of purified (2) yeast RNA in 0.1 M Tris buffer, pH 8.1, 0.5 ml of the same buffer, and 1 ml of enzyme. After incubation at 25 C for 25 min, 0.5 ml of 0.75% uranyl acetate in 25% perchloric acid is added; the suspension is mixed well and immediately centrifuged in the cold at 2000 × g for 10 min; 0.2 ml of the clear supernatant fluid is added to 6 ml of H_2O and the absorbancy of this solution is read at 260 mμ. Blanks without

† Reproduced from J. Biol. Chem. 1961. *236:* 823. With the permission of the copyright owner.

enzyme are run in parallel and their absorbancy subtracted from each sample.

A unit of *Escherichia coli* ribonuclease I is defined as the amount of enzyme which, under the above conditions, gives an absorbancy of 0.1. The assay is linear up to 0.6 absorbancy. Under these conditions, 0.1 μg of pancreatic ribonuclease gives an absorbancy of 0.215. The specific activity is expressed in units per mg of protein.

Procedure B (3)

This assay measures the release of alcohol-soluble nucleotides from C^{14}-labeled poly U or poly A by ribonuclease I and is used whenever small amounts of enzyme are to be estimated.

The reaction mixture contains in a final volume of 0.05 ml: 0.1 M KCl, 10 mM Tris buffer, pH 8.1, C^{14}-labeled poly U (7.5 μg and 13,800 dpm) or C^{14}-labeled poly A (7 μg and 21,000 dpm), and the enzyme. Controls without enzyme are run in parallel and their values subtracted from each sample. After incubation at 30 C for 20 min, the reaction is stopped by addition of 0.1 ml of a yeast RNA solution (5 mg per ml of 0.01 M Tris buffer, pH 8.1, 0.6 M NaCl, and 0.05 M $CaCl_2$) followed immediately by 1 ml of cold absolute ethanol. The resulting suspension is mixed well, kept in ice for 10 min, and then centrifuged in the cold at $2000 \times g$ for 10 min; 1 ml of the clear supernatant fluid is mixed with 10 ml of Bray's Solution (4) and counted in a liquid scintillation spectrophotometer.

A unit of *E. coli* ribonuclease I is defined as the amount of enzyme which, under the above conditions, renders 1 μg of polymer soluble in alcohol in 1 hr.

PURIFICATION PROCEDURE

Growth of *E. coli* Cells

STEP 1. Cultures of *E. coli strain* B are maintained on agar slants made from the following medium: 15 g of nutrient broth (Difco), 5 g of NaCl, 20 g of agar (Difco), 7 ml of 0.5 N KOH, and H_2O up to one liter. The cells on the slants can be stored in the refrigerator for months without loss of their viability.

STEP 2. PREPARATION OF THE MEDIUM (24 LITERS). Two 15-liter Pyrex carboys are used. Into each carboy are weighed: 72 g of $(NH_4)_2SO_4$, 72 g of vitamin-free casamino acids (Difco), and 36 g of NaCl. Each carboy is filled with about 10 liters of distilled water to dissolve the ingredients before the addition, per carboy, of 18 ml of a salt solution (16 g of $MgCl_2$, 0.3 g of $CaCl_2$, 0.1 g of $FeSO_4$ dissolved in 50 ml of distilled water) and 180 ml of a potassium phosphate buffer, pH 6.8 (34 g of KH_2PO_4 and 43.55 g of K_2HPO_4 in 500 ml of distilled water). The contents of both carboys are made up to 12 liters with H_2O. For the preculture medium, 500 ml of the above medium are withdrawn from each carboy and poured into two 1-liter Erlenmeyer flasks (if the preculture is carried out under forced aeration) or into larger containers (if the preculture is done on a shaker). Two solutions of dextrose, each containing 72 g in 600 ml of H_2O, are then prepared and from each a 25-ml sample is withdrawn and poured into two 100-ml Erlenmeyer flasks. The carboys, the preculture medium, and the four dextrose solutions are autoclaved for 1 hr at 125 C and 16 psi. (It is convenient to autoclave the carboys and the Erlenmeyer flasks containing the preculture medium with the cotton filtered aerators already fixed and clipped.) The solutions are allowed to cool down in the constant temperature room (35–37 C) where the culture will be carried out.

STEP 3. PRECULTURE. To the two Erlenmeyer flasks containing the 500 ml of medium are added, under sterile conditions, the two 25-ml dextrose solutions and then each flask is inoculated aseptically with an *E. coli* B slant. The aeration system is attached to an air supply and the air inflow is adjusted to give good aeration. Alternatively the two preculture containers can be placed on a shaker. The preculture is left to grow overnight.

STEP 4. CULTURE. On the following day, to each carboy are added the dextrose solution (575 ml) and the preculture. The forced aeration system is then adjusted to give a vigorous air stream without too much foaming. Foaming, if in excess, can be reduced by the addition of an antifoaming agent (such as propyleneglycol monolaurate, 1 ml per carboy). The growth curve is then followed by reading the absorbancy at 550 mμ of samples removed with sterile pipettes at suitable intervals. The cells are harvested at the end of the logarithmic phase of growth.

STEP 5. To harvest the cells, two large plastic containers (with a capacity of about 25 liters each) are half-filled with crushed ice and the contents of each carboy are poured into the ice. The suspension is well mixed and centrifuged in the cold in a continuous flow centrifuge (such as a Sharples). The cells are resuspended in about 400 ml of 0.01 M Tris buffer, pH 7.4, containing 0.01 M Mg^{2+} (standard buffer) well homogenized and centrifuged in the cold at about 10,000 $\times$ g for 20 min. The supernatant liquid is discarded and the washing process repeated once more. The well-packed cells are then divided into lots of about 15 g (the exact weight is recorded), conveniently wrapped in pieces of parafilm, and kept frozen. The yield is approximately 2 g of wet cells per liter of culture medium.

Isolation of Ribosomes from *E. coli* Cells (5)

STEP 1. PREPARATION OF A CELL-FREE EXTRACT. All operations are carried out at 4 C. Frozen cells, per lots of about 15 g, are ground by hand in a cold mortar with 3 parts (w/w) of alumina powder (Norton levigated alumina, Norton Abrasives, Worcester, Mass.) until a paste with a shiny appearance is obtained. This paste is thoroughly suspended in 3 volumes of standard buffer and the suspension is centrifuged at $10,000 \times g$ for 20 min. The supernatant fluid is collected and centrifuged once more to remove completely the alumina, cell debris, and unbroken cells, yielding the cell-free extract or crude extract.

STEP 2. PREPARATION OF RIBOSOMES FROM THE CRUDE EXTRACT. The cell-free extract is centrifuged in the rotor 40 of the Spinco Model L at 40,000 rev/min for 5 hr at 4 C. The supernatant liquid is decanted, the pellet of crude ribosomes is thoroughly resuspended in enough standard buffer to restore the original volume, and this suspension is centrifuged again at 40,000 rev/min for 5 hr. This process is repeated once more. The twice-washed ribosomes are thoroughly resuspended in 0.005 M Tris buffer, pH 7.4, and 0.01 M Mg^{2+} to give a concentration of about 30 mg of ribosomes/ml (a solution of 0.06 mg of ribosomes/ml has an absorbancy of 1.0 at 260 mμ). The yield is about 15–20 mg of ribosomes/g of cells (wet weight).

Purification of Ribonuclease I from *E. coli* Ribosomes (1)[†]

STEP 1. A solution of ribosomes, 15 ml (29.3 mg of ribosomes/ml) in 0.005 M Tris buffer, pH 7.4, and 0.01 M Mg^{2+} is added to an equal volume of the same buffer, which also contains 8 M urea and 0.1 M NaCl. The resulting mixture is dialyzed in the cold against three changes of 1 liter of buffer (0.01 M Tris, pH 7.4, 0.05 M NaCl, and 4 M urea) over a period of 24 hr. The solution, which is slightly turbid, is then extensively dialyzed against water (four changes each of 3 liters) in the cold to remove urea. A large precipitate appears inside the bag and is centrifuged off. The supernatant fluid is brought to pH 4.5 by addition of 5 ml of 0.2 M acetate buffer.

STEP 2. The solution is brought to 0.5 saturation with 11.2 g of $(NH_4)_2SO_4$, added in the cold with stirring. After standing for 10 min,

† Reproduced from J. Biol. Chem. 1961. *236*: 823. With the permission of the copyright owner.

the precipitate is centrifuged off and the supernatant fluid (40 ml) is brought to 0.8 saturation by adding 8.3 g of $(NH_4)_2SO_4$. The suspension is stirred in the cold for 10 min and then centrifuged. The supernatant solution is discarded and the precipitate dissolved in 10 ml of water and dialyzed against three changes of 3 liters of water in the cold. A small precipitate that forms at this stage is removed by centrifugation and the clear supernatant fluid is lyophized.

STEP 3.   A column (1 cm × 30 cm) of Amberlite CG-50 [Type II, 200–400 mesh, treated before use according to the procedure described in (6)] is buffered at pH 7.18 with 0.2 M phosphate buffer. Since the Amberlite CG-50 is a fine resin, a small plug of glass wool is placed on the column resting on the sintered glass disk to prevent clogging of the latter.† Several hold-up volumes of the buffer are run through at room temperature before use. The lyophilized material from Step 2 (25 mg) is dissolved in 1.2 ml of 0.2 M phosphate buffer, pH 7.18; any insoluble material is removed by centrifugation. Samples are withdrawn for activity and protein estimations, and the remainder is loaded on the column. After adsorption of the sample, the walls of the chromatographic tube are rinsed twice with 0.5 ml of buffer and the column is connected with a reservoir containing the same buffer to which a few crystals of chlorobutanol are added to prevent bacterial contamination. Elution is performed at room temperature at the rate of 1–1.5 ml/hr; fractions of 1-ml size are collected automatically. A 4% solution of bovine serum mercaptalbumin (or commercial crystalline albumin dialyzed versus EDTA) in water, 25 μliter, is added to each receiving tube, starting from Fraction 30. Portions of 0.05 to 0.1 ml are withdrawn from the tubes and assayed for ribonuclease I activity. The fractions containing the ribonuclease (fractions 40–50) are pooled, dialyzed in the cold against three changes of 2 liters of water (each change being left 3 hours), lyophilized, and stored at −20 C. The lyophilized preparation is stable for at least one year.

COMMENTS.   Table 1 gives the activity (assayed according to Procedure A) and protein content for each step of the procedure. The purification obtained is about 400-fold. A 730-fold purification can be obtained (1) by chromatography on Amberlite CG-50 of Step 2 under conditions different from those described here.

----

† Since it has been reported (7) that ribonuclease I is adsorbed on ultrafine glass filters and powdered glass, it is preferable to avoid the use of a sintered glass disk column and to replace it by a column fitted with the smallest possible glass wool plug covered with a layer of washed sea sand (Merck Co.). The loss of activity observed when using the sintered glass disc column amounts to about 10%.

TABLE 1. *Purification of* E. coli *Ribonuclease I*[a]

Purification step	Ribonuclease (units)	Protein (mg)	Ribonuclease (units/mg of protein)	Yield (% of activity)
Ribosomes	450	163	2.8	100
Step 1: Urea treatment and dialysis	450	90	5.0	100
Step 2: Ammonium sulfate fractionation	370	25	14.8	82
Step 3: Chromatography on Amberlite CG-50	290	0.27[b]	1072	65

[a] Reproduced from J. Biol. Chem. 1961. *236:* 823. With the permission of the copyright owner.

[b] Estimated in a parallel chromatogram with no bovine serum mercaptalbumin added to the receiving tubes.

SOME PROPERTIES OF THE ENZYME (1)

Purity of the Preparation

The purified *E. coli* ribonuclease I does not show any phosphatase activity, in the pH range 5 to 9.1, when incubated with the following substrates: *o*-carboxyphenylphosphate, *p*-nitrophenylphosphate and the four nucleosides 5'-mono, -di, and -triphosphates.

The preparation of *E. coli* ribonuclease I does not release any acid-soluble deoxynucleotides upon incubation with tritium-labeled DNA. Thus the deoxyribonuclease reported (6) to be present in the ribosomes has been removed in the course of the purification. Ribonuclease I has no activity towards Calcium bis-*p*-nitrophenylphosphate either at pH 5.1 or 8.5.

The purified *E. coli* ribonuclease I is free of ribonuclease II (3), the latter enzyme being completely destroyed after the urea treatment of Step I (see Purification of Ribonuclease I from *E. coli* Ribosomes).

Optimal pH and Stability of Ribonuclease I

The pH optimal for ribonuclease I activity is 8.1 in Tris buffer ($\mu = 0.1$). At pH 5.0 (ammonium acetate buffer) one observes only 8% of the activity assayed at pH 8.1 in Tris.

E. coli ribonuclease I is relatively stable to heat only at acid pH: It retains 53% of its activity when heated at pH 3.1 for 15 min at 100 C, but is completely inactivated after heating at pH 8.8.

The enzyme is stable in the 3.9–9.0 pH range, no activity being lost after 4 days at 4 C.

Effect of Ions upon the Activity of Ribonuclease I

Ribonuclease I activity (assayed in 0.1 M Tris, pH 8.1) is greatly enhanced by the presence of monovalent cations such as K^+ and Na^+. In 0.1 M Tris buffer, pH 8.1, containing 0.2 M NaCl or KCl the activity is about 1.6 times higher than that assayed in 0.1 M Tris buffer alone. NaF has the same effect as NaCl. Ribonuclease does not require a divalent cation for its activity: It is fully active in EDTA concentrations as high as 0.05 M.

Magnesium inhibits the activity of ribonuclease I, though not completely—in 0.1 and 0.2 M Mg^{2+} one observes, respectively, 38 and 60% inhibition. No agents capable of completely inhibiting the ribonuclease I activity have been reported (excepting, of course, denaturing agents such as sodium dodecyl sulfate). It has been reported [7] that ribonuclease I can be easily and completely removed by filtration through Millipore filters, "ultrafine" glass filters, asbestos, and powdered glass.

Mechanism of Action

E. coli ribonuclease I is an endonuclease, which rapidly hydrolyzes all internucleotide linkages in RNA producing first nucleoside 2′,3′-cyclic phosphates. The cyclic phosphodiester bond is then selectively hydrolyzed at a much slower rate to produce exclusively nucleoside 3′-phosphates; in this process, the 6-amino nucleoside 2′,3′-cyclic phosphates (adenylic acid and cytidylic acids) are hydrolyzed about 5 times faster than the 6-keto nucleoside 2′,3′-cyclic phosphates (guanylic and uridylic acids).

In the initial stages of RNA degradation by the enzyme, there is a preferential release of adenylic and uridylic residues over that of guanylic and cytidylic residues.

REFERENCES

1. SPAHR, P. F., and B. R. HOLLINGWORTH. 1961. J. Biol. Chem. *236:* 823.
2. FRISCH-NIGGEMEYER, W., and K. K. REDDI. 1957. Biochim. Biophys. Acta. *26:* 40.
3. SPAHR, P. F. 1964. J. Biol. Chem. *239:* 3716.
4. BRAY, G. A. 1960. Anal. Biochem. *1:* 279.
5. TISSIÈRES, A., J. D. WATSON, D. SCHLESSINGER, and B. R. HOLLINGWORTH. 1959. J. Mol. Biol. *1:* 221.
6. ELSON, D. 1959. Biochim. Biopyhs. Acta. *36:* 372.
7. NEU, H. C., and L. A. HEPPEL. 1964. J. Biol. Chem. *239:* 3893.

Plant Ribonucleases

K. K. REDDI

THE ROCKEFELLER UNIVERSITY

NEW YORK, NEW YORK

DISTRIBUTION

Ribonucleases have been found in all the plant extracts that have been examined. They appear to be normal components of plant cells. Purification of ribonucleases present in pea leaves (1), tobacco leaves (2), ryegrass (3) and spinach (4) has been achieved. All the purified preparations have three characteristics in common: (a) pH optimum, which is between 5 to 6; (b) disruption of all the internucleotide linkages in RNA via intramolecular transphosphorylation; and (c) preference for the secondary phosphate esters of guanosine 3'-phosphates in the initial stages of reaction. However, they differ in their ability to hydrolyze pyrimidine 2',3'-cyclic phosphates and this appears to be the intrinsic property of these preparations. On the basis of this difference they can be divided into two major groups. These will be called ribonuclease I and ribonuclease II.

$$\text{RNA} \xrightarrow[\text{ribonuclease II}]{\text{ribonuclease I}} \text{Gp! + Ap! + Up! + Cp!} \longrightarrow \text{Gp + Ap + Up! + Cp!} \quad (1)$$

$$\text{RNA} \xrightarrow{\text{ribonuclease II}} \text{Gp! + Ap! + Up! + Cp!} \longrightarrow \text{Gp + Ap + Up + Cp} \quad (2)$$

(Gp!, Ap!, Up!, and Cp! = 2',3'-cyclic nucleotides of guanosine, adenosine, uridine, and cytidine; Gp, Ap, Up, and Cp = 3'-phosphates of guanosine, adenosine, uridine, and cytidine.)

Ribonuclease I is present in pea leaves (5) and tobacco leaves (6,7). Ribonuclease II occurs in ryegrass (3), spinach (4), and also in association with the microsomes of tobacco leaf (8).

71

Determination of Activity

PRINCIPLE.   Cleavage of RNA by ribonuclease is followed by the rate of formation of mono- and oligonucleotides, which are separated from the partially digested RNA fragments by acid precipitation. The concentration of acid soluble nucleotides is determined spectrophotometrically.

REAGENTS

0.1 M Sodium acetate buffer, pH 5.1
Yeast RNA 10 mg/ml in sodium acetate buffer, pH 5.1
2 N HCl

PROCEDURES.   Reaction mixture containing 0.5 ml of 1% RNA in 0.1 M acetate buffer of pH 5.1, 0.3 ml of 0.1 M acetate buffer of pH 5.1 and 0.2 ml of enzyme, is incubated at 37 C for 1 hr. At the end of reaction time, the tubes are transferred to an ice bath and 0.37 ml of cold 2 N HCl is added to stop the reaction and to precipitate the partially digested RNA fragments. After 10 min the precipitate is removed by centrifugation in cold at 2500 rev/min for 10 min. Two-tenth ml of the supernatant fluid is made up to 10 ml with H_2O and the absorption is measured in a Beckman spectrophotometer at 260 mμ. Substrate and enzyme blanks are run side by side. The amount of ribonuclease needed to cause an increase in the optical density of 0.005 is taken as one unit of enzyme activity.

PREPARATION OF RIBONUCLEASE I

The enzyme capable of catalyzing the reaction given in equation (1) is prepared from tobacco leaves (2).

Extraction

Unless otherwise stated, all operations are performed at 4 C and all centrifugations are done at 3000 rev/min in the International Refrigerated Centrifuge. One kg of tobacco leaves, immediately after harvesting, are frozen. The frozen leaves are ground in a mechanical meat grinder. The ground material is thawed at room temperature and centrifuged in a basket centrifuge lined with a canvas bag.

Acidification

The clear supernatant liquid (800 ml) is adjusted to pH 4.5 with dilute acetic acid and the resulting precipitate is removed by centrifugation. The supernatant fluid is brought to pH 5.5 with 1 N NaOH.

Ammonium Sulfate Fractionation

To the supernatant fluid (780 ml) at pH 5.5 solid ammonium sulfate is added to 40% saturation. The precipitate is removed by centrifugation. The ammonium sulfate concentration of the supernatant liquid is raised to 80% with solid ammonium sulfate. After 1 hr the precipitate is collected by centrifugation. It is taken up in 55 ml of acetate buffer, pH 5.1, and centrifuged.

Dialysis

The clear supernatant liquid is dialyzed for 24 hr against several changes of H_2O. During the course of dialysis a precipitate is formed. The contents of dialysis bag are mixed, centrifuged, and the supernatant fluid is saved. The residue is suspended in 5 ml of 0.1 M acetate buffer, pH 5.1, and centrifuged. The combined supernatant fluids are stored overnight. A heavy precipitate that is formed on storing is removed by centrifugation. The supernatant liquid has all the ribonuclease activity. In addition, it has also considerable phosphatase activity. This fraction will be referred to as crude enzyme.

Further purification of crude enzyme to remove phosphatase by fractional precipitation with acetone is unsuccessful.

Adsorption on Alumina Cγ

Both ribonuclease and phosphatase are adsorbed on alumina Cγ between pH 4.5 and 5.6. Citrate, borate, phosphate, and acetate buffers at different pH ranges and ionic strengths do not bring about a selective elution of ribonuclease and phosphatase from alumina adsorbate. However, ribonuclease is more readily eluted by sodium β-glycerophosphate. The conditions for elution with sodium β-glycerophosphate are first established as follows. To a series of tubes one ml of crude enzyme preparation and 0.3 ml of alumina Cγ (10 mg/ml) are added. The mixture is held at 0 C for 10 min and centrifuged. The alumina adsorbate is washed in each case with 1 ml of H_2O and the washed residues are eluted at room temperature with 1 ml of sodium β-glycerophosphate of varying molarity. It is found that 0.01 M sodium β-glycerophosphate elutes about 78% of ribonuclease and 8.5% of phosphatase. Hence, 0.01 M sodium β-glycerophosphate is chosen for elution.

To 89 ml of crude enzyme solution at pH 4.5 are added 5 ml of alumina Cγ (18 mg/ml). After 10 min, the mixture is centrifuged at 2500 rev/min for 10 min. The supernatant fluid, which is free from ribonuclease activity, is discarded. The alumina adsorbate is washed once with H_2O. The washed gel is suspended in 60 ml of 0.01 M sodium β-glycerophosphate. The suspension is kept at room temperature for 15 min with occasional mixing and centrifuged. The eluate is dialyzed for 18 hr against three changes of H_2O. The adsorption on alumina Cγ and elution with sodium β-glycerophosphate is repeated three more times. In these subsequent steps, the amount of alumina Cγ used is proportional to the total activity of the ribonuclease and so is the amount of sodium β-glycerophosphate used for elution. The final preparation is completely free from phosphatase activity. The purification procedure is summarized in Table 1.

TABLE 1. *Purification of Ribonuclease I from Tobacco Leaves*

Fractions	Volume (ml)	Units Ribonuclease (/ml)	Total Units	Units (/mg of protein)	Yield (%)
First extract	800	440	350,000	110	100
Supernatant after removal of precipitate at pH 4.5	780	400	310,000	220	89
Precipitate between 40% and 85% $(NH_4)_2SO_4$ saturation	63	4,700	296,000	360	84
After dialysis (crude enzyme)	89	3,100	276,000	770	79
First eluate from alumina Cγ adsorbate	102	2,100	214,000	3,000	61
Final preparation	21	4,000	84,000	9,800	24

Properties of Ribonuclease I

CONTAMINATION WITH OTHER ENZYMES. No evidence for the presence of phosphatase in the preparations is obtained. The reaction mixture consisting of 0.1 ml of 0.1 M sodium β-glycerophosphate in 0.1 M acetate buffer of pH 5.6, 0.7 ml of 0.1 M acetate buffer of pH 5.6 and 0.2 ml of enzyme preparation is incubated for 1 hr at 37 C. At the end of the reaction time, 0.5 ml of 20% trichloroacetic acid is added to stop the reaction. In a sample, inorganic orthophosphate is determined according to the procedure of King (9).

The presence of contaminating phosphodiesterase is investigated using Ca[bis (p-nitrophenyl)phosphate]$_2$ as the substrate. The reaction mixture containing 0.5 ml of 0.1% solution of bis (p-nitrophenyl)phosphate in 0.1 M acetate buffer of pH 5.1 and 0.5 ml of enzyme preparation is incubated at 37 C. At intervals of time, 0.2 ml of the reaction mixture is withdrawn, diluted to 5 ml with H_2O, and the absorption is measured at 440 mμ. Its presence is also tested at pH 8.5 using 0.1 M Tris-HCl buffer instead of 0.1 M acetate buffer of pH 5.1. No activity could be detected.

EFFECT OF pH.   The optimum pH in two buffer systems, sodium acetate buffer and citrate-phosphate buffer (McIlvain) is 5.1.

INHIBITORS AND ACTIVATORS.   Activity is neither enhanced nor diminished by arsenate, pyrophosphate, fluoride, iodoacetic acid, and cysteine. All cations tested have inhibitory effect; $Cu^{2+} > Zn^{2+} > Cd^{2+} > Mg^{2+} > Ca^{2+}$.

STABILITY.   The enzyme is remarkably stable between pH 4.5 and 5.0 when incubated at 37 C for 18 hr. Only about 20% of the total activity is lost when the enzyme solutions at pH 4.5 are placed at 100 C for 10 min.

ACTION ON RNA (6).   Ribonuclease I acts on RNA in two stages. The first stage is an intramolecular transphosphorylation to form nucleoside 2',3'-cyclic phosphates; the second stage is a slow hydrolysis of purine cyclic nucleotides to their corresponding nucleoside 3'-phosphates. The enzyme does not hydrolyze pyrimidine 2',3'-cyclic phosphates and hence these accumulate in the digestion mixture [equation (1)].

Even though ribonuclease I brings about the cleavage of all the diester bonds in RNA, at least in the initial stages of digestion it appears to have much more preference for the secondary phosphate esters of guanosine 3'-phosphates and much less preference for the secondary phosphate esters of cytidine 3'-phosphates. This evidence has been further tested using synthetic polymers of uridylic acid (poly U) and cytidylic acid (poly C) (7).

PREPARATION OF RIBONUCLEASE II

The enzyme capable of catalyzing the reaction given in equation (2) is prepared from spinach leaves (4).

Extraction

Unless otherwise stated, all operations are carried out at 4 C. Ten kg of fresh spinach leaves are washed with tap water and ground in a meat grinder. The ground material is frozen in a Dry Ice chest. The material is thawed and refrozen. The thawed material is homogenized for 2 min in a one-gallon stainless steel Waring Blendor (Model CB-2, speed setting, 3) in 5 equal batches with a total of 5 liters of 0.1 M potassium phosphate buffer, pH 5.7. The homogenate is stirred for 2 hr and centrifuged in the International centrifuge, Model SR-3, at 2500 rev/ min for 20 min. The supernatant liquid is adjusted to pH 5.1 with cold 1 N HCl and allowed to stand overnight. The green precipitate is removed by centrifugation as above and discarded. The supernatant fluid, which is turbid, is filtered under suction with the aid of Hyflo Super Cel. The clear brown filtrate (10.6 liters), is then readjusted to pH 5.1 when necessary.

Adsorption on, and Elution from, Amberlite XE-64 Resin

A column of Amberlite XE-64 ion exchange resin, 10 cm × 20 cm, is prepared according to the procedure of Hirs (10). It is equilibrated to pH 5.1 with 0.1 M potassium phosphate buffer. The clear brown filtrate from above is allowed to pass through the column at a rate of 20 ml/min. The column is extensively washed with the pH 5.1 buffer until the E_{280} of the effluent is less than 0.100. The eluate resulting from the initial charge and from the washings has little ribonuclease activity and is discarded. The enzyme is eluted with 1 M phosphate buffer, pH 6.0, and collected in 100 ml fractions. Those having the bulk of the activity are pooled.

Fractionation with Ammonium Sulfate

To each liter of the combined eluate, 144 g of ammonium sulfate are added. The precipitate is removed by centrifugation. To each liter of the supernatant fluid, 370 g of ammonium sulfate are added and stirred for 1 hr. The precipitate is collected by centrifugation at 20,000 × g for 10 min. The precipitate is suspended in 250 ml of H_2O and dialyzed for 24 hr against several changes of H_2O. The insoluble precipitate that is formed during dialysis is removed by centrifugation. The supernatant liquid is lyophilized, yielding about 1.8 g of a light tan powder.

Chromatography on DEAE-Cellulose

The lyophilized material is dissolved in 30 ml of H_2O and dialyzed with stirring for 1 hr against 200 ml of 0.01 M sodium phosphate, pH 7.0. The dialyzed solution is allowed to pass through a DEAE-cellulose column, 5 cm × 20 cm, equilibrated to pH 7.0 with the 0.01 M buffer. After washing briefly with 0.01 M buffer, the column is washed with 0.04 M sodium phosphate buffer, pH 7.0, until the E_{280} of the effluent is less than 0.050. With a fraction collector the enzyme is eluted by the gradient technique with a mixing chamber volume of 500 ml of 0.04 M buffer into which flowed 0.1 M sodium phosphate buffer, pH 7.0. The enzyme is eluted in a sharp peak at approximately 0.07 M. The most active fractions (5 ml) are pooled, dialyzed, and lyophilized. The purified preparations are free from phosphatase activity. The purification procedure is summarized in Table 2.

TABLE 2. *Purification of Ribonuclease II from Spinach Leaves*

Fractions	Volume (ml)	Units Ribonuclease (/ml)	Total Units	Units (/ml/E_{280})
Extract	10,600	34	360,000	1.2
Combined eluate from				
Amberlite XE-64 resin	1,800	115	107,000	17
(NH$_4$)$_2$SO$_4$ precipitate	360	500	180,000	88
Combined peak tubes				
from DEAE-cellulose	270	275	74,000	3,200
After dialysis	310	250	77,500	2,950

Properties

OPTIMUM pH. Even though the ribonuclease from spinach has been purified 2500-fold, a double hump in the pH optimum curve indicates that the preparation is a mixture of ribonuclease I (pH 5.0) and ribonuclease II (pH 6.0). Ribonuclease II occurring in association with the microsomes of tobacco leaf has a pH optimum of 6.0 (8).

ACTIVATORS AND INHIBITORS. The activity of purified preparations is not affected by p-chloromercuribenzoate (0.01 M), mercaptoethanol (0.01 M), Mg^{2+} (0.001 M), Ca^{2+} (0.001 M), ethylenediaminetetraacetate (0.001 M).

STABILITY. The enzyme is fairly heat stable between pH 5 and 7, losing about 50% of its activity in 10 min at 100 C.

ACTION ON RNA. The action of ribonuclease II on RNA is similar to that of ribonuclease I. The major difference between ribonuclease II and ribonuclease I is that the former brings about the hydrolysis of both the pyrimidine and purine 2',3'-cyclic nucleotides to their corresponding nucleoside 3'-phosphates.

USES. Ribonuclease I and ribonuclease II can be used with advantage to prepare both purine and pyrimidine 2',3'-cyclic nucleotides. Ribonuclease I can also be used for determining the pyrimidine nucleoside 2'- or 3'-phosphate endings in a polyribonucleotide.

REFERENCES

1. PIERPOINT, W. S. 1956. Biochim. Biophys. Acta. *21:* 136.
2. FRISCH-NIGGEMEYER, W., and K. K. REDDI. 1957. Biochim. Biophys. Acta. *26:* 40.
3. SHUSTER, L., H. G. KHORANA, and L. A. HEPPEL. 1959. Biochim. Biophys. Acta. *33:* 452.
4. TUVE, T. W., and C. B. ANFINSEN. 1960. J. Biol. Chem. *235:* 3437.
5. MARKHAM, R., and J. L. STROMINGER. 1956. Biochem. J. *64:* 46P.
6. REDDI, K. K. 1958. Biochim. Biophys. Acta. *28:* 386.
7. REDDI, K. K. 1958. Biochim. Biophys. Acta. *30:* 638.
8. REDDI, K. K., and LJ. MAUSER. 1965. Proc. Natl. Acad. Sci., U.S. *53:* 607.
9. KING, E. J. 1932. Biochem. J. *26:* 292.
10. HIRS, C. H. W. 1955. *In* S. P. Colowick and N. O. Kaplan, editors, Methods in enzymology. Academic Press, New York. Vol. I, p. 113.

Extracellular Nuclease

from *Staphylococcus*

aureus (**1**)

JAMES N. HEINS, HIROSHI TANIUCHI, AND
CHRISTIAN B. ANFINSEN
NATIONAL INSTITUTE OF ARTHRITIS
AND METABOLIC DISEASES
NATIONAL INSTITUTES OF HEALTH
BETHESDA, MARYLAND

ASSAY

Spectrophotometric determination of the formation of acid-soluble oligo- and mononucleotides.

Method I

Reagents

1. DNA substrate:

   7% perchloric acid
   Salmon sperm DNA (Calbiochem) 2.5 mg/ml in 0.01 M NaCl
   Sodium borate, 0.1 M, pH 8.8
   $CaCl_2$, 0.1 M
   Enzyme solution

2. The reaction mixture (210 μliters) contains

   DNA solution, 100 μliters
   Borate buffer, 100 μliters

CaCl$_2$ solution, 5 μliters

Enzyme solution, 5–10 μliter (see discussion on selection of buffers)

Procedure

The reaction mixture is incubated at 37 C in siliconized glass tubes for 30 min after which the reaction is stopped by the addition of 0.5 ml of 7% perchloric acid. The tubes are placed in an ice bath for 10 min to assure complete precipitation of insoluble polynucleotides and unreacted DNA molecules, diluted with 2.7 ml of cold distilled water, and centrifuged in an International Clinical Centrifuge for 5 min. The supernatant fluid is decanted immediately and read at 260 mμ in a spectrophotometer. Appropriate reagent blanks are made by the addition of enzyme after acid precipitation. All determinations are run in duplicate.

Method II

Reagents

1. RNA substrate:

   Uranyl acetate 0.75% in 25% perchloric acid

   Sodium borate, 0.1 M, pH 8.8

   Yeast RNA [prepared by the method of Crestfield, Smith and Allen (2)] 0.4% in borate buffer

   CaCl$_2$, 0.1 M

   Enzyme solution

2. Reaction mixture (1 ml):

   RNA solution, 0.5 ml

   Borate buffer, 0.4 ml

   CaCl$_2$ solution, 0.1 ml

   Enzyme solution, 5–10 μliters

Procedure

After 30 min incubation at 37 C, the reaction is stopped by adding 0.5 ml of uranyl acetate solution. The precipitate is removed by centrifugation and 0.1 ml of the supernatant fluid is diluted to 3.1 ml with water and read as before.

A unit of activity is defined in both assays as a change of 260 mμ absorbancy of 1.0 under the conditions described. The pH optimum is 8.8 and Ca^{2+} ion is an absolute requirement. Highly active preparations require extensive dilution to fall within the linearity of the assays so that adsorption of the enzyme on glass can become a factor in variability of duplicate runs; therefore, siliconized tubes are advisable.

The enzyme activity is completely lost in the presence of EDTA, whereas citrate and phosphate stimulate deoxyribonuclease activity, and to a lesser extent ribonuclease activity, over borate by mechanisms not presently understood. Specific activity is defined as the units of activity per mg of enzyme protein, concentration of enzyme being based on $E_{280}^{1\%}$ of 11.6 for pure preparations. Fully active enzyme has 5700 units and 2000 units/mg of protein versus DNA and RNA, respectively.

ISOLATION PROCEDURE

Growth of Cells

Extracellular nuclease is produced by *Staph aureus* (Strain V8) when grown with appropriate conditions. The medium, "CCY" (3), contains (per liter) 30 g of oxoid casamino acids, 20 g of sodium β-glycerophosphate, 10 g of sodium lactate, 2.45 g of Na_2HPO_4, 0.4 g of KH_2PO_4, 6.4 mg of $FeSO_4 \cdot 7H_2O$, 6.4 mg of citric acid, 10 mg of $MnSO_4 \cdot 7H_2O$, and 20% (v/v) of oxoid yeast diffusate (pH 7.2–7.4). The organisms are grown in 100–150 liter lots overnight at 37 C with vigorous bottom aeration and then killed by the addition of Cetavlon (Cetrimide B.P., Imperial Chemical Industries, Ltd.) 10 g/100 liters of medium.

Precipitation of the Enzymes

The cells are separated by centrifugation and the enzymes in the medium are precipitated by saturating the solution with ammonium sulfate and allowing it to stand overnight at room temperature. The "crude paste" obtained in this manner is frozen awaiting further purification.

First Ammonium Sulfate Fractionation

One hundred grams of the crude paste are dissolved in 500 ml of NaH_2PO_4 buffer, 0.05 M, pH 6.1, and insoluble material separated by centrifugation. The solution is 40% saturated with solid $(NH_4)_2SO_4$ with constant stirring at room temperature and allowed to stand for 6 hr. The precipitate is removed by centrifugation in an International Centrifuge P.R.II at 4000 rev/min (2960 × g) for 20 min and discarded.

Second Ammonium Sulfate Fractionation

The supernatant fluid from the previous step is made 90% saturated with $(NH_4)_2SO_4$ as before except that the precipitated 40–90%

$(NH_4)_2SO_4$ cut is recovered quantitatively and contains approximately 60–70% of the units of activity present in the crude paste.

Removal of $(NH_4)_2SO_4$ by Dialysis

All further purification is carried out at 4 C. The precipitated material is suspended in 200 ml of 0.05 M NaH_2PO_4 buffer, pH 6.1, and dialyzed in Visking cellophane tubing, previously heated for 72 hr at 80 C to decrease the pore size, against 4 liters of the same buffer with magnetic stirring. The dialysis is carried out for 24 hr with six buffer exchanges. During this period, the larger part of the dark brown pigment, present in varying amounts depending on growth conditions since precipitation from the culture medium, diffuses out of the bag and is discarded during the exchanges. The dialyzed solution is centrifuged as before.

Ion-Exchange Chromatography Step No. 1

The supernatant solution thus obtained is applied to the carboxymethyl cellulose column (Sigma Chemical Company, medium mesh, 0.7 meq/g, 6 × 95 cm) which has been equilibrated with 0.05 M NaH_2PO_4 buffer, pH 6.1. The CM cellulose is prepared by successively washing with 1 N NaOH, water, 3 N HCl, and water. To prevent excessive solubilization of the cellulose at high pH, a high ionic strength is maintained with NaCl (2 M) during that step.

After addition of the enzyme solution, the column is washed with the same phosphate buffer until the extinction of the effluent at 280 mμ becomes less than 0.05 and a gradient elution is carried out with a mixing solution of 800 ml of 0.05 M NaH_2PO_4 buffer, pH 6.1, and a reservoir of 0.21 M K_2HPO_4 buffer, pH 8.0. One fraction is collected every 10 min with a flow rate of 75 ml/hr.

The tubes containing the active component with specific activity versus DNA substrate of greater than 3800 units are pooled, acidified to pH 6.0, and diluted 2.6 times with distilled water.

Rechromatography on CM Cellulose

The pooled component is reapplied to a CM cellulose column, 2 cm × 60 cm, prepared as before, and is eluted with an open two-compartment gradient (Varigrad) containing 1 liter of 0.05 M NaH_2PO_4 buffer, pH 6.1, and 1 liter of 0.15 M K_2HPO_4 buffer, pH 7.5. Fractions are collected every 30 min at a flow rate of 18 ml/hr. Both columns may be pumped on the effluent side by a sigma motor pump if necessary to maintain flow rates. Fractions with a constant maximum specific activity of 5700 units are pooled (pure nuclease fraction).

PROPERTIES OF ENZYME

Contaminating Enzymes

PHOSPHATASES. Both acid and alkaline phosphatases have been detected in preparations isolated by different published methods [Ohsaka, Mukai, and Laskowski (4); Anfinsen et al. (1)]. Acid phosphatase activity is separated from the nuclease by chromatography on DEAE-cellulose and alkaline phosphatase is destroyed by heating to 100 C for 3 min (4).

PROTEASES. Incubation of enzyme preparations at 25 C for 24 hr in Tris-NaCl buffer, pH 7.0, failed to produce any change in the specific activity, eliminating the likelihood of significant protease contamination.

Specificity

Staphylococcal nuclease attacks the diester bonds of both RNA and DNA. Activities against these compounds remain essentially parallel throughout purification and after selective modification of amino acid residues. Exhaustive hydrolysis produces mixtures of 3'-phosphonucleotides and dinucleotides by a combination of endo- and exonuclease action. Cyclic mononucleotides and dinucleotides are not attacked (6), and 5'-phosphate oligonucleotides inhibit enzyme activity (5). Different relative rates of hydrolysis for specific nucleotides are suggested by preliminary data but await further study.

Physical Properties

The molecular weight lies in the range of 15,000–20,000 as determined by the diffusion coefficient-sedimentation velocity and Yphantis techniques (7). Physical measurements and preliminary sequence analyses suggest a compact globular protein of high helicity without disulfide bridges.

REFERENCES

1. ANFINSEN, C. B., M. K. RUMLEY, and H. TANIUCHI. 1963. Acta Chem. Scand. 17: S270, 1963.
2. CRESTFIELD, A. M., K. C. SMITH, and F. W. ALLEN. 1956. J. Biol. Chem. 216: 185.

3. GLADSTONE, G. P., and W. E. VAN HEYNINGEN. 1957. Brit. J. Exptl. Pathol. *38:* 123.
4. OHSAKA, A., J. MUKAI, and M. LASKOWSKI. 1964. J. Biol. Chem. *239:* 3498.
5. ALEXANDER, M., L. A. HEPPEL, and J. HURWITZ. 1961. J. Biol. Chem. *234:* 3014.
6. REDDI, K. K. 1959. Biochem. Biophys. Acta. *36:* 132.
7. YPHANTIS, D. A. 1964. Biochemistry. *3:* 297.

3. Deoxyribonucleases (Endonucleases)

Pancreatic
Deoxyribonuclease I

M. LASKOWSKI, SR.
ROSWELL PARK MEMORIAL INSTITUTE
BUFFALO, NEW YORK

Reaction

Pancreatic deoxyribonuclease I hydrolyzes native DNA in a typically endonucleolytic manner (1) and produces fragments terminated in 5'-monophosphate. Early observations of Zamenhof (2,3), who, using the viscosimetric technique, observed the lag period, have been confirmed and extended. Using biologically active λ-DNA, Young and Sinsheimer (4) established that, on an average, four phosphodiester bonds are hydrolyzed (single-strand scissions) before the infectivity is lost (a double-strand scission). Denatured DNA is hydrolyzed at a somewhat slower rate than native DNA (5,6). The detachment of even a portion of purines from DNA makes it resistant to deoxyribonuclease I (7,8). Glycosylated viral DNA is more resistant to the combined consecutive action of deoxyribonuclease I and venom exonuclease (9–15), but no accurate measurements of the rate of each of these enzymes on glycosylated DNA are available.

Some of the experimental work described in this article was performed in the author's laboratory during his stay at Marquette University School of Medicine. The work was generously supported by the American Cancer Society (grants PRP-16 and E-157), the Atomic Energy Commission (grant AT(11–1)-293), and the National Science Foundation (grant GB-4274).

With all endonucleases, the products formed in the initial stages of the reaction serve as substrates in the later stages. With many endonucleases, including the pancreatic deoxyribonuclease I, successive products are progressively more resistant substrates (16). We propose the name of "Autoretardation" for this phenomenon. The period of the high rate of hydrolysis corresponds to cleavage of the most susceptible linkages. As the rate declines, the randomness of cleavages increases. In the case of deoxyribonuclease I, the initial rate is about 1000 times greater than the rate toward the end of the reaction. Thus, the previous conclusion that the pPu-pPy linkage is the most susceptible to deoxyribonuclease I (16–21) is valid only for the stage of degradation corresponding to the formation of dinucleotides, and only in the presence of Mg^{2+}.

Exhaustive digestion with very large amounts of enzyme in the presence of Mg^{2+} alone leads to a mixture containing 2% of mononucleotides, 63% dinucleotides, and 25% trinucleotides (16). The extensive hydrolysis may also be achieved with a moderate amount of enzyme, but in the presence of Mn^{2+} instead of Mg^{2+} (22,23). In this case no accumulation of pPy-pPu fragments in the digest can be detected. The amount of mononucleotides formed increases to 5.8%, and the predominant dinucleotides are of the pPu-pPu type. On the other hand, Lunt, Siebke, and Burton (15) used glycosylated T_2 phage DNA in the presence of relatively large amounts of deoxyribonuclease I and both ions Mg^{2+} and Ca^{2+}. They found the accumulation of pPy-pPu type of dinucleotides.

An interesting and totally fresh approach has been made by Bollum (24), who succeeded in synthesizing deoxyribopolymers (25) composed of two complementary chains of homopolymers dA:dT; dI:dC; and dG:dC. In the presence of Mg^{2+} alone, dA:dT polymer was digested by deoxyribonuclease I to a mixture of oligonucleotides of dT (ranging from di to penta) and dA (ranging from di to undeca). Among dT derivatives tetranucleotide predominated, among dA derivatives oligonucleotides from 5 to 7 nucleotides long predominated. In the presence of Mg^{2+} alone the dC chain of poly dI:dC was resistant to deoxyribonuclease I; the addition of Ca^{2+} or the substitution by Mn^{2+} made poly dC susceptible. Both chains of dG:dC were resistant in the presence of Mg^{2+} alone, but were hydrolyzed in the presence of Mg^{2+} and Ca^{2+}. The findings of Bollum may explain some earlier contradictory statements concerning the ionic requirements.

Substrate

Since no uniform synthetic substrate is available, native DNA is used. The most commonly used is thymus DNA prepared by the method of Kay, Simmons, and Dounce (26) (this material is now commercially available, Worthington Biochemical Corporation, Freehold, New Jersey). In the reviewer's laboratory, it was found convenient to keep the stock solution of DNA in water as recommended by Kunitz (27), 2 mg/ml. This solution is then used for any method after an appropriate dilution.

Assays

Numerous assays for deoxyribonuclease have been suggested. Since the starting substrate is always a high molecular DNA, the "autoretardation" cannot be avoided. All methods, but to a variable degree, suffer from an additional handicap. The effect measured is not constant per each enzymatic attack. This is most obvious with the viscosimetric method where only the double scissions count. With spectrophotometric methods, the location of the cleaved bond, the nature of the adjacent bases, etc., exert a strong influence on the effect measured. Presently, it seems that the pH stat represents the method in which the measured effect is relatively independent of the size, and the secondary structure of the substrate, and probably is least dependent on the adjacent bases, particularly at high pH values.

Kurnick (28) recently reviewed assays of deoxyribonuclease activity. He subdivided the assays into the following groups:

1. Measurements of the release of protons.
2. Physicochemical methods (viscosity, spectrophotometer, ultracentrifugation, etc.)
3. Changes in affinity for dyes.
4. Products of depolymerization.
5. Biological activity.
6. Histochemical methods.

To these categories we would like to add one more, the use of radioactive substrates. Several techniques in which either the liberated products or the remaining substrate are determined have been described (29–31). A method that combines the use of P^{32} DNA with the ability of nitrocellulose filters to retain the denatured DNA has been recently proposed (32). This method allows the determination of a millimicrogram of deoxyribonuclease I per ml.

The optimal concentrations of ions in the reaction medium are not easily defined, because they are interdependent (16,33,34). Table 1 from Shack and Bynum (34) shows how the optimal concentration of a bivalent cation depends on the concentration of substrate and monovalent cation.

TABLE 1.   *Dependence of Optimal Ion Concentration on Conditions of Assay (34)*

DNA (mg/ml)	pH	Na$^+$ (M)	Mg^{2+} (M)	Mn^{2+} (M)
0.02	7.0	0.005	0.0015	0.005
0.4	7.0	0.005	0.0027	0.025
0.02	7.0	0.1	0.005[a]	0.008[a]

[a] Essentially the same for 0.4 mg/ml of DNA.

An additional serious difficulty exists with crude tissue extracts or tissues other than pancreas. Even the demonstration of deoxyribonuclease I or "the deoxyribonuclease I-like enzyme" in these tissues is not a simple matter. The discovery of the specific protein inhibitor for deoxyribonuclease I (35,36) explained the difficulty in detecting deoxyribonuclease I in tissues or crude tissue extracts. The inhibitor is unstable in acid (37), whereas deoxyribonuclease I is rather stable. This finding enabled the demonstration of the wide distribution of both deoxyribonuclease I and its inhibitor in the variety of tissue (37-41). Feinstein (42,43) reported that some tissues contain a heat-stable activator of deoxyribonuclease I. Lindberg (44,45) and Zalite and Roth (46) described methods for the determination of the inhibitor in tissues and the methods for the purification of the inhibitor from calf spleen (44) and rat liver (46). Lindberg could not demonstrate the activator.

Of the numerous assay procedures only three have been selected to be described in detail on the assumption that each may be useful for a different purpose. The general characteristics are first discussed, and are followed by the detailed description of the procedure.

VISCOSIMETRIC ASSAY.   This is one of the most sensitive. It can only be used for the initial stages of the reaction. It is applicable to relatively crude systems. It has a disadvantage that only one determination can be performed at a time.

For the purpose of following the purification of an enzyme, or for the purpose of studying levels of deoxyribonuclease activity in different tissues or microbial cultures, the viscosimetric method is at best a *semiquantitative* one. However, it is a very valuable tool for the characterization of a nuclease. Endonucleases show high viscosimetric values, whereas exonucleases can barely be detected (47).

SPECTROPHOTOMETRIC ASSAY. This method is one of the most widely used, but not easily applicable to crude systems. It is recommended for the evaluation of purified preparations, because it is simple, rapid, and reproducible when the same batch of substrate is used. The assay is almost useless for rigorous kinetic studies, because the effect measured varies with the substrate, the stage of the reaction, the type of the bond cleaved, etc.

pH STAT: THE METHOD OF CHOICE WITH A FAIRLY PURI-FIED SYSTEM. A little more cumbersome than the previous, but the effect measured is less dependent on the state of the substrate, stage of the reaction, and the adjacent bases. It is accurate and reproducible.

Viscosimetric Assay

The principle of the viscosimetric method was first described in 1945 by two independent groups of workers (48,49). A solution of DNA having a specific viscosity of about 3 in 0.1 M buffer, pH 7.0, containing Mg^{2+} or Mn^{2+} (for concentrations see Table 1) (34), is placed in an Ostwald viscosimeter at 37 C. After thermal equilibration, the enzyme is added, the contents are mixed, and the viscosity measurements are made at 5-min intervals for about 20 min. The first-order velocity constant is calculated from the equation

$$K = \frac{1}{t} \ln \frac{\eta_0}{\eta_t}$$

where η_0 and η_t are specific viscosities at 0 time and at time t, respectively. One unit is set as an amount of enzyme that gives the value of $K = 1 \times 10^{-3}$.

As our knowledge progressed it became evident that cleavages inflicted early produce much higher effect on viscosity than cleavages inflicted later. It was therefore necessary to introduce the limits for enzyme concentration (50,51). Lately, the limits became quite narrow, the range of K from 9×10^{-3} to 11×10^{-3} was suggested by Osowiecki and Pakula (52).

Further analysis of their results indicated that even in this range no straight proportionality between the enzyme concentrations and K can be expected. Osowiecki and Pakula (52) plotted the value of K versus dilation (H) and showed that curves drawn for intervals of 5, 10, 15, and 20 min intercepted at the same point. To obtain an accurate result by viscosimetry the authors propose (a) to find a dilution that gives the value of K in the desirable range using a 5-min interval for the calculation of K, (b) to make two more determinations with 5-min intervals using dilution 25% higher, and 25% lower than the first.

Plot the three points and draw the curve, (c) repeat the determination with the same three concentrations—H, $H + 25\%$, $H - 25\%$—using 15-min intervals, plot the results and draw the 15-min curve through the three points. The intercept of the two curves representing 5- and 15-min intervals gives the most probable value for K at the dilution H.

Spectrophotometric Assay

The spectrophotometric assay as described by Kunitz (27) is performed at pH 5.0, not at the optimum pH 7.0.

SUBSTRATE SOLUTION. Two ml of stock solution of sodium thymonucleate + 10 ml of 0.05 M $MgSO_4$ + 10 ml of 1.0 M acetate buffer, pH 5.0, + H_2O to a volume of 100 ml. Store at 5 C. Stable for a week or longer.

Four test tubes, each containing 3 ml of substrate solution (40 μg of DNA/ml) are placed for several minutes in a water bath at 25 C. One ml of water is added to one of these tubes, the mixture is transferred to the first quartz cuvette of the thermostated spectrophotometer, and is used as a blank. Three samples of 1 ml each containing from 5 to 10 μg of deoxyribonuclease per ml are also equilibrated at 25 C. At zero time the contents of the substrate tube are poured into the enzyme tube, mixed, and transferred to the second, third, and fourth quartz cuvette, respectively, and placed in a spectrophotometer. Readings are then taken of the optical density at 260 mμ in the experimental cuvettes at intervals of 0.5 or 1 min, depending on the rate of change, for about 5 to 10 min. It is convenient to have the main switch of the spectrophotometer set continuously at the mark 1 and the density scale kept set at the zero mark for the blank; the slit opening is usually about 1 mm. The cuvettes containing the enzyme give readings above zero, the readings increasing at the rate of 0.005 to 0.02/min.†

The activity of the enzyme solution is expressed in terms of the slope of the plotted curve of optical density vs. time in minutes. This divided by the concentration of the enzyme in milligrams of protein per milliliter of the final digestion mixture gives the specific activity of enzyme in units of deoxyribonuclease activity per milligram of protein. One unit of activity is thus defined as the amount of enzyme capable of bringing about an increase in optical density at 260 mμ of one unit per minute under the given conditions of concentration of the substrate, pH, temperature, and salt concentration. Fig. 1 (27) shows curves plotted for two concentrations of enzyme. The curves generally rise slowly during

---

† With an automatic recorder, such as Gilford or Cary, reading at definite intervals is provided by the machine. Only the straight line portion of the record is used for calculations.

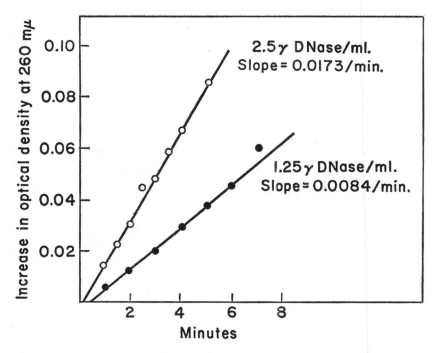

Fig. 1. Rate of increase of ultraviolet light absorption by thymus nucleic acid on digestion with deoxyribonuclease (27).

the first minute or two, depending on the concentration of enzyme; thereafter, the rate of increase in optical density becomes constant for several minutes. The slopes of the straight lines drawn through the plotted points are proportional to the concentration of enzyme in the digestion mixture.

Titration in a pH Stat

In the reviewer's laboratory this procedure has been successfully used (16,47) with the home-made instrument described in detail by Peanasky and Szucs (53). Using a standard pH stat instrument, such as that produced by the Radiometer, may require changing the volume of reactants and molarity of the titrating base.

In our laboratory (16) conditions were as follows: 1.0 mg of thymus DNA (26) in 10 ml solution, which was 7.5×10^{-3} M in respect to Mn^{2+} and 4.5×10^{-3} M in respect to EDTA, was adjusted to pH 8.0 and placed in the titration chamber, kept at 37 C under a continued flow of nitrogen. Stirring was provided by a magnetic bar. After equilibration for 5–10 min, 100 microliters of the enzyme solution (from a micropipette) were added to the mixture. The titrating base was 0.002 N NaOH. It was freshly diluted from 0.1 N NaOH prepared in CO_2-free water and kept protected.

METHOD OF ISOLATION OF CRYSTALLINE DEOXYRIBONUCLEASE† (27)

STEP 1. PRELIMINARY PURIFICATION.‡   Fresh beef pancreas is collected in ice-cold 0.25 N sulfuric acid. The glands are drained of the acid, cleaned of fat and connective tissue, and then minced coarsely in a meat grinder. The minced pancreas is suspended in about an equal volume of ice-cold distilled water, and then enough ice-cold 0.25 N sulfuric acid is added with stirring until the pH of the fluid in the suspension is about 3.0 (tested with 0.01% methyl orange on a test plate); a volume of 0.25 N acid equal to half of the water added is generally required. The suspension of the minced pancreas is stored at about 5 C for 18 to 20 hr. It is then strained through cheese cloth. The residue is resuspended in one volume of ice-cold water and strained. The combined filtrates are brought to 0.2 saturation of ammonium sulfate (114 g of the salt per liter of filtrate). The precipitate formed is filtered with suction on 30–32 cm Büchner funnel through soft, rapid filtering paper (Eaton and Dikeman, No. 617) with the aid of 10 g of Celite 503 (Johns-Manville Corporation) and 10 g of standard Supercel per liter of solution. The clear filtrate is brought to 0.4 saturation of ammonium sulfate, 121 g/liter, and refiltered with suction with the aid of 3 g of Celite 503 per liter on double paper, No. 612 on top of No. 617. The filtrate§ can be utilized for the preparation of chymotrypsinogen (56), trypsin (55), and ribonuclease (57,58). The residue, including the Celite, is suspended in five times its weight of water, the suspension is brought to 0.3 saturation of ammonium sulfate (176 g/liter of water used) and refiltered with suction on No. 617 paper, the filtrate then being discarded.

---

† The method of isolation described here is identical, except for several minor changes, with the method given in the preliminary publication (54).

‡ Preliminary purification is based on the procedure of McCarty (49). In the reviewer's laboratory the original extraction described by Kunitz and Northrop (55) was also tried. Little difference in yield of deoxyribonuclease was observed, possibly because of the protective action of other proteins.

§ It is advisable to adjust the filtrate to 0.25 N H_2SO_4 by the addition of 7 ml of concentrated sulfuric acid per liter of water used in the extraction and washing of the ground pancreas. The addition of the acid facilitates filtrations in the further procedure for the preparation of chymotrypsinogen, etc.

STEP 2. INCUBATION AT 37 C FOLLOWED BY FRACTIONA-
TION WITH AMMONIUM SULFATE. The residue is suspended in
ten times its weight of water, and the suspension is brought to 0.15
saturation of ammonium sulfate (83.7 g of salt/liter of water). The
solution is titrated to pH 3.2 (glass electrode) with about 2 ml of
5 N H$_2$SO$_4$ per liter. It is heated to 37 C and incubated for 1 hr at that
temperature. It is then cooled to about 20 C and filtered with suction
on No. 617 with the aid of an additional 5 g of Celite per liter of
suspension. The residue is discarded.

The filtrate is titrated to pH 5.3 with 5 N NaOH (about 2 ml/liter)
and brought to 0.5 saturation of ammonium sulfate (220 g/liter).
The precipitate formed, designated as "0.5 s.a.s. precipitate," is filtered
with suction on No. 617 paper with the aid of 5 g of Celite 503 per
liter of solution.

The clear filtrate is titrated with a few drops of 5 N H$_2$SO$_4$ to pH 4.0
(tested with bromcresol green on test plate) and brought to 0.7 saturation of ammonium sulfate (135 g/liter). The light precipitate formed,
designated as "0.7 s.a.s. precipitate," is filtered with suction on soft
paper with the aid of 2 g of standard Supercel per liter and stored. The
filtrate is discarded.

The "0.5 s.a.s. precipitate" (including the Celite) is then resuspended in ten times its weight of water and Step 2, including the incubation at 37 C, is repeated several times until no appreciable "0.7 s.a.s.
precipitate" is formed. The combined "0.7 s.a.s. precipitate" is suspended in about ten times its weight of water and filtered with suction
on soft paper. The Supercel residue is washed several times with water
until the washing is water clear.

STEP 3. FRACTIONATION WITH ETHYL ALCOHOL. The
combined filtrate and washings are diluted with water to a concen-
tration† of about 1% protein. The pH of the solution is adjusted with
5 N H$_2$SO$_4$ to about 3.8, and 2 ml of saturated ammonium sulfate is
added per 100 ml of solution, which is cooled in an ice salt bath to
about 2 C. One-quarter of its volume of cold 95% alcohol is added
slowly with stirring in order to keep the temperature of the solution
below 5 C. The mixture is stored for 24 hr at about 5 C and then
centrifuged at the same temperature. The residue is discarded, while
the clear supernatant solution is left at about −10 C for 24 hr and
centrifuged at the same temperature. The precipitate, called the "sec-

† The approximate concentration of protein can be determined spectrophotometrically at 280 mμ, the optical density being about 1.2 per mg of protein per ml.

ond alcohol precipitate," contains most of the enzymatic activity of the original "0.7 s.a.s. precipitate."

STEP 4. CRYSTALLIZATION. The "second alcohol precipitate" is dissolved in about ten times its volume of cold water, after which it is brought to 0.38 saturation by addition of 60 ml of saturated ammonium sulfate per 100 ml of solution. The precipitate formed is filtered with suction on hardened paper at 5–10 C. It is then suspended in three times its weight of cold water and dissolved with the aid of several drops of 0.2 or 0.5 N NaOH. The pH of the solution is not allowed to rise above 4.8. The solution, if turbid, is centrifuged clear at about 5 C. The pH of the filtrate is adjusted to 2.8 (glass electrode) with several drops of 0.2 N H_2SO_4. The heavy precipitate, which generally forms at pH about 3.5, readily dissolves as the pH of the solution reaches 3.0 or lower. The clear solution is left at 5 C overnight and then in the room at about 20 C for 6 to 8 hr. Crystals appear at room temperature. Seeding insures and hastens the crystallization, as usual.

STEP 5. RECRYSTALLIZATION. The suspension of crystals is centrifuged. The sedimented crystals are suspended in about three volumes of 0.02 saturated ammonium sulfate solution and dissolved with the aid of a few drops of 0.2 N NaOH at a pH of about 4.6. The solution, if turbid, is centrifuged, titrated to pH 2.8, and then left at 20 C. Crystallization proceeds rapidly. The crystals, filtered with suction on hardened paper at 5 C, are washed, first with ice-cold acidified 30% alcohol (1 drop of 5 N H_2SO_4 per 100 ml), then with ice-cold acetone, and dried at room temperature for several hours. The dry preparation is stored at about 5 C.

The mother liquors in Steps 4 and 5 generally yield more crystals when treated as follows:

The solution is diluted about threefold with cold water and is titrated with 0.2 N NaOH to pH about 4.6. Any insoluble material formed is centrifuged off. The clear supernatant solution is titrated with 0.2 N H_2SO_4 to pH 4.0 and then brought to 0.38 saturation of ammonium sulfate, as described in Step 4, which is then followed through in every detail.

The yield of crystalline deoxyribonuclease is rather small due partly to the fact that at pH 2.8, which is most favorable for crystallization, the protein is gradually changed into a denatured form insoluble at pH 4.6. The yield is generally 3–5 mg of dry first crystals per kilo of ground pancreas.

The extent of purification accompanying the farious steps during the process of isolation is shown in Table 2.

TABLE 2. *Extent of Purification of Deoxyribonuclease* (27)

Fraction	Specific Activity (Kunitz' units/mg)	Yield (%)
0.3 saturated $(NH_4)_2SO_4$	0.2	100
pH 3.2 at 37 C	3–5	30
20% alcohol at −10 C	5–6	15
First crystals	8–10	5
First mother liquor	5–6	10
Second crystals	8–10	
Second mother liquor	8–10	

The specific enzymatic activity, i.e., activity per milligram of protein, is expressed in terms of that of the best preparations, which is taken as equal to 10, whereas the yield is given in percent of the activity content of the first fraction, precipitated in 0.3 saturated ammonium sulfate.

OTHER METHODS OF PREPARATION

Suggestions purported to increase the yield of deoxyribonuclease I have been made (59,60), but have found little practical application. In connection with preparing chymotrypsinogen B by chromatography on CM-cellulose (61–63), it was noticed that the peak appearing immediately after chymotrypsinogen B contains deoxyribonuclease I in good yield and of fair potency. The combined peak had a specific activity approaching 2, and therefore contained 20% of deoxyribonuclease. The use of this material for further purification has not been investigated.

The assumption that crystalline pancreatic deoxyribonuclease I is highly homogeneous is no longer tenable. From the beginning it was known that some denaturation occurs during drastic crystallization at pH 2.8, and it was suspected that a partly inactivated protein is incorporated into the crystals.

Attempts to show electrophoretic heterogeneity have been made (64) and are summarized as follows:

Commercial preparations of crystalline deoxyribonuclease I have been shown to contain at least five electrophoretically distinct protein bands on cellulose acetate strips. All bands yielded a positive reaction with the periodate-Schiff reagent. Traces of proteolytic activity were detected in these preparations as measured on a casein substrate, and increased activity on treatment of the preparation with small amounts of trypsin. No amylase or ribonuclease activities were detected, and no inhibition of trypsin or chymotrypsin activities were detected under the experimental conditions used. The major band, accounting for 40–60% of the total protein has been eluted from the cellulose acetate paper and found to have deoxyribonuclease activity. One other band co-electrophoresed with chymotrypsinogen B.

The crystalline preparation is contaminated with ribonuclease to the extent of 1 part per 100,000 parts (w/w) of deoxyribonuclease I (65). The contamination can be reduced by chromatography on DEAE cellulose (65). Recently Sandeen and Zimmerman (66) described an improved method.

METHOD OF REMOVAL OF CONTAMINATING RIBONUCLEASE FROM DEOXYRIBONUCLEASE (66)

The following operations were carried out at 0–5 C: A column of DEAE cellulose (3.8 cm² × 15 cm) was equilibrated with 0.005 M potassium phosphate buffer, pH 8.0. Crystallized deoxyribonuclease (100 mg) dissolved in 20 ml of the equilibrating buffer was adjusted to pH—8.0 to 8.2†—by slow addition of 0.05 N NaOH (ca. 1.2 ml required) with constant stirring. The deoxyribonuclease was passed through the column and the column was washed with 400 ml of 0.015 M potassium phosphate buffer, pH 8.0, to remove the bulk of the ribonuclease activity. A constant gradient (1300 ml total volume) was applied from 0.03 M, pH 8.0, to 0.053 M, pH 6.0, potassium phosphate buffers. The gradient was obtained by open reservoir vessels of equal cross-sectional area. The flow rate for all operations was 4 ml/min; fractions of 20 ml were collected. In the representative chromatography shown (Fig. 2), a second constant gradient (800 ml total volume from 0 to 1.0 M NaCl, in 0.053 M potassium phosphate buffer, pH 6.0) was used to elute inactive protein (66).

Of the 77% of deoxyribonuclease activity recovered from the column, about half had constant specific deoxyribonuclease activity and reduced ribonuclease activity. This half was pooled and adjusted to pH 2.8‡ by addition of about 1/40 volume of 1 N HCl with good stirring. This acidified eluate may be stored overnight without activity loss. The chromatographic procedure described above will handle at least 200 mg of deoxyribonuclease with similar resolution. For purify-

† Yellow-gray to thymol blue indicator on spot test.
‡ Faint orange to thymol blue indicator on spot test.

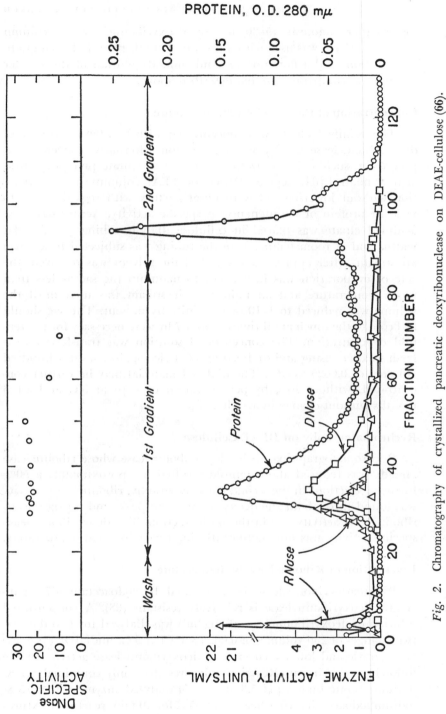

Fig. 2. Chromatography of crystallized pancreatic deoxyribonuclease on DEAE-cellulose (66).

ing smaller amounts (5–30 mg of deoxyribonuclease) a column $0.9\ cm^2 \times 15\ cm$ was used with a wash of 250 ml, 180 ml of each gradient solution, and a flow rate of 1 ml/min. Resolution of the smaller column was comparable to that described above.

Concentration of the DEAE-Cellulose Eluate

The acidified eluate was concentrated with 95–100% recovery of deoxyribonuclease activity by pervaporation. Alternative concentration procedures such as lyophilization, ammonium sulfate precipitation at acid or neutral pH, stepwise DEAE- or TEAE-columns, or pervaporation without lowering pH were unsatisfactory with regard either to yield of protein or maintenance of specific activity. Accordingly, the acidified eluate was placed in cellulose dialysis tubing (1.7 in. flat width) and at room temperature the tubing was subjected to a warm air stream. After approximately 2/3 of the solvent was removed, the rate of evaporation was insufficient to maintain the sac at less than room temperature and an unheated air stream was used until the volume was reduced to 1/10 of that initially present. The sac should feel cool to the touch at all times. About 7 hr were necessary for the tenfold concentration. The concentrated solution was transferred to a fresh smaller casing and dialyzed at 5 C twice against several hundred volumes of 0.0025 N HCl. The dialyzed material may be further concentrated, without loss, by pervaporation or kept at 5 C at least 3 months without change in activity.

Rechromatography on DEAE-Cellulose

Rechromatographing of the deoxyribonuclease whose ribonuclease already was reduced about tenfold resulted in approximately a 50% further reduction. In the second chromatography, ribonuclease activity was found throughout the deoxyribonuclease peak, and no significant ribonuclease activity was in the wash fraction. The deoxyribonuclease specific activity was not significantly improved by rechromatography.

Inactivation of Ribonuclease by Iodoacetate

Pancreatic ribonuclease is inactivated by iodoacetate (67); pancreatic deoxyribonuclease is relatively resistant (68). A concentrated solution of deoxyribonuclease (5 mg/ml) was dialyzed for two days vs. two changes of 200 volumes of 0.0025 N HCl at 5 C; undialyzed enzyme gave erratic and lower recoveries of deoxyribonuclease activity in the following experiment. Reaction mixtures (0.80 ml) contained 0.1 M sodium acetate buffer, pH 5.3, 0.8 mg of dialyzed enzyme with 0.15 M sodium iodoacetate. After heating at 55 C for 40 min, reaction mixtures were chilled and dialyzed vs. 250 volumes of 0.0025 N HCl for 16 hr at 5 C. This treatment reduced ribonuclease activity below the limits of detection with polycytidylate.

Worthington Corporation (Worthington catalog, code DPFF) sells the product which, after crystallization by the method of Kunitz (27), was subjected to electrophoresis in a free boundary continuous flow instrument (Brinkman model FF). This process removes a component carrying most of the ribonuclease activity and reduces ribonuclease to a level comparable to that obtained by the DEAE chromatography (66). Commercial preparation can further be treated with iodoacetate to inhibit last traces of contaminating ribonuclease.

PROPERTIES OF DEOXYRIBONUCLEASE I

Kunitz (27) using the method of Northrop and Anson (69) estimated the molecular weight of deoxyribonuclease I as 60,000, and a similar value was obtained by Smith (70) by electron bombardment. Polson (60) by sedimentation-diffusion found 40,000.

The isoelectric point, determined by cataphoresis of collodion particles coated with nonheated deoxyribonuclease I (27) was pH 4.7, and for the heated deoxyribonuclease I, pH 5.0. Davidson (71) quotes the isoelectric point between 5.0 and 5.2; Polson (60), using paper electrophoresis 4.7, Worthington, on the basis of their preparative electrophoresis, arrives at the value 5.2.

The amino acid analysis of the crystalline preparation has been reported by Gehrman and Okada (72).

In view of the increasing evidence for heterogeneity of crystalline deoxyribonuclease I it seems rather obvious that the above values are at best close approximations.

REFERENCES

1. LASKOWSKI, M., SR. 1961. *In* P. D. Boyer, H. Lardy, and K. Myrbäck, Editors, The enzymes. Academic Press, New York. Vol. V, p. 123.
2. ZAMENHOF, S., H. E. ALEXANDER, and G. LEIDY. 1955. J. Exptl. Med. *98:* 373.
3. ZAMENHOF, S., G. GRIBOFF, and N. MARULLO. 1954. Biochim. Biophys. Acta. *13:* 459.
4. YOUNG, E. T., II, and R. L. SINSHEIMER. 1965. J. Biol. Chem. *240:* 1274.
5. KURNICK, N. B. 1954. J. Am. Chem. Soc. *76:* 417; *76:* 4040.

6. See p. 135, The Enzymes, Vol. V.

7. TAMM, C., and E. CHARGAFF. 1951. Nature. *168:* 916.

8. TAMM, C., H. S. SHAPIRO, and E. CHARGAFF. 1952. J. Biol. Chem. *199:* 313.

9. COHEN, S. S. 1953. Cold Spring Harbor Symposia Quant. Biol. *18:* 221.

10. SINSHEIMER, R. L. 1954. Science. *120:* 551.

11. JESAITIS, M. A. 1957. J. Exptl. Med. *106:* 233.

12. VOLKIN, E. 1954. J. Am. Chem. Soc. *76:* 5892.

13. LEHMAN, I. R. 1960. J. Biol. Chem. *235:* 1479.

14. LICHTENSTEIN, J., and S. S. COHEN. 1960. J. Biol. Chem. *235:* 1134.

15. LUNT, M. R., J. C. SIEBKE, and K. BURTON. 1964. Biochem. J. *92:* 27.

16. VANECKO, S., and M. LASKOWSKI, SR. 1961. J. Biol. Chem. *236:* 3312.

17. SINSHEIMER, R. L. 1954. J. Biol. Chem. *208:* 445.

18. SINSHEIMER, R. L., and J. F. KOERNER. 1952. J. Am. Chem. Soc. *74:* 283.

19. SINSHEIMER, R. L. 1955. J. Biol. Chem. *215:* 579.

20. PRIVAT DE GARILHE, M., L. CUNNINGHAM, U.-R. LAURILA, and M. LASKOWSKI. J. Biol. Chem. *224:* 751.

21. LASKOWSKI, M. 1959. Ann. N.Y. Acad. Sci. *81:* 776.

22. HURST, R. O., and G. C. BECKING. 1963. Canad. J. Biochem. Physiol. *41:* 469.

23. BECKING, G. C., and R. O. HURST. 1963. Canad. J. Biochem. Physiol. *41:* 1433.

24. BOLLUM, F. J. 1965. J. Biol. Chem. *240:* 2599.

25. BOLLUM, F. J., E. GROENIGER, and M. YONEDA. 1964. Proc. Natl. Acad. Sci., U.S. *51:* 853.

26. KAY, E. R. M., M. S. SIMMONS, and A. L. DOUNCE. 1952. J. Am. Chem. Soc. *74:* 1724.

27. KUNITZ, M. 1950. J. Gen. Physiol. *33:* 349.

28. KURNICK, N. B. 1962. *In* D. Glick, Editor, Methods of biochemical analysis. Interscience Publishers, New York. Vol. 9, p. 1.

29. FRIEDKIN, M., and H. WOOD, IV. 1956. J. Biol. Chem. *220:* 639.

30. KORNBERG, A., I. R. LEHMAN, M. J. BESSMAN, and E. S. SIMMS. 1956. Biochim. Biophys. Acta. *21:* 197.

31. BOLLUM, F. J. 1959. J. Biol. Chem. *234:* 2733.

32. GEIDUSCHEK, E. P., and A. DANIELS. 1965. Anal. Biochem. *11:* 133.

33. WIBERG, J. S. 1958. Archives Biochem. Biophys. *73:* 537.

34. SHACK, J., and B. S. BYNUM. 1964. J. Biol. Chem. *239:* 3843.

35. DABROWSKA, W., E. J. COOPER, and M. LASKOWSKI. 1945. J. Biol. Chem. *177:* 991.

36. COOPER, E. J., M. L. TRAUTMAN, and M. LASKOWSKI. 1950. Proc. Soc. Exptl. Biol. Med. *73:* 219.

37. CUNNINGHAM, L., and M. LASKOWSKI. 1953. Biochim. Biophys. Acta. *11:* 590.

38. CRUZ-COKE, E., M. PLAZA DE LOS REYES, J. MARTENS, J. DEL NIDO, and J. ARAYA. 1951. Soc. Biol. Santiago de Chile. *9:* 38.

39. CRUZ-COKE, E., M. PLAZA DE LOS REYES, J. DEL NIDO, and J. ARAYA. 1951. Soc. Biol. Santiago de Chili. *9:* 44.

40. HENSTELL, H. H., and R. L. FREEDMAN. 1952. Cancer Res. *12:* 341.

41. KURNICK, N. B., L. J. SCHWARTZ, S. PARISER, and S. L. LEE. 1953. J. Clin. Invest. *32:* 193.

42. FEINSTEIN, R. N., and F. O. GREEN. 1956. Arch. Biochem. Biophys. *60:* 502.

43. FEINSTEIN, R. N. 1960. J. Biol. Chem. *235:* 733.
44. LINDBERG, U. 1964. Biochim. Biophys. Acta. *82:* 237.
45. LINDBERG, U. 1964. Biochem. J. *92:* 27p.
46. ZALITE, B. R., and J. S. ROTH. 1964. Arch. Biochem. Biophys. *107:* 16.
47. WILLIAMS, E. J., S.-C. SUNG, and M. LASKOWSKI, SR. 1961. J. Biol. Chem. *236:* 1130.
48. LASKOWSKI, M., and M. K. SEIDEL. 1945. Arch. Biochem. *7:* 465.
49. MCCARTY, M. 1946. J. Gen. Physiol. *29:* 123.
50. CUNNINGHAM, L., B. W. CATLIN, and M. PRIVAT DE GARILHE. 1956. J. Am. Chem. Soc. *78:* 4642.
51. WECKMAN, B. G., and B. W. CATLIN. 1957. J. Bacteriol. *73:* 747.
52. OSOWIECKI, H., and R. PAKULA. 1962. Med. Dosw. Mikrobiol. *14:* 173.
53. PEANASKY, R. J., and M. M. SZUCS. 1964. J. Biol. Chem. *239:* 2525.
54. KUNITZ, M. 1948. Science. *108:* 19.
55. KUNITZ, M., and J. H. NORTHROP. 1936. J. Gen. Physiol. *19:* 991.
56. KUNITZ, M., and J. H. NORTHROP. 1935. J. Gen. Physiol. *18:* 433.
57. KUNITZ, M. 1940. J. Gen. Physiol. *24:* 15.
58. MCDONALD, M. R. 1948. J. Gen. Physiol. *32:* 39.
59. BAUMGARTNER, W. F., R. F. JOHNSON, R. F. FINGER, and F. E. PAGENKEMPER. 1958. Arch. Biochem. Biophys. *77:* 296.
60. POLSON, G. 1957. Biochim. Biophys. Acta. *22:* 61.
61. LASKOWSKI, M., and B. KASSELL. 1960. Acta Biochim. Polonica. *7:* 253.
62. ROVERY, M., O. GUY, and P. DESNUELLE. 1960. Biochim. Biophys. Acta. *42:* 554.
63. ENENKEL, A. G., and L. B. SMILLIE. 1963. Biochemistry. *2:* 1445.
64. POTTER, J. L. Personal communication.
65. PALATNICK, J., and H. L. BACHRACH. 1961. Anal. Biochem. *2:* 168.
66. SANDEEN, G., and S. B. ZIMMERMAN. Anal. Biochem. (in press).
67. GUNDLACH, H. G., W. H. STEIN, and S. MOORE. 1959. J. Biol. Chem. *234:* 1754.
68. OKADA, S., and G. L. FLETCHER. 1961. Radiation Res. *15:* 452.
69. NORTHROP, J. H., and M. L. ANSON. 1929. J. Gen. Physiol. *12:* 543.
70. SMITH, C. L. 1953. Arch. Biochim. Biophys. *45:* 83.
71. DAVIDSON, J. N. 1953. The biochemistry of nucleic acids. Methuen, London, 2nd ed.
72. GEHRMAN, G., and S. OKADA. 1957. Biochim. Biophys. Acta. *23:* 621.

CARL A. RUDISILL LIBRARY
LENOIR RHYNE COLLEGE

Spleen Acid

Deoxyribonuclease (1,2)

GIORGIO BERNARDI

CENTER FOR RESEARCH IN MACROMOLECULES

STRASBOURG, FRANCE

Several methods have been described for the partial purification of spleen acid deoxyribonuclease (see ref. 3 for a review). The preparation of the enzyme as a homogeneous protein was first reported by Bernardi and Griffé (1). The original purification procedure has been successively modified (2). Both procedures lend themselves, with slight modifications, to the preparation of several other enzymatic activities, such as acid phosphomonoesterase (p. 236), acid ribonuclease (p. 37), exonuclease (p. 144), and nucleoside polyphosphatase. Both methods will be described because the protein composition of the two crude nuclease preparations (*vide infra*) is different. Furthermore, for a given tissue one method may be more convenient than the other.

ASSAY

Reaction

$$DNA \longrightarrow 3'\text{-P-oligonucleotides}$$

The deoxyribonuclease activity is assayed by measuring the liberation of acid-soluble oligonucleotides from DNA.

Reagents

1. The reaction mixture (total volume 2.5 ml)† contains
    a. 2.4 μmoles of DNA-P‡
        375 μmoles of acetate buffer, pH 5.0
        25 μmoles of EDTA
    b. Enzyme—if necessary, this is diluted with 0.15 M acetate buffer + 0.01 M EDTA, pH 5.0, containing 0.05% beef heart cytochrome c (Sigma Chemical Company, type V).

2. 12% Perchloric acid

Procedure

After 10 min of incubation at 37 C the reaction is stopped by addition of 0.5 ml of 12% perchloric acid. The mixture is then chilled in an ice bath for 10 min and clarified by centrifugation at 4 C. The extent of DNA hydrolysis is determined by measuring the absorption at 260 mμ of the supernatant fluid. After subtracting a suitable blank, readings are corrected for dilution with the enzyme solution and the perchloric acid.

Assays are performed using enzyme concentrations to obtain OD_{260} readings in the range 1–4. Under these conditions a linear relationship obtains between enzyme concentration and acid-soluble oligonucleotide formation. One activity unit is defined as the amount of enzyme that under the conditions defined above catalyzes in 1 min the liberation of oligonucleotides having a (corrected) OD_{260} equal to 1. If the volumes used in the assay are halved, the activity value must be divided by 2. Since the molar extinction coefficient at 260 mμ of the oligonucleotide-phosphorus present in the final, completely acid-soluble, digest is 9100, one activity unit corresponds to the liberation of 0.22 μmoles of oligonucleotide-phosphorus. The specific activity is calculated by dividing the activity by the OD_{280} of the enzyme solution.

Assay of Other Enzymatic Activities

Ribonuclease, exonuclease, and acid phosphomonoesterase activities are assayed as described on pp. 37, 144, and 236 respectively.

Phosphodiesterase activity is assayed like phosphomonoesterase; Ca [bis(p-nitrophenyl)phosphate]$_2$ is used as the substrate; the solvent

---

† If desired, all volumes may be halved.
‡ Calf thymus DNA prepared according to Kay et al. (4) was used.

is 0.25 M succinate buffer, pH 6.4; the 2 N (NH$_4$)OH solution used to stop the reaction is 0.1 M in EDTA. Under these conditions the assay detects essentially the nucleoside polyphosphatase activity (5).

PREPARATION OF CRUDE SPLEEN NUCLEASE

Two different methods, I (1) and II (2), will be described. They give rise to two different enzyme preparations, which will be called crude spleen nuclease I and II, respectively. These preparations contain among other enzymes acid deoxyribonuclease, three or more ribonucleases, and an exonuclease. The yield in acid deoxyribonuclease is slightly higher with the more laborious Method I, than with Method II, which was specifically designed for the large scale preparation of acid deoxyribonuclease and some of the accompanying enzymes.

Method I

General Directions

All operations are performed at 4 C; the precipitates are allowed to stand overnight; the centrifugations are carried out at 8000 × g for 1 hr, except where otherwise stated (a Lourdes Instruments Corp., Brooklyn, N.Y., centrifuge was used in the original work).

STEP 1. EXTRACTION. Spleens obtained at the abattoirs from freshly slaughtered pigs, are trimmed, minced, and homogenized for 3 min in a Waring Blendor with 0.15 M NaCl–0.02 M CaCl$_2$. Batches of 250 g are treated with 300 ml of solvent to which 1 ml of isooctanol has been added. The suspension is shaken for 18 hr and then centrifuged for 30 min at 3000 × g. The sediment is again homogenized with fresh solvent (1 liter/kg of spleen) and treated as before. The turbid combined supernatant fluids are centrifuged. The supernatant liquid so obtained is filtered through cheesecloth ("clarified extract").

STEP 2. FIRST AMMONIUM SULFATE FRACTIONATION. Solid (NH$_4$)$_2$SO$_4$ is added to the clarified extract (200 g/liter; this is equivalent to 0.34 saturation at 20 C), and the resulting suspension is centrifuged. The sediment is discarded. The supernatant fluid is filtered through cheesecloth and paper and saturated with (NH$_4$)$_2$SO$_4$ by adding 520 g of salt/liter. The precipitate is collected by centrifugation or filtration on paper.

STEP 3. ACID PRECIPITATION. The precipitate from the previous step is dissolved in distilled water (about 700 ml/kg of spleen) and adjusted to pH 2.5 by dropwise addition of 0.3 N HCl, under mechanical stirring. The suspension is then centrifuged and the sediment is discarded.

STEP 4. SECOND AMMONIUM SULFATE FRACTIONATION. Solid $(NH_4)_2SO_4$ is added to the supernatant fluid from the previous step (245 g/liter; 0.4 saturation at 20 C). The precipitate is removed by centrifugation and discarded. The supernatant liquid is brought to 0.8 saturation of $(NH_4)_2SO_4$ (20 C) by adding 285 g of salt/liter. The precipitate is collected by centrifugation and the supernatant fluid is discarded.

STEP 5. DIALYSIS AND LYOPHILIZATION. The precipitate obtained between 0.4 and 0.8 $(NH_4)_2SO_4$ saturation is dissolved in distilled water (about 100 ml/kg of spleen) and dialyzed against distilled water with several changes. The precipitate formed is removed by centrifugation and the supernatant fluid is freeze-dried.

Properties of Crude Spleen Nuclease I

The crude spleen nuclease I is obtained in a yield of about 1 g/kg of trimmed tissue. Whereas no loss of enzymatic activity is found upon freeze-drying, storage at −15 C of the brownish, freeze-dried preparation for several months is accompanied by some loss of activity.

The crude spleen nuclease has a specific activity equal to 3–4; its total activity is about 3,000 units/kg of trimmed tissue. The specific acid deoxyribonuclease activity of the crude spleen nuclease so obtained is about the same as that of commercial preparations of spleen acid deoxyribonuclease (Worthington, Freehold, N.J.) obtained according to the procedure of Shimomura and Laskowski (6) through dialysis against acetate buffer (Step 5).

The crude spleen nuclease contains acid phosphomonoesterase, exonuclease, nucleoside polyphosphatase activities, and basic and acid ribonuclease activities.

Method II

General directions as in Method I. All operations however, are carried out at room temperature, except where otherwise stated.

STEP 1. Hog spleens are trimmed, ground with an electrical meat grinder, and homogenized with 0.1 N H_2SO_4 (1 liter/kg of ground spleen; 1 ml of isooctanol is added to each batch). 4.2 is the final pH. 0.2 N H_2SO_4 is added to the suspension dropwise under mechanical stirring until a pH of 2.5 is obtained; about 1 liter/kg of spleen is needed. Solid $(NH_4)_2SO_4$ (243 g/liter; 0.4 saturation at 20 C) and EDTA (2.43 g/liter) are added to the suspension. This is then allowed to stand overnight at 4 C. The suspension is then centrifuged for 1 hr at $8000 \times g$ at 4 C and the sediment is discarded.

STEP 2. Solid $(NH_4)_2SO_4$ (285 g/liter; 0.8 saturation at 20 C) and EDTA (2.85 g/liter) are added to the supernatant liquid from the previous step and the suspension is stored for several days or weeks at 4 C.

The suspension is then filtered. In the original work this was done using a k_0 00 Seitz filter† with a Seitz press-filter; over 60 liters of suspension may be easily filtered through the same filter, under atmospheric to +0.5 kg/cm² pressure.

STEP 3. The filtered precipitate is dissolved in a small volume of distilled water (about 100 ml per 10 kg of spleen) and dialyzed against several changes of distilled water at 4 C for 48 hr. The precipitate that forms upon dialysis is centrifuged off.

STEP 4. The supernatant fluid is concentrated by freeze-drying and dialyzed against 0.05 M phosphate buffer, pH 6.8, and used for the chromatographic purification.

Properties of the Crude Spleen Nuclease II

The crude spleen nuclease II is obtained in a yield of about 0.2 g (dry weight)/kg of trimmed spleen.

TABLE 1. *Crude Spleen Nuclease II (Preparation HS 11)[a]*

	Total Activity	Specific Activity
Acid deoxyribonuclease	160,000	12.8
Acid ribonuclease	153,000	12.5
Acid phosphomonoesterase	600	0.048
Phosphodiesterase	185	0.015

[a] This preparation was obtained from 60 kg of hog spleen.

Its specific activity is about 10. The total activity is about 2700 units/kg of trimmed tissue. The OD_{280}/OD_{260} ratio is equal to 1.3–1.5. The properties of crude spleen nuclease II are summarized in Table 1.

† Seitz-Asbest-Werke, Bad Kreuznach, Germany.

CHROMATOGRAPHIC PURIFICATION

Three different chromatographic procedures, A, B and C, have been developed to purify the crude spleen nuclease preparation. Procedures A and B (1) have been only used on crude spleen nuclease I preparations. Procedure C has been developed more recently (2) to purify large quantities of spleen nuclease II preparations.

Column Chromatography

Hydroxyapatite was prepared according to Tiselius *et al.* (7). DEAE-cellulose was purchased from Serva, Heidelberg, Germany, and Calbiochem (Biorad Cellex D); the exchange capacities were 0.63 meq/g and 0.6 meq/g, respectively. CM-cellulose was a product of Serva; its exchange capacity was 0.65 meq/g. Sephadex, DEAE-Sephadex, and CM-Sephadex were obtained from Pharmacia AB, Stockholm, Sweden. Amberlite IRC-50 was purchased from Fisher, Philadelphia, Pa. (Rexyn CG-51) or Serva (C 950/II, 200–400 mesh); the latter product was treated according to Hirs (8) before use.

Chromatographic experiments were performed in a cold room (4 C) using a Gilson Medical Electronics fraction collector. The transmission of the effluent at 280 mμ was continuously recorded; 50–100 cm hydrostatic heads were used in most experiments. Molarity gradients were checked by refractometry using a Zeiss refractometer or by phosphorus analysis.

Procedure A

The results obtained for preparation HS I are summarized in Table 2.

STEP 1. DEAE-CELLULOSE. Crude spleen nuclease I was dissolved in water, adjusted to 0.005 M in phosphate buffer, pH 8.0, and adsorbed on DEAE-cellulose columns equilibrated with the same buffer. Under these conditions acid deoxyribonuclease is not retained. The total deoxyribonuclease activity eluted was about 10% higher than that of the starting material because of the adsorption of an inhibitor on the column. This inhibitor was later identified as sulfate ion. The adsorbed proteins could be eluted with 0.15 M acetate buffer, pH 5.0; this buffer also eluted sulfate. A brown substance, unidentified as yet, was removed from the column with 0.1 N HCl.

TABLE 2.   *Chromatographic Purification of Spleen Acid Deoxyribonuclease*
(Procedure A)[a]

	Volume (ml)	Total OD_{280}	Total Activity	Specific Activity
Crude spleen nuclease I	200	12,200	47,500	3.9
Step 1. DEAE-cellulose	814	7,090	51,200[b]	7.2
Step 2. Hydroxyapatite	289	493	36,600	74.1
Step 3. DEAE-cellulose[c]				
Step 4. Hydroxyapatite	285	157	19,500	124.2
Step 5. Hydroxyapatite	50	60.4	10,680	176.8
Step 6. IRC-50 Amberlite[d]	34	5.5	1,650	302

[a] Only the figures concerning the fractions that were processed further or the final product are given. A complete Table is given in ref. 1. The reported data refer to preparation HS 1.

[b] See text for the explanation of this increase.

[c] No data are available, since the fraction eluted at pH 8.0, $\mu = 0.005$ was immediately made 0.02 M with potassium phosphate buffer, pH 6.8, and loaded on hydroxyapatite.

[d] This chromatography was performed on a fraction (18%) of the enzyme obtained from Step 5.

STEP 2. HYDROXYAPATITE. The activity-rich fraction from Step 1 was made 0.02 M with phosphate buffer, pH 6.8, and adsorbed on hydroxyapatite. Elution was carried out stepwise, using 0.02, 0.1, 0.3, and 0.5 M phosphate buffer, pH 6.8.

STEP 3. DEAE-CELLULOSE. The 0.3 M fraction from the previous step was freeze-dried, dissolved in water, and dialyzed against 0.005 M phosphate buffer, pH 8.0, and then adsorbed on DEAE-cellulose. The fraction that was not retained was immediately made 0.02 M with phosphate buffer, pH 6.8, and absorbed on hydroxyapatite.

STEP 4. HYDROXYAPATITE. Elution was carried out in four steps: 0.02, 0.2, 0.3, and 0.5 M phosphate buffer, pH 6.8. Activity was found in the 0.2 and 0.3 M fractions. Active fractions were pooled together and adsorbed on another hydroxyapatite column.

STEP 5. HYDROXYAPATITE. Elution was carried out with a linear molarity gradient of phosphate buffer, pH 6.8, from 0.05 to 0.5 M. A single peak was eluted but the activity curve did not coincide with the optical density curve. The central fractions of the peak were pooled, concentrated by being rolled in visking cellulose tubes over dry Sephadex, frozen at an optical density at 280 mμ of about 3.0, and stored at

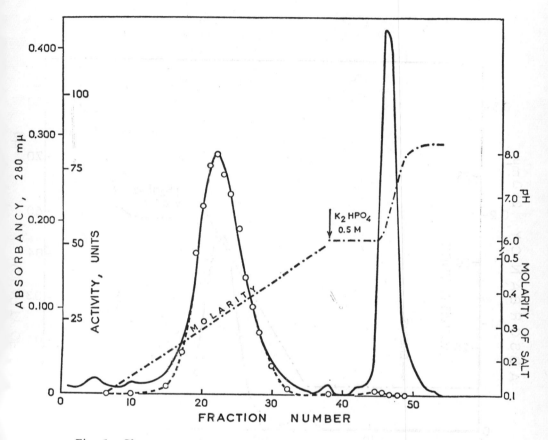

Fig. 1. Chromatography of acid deoxyribonuclease on Amberlite IRC-50 (Procedure A, Step 6; see Table 2). A molarity gradient of phosphate buffer, pH 6.0 (right-hand ordinate, lower scale) was followed by 0.5 M K₂HPO₄ (the pH of effluent is given in the right-hand ordinate upper scale). The continuous line indicates the absorption at 280 mµ. Circles indicate the deoxyribonuclease activity (left-hand, inner scale). (Reproduced from Biochemistry. 1964. *3*: 1419. With the permission of the American Chemical Society, publisher and copyright owner.)

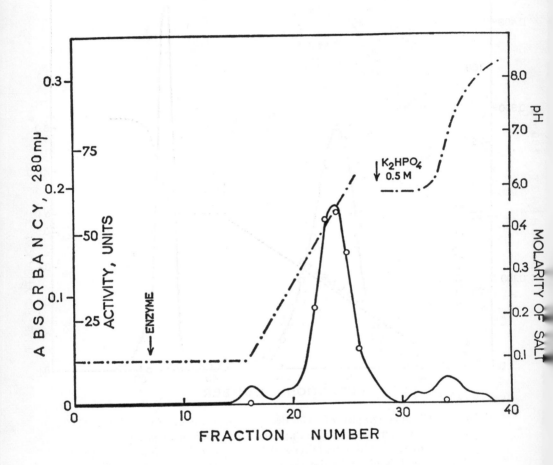

Fig. 2. Rechromatography of acid deoxyribonuclease on Amberlite IRC-50. Elution was carried out as in Fig. 1. All indications as in Fig. 1.

—60 C. A portion of the frozen enzyme was thawed and rerun on hydroxyapatite; no improvement whatsoever over Step 5 was obtained.

STEP 6. AMBERLITE IRC-50. Other samples of enzyme from the previous step were dialyzed against 0.1 M phosphate buffer, pH 6.0, and adsorbed on Amberlite IRC-50 equilibrated with the same buffer (Fig. 1). Some inactive material was not retained. A molarity gradient of phosphate buffer, pH 6.0, from 0.1 to 0.5 eluted the enzyme at a constant specific activity of 300,† the eluting molarity being extremely dependent upon the pH of the buffer. Additional inactive material was eluted with 0.5 M K_2HPO_4. Upon rechromatography the first fraction was again eluted (Fig. 2) at a constant specific activity of 300 with the molarity gradient, whereas the inactive fraction still required the pH gradient for elution.

Procedure B

STEP 1. DEAE-CELLULOSE. This was used as in Procedure A. The fraction not retained by the column contained deoxyribonuclease, phosphodiesterase, and acid phosphomonoesterase in that order; basic ribonuclease and some acid ribonuclease were also present. Adsorbed proteins were eluted with a gradient of molarity and/or pH, with 0.15 M acetate buffer, pH 5.0, as the final eluent; this resulted in a partial separation of a second acid phosphomonoesterase and the bulk of acid ribonuclease.

STEP 2. HYDROXYAPATITE. Elution was carried out as in Step 5 of Procedure A. Deoxyribonuclease was eluted immediately after a bright-red fraction showing absorption bands centered at 280, 414, 520, and 550 mμ (tentatively identified with cytochrome c). Phosphodiesterase and acid phosphomonoesterase were eluted in that order before deoxyribonuclease.

STEP 3. HYDROXYAPATITE. Elution was performed as before, the enzyme being desorbed at about 0.2 M phosphate buffer, pH 6.8. The active fractions were concentrated and frozen.

STEP 4. AMBERLITE IRC-50. Elution was performed as in Step 6 of Procedure A, with the same results upon rechromatography. The central fractions showed a constant specific activity and were pooled, dialyzed against 0.01 M phosphate buffer, pH 6.0, 0.02 M NaCl, con-

† See ref. 1 for an explanation of this lower value, compared to those obtained from Procedures B and C.

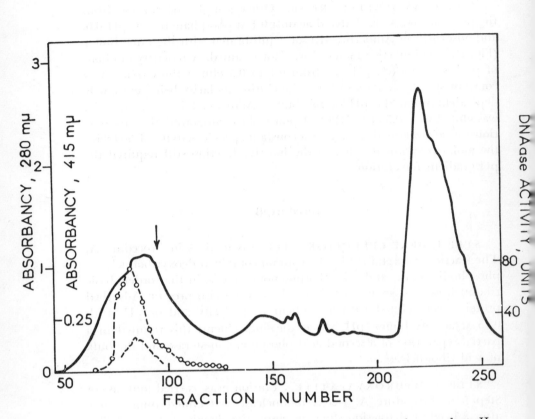

Fig. 3. Chromatography on DEAE-Sephadex A-50 of crude spleen nuclease II (Procedure C, Step 1). 330 ml of preparation HS 9 (OD_{280} = 10.3; OD_{260} = 6.9) were loaded on a 8- × 80-cm column of DEAE-Sephadex A-50 equilibrated with 0.05 M phosphate buffer, pH 6.8. This buffer was also used to elute the first protein peak. 0.5 M phosphate buffer, pH 6.8, was loaded at the fraction indicated by the arrow. 24-ml fractions were collected. The continuous line indicates the absorption at 280 mμ. Circles indicate the acid deoxyribonuclease activity (right-hand scale). The broken line indicates the absorption at 415 mμ of cytochrome c (left-hand inner scale). Fractions 50–65 were processed further. Acid and basic ribonuclease, acid phosphomonoesterase, and phosphodiesterase were also assayed; the results are shown on pp. 39 and 238.

centrated to an $OD_{280} = 2.5$, and frozen. Deoxyribonuclease activity was recovered in a final yield of 25%, taking as 100% the activity measured after Step 1. The specific activity was 350.

Procedure C

STEP 1. DEAE-SEPHADEX A-50 (FIG. 3). 10–20 g of crude spleen nuclease II in 300–500 ml of 0.05 M phosphate buffer, pH 6.8, were loaded onto a 8- × 80-cm DEAE-Sephadex A-50 column equilibrated with the same buffer. The column is then washed with the same buffer, and several enzymatic activities were not retained under these conditions: ribonuclease, nucleoside polyphosphatase, acid phosphomonoesterase, acid deoxyribonuclease, and cytochrome c.

The column is then washed with 0.5 M phosphate buffer, pH 6.8. A second large fraction, which contains acid ribonuclease activity and some acid phosphomonoesterase, is eluted. These activities are different from those present in the first peak.

STEP 2. HYDROXYAPATITE (FIG. 4). The fractions rich in deoxyribonuclease activity from the first peak of the previous step were loaded onto a 2- × 40-cm hydroxyapatite column equilibrated with 0.05 M phosphate buffer. No enzymatic activity was found in the fraction that was not retained.

A molarity gradient (0.05–0.5) of phosphate buffer, pH 6.8 (1000 + 1000 ml), eluted three main peaks of optical density. The first peak contained nucleoside polyphosphatase and a first ribonuclease, the second peak contained acid phosphomonoesterase, cytochrome c, and a second ribonuclease, and the third peak acid deoxyribonuclease.

STEP 3. CM-SEPHADEX C-50 (FIG. 5). The deoxyribonuclease-rich fraction from the previous step is dialyzed against 0.075 M phosphate buffer, pH 6.8, loaded on a 2- × 100-cm CM-Sephadex C-50 column equilibrated with 0.05 M phosphate buffer, pH 6.8. Elution is then carried out with a 0.1–0.4 M molarity gradient of phosphate buffer, pH 6.8. Acid deoxyribonuclease activity is eluted at a fairly constant specific activity in two peaks (Fig. 5). The first, minor, peak will be called deoxyribonuclease A, the second major one deoxyribonuclease B. The central parts of the two peaks are rechromatographed separately on CM-Sephadex after having reduced the phosphate molarity of the solvent to 0.075 by dialysis or Sephadex G-25 filtration. Upon rechromatography each fraction gives a single peak (Fig. 6) with a constant specific activity of about 350.

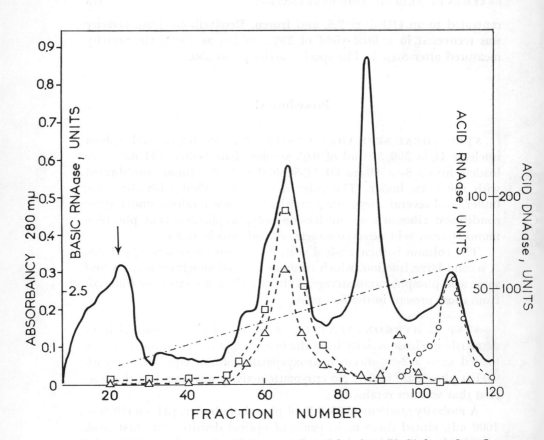

Fig. 4. Chromatography on hydroxyapatite of fractions 50–65 from Step 2 (Procedure C; Step 2). 370 ml (OD$_{280}$ = 1.48) were loaded on a 2- × 40-cm column of hydroxyapatite equilibrated with 0.05 M phosphate buffer, pH 6.8. A molarity gradient (0.05–0.5) was started at the fraction indicated by the arrow; at fraction 120 the molarity of the effluent was 0.35. 24-ml fractions were collected. The continuous line indicates the absorption at 280 mμ. Circles indicate the acid deoxyribonuclease activity (right-hand scale). Cyto-chrome c was eluted as a sharp peak centered on fraction 86 (OD$_{415}$ = 0.82; not shown on the figure). Acid ribonuclease (squares; right-hand scale) and basic ribonuclease (triangles; left-hand inner scale) are also shown. [Phospho-monoesterase and diesterase were also assayed (p. 239).] Fractions 100–115 were concentrated by freeze-drying to about 70 ml, filtered through Sephadex G-25 equilibrated with 0.075 M phosphate buffer, pH 6.8, and processed further.

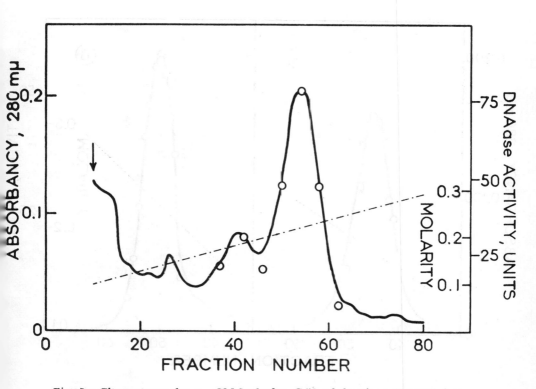

Fig. 5. Chromatography on CM-Sephadex C-50 of fractions 100–115 from Step 2 (Procedure C; Step 3). 115 ml ($OD_{280} = 0.490$) were loaded on a 2- × 100-cm column of CM-Sephadex C-50 equilibrated with 0.05 M phosphate buffer, pH 6.8. A molarity gradient (0.1–0.4) of phosphate buffer, pH 6.8, was started at the fraction indicated with an arrow (right-hand inner scale). 11-ml fractions were collected. The continuous line indicates the absorption at 280 mμ. Circles indicate the acid deoxyribonuclease activity (right-hand outer scale). Fractions 37–48 and 49–61 were processed further.

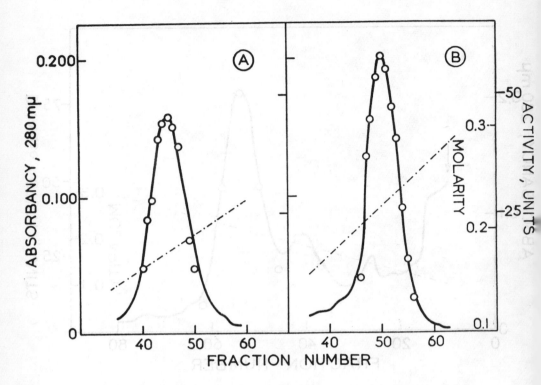

Fig. 6. Rechromatography of acid deoxyribonuclease fractions A and B on CM-Sephadex G-50. 8 OD$_{280}$ units of each acid deoxyribonuclease (preparation HS 10) fractions A and B were loaded on two 1- × 100-cm CM-Sephadex C-50 columns. A molarity gradient (0.1–0.4) of phosphate buffer, pH 6.8, was started at fraction no. 1 (right-hand inner scale). 3-ml fractions were collected. The continuous line shows the absorption at 280 mμ. Circles indicate the deoxyribonuclease activity (right-hand outer scale).

TABLE 3. *Chromatographic Purification of Spleen Acid Deoxyribonuclease (Procedure C)[a]*

	Weight (g)	Volume	Total Units	Total OD₂₈₀	Specific Activity	
					OD₂₈₀	Weight[b]
Crude spleen nuclease II	10	400	160,000	125,000	12.8	16
Step 1. DEAE-Sephadex	0.935	725	105,000	1,625	64.5	112
Step 2. Hydroxyapatite	0.193	425	61,500	225	273	318
Step 3. CM-Sephadex A[c]	0.0185	20	7,850	22.4	350	425
CM-Sephadex B[c]	0.073	30	31,000	88.5	350	425

[a] The reported data refer to preparation HS 11. All values quoted refer to the fractions that were processed further or to the final product. Fractions from the sides of the activity peaks were processed separately.

[b] Specific activity-data given in this column were obtained by dividing the activity (total units) by the dry weight (in mg) of the enzyme preparation.

[c] Values reported refer to fractions A and B, respectively (see text).

117

The central parts of the rechromatographed fractions are loaded on Sephadex G-25 equilibrated with 0.001 M acetate buffer, pH 5.0. The enzyme fractions are then concentrated by freeze-drying to an $OD_{280} = 3.0$ or higher, frozen, and stored at -60 C. These fractions are referred to as the final product in Table 3.

Acid deoxyribonuclease fractions A and B do not show any significant differences in any of the following properties: sedimentation constant (as measured both in the analytical ultracentrifuge and in sucrose density gradient centrifugation), ultraviolet spectra, elution volume from Sephadex G-100 columns, deoxyribonuclease and phosphodiesterase (*vide infra*) specific activities, color reaction with orcinol. The peptide map of the two fractions is identical, except that one particular peptide spot of fraction A is replaced by two well-resolved spots in fraction B. This is the only difference between the two fractions found so far.

No significant difference in physical properties, enzymatic activities and amino acid composition has been found between acid deoxyribonuclease B and the preparations obtained from crude spleen nuclease I (1,9).

PROPERTIES OF SPLEEN ACID DEOXYRIBONUCLEASE

Physical Properties and Amino Acid Composition (10)

These are shown in Tables 4 and 5, respectively. Recently it has been shown that the enzyme is a dimeric protein with two probably identical subunits (11).

TABLE 4. *Physical Properties of Hog Spleen Acid Deoxyribonuclease[a]*

$s°_{20, w}$ (Svedbergs)	3.4
$D_{20, w}$ $(10^{-7} cm^2/sec)^b$	7.8
$v(ml/g)^c$	0.72
MW	3.8×10^4
f/f_o	1.34
$E\ ^{1\%, 1cm}_{280\ m\mu}$	12.1

[a] Reproduced from Biochemistry. 1965. *4*:1725. With the permission of the American Chemical Society, publisher and copyright owner.
[b] This value was obtained at concentrations of 0.5% and about 0.1%.
[c] Calculated value.

TABLE 5. *Amino Acid Analysis of Hog Spleen Deoxyribonuclease*[a]

	Grams of Amino Acid Residues/100 g of Protein[b]				Moles of Amino Acid/Mole of Protein M/W 38,000	Nearest Integral Number of Residues/Mole of Protein[d]
	Hydrolysis time (hr)			Corrected Values[c]		
	22	48	72			
Lys	6.94	6.80	6.95	6.89	20.44	20
His	2.13	2.17	2.31	2.20	6.08	6
(NH₃)	(23.05)	(23.65)	(24.06)	(22.5)	(49.4)	(49)
Arg	5.04	5.55	5.37	5.46	13.30	13
Asp	10.19	10.14	9.36	9.89	32.68	33
Thr	5.44	5.20	4.80	5.63	21.16	21
Ser	8.30	8.10	7.18	8.46	36.93	37
Glu	11.03	11.09	10.66	10.93	32.19	32
Pro	7.09	7.14	6.51	6.91	27.05	27
Gly	3.88	3.97	3.87	3.90	25.99	26
Ala	4.84	4.72	4.33	4.63	24.77	25
½ Cys	1.77	1.79	1.79	1.79	6.65[e]	8
Val	2.62	3.33	3.35	3.35	12.84	13
Met	1.63	1.65	1.30	1.53	4.45	4
Ileu	2.08	2.49	2.52	2.52	8.47	8
Leu	10.47	11.13	10.49	10.67	35.87	36
Tyr	5.23	5.17	4.83	5.28	12.31	12
Phe	6.30	6.56	6.07	6.31	16.30	16
Try					6.3[f]	6
Glucosamine	3.07	3.32	3.06	3.15	7.45	(8)
Total	98.05	100.32	94.75	(99.50)		343
N recovery %	98.9	98.7	97.4			

[a] Reproduced from Biochemistry. 1965. 4:1725. With the permission of the American Chemical Society, publisher and copyright owner.

[b] Total N is 17.2%; total S is 1.0%.

[c] In calculating the corrected values, the criteria given by Tristram and Smith (14) have been followed.

[d] The selection of the integral numbers of residues has been done also taking into account results from other analyses.

[e] After performic acid oxidation: cysteic acid 8.2 residues.

[f] From N-bromosuccinimide titration.

Purity

Phosphomonoesterase activity at pH 5.0 and 6.7, nucleoside poly-phosphatase (5), and exonuclease activities were absent. Ribonuclease activity was present at a trace level in acid deoxyribonuclease preparations obtained according to Procedure B (1). No ribonuclease activity could be detected in the preparations obtained according to Procedure C (2).

Enzymological Properties

Spleen acid deoxyribonuclease is active on both DNA and a series of p-nitrophenyl phosphodiesters (1).

DEOXYRIBONUCLEASE ACTIVITY. The enzyme is able to hydrolyze both native and heat-denatured DNA; the acid-soluble oligonucleotide liberation is slower in the latter case. The initial kinetics of degradation of native DNA indicates that acid deoxyribonuclease can cause scissions of opposite bonds at the same level ("single hit" degradation) in addition to introducing single breaks on one or the other strand ("double hit" degradation) (12,13). At $\mu = 0.15$ the pH optimum appears to be close to 4.8. Mg^{2+} is slightly inhibitory above pH 4.5 and shifts the pH optimum to 4.4. EDTA enhances the enzymatic activity without shifting the pH optimum. Phosphate ion seems to be slightly inhibitory only above pH 5.0. Sulfate ion is a very strong inhibitor, the inhibition being less pronounced below pH 4.5. In succinate buffer, $\mu = 0.15$, pH = 6.7, the activity is less than 3% of that in acetate buffer, $\mu = 0.15$, pH = 5.0. At a lower ionic strength ($\mu = 0.01$) the pH optimum is shifted to a higher pH (5.5 instead of 4.8) and the enzyme shows an activity also in the 6.5–7.5 pH range.

PHOSPHODIESTERASE ACTIVITY. The enzyme shows an activity on the Ca^{2+} and Na^+ salts of bis(p-nitrophenyl)phosphate and the p-nitrophenyl esters of thymidine, deoxyguanosine, and deoxycytidine-3'-phosphates (the deoxyadenosine derivative was not assayed). The p-nitrophenyl ester of thymidine-5'-phosphate is resistant. With Ca [bis(p-nitrophenyl)phosphate]$_2$ as a substrate, the pH optimum was found to be between 5.6 and 5.9. In the 5.1–5.6 pH range the activity in acetate is about twice as large as in the succinate buffer. In the 4.0–5.6 pH range no significant changes occur upon addition of Mg^{2+} or EDTA; in the 4.0–7.0 pH range sulfate and phosphate give a very strong inhibition at a 0.01 M level. In contrast to the deoxyribonuclease activity, the phosphodiesterase activity exhibits a sigmoid type of velocity versus substrate concentration curve (11).

Soluble RNA, ribosomal RNA, and some synthetic polyribonucleotides competitively inhibit acid deoxyribonuclease in both its activities (15). Keeping the enzyme for 20 min at 60 C destroys 50% of both activities (1).

REFERENCES

1. BERNARDI, G., and M. GRIFFÉ. 1964. Biochemistry. 3: 1419.
2. BERNARDI, G., A. BERNARDI, and A. CHERSI. In preparation.
3. LASKOWSKI, M. 1961. In P. D. BOYER, H. LARDY, and K. MYRBACK, editors, Enzymes. Academic Press, New York. Vol. V, p. 123.
4. KAY, E. R. M., N. SIMMONS, and A. L. DOUNCE. 1952. J. Am. Chem. Soc. 74: 1724.
5. LASKOWSKI, M., and B. FILIPOWICZ. 1958. Bull. Soc. Chim. Biol. 40: 1865.
6. SHIMOMURA, M., and M. LASKOWSKI. 1957. Biochim. Biophys. Acta. 26: 198.
7. TISELIUS, A., S. HJERTÉN, and O. LEVIN. 1955. Arch. Biochem. Biophys. 65: 132.
8. HIRS, C. H. W. 1955. In S. P. COLOWICK and N. O. KAPLAN, editors, Methods in enzymology. Academic Press, New York. Vol. I, p. 113.
9. BERNARDI, G., M. GRIFFÉ, and E. APPELLA. 1963. Nature. 198: 186.
10. BERNARDI, G., E. APPELLA, and R. ZITO. 1965. Biochemistry. 4: 1725.
11. BERNARDI, G. 1965. J. Mol. Biol. 13: 603.
12. BERNARDI, G., and C. SADRON. 1964. Biochemistry. 3: 1411.
13. YOUNG, E. T., II, and R. L. SINSHEIMER. 1965. J. Biol. Chem. 240: 1274.
14. TRISTRAM, G. R., and R. H. SMITH. 1963. Advan. Protein Chem. 18: 227.
15. BERNARDI, G. 1964. Biochem. Biophys. Res. Comm. 17: 573.

Endonuclease I (1) from

Escherichia coli

A. DE WAARD AND I. R. LEHMAN

DEPARTMENT OF BIOCHEMISTRY

STANFORD UNIVERSITY SCHOOL OF MEDICINE

STANFORD, CALIFORNIA

Reagents

1. The reaction mixture (total volume 0.3 ml) contains

   0.067 M Tris-Cl buffer, pH 7.5
   6.7 mM $MgCl_2$
   60 μg pancreatic ribonuclease†
   20 mμmoles of P^{32}-labeled *E. coli* DNA-nucleotide (2 to 5×10^6 cpm/μmole) (2)
   Enzyme, diluted in Tris Cl buffer, 0.05 M, pH 7.5, containing 0.25 M ammonium sulfate and crystalline bovine plasma albumin (Armour Laboratories) 1 mg/ml

2. 3.5% $HClO_4$
   "Carrier," salmon sperm DNA, 2.5 mg/ml

Procedure

This assay measures the formation of acid-soluble oligonucleotides from P^{32}-labeled DNA. After incubation at 37 C for 30 min, the reac-

---

† In assays of the crude extract (Fraction I) as well as the streptomycin-ethanol fraction (Fraction II), ribonuclease is added to destroy the inhibitory RNA. All subsequent fractions are free of this inhibitor; however, ribonuclease or a comparable amount of crystalline cytochrome c is added to stabilize the enzyme during incubation.

tion is stopped by adding 0.2 ml of "carrier" DNA and 0.5 ml of cold $HClO_4$. After 5 min at 0 C the suspension is centrifuged at $10,000 \times g$ for 3 min. A sample of the supernatant fluid is pipetted into a planchet and after the addition of 1 or 2 drops of 1 N KOH, the solution is evaporated to dryness and the radioactivity is determined.

The supernatant fluids obtained from control incubations (enzyme omitted) usually contain 0.05–0.1% of the added radioactivity and this value is subtracted from each sample. A unit of enzymatic activity is defined as the amount causing the production of 0.1 μmole of acid-soluble P^{32} in 30 min. The specific activity is expressed as units per milligram of protein. With both crude extracts of E. coli and the purified enzyme, the radioactivity made acid soluble is proportional to the enzyme concentration at levels of 0.005 to 0.07 unit. The pH optimum is from 7.5 to 8.5 (Tris Cl buffer).

The purified enzyme requires added magnesium ion for maximal activity; no activity is detectable in its absence. Magnesium ion can be partially replaced by manganous ion; at 6.7 mM Mn^{2+} the activity is approximately 60% that observed with an equivalent concentration of Mg^{2+}.

ISOLATION PROCEDURE

Growth of Cells

Large-scale growth of E. coli B is carried out in a 60-liter Biogen (American Sterilizer Company). Fifty-five liters of medium containing 1.1% K_2HPO_4, 0.85% KH_2PO_4 and 0.6% Difco yeast extract are auto-claved in the Biogen. To the sterilized medium are added 3 liters of sterile 20% glucose and 2 liters of an inoculum of E. coli B grown overnight in the phosphate-yeast extract-glucose medium. The culture is aerated vigorously at 37 C. When the A_{590} of the culture reaches 1.50, 1 liter of sterile 20% glucose and 1 liter of sterile 18% yeast extract are added. At a A_{590} reading of 3.0 the cells are harvested by pumping them rapidly through a stainless steel coil submerged in a cooling bath into chilled (0 C) jars over a period of 20 min.† The temperature of the cell suspension should not exceed 10 C. The cells are then harvested by means of a Spinco refrigerated continuous flow centrifuge and stored at −20 C. The yield of cell paste is approximately 400 g.

---

† The level of endonuclease I drops rapidly with the onset of the stationary phase (3); it is therefore important to prevent cell growth from proceeding beyond this point.

Unless otherwise indicated, all operations are carried out at 0–4 C. All centrifugations are at 15,000 × g for 15 min. (See Table 1.)

TABLE 1.   *Purification of* E. coli *Endonuclease I*

Fraction	Protein (mg/ml)	Specific Activity (units/mg of protein)	Units (× 10⁻³)
I. Extract	15.5	17.2	362
II. Streptomycin-ethanol	22.5	27	249
III. Autolysis-ammonium sulfate	8.75	94	140
IV. Duolite resin	0.69	1330	78
V. Phosphocellulose	0.27	3190	73
VI. Carboxymethylcellulose	0.047	8730	45

Preparation of Extract

Four hundred grams of cells are partially thawed and suspended in 300 ml of potassium phosphate buffer, 0.15 M, pH 7.0, in a large Waring Blendor (5-liter capacity) equipped with a cooling jacket and connected to a Variac. Stirring is begun at approximately one-third of maximal speed. To the suspension are then added 1350 g of acid-washed glass beads ("Superbrite," average diameter 200 μ, obtained from the Minnesota Mining and Manufacturing Company). When the mixture appears homogeneous, an additional 1500 ml of buffer are added and the homogenization is continued for 20 min at maximal speed. The temperature of the suspension should not be permitted to rise above 12 C. After the homogenization, approximately 10 min are required for the beads to settle out. The broken cell suspension is then centrifuged and the supernatant fluid (approximately 1500 ml) is collected (Fraction I).

Streptomycin-Ethanol Fractionation

The extract is diluted with potassium phosphate buffer, 0.15 M, pH 7.0, to a protein concentration of 10 mg/ml and 0.5 volume of a freshly made 5% solution of streptomycin sulfate is added slowly with stirring. After standing for 30 min, the precipitate that forms is removed by centrifugation and the supernatant fluid (4000 ml) is collected. This solution is subjected to ethanol fractionation in two 2000-ml batches.

To 2000 ml of the supernatant fluid are added 330 ml of 96% ethanol (4 C) with vigorous stirring over a 30-min period. The temperature of the cooling bath is gradually lowered to bring the temperature of the enzyme solution to −4 C. The resulting suspension is centrifuged at −4 C and the precipitate is thoroughly drained and dissolved in 150 ml of potassium phosphate buffer, 0.25 M, pH 7.4, to yield a turbid solution (Fraction II).

Autolysis and Ammonium Sulfate Fractionation

Fraction II (360 ml) is made 1.7 mM in Mg^{2+}, then added to a stainless steel beaker immersed in a water bath at 55 C and stirred rapidly. When the temperature of the solution reaches 42 C, the beaker is immediately transferred to a 37 C bath. The suspension is incubated at 37 C for 15 to 25 min, until 95–100% of the ultraviolet absorbing material at 260 mμ has been made acid soluble.† The autolysate is then chilled to 0 C and the insoluble residue that forms during the digestion is removed by centrifugation.

To 300 ml of the supernatant fluid are added with stirring 94 g of ammonium sulfate. After 10 min, the precipitate that forms is removed by centrifugation. Ammonium sulfate (84 g) is then added to the supernatant fluid and stirring is continued for 15 min after all the ammonium sulfate has dissolved. The suspension is centrifuged and the precipitate is dissolved in 100 ml of sodium phosphate buffer, 0.05 M, pH 6.5. The solution is dialyzed against 2 changes (4 liters each) of the phosphate buffer for a total of 5 hr (Fraction III).

Duolite Chromatography

A column (30 cm × 3 cm) of Duolite CS 101 resin (Biorex 70, Na form, 200–400 mesh, Biorad Laboratories) is prepared and equilibrated with 2 liters of sodium phosphate buffer, 0.05 M, pH 6.5. Fraction III is applied to the column at the rate of 30 ml/hr. The resin is washed first with 500 ml of sodium phosphate, 0.05 M, pH 6.5, and then with 250 ml of sodium phosphate, 0.1 M, pH 7.4. A linear gradient of sodium chloride is then applied with limiting concentrations of 0.3 M and 1.0 M NaCl; both solutions are 0.1 M with respect to sodium phosphate, pH 7.4. The total gradient volume is 800 ml and the flow rate is 80 ml/hr.‡ The enzyme is eluted approximately midway through the gradient. The fractions with a specific activity of 1000 or more are

† At 10-min intervals, 1-ml portions are removed and centrifuged and the optical density of the supernatant fluid, after suitable dilution in Tris Cl buffer, 0.05 M, pH 7.4, is determined at 260 mμ. A portion of the supernatant fluid is precipitated with an equal volume of cold 1 N perchloric acid and the optical density of the acid-soluble fraction is determined.

‡ Crystallization of the sodium phosphate in the gradient reservoir can be prevented by jacketing the reservoir with a thin layer of polyurethane.

pooled (85 ml) and dialyzed for a total of 5 hr against two changes (4 liters each) of potassium phosphate buffer, 0.02 M, pH 6.5 (Fraction IV).

Phosphocellulose Chromatography

A column (20 cm × 1 cm) of phosphocellulose (Whatman Chromedia, P11) is prepared and equilibrated with 1 liter of potassium phosphate, 0.02 M, pH 6.5. Fraction IV is applied to the column at the rate of 30 ml/hr. The adsorbent is then successively eluted with 10-ml portions of potassium phosphate buffers, pH 6.5, at 0.02 M, 0.10 M, and 0.20 M. A linear gradient of potassium phosphate, pH 6.5, is then applied, with limiting concentrations of 0.2 M and 0.67 M. The total gradient volume is 200 ml and the flow rate is 20 ml/hr. The fractions with a specific activity of 2500 or greater are pooled (85 ml) and dialyzed for a total of 3 hr against two changes (4 liters each) of potassium phosphate, 0.01 M, pH 6.5 (Fraction V).

Carboxymethylcellulose Chromatography

A column (25 cm × 1.5 cm) of carboxymethylcellulose (Brown and Company, Selectacel, Type 40) is prepared and equilibrated with 1 liter of potassium phosphate, 0.01 M, pH 6.5. Fraction V is applied to the column at a rate of 20 ml/hr. After washing the adsorbent with 25 ml of potassium phosphate, 0.01 M, pH 6.5, a linear gradient of potassium phosphate, pH 7.4 is applied, with limiting concentrations of 0.04 M and 0.2 M. The total gradient volume is 400 ml and the flow rate is maintained at 40 ml/hr. Those fractions with a specific activity of 7500 or greater (40 ml) are combined and dialyzed for a total of 3 hr against 4 liters of potassium phosphate, 0.02 M, pH 7.4 (Fraction VI). The pooled carboxymethylcellulose fraction is then taken to dryness by lyophilization and dissolved in 4 ml of distilled water.

Stability of Enzyme Fractions

Fractions I, II, and III have shown no significant decrease in activity upon storage at −20 C for 6 months. Fractions IV, V, and VI lose activity rapidly on storage at −20 C; however, no loss in activity has been detected when these fractions are kept at 0 C for a 4-month period. Fraction VI concentrated by lyophilization has shown no decrease in activity when stored at −20 C for 4 months.

Comments on Purification Procedure

The enzyme preparation obtained by this procedure is still physically inhomogeneous; specific activities as high as 30,000 have been observed after gel filtration of Fraction IV on Sephadex G75 followed by chromatography of the Sephadex fraction on phosphocellulose and carboxymethylcellulose. Such preparations have approached physical homogeneity as judged by acrylamide gel electrophoresis. The gel filtration step is, however, at present unsuitable as a routine procedure since enzymatically active aggregates, often in large amounts, are separated by the gel filtration from a "monomeric" form of the enzyme. The aggregates are eluted from the Sephadex column mixed with much contaminating protein. The amount of "monomeric" form (defined as that material eluted after approximately three hold-up volumes have passed through the column) is variable. This enzyme fraction, however, is essentially free of ribonuclease activity.

To isolate an endonuclease I preparation free of significant ribonuclease contamination, the following procedure may be used: Fraction IV (50 ml) is dialyzed against a 30% solution of polyethylene glycol in potassium phosphate buffer, 0.05 M, pH 6.5, until the volume is reduced to 12 ml. The enzyme solution containing approximately 2 mg of protein/ml is then applied to a Sephadex G75 column (80 cm × 1 cm) equilibrated with potassium phosphate, 0.05 M, pH 6.5. Elution is carried out with the same buffer. The pass-through fraction contains the aggregated form of the enzyme, whereas the "monomeric" form, free of ribonuclease activity, is eluted after three hold-up volumes.

PROPERTIES OF ENZYME

Contamination with Other Enzymes

Fraction VI of endonuclease I is free of *E. coli* exonucleases I, II, and III (4) as judged by the absence of mononucleotides among the products after extensive degradation of both native and denatured DNA. It is also free of detectable acid or alkaline nucleotidase activity (<0.5% of the endonuclease activity).

Fraction VI does contain a significant level of ribonuclease activity, probably the ribonuclease I described by Spahr and Hollingsworth (5). The ribonuclease can, however, be largely removed by gel filtration on Sephadex as described above.

Specificity

E. coli endonuclease I degrades native DNA at a sevenfold greater rate than denatured DNA. It carries out a purely endonucleolytic attack on DNA yielding a limit digest whose oligonucleotides have an average chain length of approximately 7; they are terminated by 5'-

phosphoryl groups. The isolated oligonucleotides are neither cleaved by high concentrations of the enzyme, nor can they inhibit the hydrolysis of DNA when added in equal concentration (of nucleotide residues).

Attempts to demonstrate some base specificity for the endonuclease have not yielded decisive results. Thus, although less than 5% of the oligonucleotides found in a limit digest are terminated by deoxyadenosine at the 3′-hydroxyl end, implying that bonds of the type . . . pApX . . . are relatively resistant to the action of the endonuclease, this finding in itself cannot account for a limit digest of chain length as great as 7. Clearly, a minimal substrate size requirement, perhaps in addition to some other as yet undetermined features, must impose the limit observed. Of interest in this regard is the observation that the dAT copolymer is degraded more rapidly and to a greater extent (average chain length about 4) than DNA. By contrast, the dGdC polymer is highly resistant to the endonuclease.

Recently, Studier (6) utilizing the technique of zone sedimentation of DNA at neutral and alkaline pHs has observed that, unlike pancreatic deoxyribonuclease, which is known to introduce single-strand scissions in DNA, *E. coli* endonuclease I appears to cleave both strands of a DNA double helix at or near the same level.

Other Properties

Endonuclease I is present in crude extracts bound to an inhibitory RNA, which is removed during purification (autolysis step). The purified enzyme can be inhibited by a variety of RNAs including those from *E. coli*, guinea pig liver, and tobacco mosaic virus. Of the RNAs tested, sRNA from *E. coli* is the most active. The kinetics of the enzyme inhibited by sRNA show that the inhibition is competitive and the K_I is approximately 1×10^{-8} M (RNA nucleotide) (7). Poly A and poly U individually are completely inactive as inhibitors; however, when these two polymers are mixed under conditions known to yield the 1:1 double-stranded complex, the resulting complex is a more effective inhibitor than even sRNA from *E. coli* (4). This result suggests that some ordered helical structure is necessary to permit a polyribonucleotide to serve effectively as an inhibitor of the endonuclease.

REFERENCES

1. LEHMAN, I. R., G. G. ROUSSOS, and E. A. PRATT. 1962. J. Biol. Chem. *237:* 819.
2. LEHMAN, I. R. 1960. J. Biol. Chem. *235:* 1479.
3. SHORTMAN, K., and I. R. LEHMAN. 1964. J. Biol. Chem. *239:* 2964.

4. LEHMAN, I. R. 1963. *In* J. N. DAVIDSON and W. COHN, editors, Progress in nucleic acid research. Academic Press, New York. Vol. 2, p. 83.

5. SPAHR, P. F., and B. R. HOLLINGSWORTH. 1962. J. Biol. Chem. *236:* 823.

6. STUDIER, W. F. 1965. J. Mol. Biol. *11:* 373.

7. LEHMAN, I. R., G. G. ROUSSOS, and E. A. PRATT. 1962. J. Biol. Chem. *237:* 829.

Cyclic Phosphodiesterase

of *Escherichia coli*

YASUHIRO ANRAKU
NATIONAL INSTITUTE OF ARTHRITIS
 AND METABOLIC DISEASES
NATIONAL INSTITUTES OF HEALTH
BETHESDA, MARYLAND

ASSAY

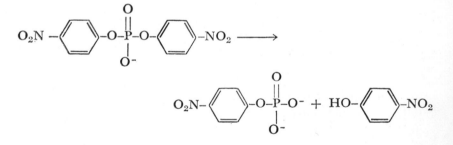

Reagents

1. The reaction mixture (total volume 2 ml) contains

   0.05 M Acetate buffer, pH 5.7
   0.5 mM $CoCl_2$

0.5 mM Di-*p*-nitrophenyl phosphate
Enzyme

2. 0.3 N NaOH

Procedure

This assay measures the formation of *p*-nitrophenol from di-*p*-nitrophenyl phosphate. With the enzyme from *Escherichia coli*, this assay is highly specific for cyclic phosphodiesterase and can be used to measure the enzymatic activity during the purification procedure (for more details, see the section *Substrate Specificity*).

After 20-min incubation at 37 C, the reaction is stopped by adding 1 ml of 0.3 N NaOH (reagent 2). The resulting mixture is diluted to 6 ml by addition of 3 ml of water and the intensity of the yellow color developed due to *p*-nitrophenol is measured in a 1-cm quartz cuvette with a spectrophotometer (Hitachi-Perkin Elmer, model 139) at 420 mμ. A suitable blank, prepared by addition of enzyme to the reaction mixture after the incubation, is run with each set of assays. The amount of *p*-nitrophenol released is determined from a calibration curve prepared with *p*-nitrophenol as a standard under the above conditions.

One unit of enzyme is defined as the amount that under the above conditions hydrolyzes 1 μmole of di-*p*-nitrophenyl phosphate per hour. Specific enzyme activity is defined as the units per milligram of protein. Under the conditions described, the amount of *p*-nitrophenol released is proportional to the enzyme concentration from 0.2 to 1.0 units and to the time of incubation for more than 30 min. The optimal pH value is between 5.5 and 6.5 in acetate buffer.

FORMATION OF ENZYME AND GROWTH OF CELLS

Formation of Enzyme in Various Strains

The formation of the enzyme varies with the strain. *E. coli* strain B usually has a high enzyme level. Among the strains examined, the highest specific activity is shown in strain 165. Typical results on enzyme formation of several strains cultured in broth are presented in Table 1 (2).

Formation of Enzyme Under Various Conditions

The formation of the enzyme in strain B varies with the culture medium (Table 2). Maximal specific activity of the enzyme is reached

TABLE 1. *Cyclic Phosphodiesterase Activity in Various Strains of* E. coli *(2)*[a]

Strain	Late Exponential Phase		Stationary Phase	
	Protein (mg/ml)	Specific Activity (units/mg of protein)	Protein (mg/ml)	Specific Activity (units/mg of protein)
B	0.58	0.50	0.84	0.49
F-2[b]	0.21	0.19	0.22	0.20
U-3[c]	0.72	0.14	1.00	0.16
E-15[d]	0.63	0.13	0.80	0.12
W-25[e]	0.56	0.18	0.78	0.19
H-5[f]	0.62	0.19	0.91	0.27
165	0.56	0.77	0.82	0.84

[a] Bacteria were grown in broth. The medium contained per liter: 10 g of meat extract, 10 g of peptone, and 2 g of NaCl. The pH was adjusted at 7.4. The enzyme activity was determined under the conditions described in "Assay."

[b] Uracil or cytosine, and arginine requiring.

[c] Hfr (λ), phosphatase Cr+.

[d] Hfr (λ), proline and thiamine requiring, phosphatase deletion.

[e] Hfr (λ), purine requiring.

[f] Hfr.

U-3, E-15, and W-25 were obtained through Dr. T. Horiuchi. H-5 was obtained through Dr. J. Tomizawa. Strain 165 is *E. coli* N.C.T.C. 1100 and was given by Dr. H. E. Wade through Dr. L. A. Heppel.

at the late exponential or stationary phase (3). In medium C, a high enzyme yield is obtained, but about 5 times as much of a nonspecific acid phosphatase is formed as in medium A (4). For preparation of the enzyme, it is best to add glucose or lactate to the medium as a carbon source.

Growth of Cells

Large scale production of cells is performed by tank culture. The best yield of cells and the highest enzyme activity have been obtained with a lactate–peptone medium as follows: A solution is obtained by mixing 2.78 kg of $Na_2HPO_4 \cdot 12H_2O$, 420 g of KH_2PO_4, 100 g of NaCl, 200 g of NH_4Cl, 2.92 g of $CaCl_2$, 44 g of $MgSO_4 \cdot 7H_2O$, 48 mg of $FeCl_3$, 2 kg of sodium lactate, 1 kg of peptone (Kyokuto Company, Japan), and 200 liters of water in a stainless steel tank. The pH of the medium is adjusted to 7.15 by adding solid NaOH. The contents are sterilized

TABLE 2. *Cyclic Phosphodiesterase Activity of* E. Coli B *in Various Culture Media* (3)

Medium	Phase	Protein (mg/ml)	Cyclic Phosphodiesterase Activity (units/ml)	Specific Activity (units/mg of protein)	Acid Phosphatase[a] Activity (units/ml)
Broth	Late exp.	0.58	0.29	0.50	—[b]
	Stationary	0.84	0.41	0.49	—[b]
A[c]	Late exp.	0.80	0.38	1.10	0.015
	Stationary	0.90	1.10	1.22	0.022
B[d]	Late exp.	0.67	0.53	0.80	0.015
	Stationary	1.00	0.30	0.80	0.019
C[e]	Late exp.	0.37	0.72	1.95	0.070
	Stationary	0.48	0.60	1.25	0.077

[a] The reaction mixture contained, in a total volume of 2 ml, 5×10^{-4} M p-nitrophenyl phosphate, 0.1 M acetate buffer, pH 5.0 and enzyme. After 20 minutes incubation at 37 C, the reaction was stopped by adding 1 ml of 0.3 N NaOH. The resulting mixture was diluted to 6 ml by adding 3 ml of water and the amount of p-nitrophenol released was determined as described in "Assay." One unit of enzyme is defined as the amount that under the above conditions hydrolyzes 1 μmole of p-nitrophenyl phosphate per hour.

[b] The dashes indicate that no test was made.

[c] The medium contained per liter: 10 g of casamino acid (Difco), 10 g of glucose, 3 g of NaCl, 11 mg of $CaCl_2$, 250 mg of $MgSO_4 \cdot 7 H_2O$, 1.30 g of KH_2PO_4, and 7.30 g of Tris, pH 7.4.

[d] The medium contained per liter: 5.0 g of peptone (Kyokuto), 4 g of glucose, 13.9 g of $Na_2HPO_4 \cdot 12 H_2O$, 2.1 g of KH_2PO_4, 0.5 g of NaCl, 1.0 g of NH_4Cl, 11 mg of $CaCl_2$, 220 mg of $MgSO_4 \cdot 7 H_2O$, and 0.24 mg of $FeCl_3$, pH 7.4.

[e] The 4 g of glucose in Medium B was replaced by 1 g of potassium succinate.

by autoclaving at 1 kg/cm² pressure (110 C) for 30 min. When the temperature of the medium decreases to 37 C, 2 liters of a culture of *E. coli* B that has been shaken for 24 hr is introduced into the tank to start the cultivation. The contents are aerated vigorously and stirred mechanically at 37 C.

The growth of cells is determined by measuring the turbidity of samples taken at intervals. After cultivation for 6 hr the cells reach the late exponential phase and they are then harvested with a Sharpless centrifuge in the cold. The yield of cells is approximately 5.6 g wet weight per liter. Antifoam agents, such as soy bean oil, adversely affect the yield of the enzyme activity.

Under the above conditions, the specific activities of cyclic phospho-diesterase and nonspecific acid phosphatase are 2.47 and 0.15 units per mg of protein, respectively. The formation of a nonspecific alkaline phosphatase is negligible. The wet cell pellets are immediately frozen without further washing and stored at −15 C. They may be stored for about a year without appreciable loss of activity.

ISOLATION PROCEDURE

The procedure for purification of the cyclic phosphodiesterase is not completely established. Two procedures for its isolation are de-scribed in this article. By Procedure A a preparation of high purity is obtained (1), but Procedure B is quicker (2). Unless otherwise stated, all procedures were carried out below 4 C.

Procedure A

Step I. Preparation of Crude Extract

The cells are usually disintegrated in a French pressure cell (Ohtake Company, Japan). Toluolysis of the cell suspension causes slight in-activation of the enzyme. The preparation can be sonicated at 10 kc/sec (Kubota Company, Japan), but treatment for more than 5 min causes a considerable loss of activity.

One hundred grams of frozen E. coli cells from a culture in glucose–peptone medium (1) are suspended in 300 ml of 0.05 M Tris buffer, pH 7.4, containing 0.02 M $MgSO_4$. A 70-ml portion of the suspension is passed through the French pressure cell (400 kg/cm²). Disrupted cells are pooled in an ice bath until all treatments are completed. The pooled, disrupted cell suspension is then centrifuged for 20 min at 10,000 × g. The precipitates are washed with an appropriate volume of the same buffer, centrifuged, and discarded. The supernatant fluid and washings are combined, recentrifuged as above, and made up to a final volume of 420 ml with the buffer (Fraction I, Table 3).

Step II. 78,000 × g Soluble Fraction

This fraction (Fraction II) is obtained by centrifugation for 180 min at 78,000 × g using a Hitachi preparative ultracentrifuge, Type 40P with an RP 30-225 rotor. The 78,000 × g precipitate has no detectable enzyme activity. By sedimenting the ribosome fraction in this step, most of the ribonuclease activity is eliminated from Fraction II.

TABLE 3. *Purification of Cyclic Phosphodiesterase of* E. coli *B by Procedure A* (1)[a]

Fraction[b]	Protein (mg/ml)	Activity (units/ml)	Specific Activity (units/mg of protein)	Recovery (%)
I. Crude extract	21.1	20.2	0.96	100
II. 78,000 × g supernatant fluid	14.5	21.5	1.49	98
III. First ammonium sulfate	26.0	40.0	1.55	38
IV. Second ammonium sulfate	31.7	48.8	1.55	16
VI. DEAE-cellulose	0.149	11.0	73.9	13
VII. DEAE-Sephadex[c]	0.01	8.54	853	12

[a] Enzyme units were recalculated in terms of the units defined in "Assay."
[b] Fraction V was omitted.
[c] Main fraction.

Step III. First Ammonium Sulfate Fractionation

Fraction II is first brought to 42.5% saturation with saturated ammonium sulfate solution: To 385 ml of Fraction II a solution of 285 ml of ammonium sulfate (saturated at 0 C) are added, dropwise, with gentle stirring. The solution is kept at pH 7.4–7.5 by addition of 3% ammonium hydroxide as needed. After removal of the precipitate by centrifugation for 20 min at 10,000 × g, 170 g of solid ammonium sulfate are added as above to 640 ml of the supernatant fluid to give 83% saturation. The solution is allowed to stand for 10 min after the addition. Then the precipitate is collected by centrifugation and dissolved in 0.05 M Tris buffer, pH 8.8, to give a final volume of 80 ml (Fraction III).

Step IV. Second Ammonium Sulfate Fractionation

Solid ammonium sulfate (15 g) is added to 80 ml of Fraction III to bring it to 25% saturation. The bulky precipitate is removed by centrifugation, and a further 21.9 g of ammonium sulfate are added to the supernatant solution to give 60% saturation. The pH of the solution is maintained at 8.8 throughout the treatments by addition of 3% ammonium hydroxide. The precipitate is collected and dissolved in 0.005 M Tris buffer, pH 7.6. The clear solution (Fraction IV, 28 ml) may be stored in the frozen state.

Step V. Gel Filtration

A Sephadex G-50 column (2.8 cm × 45 cm, medium, Pharmacia) is prepared and equilibrated with 0.005 M Tris buffer, pH 7.6. Fraction IV is introduced onto the column, which is then eluted with 0.001 M β-mercaptoethanol in 0.001 M Tris buffer, pH 7.6. Fractions are collected in 10-g portions (Toyo fraction collector, rectangular balance-operated type), at a flow rate of 30 g/hr.

The enzyme is eluted in Fractions 11–20 and recovery is almost complete. β-Mercaptoethanol is necessary to protect the enzyme activity in this process. The pooled effluent (Fraction V) is free from residual ammonium sulfate. It is also possible to remove residual ammonium sulfate by dialysis, but we have occasionally observed that this causes a considerable loss of the activity.

Step VI. Chromatography on DEAE-Cellulose

DEAE-cellulose (0.9 meq/g, Brown Company) is washed before use by the method of Peterson and Sober (5). A column of DEAE-cellulose (3.2 cm × 35 cm) is prepared and equilibrated by washing with 3 liters of 0.005 M Tris buffer, pH 8.8. Fraction V is layered on the column, and the adsorbent is washed with 150 ml of the same buffer. Elution with a linear gradient of NaCl is obtained by placing 1 liter of the same buffer in the mixing vessel and 1 liter of 0.5 M NaCl in the buffer in the second container. The fraction size is 10 g, and the flow rate is 30–35 g/hr. The enzyme activity is eluted between Fractions 62 and 82, and the recovery is approximately 90%. No detectable activity is found in the other fractions. The activity is eluted at 0.06–0.1 M salt concentration, as judged by conductivity measurements. Fractions 66 to 74 are combined (Fraction VI), and dialyzed for 3 hr against 50 volumes of the buffer used for elution. The buffer is changed twice during the dialysis.

Step VII. Chromatography on DEAE-Sephadex

Washed DEAE-Sephadex A-50† (medium, 3.0 meq/g, Pharmacia) is packed in a column (2.2 cm × 18 cm) and equilibrated by washing with 0.005 M Tris buffer, pH 8.8. Fraction VI (100 ml) is passed into the column that is then washed with 100 ml of a solution of 0.01 M NaCl in the above buffer. After washing, a linear gradient is applied with 0.01 and 0.1 M NaCl in the buffer as limiting concentrations; 500 ml of each

---

† DEAE-Sephadex A-50 was treated before use as follows: It was allowed to swell in an excess of water. The fine particles were removed by decantation, and the Sephadex was washed with an appropriate volume of 0.5 N HCl, water, 0.5 N NaOH, and water until the washings became nearly neutral.

buffer are employed as described in Step VI. Fractions of 5 g are collected at a flow rate of 20–30 g/hr. The enzyme activity is eluted between Fractions 210 and 235, and its recovery in these fractions is at least 95%.

Fractions 213 to 224 are pooled and dialyzed for 15 hr against 50 volumes of Tris buffer, 0.005 M, pH 7.6, containing 1×10^{-5} M EDTA. The dialysis fluid is changed three times. This fraction is dialyzed against the same buffer without EDTA for a further 24 hr (Fraction VII, 60 ml). The results of the enzyme purification are summarized in Table 3. Usually, the over-all purification obtained by these procedures is between 500- and 1,000-fold.

Procedure B

The cyclic phosphodiesterase is one of *Peri-enzymes* reported by Neu and Heppel (6). The enzyme can be released easily from cells when they are converted to spheroplasts by EDTA-lysozyme, or by the method of *"cold water wash"* (6). Procedure B (2) is a combination of the methods of Neu and Heppel (6) and of Anraku (1).

Step I. Cell Suspension

One hundred grams of frozen cells, from a culture in the lactate–peptone medium described in the section *Growth of Cells*, are thawed and uniformly suspended in 0.005 M Tris buffer, pH 7.4, containing 1 mM EDTA. The cell suspension thus obtained (Fraction I, Table 4) is kept at 20 C, and stirred vigorously for 2 hr using a magnetic stirrer.

TABLE 4. *Purification of Cyclic Phosphodiesterase of E. coli B by Procedure B (2)*

Fraction	Protein (mg/ml)	Specific Activity (units/mg of protein)	Total Activity (units)
I. Cell suspension	12.0	2.47	31,400
II. Tris-EDTA eluate	1.92	8.75	17,000
III. Protamine supernatant	1.60	9.38	16,500
IV. DEAE-cellulose	2.22	22.7	12,100
V. DEAE-Sephadex:			
Peak fraction	0.06	355	4,000
Total recovered			11,000

Step II. Tris-EDTA Eluate

The cell suspension is then centrifuged at 10,000 × g for 10 min. The slightly turbid supernatant solution (Fraction II) contains 55–70% of the total enzyme activity. If the temperature is lower during this treatment, the release of activity decreases proportionally. Washing of the residual pellets, after this treatment, yields less than 5% activity; complete solubilization takes place when the residual pellets are disrupted by sonication.

When 0.005 M Tris buffer, pH 7.4, containing 1 mM EDTA and 20% sucrose is used as a solubilizing buffer, the activity released under the above conditions is approximately the same as with Tris-EDTA. When EDTA and sucrose are not added to the buffer, the activity released corresponds to less than 50% of the total activity. Fraction II contains 12–17% of the total protein, and 8–10% of the total RNA and DNA, respectively. Ribonuclease and nonspecific acid phosphatase activities released in Fraction II are approximately of the order of 56 and 53%, respectively.

Step III. Protamine Supernatant Fluid

To 1010 ml of Fraction II is added dropwise 100 ml of 0.5% protamine solution (Wako Chemicals Company, Japan) with gentle stirring. A white, thread-like precipitate begins to appear immediately, and the solution becomes clear after the addition of approximately half of the protamine solution. On subsequent addition of the other half, the solution becomes turbid due to the formation of a fine precipitate. After standing for 30 min, the mixture is centrifuged at 10,000 × g for 15 min. The clear, light yellow supernatant fluid (Fraction III) contains more than 98% of the activity. The RNA and DNA contents of this fraction are less than 10 and 1 μg/ml, respectively.

Step IV. Chromatography on DEAE-Cellulose

Fraction III (1,100 ml) is brought to pH 8.8 with approximately 12 ml of 1 M Tris, and then placed on a column of DEAE-cellulose (4.6 cm × 25 cm, 0.9 meq/g, Brown Company) equilibrated with 0.01 M Tris buffer, pH 8.8. The column is then washed with 50 ml of the same buffer. Linear gradient elution is then started. The mixing vessel contains 800 ml of the above buffer, and the reservoir contains 800 ml of a solution of 0.5 M NaCl in the same buffer. The fractions are collected in 12-g portions, and the flow rate is 35–40 g/hr.

The enzyme activity first appears in fraction 130. Approximately 95% of the units adsorbed on the column are recovered in fractions 130 to 160. The volume of eluate that contains the activity is one quarter of the original volume. Fractions 133 to 152 are combined to give Fraction IV (240 ml) in which 30% of the protein applied on the column is recovered. Fraction IV still contains nonspecific acid phosphates and ribonuclease in amounts equivalent to 26 and 5.1% of their activities in Fraction I.

Step V. Chromatography on DEAE-Sephadex

Fraction IV is placed on a column of DEAE-Sephadex A-50 4.6 cm × 8 cm, medium, 3.0 meq/g, Pharmacia) equilibrated by washing with 0.01 M Tris buffer, pH 8.8. After the solution has passed through the column, linear NaCl gradient elution is established with 500 ml of the same buffer in the mixing vessel and 500 ml of the same buffer containing 0.1 M NaCl in the second reservoir. The fraction size is 5 g, and the flow rate is 40 g/hr. At least 90% of the activity applied on the column is recovered in fractions 170 to 250 in which the concentration of NaCl is approximately 0.06 to 0.1 M.

Comments

A summary of a typical preparation of Procedure B is shown in Table 4. The over-all purification obtained thus far is between 100- and 150-fold.

The purified enzyme preparations from the final Fraction of either Procedure A or Procedure B are dialyzed well against 0.005 M Tris buffer, pH 7.4. If necessary, they are then concentrated with washed, dried Sephadex G-50, and are stored at 4 C or in a frozen state at −15 C. Under the above conditions, there is 20–30% loss of activity in 2 months at 4 C. When stored at −15 C, there is only 30% loss of activity after a year. The stability of the lyophilized preparation has not yet been investigated thoroughly.

PROPERTIES OF THE ENZYME

Contamination with Other Enzymes

No evidence for the presence of ribonuclease or other nucleases in Fraction VII of Procedure A has so far been obtained (1).† Fraction V of Procedure B (2.0 units) was incubated with 5 mg of yeast RNA in

† Thus, when the enzyme (15 units) was incubated with 3 mg of ribosomal RNA (*E. coli*), soluble RNA (*E. coli*), and DNA (calf thymus) under the reported conditions (1) for 1 hr, 0.3, 0.4, and 0.1%, respectively, of the total nucleotides of the substrates rendered acid soluble.

0.05 M Tris buffer, pH 7.6, in a total volume of 1 ml for 1 hr at 37 C. 0.5 to 0.7% of the total nucleotides could be detected as cold perchloric acid–uranyl acetate soluble material (7,8). Thus less than 0.001 unit per ml of ribonuclease, if any, is present.

The possibility of contamination of the preparation with a non-specific acid phosphatase was investigated. The reaction mixture contained, in a total volume of 2 ml, 5×10^{-4} M p-nitrophenyl phosphate, 0.1 M acetate buffer, pH 5.0, and 1.5–2.0 units of enzyme from the final fraction of either Procedure A or Procedure B. After incubation for 1 hr at 37 C, no release of p-nitrophenol was observed.

ATP, ADP, and 5′-AMP were incubated with 2.0 units of the final preparation of Procedure B under the conditions described in "Assay" for 30 min. Approximately 7% of the organic phosphorus contained in these compounds was converted to inorganic phosphate.

Specificity

The cyclic phosphodiesterase purified by the above procedures has specific 3′-nucleotidase activity in the same molecule. The ratio of the two specific activities is constant throughout the purification procedure (1). Evidence supporting the presence of a single enzyme with two activities is obtained by experiments on the pH optimum, requirements for ions, heat stability (1), and sedimentation analysis in a sucrose density gradient (9). Results indicating that the two active sites are different is obtained by kinetic analyses (10).

Based on these findings, the cyclic phosphodiesterase and the 3′-nucleotidase are considered to be a "double-headed" enzyme. Thus the four chief nucleoside 2′,3′-cyclic phosphates are hydrolyzed by a purified enzyme preparation to the nucleosides and inorganic phosphate at the same rate *via* the corresponding nucleoside 3′-monophosphates (10). The substrate specificities of the cyclic phosphodiesterase and the associated 3′-nucleotidase are summarized in Table 5.

0.165 mg of adenosine(3′-5′)-phosphoryl-adenosine 2′,3′-cyclic phosphate (ApA-cyclic-p)† was incubated with 1.7 units of the enzyme from Fraction V of Procedure B under the present assay conditions. After incubation for 20 and 60 min, 30 and 50%, respectively, of the phosphate in the 2′,3′-hydroxyl end were converted to inorganic phosphate. The reaction products were also analyzed by paper electrophoresis. ApA was detected as a major product, and a small amount of adenosine was also found (2). Maruyama and Mizuno (11) have shown that the

† Adenosine(3′-5′)-phosphoryl-adenosine 2′,3′-cyclic phosphate used was a generous gift from Dr. N. Imura. It was prepared by hydrolyzing polyadenylic acid with crystalline bovine pancreatic ribonuclease.

TABLE 5.   *Relative Activity of Cyclic Phosphodiesterase with Various Phosphate Compounds* (1,2,10)

Cleavage of Diester Bond		Cleavage of Monoester Bond	
Substrate	Relative Activity	Substrate	Relative Activity
Uridine 2',3'-cyclic phosphate	100	3'-UMP	100
		3'-AMP	76
Di-p-nitrophenyl phosphate	20	3'-CMP	86
p-Nitrophenyl-5'-UMP	0.1	Spongouridine 3'-phosphate	1.0
ADP	0.8	2'-AMP	7.1
UDP	2.4	2'-CMP	9.5
ATP	0.2	5'-UMP	0.9[a]
UTP	2.0	5'-AMP	3.3[a]
		5'-CMP	4.6[a]
		5'-GMP	0.9[a]
		3'-dAMP	3[b]
		3'-dCMP	5[b]
		3'-dGMP	6[b]

[a] The reaction was carried out in Tris buffer 0.025 M, pH 7.5, instead of acetate buffer 0.025 M, pH 5.7.

[b] These velocities are approximate values. The deoxyisomers of the 3'-mononucleotide were generous gifts from Dr. A. Ohsaka. They were prepared by the exhaustive digestion of calf thymus DNA with purified *Micrococcal* nuclease.

cyclic phosphodiesterase can eliminate the cyclic phosphate at the 2',3'-hydroxyl end of oligonucleotides with an average chain length of 10 to 15 nucleotides.

The cyclic phosphodiesterase is highly specific for ribonucleoside 2',3'-cyclic phosphates. However, of the synthetic chromogenic substrates examined it specifically hydrolyzes di-p-nitrophenyl phosphate (Table 6) (3). This finding is very interesting, but the reason for it is unknown. However, because of this specificity, di-p-nitrophenyl phosphate is the best substrate for use in the purification of the enzyme from the cells of *E. coli* (1).

Molecular Size

A preliminary attempt to estimate the molecular size of the enzyme was performed by centrifugation of the enzyme in a sucrose gradient (9). The conditions used in the method of Martin and Ames (12) were followed, and centrifugation was carried out at 38,000 rev/min for 10

TABLE 6.   *Rates of Hydrolysis of Various Synthetic Substrates
by Phosphodiesterases and Ribonuclease (3)*

Substrate	Relative Rate of Hydrolysis by		
	Cyclic Phosphodiesterase of *E. coli*	Phosphodiesterase from Snake Venom[a]	Ribonuclease of *E. coli*
Di-*p*-nitrophenyl phosphate	100	100	Not hydrolyzed
p-Nitrophenyl-5'-(2',3'-*O*-isopropyridene)-UMP	4	950	Not hydrolyzed
p-Nitrophenyl-5'-UMP	1	1300	Not hydrolyzed

[a] Phosphodiesterase from snake venom of *T. flavovirides,* a crotalid.

hr, using bovine serum hemoglobin S and crystalline bovine pancreatic ribonuclease (Worthington) as internal protein standards. Samples of the enzyme from Fraction VII of Procedure A, Fraction VII after heat-treatment at 55 C for 5 min, and Fraction IV of Procedure A were centrifuged. In all cases, the enzyme sedimented at the same position as bovine hemoglobin S. Thus, from the molecular weights of the two standards, a rough estimate of the molecular weight of the enzyme is about 68,000.

Other Properties

The cyclic phosphodiesterase is activated specifically by cobalt ion. Thus, 1×10^{-3} and 1×10^{-4} M of cobalt ion activates the enzyme 5.3 and 3.7 times, respectively (1). Zinc and copper are inhibitory, whereas magnesium, manganese, barium, and calcium have no appreciable effect on the enzyme (1).

Sodium chloride at a concentration of 0.3 M inhibits the enzyme activity by 10%. Potassium chloride decreases the activity to the same extent as sodium chloride. Ammonium sulfate is inhibitory to the enzyme. Thus, 0.05, 0.1, and 0.3 M ammonium sulfate decrease the activity by 40, 51, and 40%, respectively, under the conditions described (2).

EDTA and potassium cyanide, which are metal-chelating agents, inhibit the enzyme (1). SH reagents, such as iodoacetate and *p*-chloromercurybenzoate at a concentration of 1×10^{-3} M have no effect on the enzyme activity (9).

The enzyme from Fraction VII of Procedure A is activated by heat treatment at below 55 C and completely inactivated by treatment at over 70 C. Maximum activation is achieved by treatment at 55 C on treatment for 5 min (1).

Equimolar concentrations of uridine and 5'-UMP do not inhibit the hydrolysis of uridine 2',3'-cyclic phosphate by the enzyme (10). Phosphate ion does not show any inhibitory effect on the cleavage of the diester bond of uridine 2',3'-cyclic phosphate by the enzyme. However, phosphate (0.1 M phosphate buffer, pH 7.5) completely inhibits the hydrolysis of di-*p*-nitrophenyl phosphate by the enzyme (3). The reason for this is unknown.

REFERENCES

1. ANRAKU, Y. 1964. J. Biol. Chem. *239:* 3412.
2. ANRAKU, Y., and D. MIZUNO. To be published.
3. ANRAKU, Y. 1965. Thesis, "Enzymatic study and regulatory mechanism of the pathways of ribonucleic acid degradation in *Escherichia coli.*" University of Tokyo.
4. VON HOFSTEN, B. 1961. Biochim. Biophys. Acta. *48:* 171.
5. PETERSON, E. A., and H. A. SOBER. 1962. *In* S. P. COLOWICK and N. O. KAPLAN, editors, Methods in enzymology. Academic Press: New York. Vol. V, p. 3.
6. NEU, H. C., and L. A. HEPPEL. 1964. Biochem. Biophys. Res. Commun. *17:* 215.
7. ANRAKU, Y., and D. MIZUNO. 1965. Biochem. Biophys. Res. Commun. *18:* 462.
8. ANRAKU, Y., and D. MIZUNO. 1965. Sym. Enzyme Chem. (Tokushima). *17:* 101.
9. ANRAKU, Y., and D. MIZUNO. 1964. Sym. Enzyme Chem. (Tokyo). *16:* 131.
10. ANRAKU, Y. 1964. J. Biol. Chem. *239:* 3420.
11. MARUYAMA, H., and D. MIZUNO. 1965. Biochim. Biophys. Acta. *108:* 593.
12. MARTIN, R. C., and B. N. AMES. 1961. J. Biol. Chem. *236:* 1372.

Spleen Exonuclease (1)

GIORGIO BERNARDI AND ALBERTO BERNARDI
CENTER FOR RESEARCH IN MACROMOLECULES
STRASBOURG, FRANCE

A method for the partial purification of spleen exonuclease (also called spleen phosphodiesterase) was described in 1960 by Hilmoe (2) and later improved by Razzell and Khorana (3). An enzymatic preparation of comparable specific activity may be obtained with the less laborious procedure described here. Some preliminary data for the further purification of this preparation are also given.

ASSAY

Reaction

$$3'\text{P-oligonucleotides} \longrightarrow 3'\text{P-mononucleotides}$$

The exonuclease activity is assayed by measuring the liberation of mononucleotides from $3'$P-deoxyribooligonucleotides, obtained by exhaustive digestion of DNA by spleen acid deoxyribonuclease. The average size of the oligonucleotides present in these digests is 8–9, and the smallest fragments are tetranucleotides (4). The p-nitrophenyl ester of thymidine $3'$-phosphate may also be used for the assay (3), although this substrate is also slowly hydrolyzed by spleen acid deoxyribonuclease (5).

Other substrates have serious drawbacks: (a) Bis(p-nitrophenyl) phosphate is a very poor substrate and is also hydrolyzed by spleen acid deoxyribonuclease (5) and spleen nucleoside polyphosphatase (6). (b) RNA "core," the water-undialyzable $3'$P-ribooligonucleotides obtained by exhaustive digestion of RNA with pancreatic ribonuclease, is also hydrolyzed by spleen ribonucleases (7,8) that are contaminants of spleen exonuclease.

Reagents

1. The reaction mixture (total volume 1.25 ml) contains

   a. 1.2 μmoles of deoxyribooligonucleotide-P (This is the product of exhaustive digestion of DNA by spleen acid deoxyribonuclease.)

      12.5 μmoles of EDTA

      187.5 μmoles of acetate buffer, pH 5.0

   b. Enzyme—if necessary this is diluted with 0.15 M acetate buffer, 0.1 M EDTA, pH 5.0, containing 0.05% beef heart cytochrome c (Sigma Chemical Company, type V)

2. 2.5% Perchloric acid containing 0.25% uranyl acetate

Procedure

After 10 min of incubation at 37 C the reaction is stopped by adding 1.25 ml of the perchloric acid–uranyl acetate reagent. The mixture is chilled for 10 min in an ice bath and clarified by centrifugation at 4 C. The optical density at 260 mμ of the supernatant fluid is measured and a suitable blank is subtracted. One activity unit is the amount of enzyme that liberates mononucleotides having at 260 mμ an optical density equal to one, under the conditions given above. The specific activity is calculated by dividing the activity by the optical density at 280 mμ of the enzyme solution. Assays are performed using enzyme concentrations to obtain OD_{260} readings not higher than 2.5. Under these conditions a linear relationship is obtained between enzyme concentration and mononucleotide liberation.

A comparison was made between the activities measured by the present method and those measured by the procedure of Razzell and Khorana (4). The initial hydrolysis rates were compared by using an enzyme fraction, purified by the chromatographic procedure described below and two additional chromatographic steps on hydroxyapatite and DEAE-Sephadex, respectively. One activity unit, as defined above, was found to liberate 1.8 μmoles of p-nitrophenol per hour from the p-nitrophenyl ester of thymidine-3′-phosphate (this was a preparation of Dr. H. Schaller). Contaminating enzymatic activities (acid deoxyribonuclease, acid and basic ribonucleases, acid phosphomonoesterase) were assayed as described elsewhere (pp. 37, 102, 236).

PREPARATION OF CRUDE SPLEEN EXONUCLEASE

Preparation Procedure

A crude spleen nuclease preparation is obtained by the following method derived from the procedures used to obtain the crude spleen nucleases (see pp. 104–106). All operations are carried out at room temperature, except where otherwise stated. Hog spleens are trimmed, ground with an electrical meat grinder, and homogenized with 0.1 N H_2SO_4 (1 liter/kg of ground spleen; 1 ml of isooctanol is added to each batch). The final pH is about 4.2. The suspension is centrifuged for 40 min at 44000 $\times$ g in a Spinco model L centrifuge. Solid $(NH_4)_2SO_4$ (176 g/liter; 0.3 saturation at 20 C) and EDTA (3.72 g/liter) are added to the clear supernatant fluid (*clarified extract*). The precipitate that forms is removed by filtration on a Seitz filter (p. 106). Solid $(NH_4)_2SO_4$ (198 g/liter; 0.6 saturation at 20 C) and EDTA (3.72 g/liter) are added to the clear filtrate. The precipitate that forms is collected by filtration on a Seitz filter, dissolved in a small volume of distilled water, dialyzed against distilled water at 4 C, clarified by centrifugation, and concentrated by freeze-drying.

Properties of the Clarified Extract and the Crude Spleen Exonuclease

The *clarified extract* has a total activity of 13,000 units/kg of spleen, a specific activity of 0.4, and an OD_{280}/OD_{260} ratio of 1.55. The crude spleen exonuclease has a total activity of 3500 units/kg of spleen, a specific activity of about 4, and an OD_{280}/OD_{260} ratio of 1.75. The properties of crude spleen exonuclease are summarized in Table 1. The loss in activity occurring when going from the *clarified extract* to the

TABLE 1. *Properties of Crude Spleen Exonuclease*[a]

	Total Activity	Specific Activity
Exonuclease	45,000	3.9
Acid ribonuclease	200,000	17.5
Acid deoxyribonuclease	7,500	0.65
Acid phosphomonoesterase	6,000	0.48

[a] This preparation was obtained from 13 kg of spleen.

crude spleen exonuclease seems to be mainly due to the dialysis against distilled water; it may be greatly reduced by dialyzing the enzyme preparation against 0.1 M acetate buffer, pH 5.0.

CHROMATOGRAPHIC PURIFICATION

The chromatographic purification of spleen exonuclease is derived from the purification procedures developed to prepare spleen acid deoxyribonuclease. Column chromatography is performed as already described (see p. 107). A summary of the purification is given in Table 2.

TABLE 2.   *Chromatographic Purification of Spleen Exonuclease*

	Volume	Total OD_{280}	Total Units	Specific Activity
Crude spleen nuclease	80	9,130	36,000	3.9
Step 1. CM-Sephadex[a]	300	157	9,000	57
Step 2. Hydroxyapatite (fractions 35–38)	60	11.1	5,650	500

[a] The values reported refer to the fractions loaded on hydroxyapatite as assayed after the dialysis step. The recovery of activity from CM-Sephadex, as assayed before dialysis, was essentially complete.

Step 1.   CM-Sephadex C-50 (Fig. 1)

Crude spleen exonuclease, dialyzed against 0.1 M acetate buffer, pH 5.6, is loaded on a CM-Sephadex C-50 column equilibrated with the same buffer. A molarity gradient (0.1 to 1.0) of acetate buffer, pH 5.6, was used to elute the proteins. Two acid phosphomonoesterase activity peaks are eluted at the beginning of the gradient and at 0.4 M acetate, respectively. The exonuclease activity is eluted at a molarity of 0.7, between two acid ribonuclease activity peaks.

Step 2.   Hydroxyapatite (Fig. 2)

The exonuclease-rich fractions are pooled, dialyzed against 0.05 M phosphate buffer, pH 6.8, and loaded on a hydroxyapatite column. Elution is carried out with a molarity gradient (0.05 to 0.5) of phosphate buffer, pH 6.8. Exonuclease activity very closely follows an ribonuclease activity peak eluted at 0.1 M.

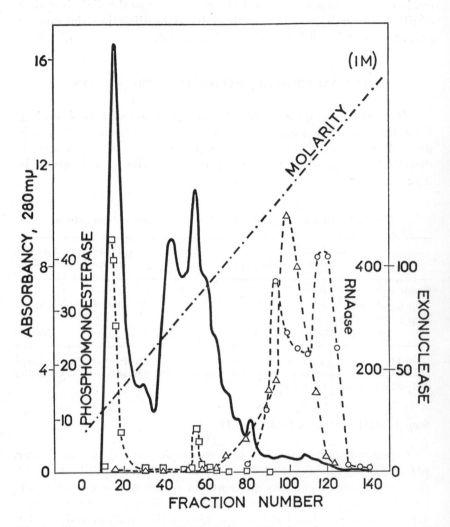

Fig. 1. Chromatography on CM-Sephadex C-50 of crude spleen exonuclease (Step 1). 80 ml of crude spleen exonuclease ($OD_{280} = 114$; $OD_{260} = 65$) were loaded on a 3- $\times$ 90-cm column of CM-Sephadex C-50 equilibrated with 0.1 M acetate buffer, pH 5.6. A molarity gradient (0.1–1 M) was used for the elution. 20 ml fractions were collected. The continuous line indicates the absorption at 280 mμ. Squares indicate the acid phosphomonoesterase activity (left-hand inner scale); circles, the acid ribonuclease activity (right-hand inner scale); triangles, the exonuclease activity (right-hand outer scale).

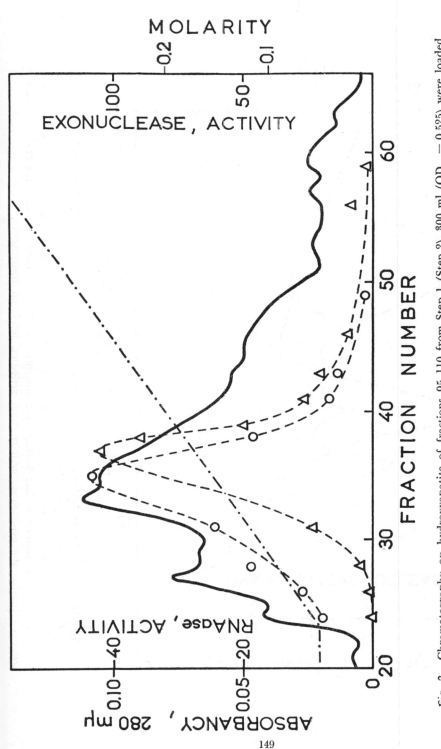

Fig. 2. Chromatography on hydroxyapatite of fractions 95–110 from Step 1 (Step 2). 300 ml (OD$_{280}$ = 0.525) were loaded on a 2- × 38-cm column of hydroxyapatite equilibrated with 0.05 M phosphate buffer, pH 6.8. A molarity gradient (0.05–0.5) of phosphate buffer was used for the elution (right-hand outer scale). 15-ml fractions were collected. The continuous line indicates the absorption at 280 mμ. Circles indicate the acid ribonuclease activity (left-hand inner scale); triangles, the exonuclease activity (right-hand inner scale).

149

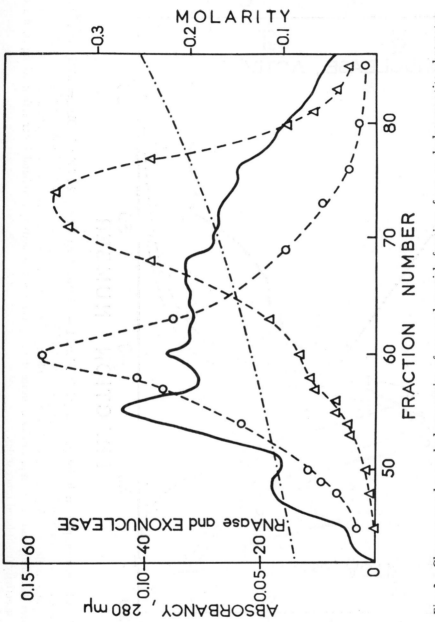

Fig. 3. Chromatography on hydroxyapatite of exonuclease-rich fractions from an hydroxyapatite chromatography. 180 ml (OD$_{280}$ = 0.215) were loaded on a 2- × 20-cm column of hydroxyapatite equilibrated with 0.05 M phosphate buffer, pH 6.8. A molarity gradient (0.05–0.4) was used for the elution (right-hand scale). 6-ml fractions were collected. The continuous line indicates the absorption at 280 mμ. Circles indicate the acid ribonuclease activity; triangles, the exonuclease activity (both activities, left-hand inner scale).

Further Purification

Two different types of chromatography were tried on exonuclease fractions derived from Step 2, in order to purify the enzyme from the contaminating ribonuclease activity.

The first one is a rechromatography run on hydroxyapatite using a shallower molarity gradient (Fig. 3). An improved separation of the ribonuclease and the exonuclease activities was obtained, and the exonuclease fractions showed a higher specific activity than those obtained from the first hydroxyapatite chromatography. The second type of chromatography tried was on DEAE-Sephadex A 50, using a molarity gradient (0.01–0.3 M) of phosphate buffer, pH 6.8, to elute the proteins (Fig. 4). A very satisfactory separation of the two enzymatic activities was obtained.

Properties of the Enzyme

The specific activity of the exonuclease fraction from Step 2 is 500; that of the peak fraction of the hydroxyapatite rechromatography is 770. By assuming, on the basis of the biuret reaction, an $E_{280}^{1\%} = 10$ for spleen exonuclease, these specific activities are equivalent to 900 and 1400 units of Razzell and Khorana (3), respectively. These values are well above that of Hilmoe's preparation [estimated to 470 by Razzell (9)], and comparable to those (995–2040) of the preparation by Razzell and Khorana (3).

A higher specific activity is likely to be associated with the DEAE-Sephadex exonuclease fraction (Fig. 4); however, the optical density at 280 mμ was so low that the specific activity could not be assessed.

Several possible contaminating activities were checked on the DEAE-Sephadex exonuclease fraction. No endonucleolytic attack on DNA was detected by viscometry, using exonuclease concentrations and digestion times such that acid-soluble nucleotides could be demonstrated. Acid phosphomonoesterase activity could be detected in trace amount by using large enzyme concentrations and very long digestion times (17 hr). Yeast-soluble RNA was hydrolyzed at only about half the rate shown by high molecular weight DNA. The hydrolysis rate was essentially the same in 0.15 M acetate buffer–0.01 M EDTA, pH 5.0, and in 0.1 M phosphate buffer–0.01 M MgCl$_2$, pH 7.2. This is in contrast with the results obtained when digesting soluble RNA with the ribonuclease fraction eluted from the DEAE-Sephadex column (Fig. 4). In this case, the ratio of acid to basic ribonuclease activity (using the buffers indicated above) equals 50. This finding may be considered as a preliminary evidence supporting the idea that the very slow digestion

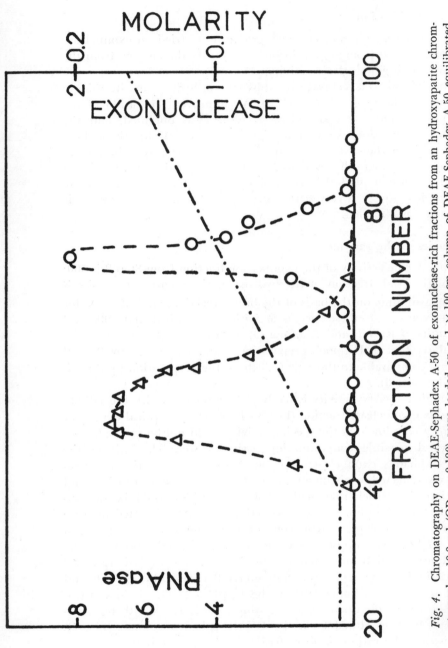

Fig. 4. Chromatography on DEAE-Sephadex A-50 of exonuclease-rich fractions from an hydroxyapatite chromatography. 10.8 ml (OD$_{280}$ = 0.120) were loaded on a 1-× 100-cm column of DEAE-Sephadex A-50 equilibrated with 0.01 M phosphate buffer, pH 6.8. A molarity gradient (0.01–0.3 M) was used for the elution (right-hand outer scale). 2.7-ml fractions were collected. Circles indicate the ribonuclease activity (left-hand inner scale); triangles, the exonuclease activity (right-hand inner scale).

of transfer RNA by the exonuclease fraction is basically due to a true exonucleolytic attack on contaminating ribosomal RNA fragments present in the transfer RNA preparation or on pre-existing, ribonuclease provoked, breaks in the transfer RNA.

REFERENCES

1. BERNARDI, A., and G. BERNARDI. In preparation.
2. HILMOE, R. J. 1960. J. Biol. Chem. 235: 2117.
3. RAZZELL, W. E., and H. G. KHORANA. 1961. J. Biol. Chem. 236: 1144.
4. CARRARA, M., and G. BERNARDI. In preparation.
5. BERNARDI, G., and M. GRIFFÉ. 1964. Biochemistry. 3: 1419.
6. LASKOWSKI, M., and B. FILIPOWICZ. 1958. Bull. Soc. Chim. Biol. 40: 1865.
7. MAVER, M. E., and A. E. GRECO. 1962. J. Biol. Chem. 211: 907.
8. BERNARDI, A., and G. BERNARDI. In preparation.
9. RAZZELL, W. E. 1963. In S. P. COLOWICK and N. O. KAPLAN, editors, Methods in enzymology. Academic Press, New York. Vol. VI, p. 247.

Exonuclease

(Phosphodiesterase)

and Other Nucleolytic

Enzymes from Venom

M. LASKOWSKI, SR.

ROSWELL PARK MEMORIAL INSTITUTE

BUFFALO, NEW YORK

Terminology

In an attempt to create a classification of nucleolytic enzymes useful in the period of rapidly advancing knowledge, it was proposed (1) to restore the original meaning of the term phosphodiesterase (2,3) to a group name for all enzymes hydrolyzing phosphodiester bonds. At the same time (1,4) four (then known) criteria for subdivision of nucleo-phosphodiesterases have been discussed. One of these criteria, which unfortunately is not an absolute one, is based on exo- and endonucleolytic mode of action (4,5). In the laboratories in which several nucleolytic enzymes, present in the same organism, were studied, the proposal has been found useful and the terminology has been adopted (6,7). At the moment of this writing the chance for encountering the terms

Some of the experimental work described in this article was performed in the author's laboratory during his stay at Marquette University School of Medicine. The work was generously supported by the American Cancer Society (grants PRP-16 and P-157), the Atomic Energy Commission (grant AT(11–1)293), and the National Science Foundation (grant GB-4274).

"venom phosphodiesterase" and "venom exonuclease" are about equal. Both terms are used throughout this article interchangeably.

Enzymes in Venom

For some time now venom has been known to possess four enzymes (8–15) capable of hydrolyzing phosphate bonds: two phosphodiesterases (an exonuclease and an endonuclease) and two phosphomonoesterases (5'-mononucleotidase and the nonspecific alkaline phosphatase of venom). The additional fifth enzyme, a ribonuclease, with a pH optimum of 7.6, and requiring Mg^{2+} has been recently reported (16,17) in Siberian snakes, and independently in the venom of Russell's viper (18). It is probably common to most venoms. The work is too recent to discuss this ribonuclease in detail.

The distribution of di- and monophosphatases among different species of snake has been studied by several authors (8–10,14,15) with the hope that a venom particularly rich in phosphodiesterases, or particularly poor in monophosphatases can be found. Although a significant

TABLE 1. *Phosphatase Activities of Formosan Snake Venoms* (10)

Enzymes / Venoms	Phosphodi-esterase	Phosphomono-esterase	5'-Nucleo-tidase
	Unit per Mg of Dried Venom		
Naja naja atra (Formosan cobra)	1.078	0.101	720
Bungarus multicinctus (Banded krait)	0.022	0.132	6
Vipera russellii formosensis (Russell's viper)	3.955	0.006	270
Trimeresurus macrosquamatus (Formosan habu)	3.008	0.054	2140
Trimeresurus gramineus (Green habu)	3.116	0.052	2320
Agkistrodon acutus (Hyappoda)	1.382	0.013	1211

variation in the contents of the four enzymes was detected, no venom was found which was naturally devoid of undesirable monophosphatases. Table 1 (10) and Table 2 (15) are reproduced from different papers, the units used by the two groups of workers are not identical and only relative values within each table are significant.

TABLE 2. *Levels of Enzymes in Five Snake Venoms*[a] (15)

Species of Venom	Units of Enzyme × 10³ per Mg of Dry Venom				Ratio of Enzymes: Phosphodiesterase = 1.0		
	Phospho-diesterase	Nonspecific Phosphatase	5'-Nucleo-tidase	Endo-nuclease	Nonspecific Phosphatase	5'-Nucleo-tidase	Endo-nuclease
Agkistrodon piscivorus	7.8	0.55	495	3.3	0.070	64	0.42
Bothrops atrox	36	1.8	1070	3.4	0.050	30	0.095
Crotalus adamanteus	25	1.3	1390	8.8	0.052	56	0.35
Crotalus atrox	8.7	0.39	860	2.8	0.045	99	0.32
Naja nigricollis	17	54	360	1.1	3.2	21	0.065

a Activity expressed in international units (micromoles of substrate per minute, at 25 C).

Mode of Action

Venom exonuclease hydrolyzes nucleic acids and derivatives by a consecutive liberation of 5'-mononucleotides. Venom exonuclease attacks all kinds of nucleic acids regardless of the native or denatured state, the type of sugar, and the size of the molecule. There is suggestive evidence that denatured DNA, and particularly oligonucleotides, are better substrates than native highly polymerized nucleic acids. On the other hand, glucosylated DNA, which is susceptible to *Escherichia coli* exonuclease (**19,20**) appears to be a poorer substrate (see p. 85, deoxyribonuclease). DNA that was irradiated with ultraviolet light is resistant to phosphodiesterase; more accurately, the action of phosphodiesterase is blocked by dimerized thymine, resulting in products of the type pXp_{TpT}, where p_{TpT} represents the thymine dimer (**21**).

The uridine and pseudouridine residues can be modified by reacting with 1-cyclohexyl-3-(2 morpholinyl-(4)-ethyl)-carbodiimide metho-*p*-toluene-sulfonate (**22,23**). The modified residues block the action of venom diesterase as shown in Table 3 (**24**).

TABLE 3.   *Percentage Hydrolysis with*
Snake Venom Diesterase (**24**)

		Products
UpA	100	(U,pA)
$\overline{U}$pA	25	($\overline{U}$,pA)
ΨpA	88	(Ψ,pA)
$\overline{\Psi}$pA	45	($\overline{\Psi}$,pA)
CpU	93	(C,pU)
Cp$\overline{U}$	0	—
CpΨ	53	(C,pΨ)
Cp$\overline{\Psi}$	0	—
UpC	94	(U,pC)
$\overline{U}$pC	40	($\overline{U}$,pC)

Note: Ψ = pseudouridine; $\overline{U}$ = chemically blocked uridine; $\overline{\Psi}$ = chemically blocked pseudouridine.

The proximity of the 3'-hydroxyl group or the proximity of the 3'-monophosphate group exerts a pronounced influence on the action of venom exonuclease. Chains bearing 5'-monophosphate are the best substrates. They are attacked in the indicated order (25,26) and require a relative amount of enzyme of 1.

$$\overset{2\qquad 1}{\swarrow\ \ \swarrow}$$
$$\text{pX p Y pZ} \tag{1}$$

The chains that are deprived of the terminal 5′-monophosphate are attacked in the same order, but are poorer substrates and require a tenfold greater amount of enzyme.

$$\overset{2\qquad 1}{\swarrow\ \ \swarrow}$$
$$\text{X pY pZ} \tag{2}$$

In the chains bearing 3′-monophosphate, the nucleoside is the first product to be liberated (27).

$$\overset{1\qquad 2}{\swarrow\ \ \swarrow}$$
$$\text{X pY pZp} \tag{3}$$

These compounds are very resistant to phosphodiesterase and require a relative amount of enzyme at least 1000-fold higher than that required for the complete hydrolysis of the compounds bearing 5′-monophosphate.

Uses of Exonuclease

The mechanism of the reaction suggests uses of the enzyme. Thus exonuclease has been used (28) to degrade the (right) amino acid accepting terminus of sRNA or the right portions of sRNA molecules (29). Exonuclease was also used (in analogy to carboxypeptidase) to determine the sequence in the proximity of the (right) terminus of the chain that bears the 3′-hydroxyl group, e.g., four terminal positions in Tobacco Mosaic Virus (30).

Much more widely, exonuclease has been used for the identification of the left terminus. The enzyme was even used in the determination of the left terminus in chains as long as that of Tobacco Mosaic Virus (31). Chains bearing no monophosphate on either terminus are used directly, chains bearing monophosphate are used after dephosphorylation with a monophosphatase. Only on occasions has phosphodiesterase been used to determine both termini in chains bearing 3′-monophosphate (14,32). This requires a very large amount of the very pure enzyme.

An elegant application of phosphodiesterase [in analogy to the Edman–Konigsberg method (33–35) in peptides] has been proposed by Holley et al. (36). This method is applicable only to a homogeneous ribooligonucleotide of known composition but unknown sequence, bearing no monophosphate on either end. The compound is first hydrolyzed with a very small amount of exonuclease, and is chromato-graphed in 7 M urea according to Tomlinson and Tener (37). The procedure segregates the mixture of products according to their length; each peak contains material that is shorter by one nucleotide than the material in the next peak (no compound bears a monophosphate). The peaks are now subjected to alkaline hydrolysis and only the (right) terminal nucleoside is identified in each peak. This establishes the sequence.

Assay

Venom exonuclease is usually assayed with synthetic substrates; either Ca-bis-p-nitrophenyl phosphate or p-nitrophenyl thymidine 5′-phosphate. Both are commercially available from the Sigma Chemical Company, St. Louis, Missouri, and Calbiochem, Los Angeles, California.

The modest advantages of Ca di-p-nitrophenyl phosphate are that it is cheap, uniform, and that it is still used by the commercial manufacturers of enzymes. The results obtained with this substrate are directly comparable with the manufacturer's specification, and with the values reported in older literature.

The reaction mixture contains 1.0 ml of 0.1 M Tris-HCl buffer, pH 8.9, 1.2 ml of 0.001 M calcium di-p-nitrophenyl phosphate, 0.2 ml of enzyme solution, and water up to 3 ml. The blank contains 1.0 ml of 0.1 M Tris buffer, 1.2 ml of 0.001 M substrate, and water up to 3 ml. The reaction is carried out at 37 C in a thermostated spectrophotometer equipped with a recorder, such as Gilford, at 400 mμ. The liberation of 0.1 μmole of p-nitrophenol in a total volume of 3 ml corresponds to ΔA_{400} of 0.400 (1 μmole/ml of p-nitrophenol gives an absorbancy at 400 mμ of 12.0). One unit of enzyme is defined as the liberation of 1 μmole/min. To recalculate from units found at 37 C to the international units (38) at 25 C, a coefficient of 0.44 is used. The specific activity is expressed as international units/mg of enzyme protein.

If a recording spectrophotometer is not available the reaction may be read manually at 1-min intervals and the average ΔA_{400}/min calculated. Another alternative is to incubate for a definite period of time in the test tubes, stop the reaction by the addition of 3 ml of 0.05 M NaOH, and read at 400 mμ.

The best substrate for venom exonuclease is p-nitrophenyl-pT. Its V_{max} value has been reported (39) as about 1000 times higher than that for bis-p-nitrophenyl phosphate. Even more important is the fact that it is specific for exonucleases that are 5′-monoester formers, and distinguishes them from 3′-monoester formers, such as spleen phosphodiesterase. A minor disadvantage (probably a temporary one) is that two samples obtained from two different sources gave V_{max} values that differed by a factor of 2 (40).

The substrate with very similar properties of specificity and affinity to phosphodiesterase, α-naphtyl-pT was synthesized (41) and was found particularly useful in histochemical work (42). A similar reagent 3-pyridyl-pT was synthesized and used for kinetic studies (43). The spectrum changes upon exposure to phosphodiesterase. The increase at 310 mμ is a convenient measure of activity with this reagent.

When very small quantities of phosphodiesterase are to be detected and measured, e.g., during the purification of 5'-nucleotidase (see p. 170), sodium p-nitrophenyl-pT must be used as the substrate. In this case a bivalent metal must be added: either Mg^{2+} or Ca^{2+}. We have used 1.2 ml of 0.002 M substrate, 1.2 ml of 0.001 M $CaCl_2$, 0.2 of enzyme, and water up to 3 ml. To recalculate from 37 to 25 C the values for activity are multiplied by 0.70.

Direct Assay for Contaminating Monophosphatases

Since the value of the exonuclease preparation depends highly on the efficient removal of monophosphatases, the assays for 5'-nucleotidase, and the nonspecific alkaline phosphatase are included (see p. 169).

Another and probably the most direct way to express the relative contamination of exonuclease by monophosphatase is to test the preparation of exonuclease on a deoxyribo*di*nucleotide bearing 3'-monophosphate, d-XpYp (14). The mixture of dinucleotides may be conveniently prepared by exhaustively digesting DNA with micrococcal nuclease (44). The individual dinucleotides are then separated on Dowex 1-X2 (45). Ten to fifteen A_{270} units of the dinucleotide (14) are digested with 0.2 international units of exonuclease, in 1 ml of 0.1 M Tris-HCl buffer, pH 8.9, containing 0.01 M $MgCl_2$, for 12, 24, 36, and 48 hr, at which times 0.2-ml portions are withdrawn and subjected to two-dimensional chromatography according to Felix *et al.* (27). If no monophosphatase is present only a nucleoside X and a nucleoside 3',5'-diphosphate should be formed as a result of hydrolysis. The appearance of nucleotides (pY + Yp) or the difference in absorbance between pYp and X represent the measure of the phosphatase activity.

A two-dimensional chromatographic method (27) has been devised for the purpose of separating nucleosides, nucleotides, and nucleoside-3',5'-diphosphates. The method is particularly useful with deoxyribonucleic acid derivatives, because C and T are widely separated. With ribonucleic acid, C and U touch or almost touch one another. However,

with appropriate precautions the technique also yielded reliable results
with RNA (46). Chromatography in the first direction was accomplished in the solvent suggested by Palladini and Leloir (47) and used by
Bergkvist (48). The solvent was composed of 75 parts of 95% ethanol
and 30 parts of 1 M ammonium acetate adjusted to pH 7.5. Chromatography was carried out on large sheets of Whatman No. 3MM paper
(57 cm × 46 cm) and for the first direction the longer side of the paper
was used. The development in this solvent lasted about 20 hr; however, the variability was quite wide—17–24 hr—in spite of the fact that
room temperature was regulated at 23 ± 1 C. The development was
stopped when the solvent front approached the edge of the paper. This
solvent separates three groups of compounds: Nucleosides travel close
to the solvent front (R_F 0.78–0.95), nucleotides move to an intermediate

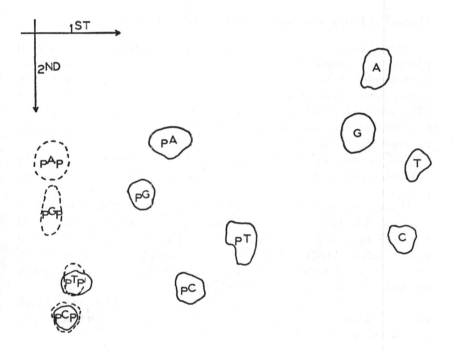

Fig. 1. A composite chart of two chromatographic runs in two dimensions.
In both experiments the first direction, in 95% ethanol, 75 parts; 1 M ammonium acetate, pH 7.5, 30 parts; 16 hr; room temperature (25 C); the second
direction in saturated ammonium sulfate, 80 parts; water, 18 parts; isopropanol, 2 parts, 12 hr. The first experiment (solid line) contained a mixture
of 4 deoxyribonucleosides, 4 deoxyribonucleotides, and 2 deoxyribonucleoside
diphosphates (pCp + pTp). The second experiment contained a mixture of
4 deoxyribonucleoside diphosphates (27).

position (R_F 0.29–0.53), and nucleoside-3',5'-diphosphates move very slowly (R_F 0.03–0.08). In the second direction, one of the solvents proposed by Markham and Smith (49) was used. It is composed of 2 parts of isopropanol (freshly redistilled), 18 parts of water, and 80 parts of saturated ammonium sulfate. The development of the paper in the short (second) direction lasted an average of about 9 hr, also with wide variations. The papers from the same box run usually fairly close; the papers from different boxes differ greatly.

In the second solvent the four components of each group separate. Fig. 1 (27) illustrates the results of such separations.

For the experiments performed on a larger scale the chromatography on Dowex 1-X2 described by Georgatsos and Laskowski (13) with the modifications of Winter and Bernheimer (50) is recommended.

Method of Preparation of Venom Exonuclease

Several recent reviews deal with methods of preparation of venom phosphodiesterase (51–53). Numerous techniques of purification have been developed in different laboratories (39,54–62). Most of the techniques have at least two features in common: acetone precipitation at pH around 4.0 [originally introduced by Sinsheimer and Koerner (63, 64)] and at least one chromatography to eliminate the remaining monophosphatases.

The decision as to which technique is to be used depends on (a) availability of venom (species and quantity); (b) requirements for purity.

Until recently, in the author's laboratory, venom of *Bothrops atrox* was available in large amounts and requirements for purity could therefore be rather rigorous. The method has been modified several times (65,27,66,14,67). Where the *Bothrops atrox* venom is available, the technique of Björk (67) is recommended. This technique has been checked many times and is described in detail below.

Unfortunately, this technique is not applicable to venoms of all species of snake. *Agkistrodon piscivorus* (68) and *Hemachatus haemachates* (40) are the striking examples of nonconformity to the method. Fortunately, the venom of *Crotalus adamanteus* is sufficiently similar to that of *Bothrops atrox* to fit the major steps of the previously developed method. Minor modifications, however, are required. At the moment of this writing no well documented method applicable to the venom of *Crotalus adamanteus* can be recommended, except that step 1 should be performed according to the method of Williams *et al.* (66) rather than by Björk's modification (67). The older method (66) requires the removal of the second acetone precipitate by simply lowering temperature from 0 to −17 C, whereas in Björk's modification the second acetone precipitate is obtained by increasing the concentration of acetone from 42 to 45% and decreasing temperature to −17 C.

STEP 1. Ten grams of venom are dissolved in 600 ml of water and stirred for 30 min in an ice bath (69). The small precipitate is removed by filtration on a Büchner funnel. The liquid is transferred to the ice bath, and 400 ml of ice-cold 0.5 M acetate buffer, pH 3.8,† are added with stirring and followed by 725 ml of acetone (precooled to −20 C) to attain a concentration of 42%. The mixture is stirred for 30 min and centrifuged in a Servall refrigerated centrifuge at 0 C for 15 min. The heavy yellow precipitate is discarded.‡ The clear supernatant solution is transferred to the bath at −17 C, and 95 ml of −20 C acetone§ are added with stirring (45% acetone concentration), stirred for 2 hr, and the precipitate that forms (precipitate 2) is removed by centrifugation at −17 C. To the supernatant solution 180 ml of −20 C acetone‖ are added with stirring. The mixture is stirred for 1 hr and is centrifuged at −17 C. The precipitate (precipitate 3) is dissolved in water to give an absorbancy A_{230} of about 11/ml. At this stage, the preparation usually contains about 70% of phosphodiesterase and only about 0.05% of monophosphatases.

STEP 2. To the solution 0.1 of its volume of 1.0 M Tris-HCl buffer, pH 8.9, is added and the solution is adjusted to 8.0. The mixture is cooled to 0 C and 0.5 volume of ethanol (95% counted as 100%) precooled to −20 C is added to attain 33% concentration. The precipitate that forms is removed by centrifugation, and the liquid transferred to a −17 C bath treated with an additional 1.5 volume of ethanol to attain 66% concentration. After 30 min stirring at this temperature, the mixture is centrifuged at −17 C. The precipitate is dissolved in water to give an absorbancy $A_{280} = 11.0$.

STEP 3. To the enzyme solution 0.1 of its volume of 2 M sodium acetate buffer of pH 4.0 is added. The solution is cooled in an ice bath, treated with cold (−20 C) acetone to attain 45% (assuming the volumes are additive) and transferred to a −17 C bath for ½ hr. The mixture is centrifuged at −17 C and the precipitate is discarded. The supernatant solution is treated with acetone (−20 C) to attain 50%

† In the method of Williams et al. (66), pH is 4.0. For the detailed description see p. 168.

‡ In reality it is saved for the preparation of venom endonuclease, and both monophosphatases. As yet, however, we are unable to ascertain whether the methods described for Bothrops (13,14) are applicable to Crotalus.

§ With Crotalus venom no acetone should be added at this time.

‖ With Crotalus venom 275 ml of acetone should be added.

concentration. After 1 hr at −17 C, the precipitate is collected by centrifugation, and dissolved in a minimum amount of 0.1 M Tris-HCl
buffer, pH 8.9.

STEP 4.   The solution is applied to a Sephadex G-100 column
previously equilibrated with 0.02 M Tris-HCl buffer, pH 8.9, Fig. 2.
Phosphodiesterase appears in the first peak. The removal of contaminating monophosphatases is not efficient, but over-all purification justi-
fies this step.

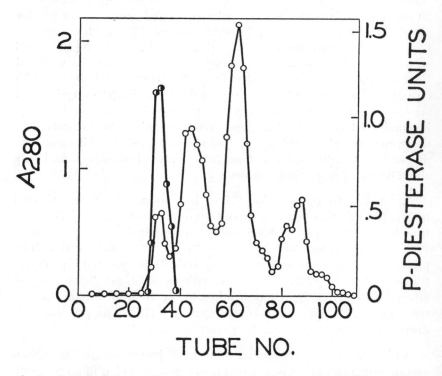

Fig. 2.   Step 4 of the purification procedure. Gel filtration of the precipitate
from Step 3 on a Sephadex G-100 column (4.4 cm × 50 cm; 760 ml, total volume). The precipitate had been dissolved in 35 ml of 0.1 M Tris-HCl, pH 8.9.
Equilibrating and eluting buffer, 0.02 M Tris-HCl, pH 8.9. Fraction volume,
6.0 ml. The first 150 ml of eluate were collected separately before starting the
fraction collector. White circles indicate protein concentration expressed as
A_{280} per ml; split circles, phosphodiesterase activity, units per 0.2 ml (67).

STEP 5.   The peak containing the exonuclease is charged on a
DEAE-cellulose column, previously equilibrated with 0.02 M Tris-HCl,
pH 8.9, Fig. 3. Elution with the same buffer removes a small peak de-

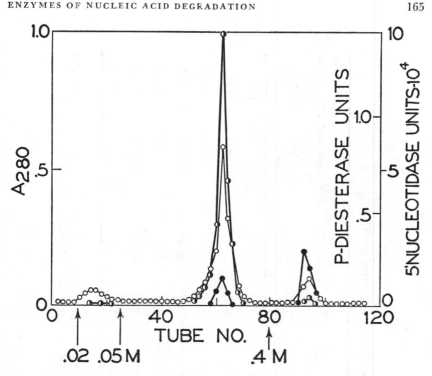

Fig. 3. DEAE-cellulose chromatography of the phosphodiesterase peak from Step 4 (tubes 28–36 in Fig. 2). Column dimensions, 1.9 cm × 34 cm; total volume, 96 ml. Equilibrating buffer, 0.02 M Tris-HCl, pH 8.9. Stepwise elution with Tris-HCl buffers of pH 8.9 and indicated molarity. Fraction volume, 6.0 ml. White circles indicate protein concentration expressed as A_{280} per ml; split circles, phosphodiesterase activity, units per 0.2 ml; black circles, 5'-nucleotidase activity, units per 0.1 ml × 10^4 (**67**).

void of activity. A change to 0.05 M Tris-HCl, pH 8.9, elutes most of the phosphodiesterase, still containing some monophosphatase. This peak is collected and frozen. A change to 0.4 M buffer removes the rest of monophosphatases contaminated with some phosphodiesterase. This peak is discarded.

STEP 6.† Phosphodiesterase from Step 5 is dialyzed against 0.1 M sodium acetate buffer, pH 6.0, and heated in a water bath at 60 C for 80 min. The temperature is not allowed to exceed 60 C. After heating, the sample is cooled rapidly in an ice bath and then frozen. Table 4 summarizes the purification procedure.

† This step has been verified only for the venom of *Bothrops atrox*.

TABLE 4. *Summary of Purification Procedure* (**67**)

Step	pH	Total A_{280}	Phosphodiesterase Total Activity (units)	Potency[a]	5'-Nucleotidase Total Activity (units)	Nonspecific Phosphatase Total Activity (units)
Crude venom (10 g)		13,290	124.6	0.0093	8,107	15.9
1. Acetone precipitation	3.8	4,014	86.7	0.0216	0.0845	0.110
2. Ethanol precipitation	8.9	488	56.4	0.116	0.0155	0.057
3. Acetone precipitation	4.0	284	50.7	0.179	0.0078	0.050
4. Sephadex G-100	8.9	24.2	43.1	1.78	0.0066	0.043
5. DEAE-cellulose	8.9	10.8	25.9	2.39	0.0021	0.026
6. Dialysis and heating to 60 C[b]	6.0	10.3	11.7	1.14		0.006

[a] Potency is synonymous with specific activity.
[b] The ratio phosphatase/phosphodiesterase = 0.006/11.7 = 1/1950 represents not only the relative activities, but also the relative number of monophosphate and diphosphate bond cleavages, because the units for both enzymes are defined on the same basis.

Other Methods

For the venom of *Hemachatus haemachates,* for which the acetone step does not work, Björk modified (40) his previous method (70) to prepare a somewhat less potent phosphodiesterase than that of *Bothrops,* yet, sufficiently free from the contaminating monophosphatases to be useful in the studies of sequence.

STEP 1. Column of DEAE-cellulose (73 cm × 2.4 cm) is adjusted to pH 8.6 with 0.005 M Tris-HCl. It is charged with 500 mg of venom. The eluting buffer is 0.33 M Tris-HCl, pH 8.6. The first small phosphodiesterase peak is discarded, and the main peak is directly applied to a Sephadex G-100 column.

STEP 2. Column of G-100 Sephadex (21 cm × 1.9 cm) is equilibrated with 0.01 M sodium acetate buffer, pH 4.8. The sample is charged and is eluted with the equilibration buffer. Since the volume of the sample is roughly equal to the void volume of the column, the enzyme peak is quite broad.

STEP 3. Phosphodiesterase from Step 2 is chromatographed on a Dowex 50 column (24 cm × 1 cm), which had been equilibrated with 0.01 M sodium acetate, pH 4.8. Elution is performed with a combined pH and concentration gradient to 0.3 M sodium acetate, pH 5.8. Phosphodiesterase is eluted in a second peak, together with some nonspecific phosphatase, but is well separated from 5'-nucleotidase, which appeared with more concentrated buffer in a broad and heterogeneous protein zone.

STEP 4. The enzyme from Step 3 is precipitated by 65% acetone. It is stored at −26 C in a closed bottle without washing or drying. When needed, a small portion of the enzyme is dissolved in 0.1 M sodium acetate, pH 6.0, and is heated at 60 C for 60 min. After this treatment the ratio of nonspecific phosphatase to phosphodiesterase was about 1/2000, the potency† about 1.

Other Methods, Venom of *Crotalus*

In the United States the venom of *Crotalus adamanteus* is the one most widely used. As yet, no phosphodiesterase preparation of a quality equal to that from *Bothrops* venom has been obtained from the *Crotalus* venom, even though several steps of the previously described methods (27,66,67) are applicable to the venom of *Crotalus.* Partly purified phosphodiesterase of *Crotalus* is commercially available from

† The term potency as used throughout this article is synonymous with specific activity.

the Worthington Biochemical Corporation. This preparation is obtained by Step 1 of the method of Williams *et al.* (**66**). It can be used directly for the digestion of short-chain oligonucleotides bearing 5′-monophosphate. However, it still contains an easily detectable amount of each of the two monophosphatases, and is not quite safe for the digestion of higher (hexa to deca) oligonucleotides bearing no monophosphoryl groups. A simple additional step introduced by Keller (**60**) decreases the contamination by monophosphatase $1/4$–$1/5$ of the level of the commercial preparation.

Starting with the venom of *Crotalus adamanteus* the following method can be used [Step 1 (**66**), Step 2 (**60**)]:

Venom (2 g) is dissolved in 120 ml of cold water, stirred for 30 min at 0 C, and filtered on a Büchner funnel through Whatman No. 3 paper. The clear solution is placed in an ice bath and treated with 80 ml of cold 0.5 M acetate buffer, pH 4.0, and then with 145 ml of acetone (−20 C) to attain a concentration of 42%. The mixture is stirred for 30 min and centrifuged in a Servall refrigerated centrifuge at 0 C for 15 min. The heavy yellow precipitate (Precipitate 1) is discarded. The clear supernatant solution is transferred to a bath at −17 C, stirred for 2 hr, and the precipitate that forms (Precipitate 2) is removed by centrifugation at −17 C. The clear supernatant solution is transferred to the −17 C bath, and 55 ml of −20 C acetone are added with stirring. The mixture is stirred for 1 hr and centrifuged at −17 C. The precipitate (Precipitate 3) is dissolved in water (20 ml), adjusted to pH 7.5, and lyophilized. This stage corresponds to the commercial preparation of Worthington (VPD).

The contents of a 5–6-mg bottle of commercial VPD, or the equivalent amount of lyophilized preparation from the previous step are dissolved in 1 ml of water. This solution on analysis shows from 8 to 12 absorbancy units, determined at 280 mμ. The solution of VPD is applied to a Dowex 50 column (Dowex 50 W-X8, 200–400 mesh, 1.9 meq/ml of wet volume, Baker analyzed reagent, previously washed with 5 N NaOH, 1 N NaOH, water, and 0.3 M sodium acetate buffer, pH 5.8). A 7-ml column of washed resin, 0.6 cm × 20 cm, is equilibrated with 0.005 M acetate, pH 5.8. The column is operated at room temperature by hand, as the total effluent to be analyzed is about 4 ml. The dead volume of column is about 2.2 ml.. A convenient test for protein is run on each drop by withdrawing a few microliters into a fine capillary and then drawing up 0.6 N HClO₄ so that the solutions mix in the capillary. Turbidity can be seen with as little as 0.2 mg of protein/ml. The application of 1 ml of VPD solution is followed by 0.005 M acetate, pH 5.8. The purified VPD emerges between about 2.2 and 4.0 ml of effluent, the exact volume being determined by the capillary protein test.

Before the purified VPD is frozen for storage the pH of the solution is adjusted to about 7.5. Recovery of activity is about 60% and of A_{280} units about 45%. The loss of activity is due to retention of VPD on the Dowex 50 and occurs only the first time that a column is used. If a column that has been used and loaded in the above fashion is washed with 0.3 M acetate, pH 5.8, reequilibrated with 0.005 M acetate, pH 5.8, and used again, recovery of activity will be practically quantitative and recovery of A_{280} units will be about 80%. A loaded column can be used repeatedly in this way. It must be kept at 4 C when it is not in use.

Properties of the Enzyme

No reliable values for either the isoelectric point, the molecular weight, or the amino acid composition are available. They probably will not be forthcoming in the near future, since it seems futile to determine these values on preparations, the homogeneity of which is doubtful.

THE NONSPECIFIC ALKALINE MONOPHOSPHATASE

The nonspecific alkaline monophosphatase was discovered by Sulkowski (14) in the venom of *Bothrops atrox*. It is also present in the venoms of *Crotalus adamanteus* (14,15), *Crotalus atrox* and *Agkistrodon piscivorus* (15), *Hemachatus haemachates* (40), and probably all others. It has been considerably purified and can be prepared almost free from phosphodiesterase and 5′-nucleotidase (14).

Since several monophosphatases can be prepared in a state of even higher purity, the detailed method of purification of venom phosphatase is not considered worthy of inclusion in this chapter. The assay procedure, however, appears to be quite important, because this monophosphatase is tenaciously bound to exonuclease, yet must be eliminated from the exonuclease preparations.

Assay

The nonspecific phosphatase is routinely determined with *p*-nitrophenyl phosphate, which is not hydrolyzed by 5′-nucleotidase. The reaction mixture contained 1.0 ml of 0.1 M glycine–NaOH buffer, pH 9.5, 1.2 ml of 0.001 M *p*-nitrophenyl phosphate, 0.3 ml of 0.1 M $MgCl_2$, 0.1 ml of enzyme solution, and water up to 3.0 ml. The mixture is incubated for 15 min at 37 C. The reaction is stopped by adding 3 ml of 0.05 N NaOH. The absorbancy is measured at 400 mμ against a blank that contained all reagents except the enzyme. One unit of activity is defined as the amount of enzyme that liberates 1 μmole of p-nitrophenol/min at 25 C. To recalculate values obtained at 37 C, a factor of 0.70 was established experimentally and must be used.

5'-NUCLEOTIDASE

The 5'-nucleotidase from the venom of *Bothrops atrox* can be obtained practically free from phosphodiesterase. It seems likely that the method described below will also work with the venom of *Crotalus*. The enzyme is quite specific and attacks only 5'-mononucleotides. The purified enzyme may serve as a useful reagent for (a) the determination of 5'-mononucleotides in a heterogeneous digestion mixture, (b) the removal of 5'-mononucleotides from a mixture containing both 5' and 3' mononucleotides. Linn and Lehman (69), Josse (personal communication) (71), and the author have used it successfully.

Assay

ANALYTICAL METHODS. 5'-Nucleotidase is determined by the modified method of Sinsheimer and Koerner (63). The reaction mixture contains: 0.1 ml of 1 M glycine buffer, pH 9.0, 0.1 ml of 0.1 M MgCl$_2$, 0.3 ml of 0.01 M AMP, 0.1 ml of enzyme solution, and water to a total volume of 1 ml. The mixture is incubated for 15 min at 37 C. The liberated phosphate is determined according to Fiske and Subbarow (72). In accordance with the recommendation of the Commission on Enzymes of the International Union of Biochemistry (73), 1 unit is defined as the amount of enzyme liberating 1 μmole of inorganic phosphate/min at 25 C. The velocities at 37 C and at 25 C were carefully compared and the coefficient of 0.25 has been used to recalculate the results obtained at 37 C into units, as defined. Potency is expressed as units of activity per A_{280} of enzyme solution.

Method of Preparation (14)

The starting material is the 42% acetone precipitate obtained as a by-product in the preparation of phosphodiesterase (64,65). It was collected by centrifugation and kept at -20 C. An identical precipitate has also served as a starting material for the purification of venom endonuclease (13). In the case of 5'-nucleotidase, however, the prolonged storage, after exposure to acetone at pH 4.0, resulted in partial destruction of the enzyme and a relative decrease in potency in this

TABLE 5. *Summary of Purification Procedure of 5'-Nucleotidase* (14)

Step	Total A_{280}	Total Activity (units)	Potency	Total Activity of Phosphodi- esterase (units)	Ratio 5'-Nucleo- tidase: Phospho- diesterase
1. Extract from 42%[a] acetone precipitate	2,692	6,581	2.4	37	178
2. Repetition of 42% acetone precipitation	1,199	6,455	5.4	10.7	603
3. Ammonium sulfate	57	2,016	35.3	0.24	8,400
4. Sephadex G-100	13	1,727	133	0.08	21,587
5. DEAE-cellulose	1.1	725	630	0.02	36,250

[a] Potency of 5'-nucleotidase in crude venom, 0.62.

material. If dried venom is used as a starting material, and the 42% acetone precipitate is worked up immediately, the yield is improved and the potency in the first step is of the order 5–7 (Table 5). The reason for not using dry venom is monetary. Venom is generally too expensive to neglect phosphodiesterase.

STEP 1. The 42% acetone precipitate obtained from 30 g of venom is suspended in 500 ml of 0.1 M Tris-HCl buffer, pH 8.0, and is stirred for 1 hr at 5 C with the aid of a magnetic stirrer. The undissolved material is centrifuged off (15 min, 10,000 × g) and discarded. The supernatant solution is dialyzed overnight against 4 liters of distilled water stirred with a magnetic stirrer.

STEP 2. To the dialyzed solution, 2 M sodium acetate buffer, pH 4.0, is added to attain 0.2 M final concentration. The solution is transferred to the Aminco cooling bath kept at −17 C, and acetone, precooled to −20 C, is poured from a measuring cylinder to attain a final concentration of 42%. The mixture is stirred for 30 min, and centrifuged (30 min, 10,000 × g) at −17 C. The supernatant solution is discarded, and the precipitate is immediately suspended in 70 ml of 0.05 M Tris-HCl buffer, pH 7.0. After being stirred for 30 min at 5 C, the undissolved material is centrifuged off and discarded. The supernatant solution is dialyzed against two 4-liter changes of 0.01 M Tris-HCl buffer, pH 7.0. The precipitate that forms during dialysis is centrifuged off and discarded.

STEP 3. To the supernatant solution, 1 M Tris-HCl buffer, pH 7.5, is added to attain a final concentration of 0.05 M. The solution is placed in an ice bath and solid ammonium sulfate is added to attain 60% saturation.†
After standing for 30 min, the mixture is centrifuged (15 min, 20,000 × g) at 0 C, and the precipitate is discarded. The concentration of ammonium sulfate is then raised to 65% saturation. After 60 min at 0 C, the mixture is centrifuged, and the precipitate is again discarded. The concentration of ammonium sulfate is then raised to 70% saturation, the mixture is allowed to stand for 60 min at 0 C, it is centrifuged at 0 C, and the supernatant solution is discarded.

STEP 4. The precipitate is dissolved in 5 ml of 0.05 M Tris-HCl buffer, pH 7.5, and is filtered through the column of Sephadex G-100, with the same buffer used for displacement. The bulk of 5′-nucleotidase appears in the ascending part of the first protein peak (Fig. 4). The

---

† Ammonium sulfate for a given concentration is calculated from the formula of Noda and Kuby (74).

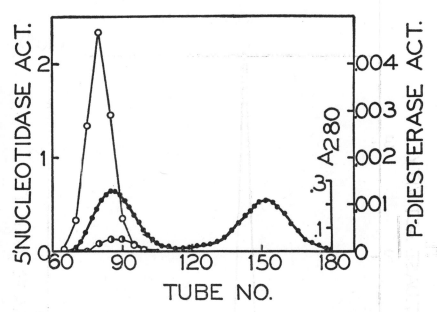

Fig. 4. Step 4 of the purification procedure. Elution pattern of 5′-nucleotidase and phosphodiesterase from a Sephadex G-100 column (4.4 cm × 50 cm; 700 ml, total volume). Flow rate, 3.8 ml/tube, 15 tubes/hr at 4 C. Elution with 0.05 M Tris-HCl, pH 7.5. Measurements of enzymatic activity were performed at 37 C. They were recalculated for 25 C with the use of the factors reported in "Analytical Methods," and expressed in units as defined in that section. Black circles indicate protein concentration expressed as A_{280} per ml; white circles, activity of 5′-nucleotidase, units per 0.1 ml of eluent; split circles, activity of phosphodiesterase, units per 0.2 ml (14).

contents of tubes 68–88† are pooled and dialyzed overnight against 6 liters of 0.01 M Tris-HCl buffer, pH 7.5, stirred with a magnetic stirrer.

STEP 5.   The dialyzed material is applied to the DEAE-cellulose column, previously equilibrated with 0.01 M Tris-HCl buffer, pH 7.5. Elution is carried out stepwise, first with 0.01, then with 0.05, and finally with 0.2 M Tris-HCl buffer of the same pH. The elution pattern is shown in Fig. 5. Most of the 5′-nucleotidase appears in the 0.05 M buffer. In spite of considerable purification, the enzyme is not chro-

---

† Should only tubes 68 to 75 be collected (Fig. 4), 75% of the total activity would be lost, but the 5′-nucleotidase obtained would contain so little phosphodiesterase that it could be detected only with *p*-nitrophenyl 5′-thymidylate. This substrate was found in our laboratory to be 70 times more sensitive than calcium di-*p*-nitrophenyl phosphate at 37 C (at 25 C, the factor was 115). The difference is smaller than that reported by Razzell and Khorana (39), but both substrates used by us were commercial products, which might explain the discrepancy.

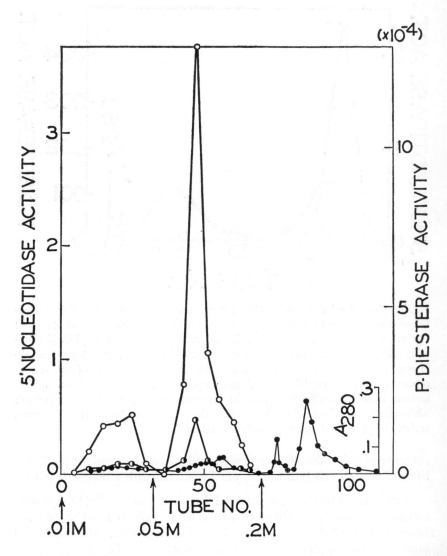

Fig. 5. Step 5 of the purification procedure. Elution pattern of 5′-nucleo-tidase and phosphodiesterase from the DEAE-cellulose column (1 cm × 30 cm). Flow rate, 3.7 ml/tube, 5 tubes/hr, 4 C. Stepwise elution Tris-HCl buffer, pH 7.5, of indicated molarity; black circles indicate protein concentration ex-pressed as A_{280} per ml; white circles, activity of 5′-nucleotidase, units per 0.1 ml; split circles, activity of phosphodiesterase, units per 0.2 ml (14).

matographically pure, and the potency varies throughout the peak. The maximal value, 1250, is found for tube 47 (for clarity, potency is not plotted in Fig. 5).

The yield and the extent of purification at each step of the procedure are summarized in Table 5.

Björk (75) obtained 5'-nucleotidase about twice as potent as that described above. The starting material was a South African venom *Hemachatus haemachates*. Since the venom of *Crotalus adamanteus* appears to resemble *Bothrops atrox* in several respects, the method of Sulkowski *et al.* (14) is given, and the points of differences are copied from Björk (75).

The procedure is essentially the same as described by Sulkowski *et al.* (14), but with the following modifications: About 90% of the 5'-nucleotidase was recovered in the 42% acetone precipitate (see p. 172) of crude *C. adamanteus* venom at pH 4.0 (27,64,69), but in the case of *H. haemachates* venom it was found necessary to increase the acetone concentration to 45% in order to get a similar yield. Making the precipitation at pH 3.8 as in the first step of the purification procedure for phosphodiesterase (67) resulted in a heavy loss of 5'-nucleotidase activity. After gel filtration on Sephadex G-100 (see p. 172 and Fig. 4), the first 30% of the enzyme peak contains so little phosphodiesterase that it can only be determined with *p*-nitrophenyl-5'-thymidylate. The rest of the peak is pooled and concentrated by vacuum dialysis (76), and then refiltered through the same Sephadex column. The enzyme peak from this run is also divided into two parts, and the second part of it is concentrated and gel filtrated as before. The first 30% of the 5'-nucleotidase peaks from the three consecutive runs are then pooled and dialyzed as described (14). As the total recovery of the enzyme in the Sephadex filtrations is close to 100%, the yield of this step is 60% (some activity is lost during concentration). The modification seems justified by its 70-fold better elimination of phosphodiesterase.

In the DEAE-cellulose chromatography (Step 5, p. 174) some changes in buffer concentrations were made. Fig. 6 shows a chromatogram on a 35-ml column (1.2 × 31 cm), equilibrated with 0.01 M Tris-HCl (pH 7.5). The 5'-nucleotidase from 10 g of crude *H. haemachates* venom was purified through the precipitation and Sephadex filtration steps and applied to the DEAE-cellulose column. After washing through with starting buffer, stepwise elution is performed with 0.04 and 0.3 M buffers of the same pH. More than 80% of the applied activity was eluted with 0.04 M buffer in a symmetrical peak with a constant potency of 1200, which is about the same as the highest value previously found for a single tube (14).

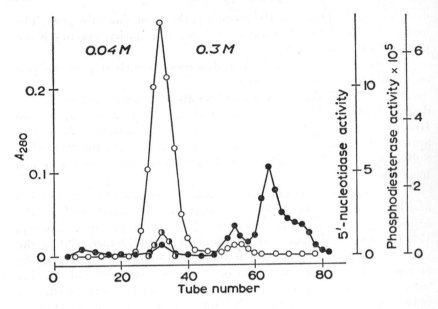

Fig. 6. Chromatogram of 5′-nucleotidase from the gel-filtration step on a 35-ml column of DEAE-cellulose. Applied volume 28 ml. Fraction volume 3.5 ml. Flow rate 15 ml/hr. Starting buffer 0.01 M Tris-HCl (pH 7.5). Stepwise elution with Tris-HCl of the same pH and of indicated molarity. Black circles indicate protein concentration expressed as A_{280} units per ml; split circles, phosphodiesterase activity; white circles, 5′-nucleotidase activity expressed as units per ml of enzyme solution (75).

VENOM ENDONUCLEASE

A second nucleophosphodiesterase, an endonuclease, has been observed in snake venoms (11,12,15). Georgatsos and Laskowski (13) purified this enzyme from the venom of *Bothrops atrox* and established that it has no specificity toward the sugar moiety and that it is a 3′-monoester former. It has an optimum activity at pH 5.0, requires no magnesium. During the early stages of digestion of DNA it has a preference toward Gp-Gp linkage. With DNA as substrate the reaction does not proceed much beyond the pentanucleotide stage, even with a comparatively large amount of enzyme. With sRNA as substrate (77) the reaction proceeds further and a small amount of dinucleotides is formed. No data concerning the preferential linkage with RNA are available. Similarity in composition of the two venoms suggests that the method as described below may be applicable to *Crotalus adamanteus* (15).

Assay

Assay of endonuclease has been followed by the spectrophotometric method of Kunitz (see deoxyribonuclease I for the detailed description) except that in crude venom the modification of Richards *et al.* (15) is necessary. The modification is described below.

Endonuclease is determined as follows: The substrate consists of DNA, 0.04 mg/ml in 0.2 M Na acetate buffer, pH 5.0. Three ml of substrate and 1 ml of enzyme (venom) are mixed and transferred to the spectrophotometer, where they are incubated at 37 C. Changes in A_{260} and A_{330} are followed against a blank of substrate and water until A_{330} begins to increase at a substantial rate. If this occurs before enough points have been recorded to determine a straight line for A_{260} against time (see Fig. 7), the assay is repeated using a more highly diluted venom. Satisfactory results are obtained with dilutions of between 1:75 and 1:110, under which conditions A_{330} remained relatively stable for

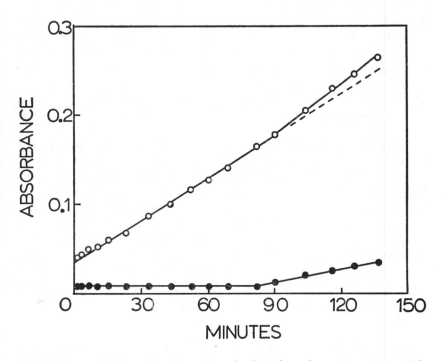

Fig. 7. Determination of endonuclease in *Crotalus adamanteus* venom. The procedure followed was that of Kunitz (38), modified as described in the experimental section. The solution assayed contained 1.85×10^{-1} mg of dry venom/ml. White circles indicate A_{260}; black circles, A_{330} (15).

between 1 and 2 hr. A unit of endonuclease is defined as the amount of enzyme giving an increase in absorbance at 260 mμ of 1.0/min.

The assay of endonuclease in *Crotalus adamanteus* venom by the procedure just described is illustrated in Fig. 7. The onset of the development of turbidity in the solution is clearly indicated by the break in the curve for A_{330}, and a corresponding break in the curve for A_{260} is also visible. Activity can be calculated from the portion of the A_{260} curve obtained before A_{330} began to rise. In certain other cases, A_{330} increased very slowly throughout the course of the measurement, with or without showing a break at some point. In such cases, the slope of A_{330} is subtracted from the slope of A_{260} under the assumption that the loss of light by scattering is approximately the same at the two wavelengths.

Preparation of Venom Endonuclease

The 42% acetone precipitate obtained as a by-product during the preparation of venom phosphodiesterase according to the modified (**66**) method of Koerner and Sinsheimer (**64**) served as a starting material. Immediately after centrifugation the precipitate is suspended in a small volume of water and lyophilized. The dry powder is stored in a cold room for several months. The potency of endonuclease (0.002) in this fraction is only slightly higher than in the original venom, but this material is available in large quantities and is already poor in phosphodiesterase.

STEP 1. Four and one-half grams of the 42% acetone precipitate of crude venom are suspended in 300 ml of cold water, and the suspension is stirred in the cold room for approximately 12 hr. The nondissolved material is centrifuged off and discarded. The supernatant is heated in a 60 C water bath for 30 min, then transferred to an ice bath. When the solution has cooled to room temperature (24 C), the precipitate is removed by centrifugation and discarded. During this step, 90% of the contaminating 5′-nucleotidase and about 40% of the remaining phosphodiesterase are removed. An increase of 20–50% in the total activity of the endonuclease, which could have been due to a partial removal of the DNA-precipitating agent, has also been noted after this step.

STEP 2. To the supernatant solution of Step 1, enough 0.2 M calcium gel prepared according to Keilin and Hartree (**78**) is added to attain a concentration of 0.03 M with respect to calcium phosphate. The suspension is stirred for 30 min at room temperature and the calcium phosphate removed by centrifugation. The supernatant solu-

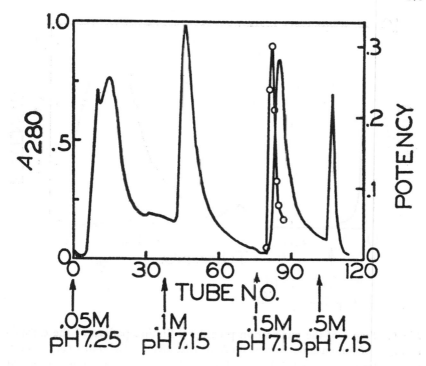

Fig. 8. Step 4 of the purification procedure. Elution pattern of the first chromatography of endonuclease on DEAE-cellulose. Column 1 cm × 20 cm, flow rate 3 ml/tube, 4–6 tubes/hr at 4 C. Elution with Tris-HCl buffer of the indicated molarity and pH. Solid line indicates protein concentration expressed as absorbancy at 280 mμ; white circles, potency of venom endonuclease. The contents of tubes 80–90 were pooled and used for further purification (13).

tion is dialyzed against 20 volumes of water at 4 C for approximately 16 hr.†

The calcium gel removes most of the remaining 5′-nucleotidase and approximately half of the remaining phosphodiesterase activities. It also removed the agent that causes precipitation of DNA.

STEP 3. The dialyzed solution from Step 2 is brought to 50% saturation with solid ammonium sulfate‡ at 0 C, and centrifuged at 0 C.

---

† It is imperative that one proceed with Step 2 immediately after Step 1. If the unbuffered system is allowed to stand for a prolonged period the endonuclease is also adsorbed on the gel. Should this occur, the enzyme can be eluted by 0.2 M Tris-HCl buffer, pH 8.9, with the subsequent steps remaining the same.

‡ Ammonium sulfate for a given saturation is calculated from the formula of Noda and Kuby (74).

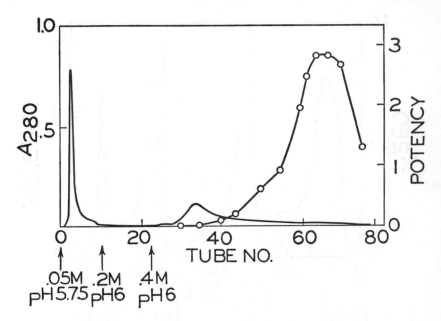

Fig. 9. Step 5 of the purification procedure. Elution pattern of the chromatography of venom endonuclease on Amberlite IRC-50. Column 1 cm × 20 cm, flow rate 3 ml/tube, 4–6 tubes/hr at 4 C. Elution with sodium acetate buffer of the indicated molarity and pH. Solid line indicates protein concentration expressed as absorbancy at 280 mμ; white circles, potency of venom endonuclease. The contents of tubes 44–77 were pooled for further purification (13).

The precipitate is discarded. To the supernatant fluid, solid ammonium sulfate is added to attain 90% saturation. The precipitate is collected and dissolved in approximately one-twentieth the original volume of 0.1 M Tris-HCl buffer, pH 8.9. The solution is dialyzed against 4 liters of 0.025 M Tris-HCl buffer, pH 7.25.

STEP 4.   From this point on all manipulations are performed at 4 C. The dialyzed solution from the previous step is applied to a 20 × 1-cm DEAE column previously equilibrated with the buffer used for dialysis. The same buffer is used as a starting eluent. The elution pattern is illustrated in Fig. 8. The first peak contains the remaining phosphodiesterase and 5′-nucleotidase activities, while the third contains the endonuclease. The endonuclease activity is eluted on the ascending side of the third peak, so that it is not advisable to allow the second peak to trail. The trailing may be avoided by switching to the higher molarity buffer immediately after the steep portion of the descending part of peak 2 has been eluted. The contents of the tubes with improved endonuclease potency are combined, lyophilized to approximately one-third the original volume, and dialyzed against 6 liters of water for 10–12 hr. The lyophilization and the dialysis are repeated once more to insure reduction in volume and removal of salt. At this point the enzyme is frozen and kept at −20 C until three or more preparations are accumulated.

STEP 5.   The combined preparations are dialyzed against 4 liters of 0.05 M sodium acetate buffer, pH 5.75, for 12 hr and applied on a 20- × 1-cm Amberlite IRC-50 column, previously equilibrated with the same buffer. The elution is continued with the same buffer till no more protein emerges from the column (Fig. 9). The enzyme emerges

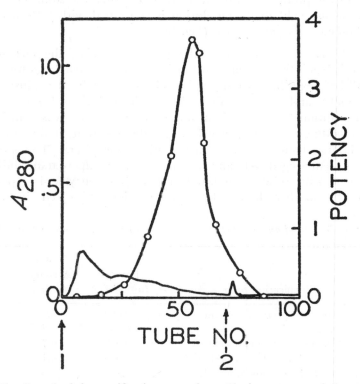

Fig. 10.   Step 6 of the purification procedure. Elution pattern of the second chromatography on DEAE-cellulose. Column 0.5 cm × 25 cm, flow rate 3 ml/tube, 2–3 tubes/hr at 4 C. Elution: at arrow 1 with linear gradient, between 0.075 and 0.15 M Tris-HCl buffer, pH 7.15 (125 ml in each of two chambers of the gradient); at arrow 2 with 0.15 M Tris-HCl buffer, pH 7.15. Solid line indicates protein concentration expressed as absorbancy at 280 mμ; white circles, potency of venom endonuclease. The contents of tubes 33–66 were pooled for further purification (13).

with 0.4 M buffer, pH 6, on the descending part of the peak. The contents of the tubes containing endonuclease with improved potency are combined, lyophilized to one-third the original volume, and dialyzed against water. The lyophilization and dialysis are repeated and the enzyme solution is reduced to a volume of 1–2 ml.

STEP 6. The enzyme solution from Step 5 is dialyzed against 2 liters of 0.075 M Tris-HCl buffer, pH 7.15, for 12 hr and applied to a 0.5- × 25-cm DEAE column, previously adjusted to the same buffer. As soon as all the enzyme solution passes into the column, the latter is connected with Peterson and Sober's "Varigrad" (79) containing a linear gradient of 0.075 and 0.150 M Tris-HCl buffer, pH 7.15. If all of the protein has not emerged by the time the solutions in the Varigrad are exhausted, the elution is continued with 0.15 M buffer until no more enzyme appears (Fig. 10).

STEP 7. The portion of the peak containing the enzyme in Step 6 is lyophilized to one-third of its volume, dialyzed against water for 12 hr, lyophilized to approximately 5 ml, dialyzed against water once more, and finally reduced by lyophilization to 1 ml. A saturated solution of ammonium sulfate is added dropwise until the first cloudiness appears, which after the solution stands for several hours changes to a semicrystalline precipitate. The precipitate is centrifuged off and discarded. The supernatant fluid is saturated with solid ammonium sulfate. The enzyme is separated from the mother liquor by centrifugation, dissolved in water,

TABLE 6. *Yield and Extent of Purification of Venom Endonuclease* (13)

Purification Step	Potency (units/A_{280})	Total Activity (units)	Yield (%)
42% acetone precipitate of venom	0.002	5.4	100
Step 1. Heating at 60 C	0.007	6.4	118
Step 2. Calcium gel adsorption	0.008	4.7	87
Step 3. Ammonium sulfate fractionation	0.015	4.1	76
Step 4. DEAE, first chromatography	0.14	1.5	28[b]
Step 5. Amberlite IRC-50, chromatography[a]	1.0	1.2	22
Step 6. DEAE, second chromatography	2.0	1.0	18
Step 7. Ammonium sulfate fractionation	2.5	0.9	16

[a] From Step 5 onward the values given are calculated as if one preparation were carried all the way to Step 7. In reality, three or more preparations from Step 4 were combined and carried through the next three steps.

[b] The low yield in this step is due to the fact that only the contents of tubes with potency higher than the one charged were combined and processed further.

dialyzed against water, and kept frozen. Table 6 summarizes the purification procedure. The potency of the final product is of a similar order of magnitude (2.5 u/A_{280}) as that of the crystalline deoxyribonuclease I, measured under identical conditions (8 u/A_{280}). Even in the deepfreeze (-20 C) the enzyme loses 70% of its activity after 6 months of storage. The yield is about 3 mg (3 A_{280} units) from 40 g of the "42% acetone fraction" obtained from 100 g of venom. In view of this, only a limited characterization was possible, and physical studies were excluded.

Properties of Venom Endonuclease

The optimal pH of the nuclease action was determined in sodium acetate buffer of constant ionic strength (0.2) and varying pH values.

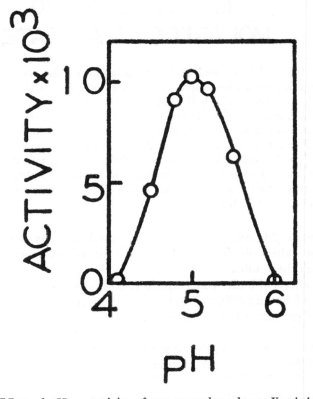

Fig. 11. Effect of pH on activity of venom endonuclease. Kunitz's spectrophotometric method (38) was used. The reaction cells contained 3 ml of DNA solution (0.04 mg/ml in H_2O, 0.05 ml of enzyme solution (0.01 unit), 0.15 ml of H_2O, and 0.8 ml of 1 M sodium acetate of the indicated pH (13).

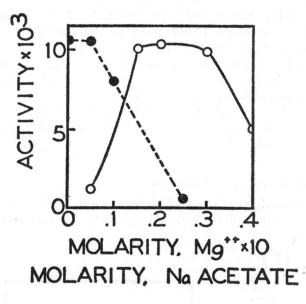

Fig. 12. Effect of buffer and Mg^{2+} concentrations on the activity of venom endonuclease. Kunitz's spectrophotometric method (38) was used. For the determination of the optimal buffer concentration, the reaction cells contained 3 ml of DNA (0.04 mg/ml in H_2O), 0.05 ml of enzyme (0.01 unit), a calculated quantity of 1 M sodium acetate buffer, pH 5.0, to attain the indicated molarity, and water to a total volume of 4 ml. For the determination of the effect of Mg^{2+} the reaction cells contained 3 ml of DNA (0.04 mg/ml), 0.05 ml of enzyme, a calculated volume of 0.25 M $MgCl_2$ to attain the indicated molarity, and water to a total volume of 4 ml. White circles indicate effect of buffer; black circles, effect of Mg^{2+} (13).

The Kunitz (38) assay method was employed. Activity was calculated from the values obtained in the first 9 min of the reaction. Fig. 11 illustrates the results.

The effects of buffer concentration and Mg^{2+} were measured by the method of Kunitz (38). Sodium acetate buffers of varying concentrations and constant pH (5.0) were tested. Concentrations lower than 0.15 M and higher than 0.4 M are inhibiting. Magnesium chloride introduced into the system in the presence of 0.2 M sodium acetate, pH 5.0, proved inhibiting at concentrations higher than 5×10^{-3} M (Fig. 12).

Even though purified preparations have not been used for heat and pH stability studies, the crude enzyme was tested under various conditions. It was found that, in the presence of 0.1 M sodium acetate buffer, the enzyme is stable at pH 6.0 but loses more than half of its activity at pH 4.0, both when it is boiled for 30 sec and when it is left at 4 C for

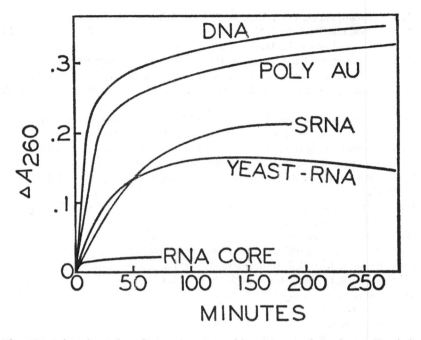

Fig. 13. Digestion of various substrates with venom endonuclease. Kunitz's spectrophotometric method (38) was used. The reaction mixtures contained 0.8 ml of 1 M sodium acetate buffer, pH 5.0, 0.2 ml of enzyme solution (potency toward DNA 1.8), 3.0 ml of substrate. The concentrations of the various substrates in A_{260} units/ml of final reaction mixture were DNA, 1.96; Poly AU, 1.75; yeast RNA, 2.05; sRNA, 2.19; RNA core, 2.7 (13).

72 hr. At pH 8.0 in the presence of 0.1 M Tris-HCl buffer the enzyme is stable under both of the previously mentioned conditions.

The purification procedure for the endonuclease was devised on the basis of its deoxyribonuclease activity. However, the purified enzyme exhibits toward RNA an activity of a similar order of magnitude (Fig. 13), except for the "RNA core," which is resistant to the enzyme.

REFERENCES

1. SCHMIDT, G., and M. LASKOWSKI. 1961. *In* P. D. Boyer, H. Lardy, and K. Myrbäck, editors, The enzymes. Academic Press, New York. Vol. V, p. 1.
2. UZAWA, S. 1932. J. Biochem. (Tokyo). *15:* 19.
3. GULLAND, J. M., and E. M. JACKSON. 1938. Biochem. J. *32:* 590.
4. LASKOWSKI, M., SR. 1961. *In* P. D. Boyer, H. Lardy, and K. Myrbäck, editors, The enzymes. Academic Press, New York. Vol. V, p. 123.

5. LASKOWSKI, M., SR. 1959. Ann. N. Y. Acad. Sci. *81:* 776.
6. LEHMAN, I. R. 1963. *In* J. N. Davidson and W. E. Cohn, editors, Progress in nucleic acid research. Academic Press, New York. Vol. II, p. 83.
7. OLESON, A. E., and J. F. KOERNER. 1964. J. Biol. Chem. *239:* 2935.
8. YANG, C. C., and S. KAKEMURA. 1958. J. Formosan Med. Assoc. *57:* 349.
9. YANG, C. C., S. IWANAGA, and S. KAWACHI. 1958. J. Formosan Med. Assoc. *57:* 525.
10. CHEN, C.-S., and C.-C. SU. 1959. Yamaguchi Medical College J. *8:* 570.
11. HAESSLER, H. A., and L. CUNNINGHAM. 1957. Exp. Cell Res. *13:* 304.
12. LASKOWSKI, M., G. HAGERTY, and U.-R. LAURILA. 1957. Nature. *180:* 1181.
13. GEORGATSOS, J. G., and M. LASKOWSKI, SR. 1962. Biochemistry. *1:* 288.
14. SULKOWSKI, E., W. BJÖRK, and M. LASKOWSKI, SR. 1963. J. Biol. Chem. *238:* 2477.
15. RICHARDS, G. M., G. DU VAIR, and M. LASKOWSKI, SR. 1965. Biochemistry. *4:* 501.
16. VASILENKO, S. K. 1963. Biokhimiya. *28:* 602.
17. BABKINA, G. T., and S. K. VASILENKO. 1964. Biokhimiya. *29:* 268.
18. MCLENNAN, B. D., and B. G. LANE. 1965. Fed. Proc. *24:* 602.
19. LEHMAN, R. I. 1960. J. Biol. Chem. *235:* 1479.
20. LEHMAN, R. I., and E. A. PRATT. 1960. J. Biol. Chem. *235:* 3254.
21. SETLOW, R. B., W. L. CARRIER, and F. J. BOLLUM. 1964. Biochim. Biophys. Acta. *91:* 446.
22. GILHAM, P. T. 1962. J. Am. Chem. Soc. *84:* 687.
23. LEE, J. C., N. W. Y. HO, and P. T. GILHAM. 1965. Biochim. Biophys. Acta. *95:* 503.
24. GILHAM, P. T. Personal communication.
25. SINGER, M. F., R. J. HILMOE, and H. G. KHORANA. 1958. Fed. Proc. *17:* 312.
26. RAZZELL, W. E., and H. G. KHORANA. 1958. J. Am. Chem. Soc. *80:* 1770.
27. FELIX, F., J. L. POTTER, and M. LASKOWSKI. 1960. J. Biol. Chem. *235:* 1150.
28. PRICE, J., P. BERG, E. J. OFENGAND, F. H. BERGMANN, and M. DIECKMANN. 1959. Proc. Nat. Acad. Sci. U.S. *45:* 319.
29. NIHEI, T., and G. L. CANTONI. 1963. J. Biol. Chem. *238:* 3991.
30. SINGER, B., and H. FRAENKEL-CONRAT. 1963. Biochim. Biophys. Acta. *72:* 534.
31. SUGIYAMA, T., and M. FRAENKEL-CONRAT. 1963. Biochemistry. *2:* 332.
32. VANECKO, S., and M. LASKOWSKI. 1962. Biochim. Biophys. Acta. *61:* 547.
33. EDMAN, P. 1950. Acta. Chem. Scand. *4:* 277.
34. EDMAN, P., and K. LAUBER. 1956. Acta. Chem. Scand. *10:* 466.
35. KONIGSBERG, W., and R. J. HILL. 1962. J. Biol. Chem. *237:* 2547.
36. HOLLEY, R. W., J. T. MADISON, and ADA ZAMIR. 1964. Biochem. Biophys. Res. Comm. *17:* 389.
37. TOMLINSON, R. V., and G. M. TENER. 1963. Biochemistry. *2:* 697.
38. KUNITZ, M. 1950. J. Gen. Physiol. *33:* 349.
39. RAZZELL, W. E., and H. G. KHORANA. 1959. J. Biol. Chem. *234:* 2105.
40. BJÖRK, W. Personal communication.
41. SIERAKOWSKA, H., H. SZEMPLINSKA, and D. SHUGAR. 1963. Acta. Biochim. Polon. *10:* 399.
42. SIERAKOWSKA, H., and D. SHUGAR. 1963. Biochem. Biophys. Res. Comm. *11:* 70.

43. WIGLER, P. W. 1963. J. Biol. Chem. *238:* 1767.
44. OHSAKA, A., J.-I. MUKAI, and M. LASKOWSKI, SR. 1962. J. Biol. Chem. *239:* 3498.
45. SULKOWSKI, E., and M. LASKOWSKI, SR. 1962. J. Biol. Chem. *237:* 2620.
46. FRAENKEL-CONRAT, H., and B. SINGER. 1962. Biochemistry. *1:* 120.
47. PALLADINI, A. C., and L. F. LELOIR. 1952. Biochem. J. *51:* 426.
48. BERGKVIST, R. 1956. Acta. Chem. Scand. *11:* 1465.
49. MARKHAM, R., and J. D. SMITH. 1952. Biochem. J. *52:* 558.
50. WINTER, J. E., and A. W. BERNHEIMER. 1964. J. Biol. Chem. *239:* 215.
51. BUTLER, G. C. 1955. *In* S. P. Colowick and N. O. Kaplan, editors, Methods in enzymology. Academic Press, New York. Vol. II, p. 561.
52. RAZZELL, W. E. 1963. *In* S. P. Colowick and N. O. Kaplan, editors, Methods in enzymology. Academic Press, New York. Vol. VI, p. 231.
53. PRIVAT DE GARILHE, M. 1964. Les nucleases. Hermann, Paris.
54. HURST, R. O., and G. C. BUTLER. 1951. J. Biol. Chem. *193:* 91.
55. MAENO, H., and S. MITZUHASHI. 1961. J. Biochem. (Japan). *50:* 434.
56. OHSAKA, A. 1958. J. Biochem. (Japan). *45:* 259.
57. BOMAN, H. G., and U. KALETTA. 1957. Biochim. Biophys. Acta. *24:* 619.
58. BJÖRK, W. 1961. Biochim. Biophys. Acta. *49:* 195.
59. LANE, B. G., J. DIEMER, and C. A. BLASHKO. 1963. Cand. J. Biochem. Physiol. *41:* 1927.
60. KELLER, E. B. 1964. Biochem. Biophys. Res. Comm. *17:* 412.
61. LANGEN, P. 1961. Biochem. Z. *334:* 65.
62. NIKOLSKAYA, I. I., N. M. SHALINA, and E. I. BUDOWSKI. 1962. Biochim. Biophys. Acta. *64:* 197.
63. SINSHEIMER, R. L., and J. F. KOERNER. 1952. J. Biol. Chem. *198:* 293.
64. KOERNER, J. F., and R. L. SINSHEIMER. 1957. J. Biol. Chem. *228:* 1049.
65. PRIVAT DE GARILHE, M., and M. LASKOWSKI. 1955. Biochim. Biophys. Acta. *18:* 370.
66. WILLIAMS, E. J., S.-C. SUNG, and M. LASKOWSKI, SR. 1961. J. Biol. Chem. *236:* 1130.
67. BJÖRK, W. 1963. J. Biol. Chem. *238:* 2487.
68. RICHARDS, G. M. Unpublished.
69. LINN, S., and I. R. LEHMAN. 1965. J. Biol. Chem. *240:* 1294.
70. BJÖRK, W. 1961. Biochim. Biophys. Acta. *49:* 195.
71. JOSSE, J. W. Personal communication.
72. FISKE, C. H., and Y. SUBBAROW. 1925. J. Biol. Chem. *66:* 375.
73. I.U.B. Symposium Series. 1961. Report of the commission on enzymes. Pergamon Press, New York. 1961. Vol. 20.
74. NODA, L., and S. A. KUBY. 1957. J. Biol. Chem. *226:* 541.
75. BJÖRK, W. 1964. Biochim. Biophys. Acta. *89:* 483.
76. VON HOFSTEN, B., and S.-C. FALKBRING. 1960. Anal. Biochem. *1:* 436.
77. MOYER, C. F., C. MCEVOY, and M. LASKOWSKI, SR. Unpublished.
78. KEILIN, D., and E. F. HARTREE. 1938. Proc. Roy. Soc. (London). *B124:* 397.
79. PETERSON, E. A., and H. A. SOBER. 1960. *In* P. Alexander and R. J. Block, editors, A laboratory manual of analytical methods of protein chemistry. Pergamon Press, New York. Vol. I, p. 88.

Preparation of Lamb Brain Phosphodiesterase

J. W. HEALY, D. STOLLAR, AND L. LEVINE
GRADUATE DEPARTMENT OF BIOCHEMISTRY
BRANDEIS UNIVERSITY
WALTHAM, MASSACHUSETTS

ASSAY METHOD

PRINCIPLE. The immunological assay method is based on the determination of denatured DNA before and after treatment with the phosphodiesterase. Denatured DNA reacts more effectivly than native DNA with antibodies directed toward DNA obtained by immunization of rabbits with ruptured T-even bacteriophage (1), methylated bovine serum albumin-DNA complexes (2,3), purinoyl, uracil, or various ribonucleotide conjugates of serum albumin (4–6), and uridine-multichain synthetic polypeptide conjugates (7). The serological reaction is sensitive to a decrease in the molecular weight of the thermally denatured DNA. Fragmentation of the DNA results in loss of serological activity. Endonucleolytic cleavage of the DNA is more effective than exonucleolytic cleavage in decreasing the size of DNA as measured serologically (8).

IMMUNOCHEMICAL ASSAY OF DEOXYRIBONUCLEASE ACTIVITY

Enzyme is incubated with 32 μg of either heat-denatured or native DNA at 37 C, in the presence of 5×10^{-4} M $MgSO_4$, 0.01 M 2-mercaptoethanol, and 0.025 M phosphate buffer, pH 7.4, in a total volume of 1.0

ml. Samples of this reaction mixture, withdrawn immediately after addition of the enzyme (zero time) and after various periods of incubation, are diluted 400-fold in ice-chilled veronal buffer to terminate the reaction and to bring the DNA to a concentration suitable for the immunologic assay. If native DNA is used as the substrate, it is boiled after this dilution. Varying concentrations of the diluted samples are reacted with antibodies to denatured DNA, and quantitative C' fixation curves are obtained (9). From these curves, the maximal amount of C' fixation is found for each sample, and the loss in maximal C' fixation is measured as a function of deoxyribonuclease activity. One unit of enzyme is arbitrarily defined as that amount which caused a 50% loss of maximal C' fixation in 20 min under the conditions described above.

PURIFICATION OF LAMB BRAIN PHOSPHODIESTERASE (10)

All steps in the purification (Table 1) are carried out at 2–4 C, with the exception of acetone fractionation, which is done at −5 C.

Four frozen whole lamb brains are thawed and homogenized in 300 ml of 0.15 M NaCl for 10 min in a Waring Blendor. The homogenized brain (550 ml) is centrifuged in a Spinco model L centrifuge at 105,000 × g for 180 min. The supernatant fluid (370 ml) is saved, and acetone is added to it to give a final acetone concentration of 20%. After 10 min, the precipitate that forms is removed and acetone is added to the supernatant fluid to give a final acetone concentration of 40%. The precipitate that forms is saved after centrifugation and is suspended in 100 ml of 0.001 M phosphate buffer, pH 7.4, with gentle stirring. This suspension is centrifuged and the supernatant fluid saved, and dialyzed for 18 hr against 0.1 M 2-mercaptoethanol in 0.001 M phosphate buffer, pH 7.4. To concentrate the enzyme, an equal volume of neutralized saturated $(NH_4)_2SO_4$ is added to the dialysate; the resulting precipitate is saved, and dissolved in 20 ml of 0.15 M Tris buffer, pH 8.0. The dialysate is added to a 40 ml slurry of DEAE, which has been equilibrated with Tris buffer (0.01 M, pH 8.0, and 2-mercaptoethanol, 0.1 M). The mixture is stirred with a glass rod for 30 min; the supernatant fluid is collected after centrifugation.

PROPERTIES

The enzyme attacks thermally denatured DNA more effectively than native DNA. The products of an extensively digested calf thymus DNA preparation were hexonucleotides and larger.

INHIBITORS. The enzyme is inhibited by p-chloromercuro-benzoate and disodium ethylenediamine tetraacetate.

EFFECT OF pH. The enzyme activity varies little between pH 7.3 and 9.0, but is reduced by half at pH 6.0.

DIVALENT CATION REQUIREMENT. 5×10^{-3} M Mg^{2+} is optimal for enzymatic activity.

STABILITY. The purified enzyme is labile at pH 5.0 and is destroyed during lyophilization or freezing. It is stable at 2–4 C in the presence of 0.01 M mercaptoethanol.

NaCl CONCENTRATION. The enzyme activity is optimal in 0.03 M NaCl and is reduced by half at 0.07 M and 0.005 M.

TABLE 1. *Purification of Lamb Brain Phosphodiesterase*

Enzyme Fraction	Total Volume (ml)	Activity (units/ml)	Protein (mg/ml)	Specific Activity (units/mg of protein)	Total Units
Supernate of homogenate	370	540	11	49	199,800
Acetone, 20–40% fraction	91	1,250	6.8	191	113,750
Ammonium sulfate, 0–50%	20	2,750	12.1	227	55,000
DEAE-cellulose eluate	34	440	0.05	3,780	14,920

REFERENCES

1. LEVINE, L., W. T. MURAKAMI, H. VAN VUNAKIS, and L. GROSSMAN. 1960. Proc. Natl. Acad. Sci., U.S. *46:* 1038.
2. PLESCIA, O. J., W. BRAUN, and N. C. PALCZUK. 1964. Proc. Natl. Acad. Sci., U.S. *52:* 279.
3. PLESCIA, O. J., N. C. PALCZUK, W. BRAUN, and E. CORA-FIGUEROA. 1965. Science. *148:* 1102.
4. BUTLER, V. P., S. W. TANENBAUM, and S. M. BEISER. 1965. J. Exptl. Med. *121:* 19.
5. BEISER, S. M., S. W. TANENBAUM, and B. F. ERLANGER. 1964. Nature. *203:* 1381.
6. TANENBAUM, and S. M. BEISER. 1963. Proc. Natl. Acad. Sci., U.S. *49:* 662.
7. SELA, M., H. UNGER-WARON, and Y. SHECTER. 1964. Proc. Natl. Acad. Sci., U.S. *52:* 285.

8. MURAKAMI, W. T., H. VAN VUNAKIS, L. GROSSMAN, and L. LEVINE. 1961. Virology. *14:* 190.
9. WASSERMAN, E., and L. LEVINE. 1960. J. Immunol. *87:* 290.
10. HEALY, J. W., D. STOLLAR, M. I. SIMON, and L. LEVINE. 1963. Arch. Biochem. Biophys. *103:* 461.

Potassium-Activated Phosphodiesterase (Ribonuclease II)† from *Escherichia coli*

MAXINE F. SINGER
NATIONAL INSTITUTE OF ARTHRITIS
AND METABOLIC DISEASES
NATIONAL INSTITUTES OF HEALTH
BETHESDA, MARYLAND

ASSAY

$$(\text{C}^{14}\text{-AMP})_n \xrightarrow{\text{Mg}^{2+},\ \text{K}^+} n\ \text{C}^{14}\text{-5}'\text{-AMP}$$

Reagents

1. The reaction mixture (total volume 0.1 ml) contains

   0.1 M Tris buffer, pH 7.5
   0.1 M KCl
   1.5 mM $MgCl_2$

---

† Spahr (1) has suggested that the various ribonucleases of *E. coli* be designated by Roman numerals. The so-called *ribosomal* (or *latent*) ribonuclease is *E. coli* ribonuclease I (2; also this volume, p. 64).

2.0 mM†C^{14}-labeled poly A‡ (approximately 30,000 cpm/μmole)
Enzyme

2. 2.5% perchloric acid
3. Approximately 1.2 N NH$_4$OH
4. Bray's solution (3) (for liquid scintillation counting)
5. Bovine serum albumin, 10 mg/ml; the albumin is dialyzed for 2 days against 1 mM EDTA and then for 2 days against distilled water

Principle

This assay measures the formation of C^{14}-labeled 5'-AMP (acid soluble) from the hydrolysis of C^{14}-labeled poly A (acid insoluble). Various alternative procedures are also convenient. Thus, other C^{14}-labeled homopolymers may be used as substrates. If poly U is used the unhydrolyzed polymer must be precipitated by alcohol–salt mixtures (1). If labeled polymers are unavailable, the formation of acid-(or alcohol-) soluble, ultraviolet-absorbing material can be measured.

Procedure

The reaction is started by the addition of enzyme. After 20 min of incubation at 37 C, 0.4 ml of cold, 2.5% HClO$_4$ (Reagent 2) is added, and the contents of the tube are mixed. The tubes are allowed to stand for 10 min at 4 C, are then centrifuged at about 2500 × g for 10 min, and 0.3 ml of the supernatant fluid are placed in a scintillation vial. Reagent 3 (0.1 ml) is added and then 10 ml of Reagent 4. Radioactivity is determined at suitable settings of a liquid scintillation counter. The radioactivity of the polymer substrate may be determined by adding a sample of the polymer stock solution to an already counted experimental vial, and counting. The concentration of polymer may be determined by measuring the total phosphate concentration or by determining its ultraviolet absorbance. The molar extinction coefficient of poly A at 257 mμ at pH 7.0 is 10,500 (4). A zero time blank is run with each set of assays and the acid-soluble counts found in the zero time are subtracted from each sample. The μmoles of 5'-AMP produced in the 0.1 ml reaction mixture are calculated. One unit is equal to the production of one μmole of 5'-AMP per hour and specific activity is units per mg protein. Protein is determined by the method of Lowry et al. (5). In those cases where small amounts of protein must

† All polymer concentrations are expressed as moles of mononucleotide unit.
‡ Abbreviations: Polyadenylic, polyuridylic, and polycytidylic acids are poly A, poly U, and poly C, respectively. 5'-Adenosine monophosphate is 5'-AMP; diethylaminoethyl cellulose is DEAE; ethylenediaminetetraacetate is EDTA; tris(hydroxymethyl)-aminoethane is Tris.

be determined a modification (6) of the Lowry method is used. Under the conditions described, the extent of polymer hydrolysis is proportional to the time of incubation until at least 50% of the polymer is hydrolyzed. Hydrolysis is not strictly dependent on enzyme concentration with the crudest fractions; it is so after the protamine step. Starting with fractions obtained after DEAE-cellulose chromatography, bovine serum albumin (Reagent 5) (final concentration, 1 mg/ml) is included in the assay mixtures.

ISOLATION OF RIBONUCLEASE II
FROM *E. COLI* EXTRACTS (7)

Growth of Cells

Escherichia coli, strain B, may be grown in various standard media (for example, see references 1, 7, and 8) and are harvested in the early logarithmic phase of growth. Cells obtained from the late logarithmic or stationary phase yield extracts containing ribonuclease II of lower specific activity. However, the absolute yield of enzyme for a given volume of growth medium is lowered considerably by harvesting in early logarithmic phase. The cells are washed once with 1.19% KCl containing 5 mM $MgCl_2$ and may be stored frozen, as a pellet, until required. It is advantageous to use a growth medium containing a relatively high concentration of inorganic phosphate in order to eliminate *E. coli* alkaline phosphatase (9) as an interfering enzyme.

Preparation of Extracts

Cell extracts may be prepared in one of three ways. (a) Cells are ground, in the cold, with 3 weights of alumina and extracted with buffer. (b) A suspension of cells in buffer is passed through a French pressure cell at 8000 lb/sq in. (c). A suspension of cells is subjected to high-frequency sonic vibration in a Branson Sonifier for a total of 40 sec. The temperature is maintained below 10 C by means of an ethanol–dry ice bath and by limiting any one period of treatment to 20 sec.

With all three procedures 5 ml of Buffer A (0.01 M Tris, pH 7.5, 5 mM $MgCl_2$, 1 mM β-mercaptoethanol) are used per gram of cells. The resulting broken cell suspension is centrifuged for 1 hr at 20,000 × g. The supernatant fluid is the crude extract (Fraction I).

Purification Procedure

The results of a typical purification are presented in Table 1 (7). In this case 40 g of cells (obtained from about 30 liters of culture) were

TABLE 1. *Purification of Ribonuclease II of* Escherichia coli *(7)*

Fraction	Description	Units/ml	Specific Activity	Total Units
I	20,000 × g supernatant fluid	181	6.9	16,500
II	Streptomycin supernatant fluid	58	6.4	14,500
III	Protamine supernatant fluid	23	3.7	5850
IV	CdCl$_2$ precipitate	39	16.0	4813
V	(NH$_4$)$_2$SO$_4$ (40–52)	202	25.2	3230
VI	DEAE (tubes 43–49)	40	572	1920
VII	Hydroxylapatite	212[a]	2120[a]	424[a]

[a] The values for the peak tube of the hydroxylapatite column are given. See the text for a more complete description.

used. All operations are at 4 C, and the addition of reagents to enzyme solutions is always carried out with efficient mechanical stirring.

STREPTOMYCIN AND PROTAMINE TREATMENT. The crude extract (Fraction I) is diluted to 13 mg of protein/ml with Buffer A. One half a volume of a 1% neutral solution of streptomycin sulfate is added dropwise. The suspension is stirred for 20 min and centrifuged for 1 hr at 20,000 × g. The supernatant fluid (Fraction II) is treated with a 1% solution of protamine sulfate that has been adjusted to pH 7 (3.8 ml of protamine sulfate solution per 100 ml of Fraction II). The suspension is centrifuged at 20,000 × g for 30 min and the supernatant fluid (Fraction III) is collected.

CdCl$_2$ FRACTIONATION. For each 100 mg of protein in Fraction III, 0.26 ml (26 µmoles) of a 0.1 M solution of CdCl$_2$ is added dropwise. The suspension is stirred for 10 min and then centrifuged for 20 min at 20,000 × g. The yellow precipitate is dissolved in one half the original volume of Fraction III of Buffer A (Fraction IV).

AMMONIUM SULFATE FRACTIONATION. Fraction IV is treated dropwise with 55.1 ml of a saturated solution of (NH$_4$)$_2$SO$_4$ (saturated at room temperature and adjusted to pH 7.7 with NH$_4$OH) per 100 ml (30% saturation). After 10 min of stirring the suspension is centrifuged for 20 min at 13,000 × g. Each 100 ml of the supernatant fluid is treated with 8.3 ml of saturated (NH$_4$)$_2$SO$_4$ and the precipitate is removed in the same manner. The resulting supernatant fluid (40% saturation) is brought to 52% saturation by the addition of 25 ml of saturated (NH$_4$)$_2$SO$_4$/100 ml. After centrifugation the precipitate (40–

52% cut) is dissolved in Buffer A (approximately 13 ml for each 100 ml of Fraction IV used) (Fraction V).

DEAE-CELLULOSE CHROMATOGRAPHY. A procedure for the chromatography of 15 ml (120 mg) of Fraction V is given. A column (16 cm × 6.2 cm²) of DEAE-cellulose (Type 20, Brown and Company, Berlin, N.H.) is prepared and equilibrated with Buffer A. Fifteen milliliters of Fraction V are diluted to 45 ml with Buffer A and the solution is passed through the column at a rate of about 0.5 ml/min. The column is washed with 30 ml of Buffer A and eluted in stepwise fashion with Buffer A containing KCl as follows: 150 ml of 0.1 M KCl, 200 ml of 0.13 M KCl, and 200 ml of 0.15 M KCl. Eight-milliliter fractions are collected every 5 min. Approximately 100% of the enzyme units placed on the column are recovered in tubes 41–62 with specific activities ranging from 100 at the beginning and end of the peak to 630 in the peak tube (No. 48). Tubes 43–49 are pooled (Fraction VI).

HYDROXYLAPATITE CHROMATOGRAPHY. A column (0.66 cm² × 7.5 cm) of hydroxylapatite (Hypatite C, Clarkson Chemical Company, Inc., Williamsport, Penna.)† is prepared and equilibrated with Buffer A. Forty-eight milliliters of Fraction VI are diluted to 130 ml with Buffer A and the solution is passed through the column at a rate of 5 ml/hr.† The column is then eluted with a linear gradient: The mixing chamber contains 75 ml of Buffer A and the reservoir 75 ml of Buffer A containing 0.3 M potassium phosphate buffer, pH 7.5. The column is eluted at a rate of 2.8 ml/hr† and 2-ml fractions are collected. Approximately 98% of the units placed on the column are recovered in tubes 21 through 30, with specific activities ranging from 256 to 2200. The peak tube, No. 23 (corresponding to 0.082 M potassium phosphate) has a specific activity of 2120 (Fraction VII). Tubes 22 to 26 contain 70% of the original activity and all have specific activities over 1000.

Storage of Purified Enzyme

Enzyme purified through the hydroxylapatite step is relatively unstable under most common storage conditions. However, it is completely stable for at least 6 months if the solution is made 1 mg/ml in dialyzed bovine serum albumin (Reagent 5), and is stored at −85 C in small portions. Repeated freezing and thawing should be avoided.

---

† Hydroxylapatite may also be obtained from Bio-Rad Laboratories, Richmond, California. This material has a much faster flow rate than hydroxylapatite routinely obtained from Clarkson Chemical Company.

Contamination with Other Enzymes

Enzyme purified as described above (Fraction VII) has been found to be essentially free of deoxyribonuclease (acting on either native or denatured DNA), of the cobalt-stimulated 5′-nucleotidase (10), of alkaline (9) and acid (2,9) phosphatase, and of polynucleotide phosphorylase (11,12). The activity of the ribosomal (or latent) ribonuclease I (2) is at most 1% of that of ribonuclease II and in some preparations is much less. Similarly, *E. coli* cyclic phosphodiesterase activity (13) is less than 1% of the ribonuclease II activity.

ISOLATION OF RIBONUCLEASE II FROM *E. COLI* RIBOSOMES (1)

This method depends on the fact that when a crude extract of *E. coli* B, prepared in Mg²⁺, is fractionated into supernatant fluid and ribosomes by ultracentrifugation, about two-thirds of the ribonuclease II activity sediments with the ribosomes (1,7,15). Both ribonuclease I and ribonuclease II are released from ribosomes by dialysis against 0.05 M EDTA and the two enzymes are then separated by chromatography on Amberlite CG-50 resin. Additional purification is obtained by gel filtration on Sephadex G-200 and chromatography on DEAE-cellulose.

Growth of Cells and Preparation of Ribosomes (1)

The procedure for the growth of *E. coli* and the preparation of ribosomes is described by Spahr, this volume, page 64.

Purification Procedure

The results of a typical purification are presented in Table 2 (1). Except as indicated, all operations are carried out at 4 C.

EDTA TREATMENT AND DIALYSIS OF RIBOSOMES. Each of two batches of a ribosomal suspension (59 ml each) containing 15 mg of ribosomes per ml (approximately 6 mg of protein/ml) are treated with 10 ml of 1 M KCl in 10 mM Tris buffer, pH 7.5, and 10 ml of 0.25 M EDTA in the same buffer. Each suspension is then dialyzed for 24 hr at room temperature against 4 liters of a solution containing 0.05 M EDTA, 0.1 M KCl, and 10 mM Tris buffer, pH 7.5. The dialysis fluid is changed twice during the 24 hr. A precipitate forms in the bags. The suspensions are then dialyzed, in the cold, against 4 liters of Tris buffer, pH 7.5, as follows: 12 hr against 0.01 M; 15 hr against

TABLE 2. *Purification of Ribonuclease II from* E. coli *Ribosomes* (1)[a]

Fraction	Description	Total Protein (mg)	Total Units[b]	Specific Activity[b] (units/mg of protein)
I	Ribosomes	707	485	0.69
II	EDTA-treated ribosomes	407	4350[c]	10.7[c]
III	Amberlite CG-50	211	1350[d]	6.4[d]
IV	Sephadex G-200	58	230	4.0
V	DEAE-cellulose[e]	1	37	37
Va	DEAE-cellulose[f]	8	145	18.1

[a] This table summarizes a purification starting from 118 ml of a suspension of twice washed ribosomes (1.77 g) containing 707 mg of protein.

[b] Assayed with poly U as substrate. The enzyme units, namely, one unit equal to one μmole of UMP produced per hour, are calculated from the data given by Spahr in which one unit equalled one microgram poly U degraded per hour. For this calculation it was assumed that one mg of poly U is approximately equivalent to 3 μmoles of UMP. Note that these units are not comparable to the units in Table 1 since assay conditions differ. The assays reported in this table were carried out at 30 C in a solution containing 0.5 mм Mg^{2+}, 0.01 м Tris, pH 7.5, and 0.1 м KCl.

[c] Combined activities of ribonuclease I and ribonuclease II released by EDTA treatment of the ribosomes.

[d] The activity at this stage usually equals that found in the ribosomes (1).

[e] Peak tubes of the chromatogram, i.e., No. 17 (Figure 3, reference 1).

[f] Pooled fractions of the chromatogram (Figure 3, reference 1).

0.005 м; and 12 hr against 0.001 м. The large precipitate that has formed is removed by centrifuging for 30 min at 15,000 $\times$ g and the opalescent supernatant fluid is lyophilized (Fraction I).

AMBERLITE CG-50 CHROMATOGRAPHY. A column (15 cm $\times$ 2 cm^2 of Amberlite CG-50 (type II, 200–400 mesh) is buffered at pH 7.2 with 0.01 м Tris. Fraction I is dissolved in 16 ml of H_2O, loaded on the column, and the column is washed with 0.5-ml portions of buffer before connecting it to a reservoir containing the same buffer. The column is then eluted with this buffer at a rate of 10 ml/hr and 10-ml samples are collected. Tubes 3–5 contain ribonuclease II and are pooled and lyophilized (Fraction III).

SEPHADEX G-200 CHROMATOGRAPHY. A column (46 cm $\times$ 12.5 cm^2) of Sephadex G-200 is prepared and washed with several volumes of 0.05 м potassium phosphate buffer, pH 7.5. A disk of Whatman No. one paper is placed on top of the column. Fraction III is dissolved in 6 ml of the same buffer and layered carefully on top of the gel. After allowing the enzyme solution to enter the gel, the column is washed with 2-ml portions of buffer and then eluted with the same buffer at a rate of 16 ml/hr. Ten-ml fractions are collected. The fractions are assayed for polynucleotide phosphorylase (see pp. 245–262, this volume) and for ribonuclease II and fractions containing ribonuclease II free of polynucleotide phosphorylase are pooled (Fraction IV). Ribonuclease II is eluted after an initial peak of polynucleotide phosphorylase on this column.

DEAE-CELLULOSE CHROMATOGRAPHY. A column of DEAE-cellulose (18 cm × 1.5 cm²) is buffered with 0.05 M potassium phosphate, pH 7.5, and Fraction IV is passed through the column at a rate of 20 ml/hr. The column is washed with the same buffer and 20-ml fractions are collected. After 9 fractions (180 ml) are collected, the column is eluted with an exponential gradient of potassium phosphate buffer, pH 7.5, as follows: The mixing chamber contains 500 ml of 0.05 M, the reservoir, 0.25 M. Twenty-milliliter fractions are collected; tube 17 (Fraction V) is the peak fraction for ribonuclease II activity (7 tubes after start of gradient elution). Suitable tubes are pooled (Fraction Va); 2.5 mg of bovine serum mercaptalbumin are added per 10 ml and the solution is dialyzed against 4 liters of 2 mM Tris buffer, pH 7.5, for 12 hr. The resulting solution is lyophilized and stored at −200 C.

Storage of Purified Enzyme†

The dialysis and lyophilization of the pooled fractions from the DEAE chromatography may result in the loss of from 20 to 40% of the activity. However, the remaining activity is perfectly stable for at least 1 year when the lyophilized enzyme is kept at −20 C.

Contamination with Other Enzymes (1)

Enzyme purified as described above (Fraction V) is free of deoxyribonuclease (acting on either native or denatured DNA), of ribonuclease I, of acid and alkaline phosphatase, and polynucleotide phosphorylase.

COMMENTS ON THE ENZYME PREPARATIONS

The preparation from *E. coli* extracts results in the purification of ribonuclease II approximately 600-fold over the activity of the protamine sulfate supernatant fraction (7,15 and Table 1). It should

† Spahr, P. F. Personal communication.

be noted that just as about two-thirds of the total ribonuclease II activity sediments with the ribosomes (1,7,15), about two-thirds of the total activity is lost upon precipitation of RNA of crude extracts with protamine sulfate. The preparation from ribosomes (1 and Table 2) results in purification of ribonuclease II approximately 55-fold over the activity of the ribosomes. Although the units in Tables 1 and 2 are not strictly comparable, the turnover number for enzyme purified from protamine sulfate supernatant fraction is at least one order of magnitude greater than that purified from ribosomes. Nevertheless, enzyme purified from ribosomes is useful for many purposes since it is free of the pertinent contaminating enzymes (1).

Ribonuclease I represents one of the most serious possible contaminants of ribonuclease II. An obvious advantage is attained by purifying ribonuclease II from a mutant organism that lacks ribonuclease I. Such an organism, called MRE-600, has been described by Wade.[†] By slight modifications of the procedures described above, ribonuclease II can be purified from either extracts[‡] or ribosomes[§] of MRE-600. In the case of purification from extracts (Table 1), the enzyme from MRE-600 did not precipitate with $CdCl_2$ and the $(NH_4)_2SO_4$ fractionation was performed on the supernatant fluid obtained after $CdCl_2$ treatment.

PROPERTIES OF THE ENZYME

Effects of Ions and pH

Ribonuclease II requires the presence of both a monovalent cation and a divalent cation (1,7). K^+ or NH_4^+ will fulfill the requirement for a monovalent ion; Na^+ and Li^+ will not. Mg^{2+} or Mn^{2+} will fulfill the requirement for divalent ion; Ca^{2+} and Zn^{2+} are inhibitory. An excess of either type of required ion is inhibitory and the optimal concentration appears to depend on the particular ion as well as the particular polyribonucleotide substrate. The available data are summarized in Table 3.

The pH optimum of ribonuclease II is between pH 7 and 8; the relative activity at various pH values depends somewhat on the buffer used (1,7).

[†] Wade, H. E. Personal communication to Dr. Leon A. Heppel.
[‡] Singer, M. F., and G. T. Tolbert. Unpublished experiments.
[§] Spahr, P. F. Personal communication.

TABLE 3.   *The Effect of Ions on Ribonuclease II* (**1, 7**)

Polyribonucleotide Substrate	Optimal Ion Concentration			
	Mg^{2+} (mM)	Mn^{2+} (mM)	K^+ (M)	NH_4^+ (M)
Poly U	0.5–1.0[a]	0.1–1.0[a]	0.05–0.10[b]	0.01–0.10[b]
Poly C			0.05[c]	
Poly A	1.5[a]		0.10[c]	

[a] Determined in the presence of 0.1 M KCl.
[b] Determined in the presence of 0.5 mM magnesium acetate.
[c] Determined in the presence of 1.5 mM $MgCl_2$.

Substrate Specificity

Ribonuclease II is specific for polyribonucleotides; as described above, the various preparations do not hydrolyze DNA (**1,7**). Various polyribonucleotides, both homopolymers and copolymers, as well as preparations of natural RNA are hydrolyzed by the enzyme (**1,7,15,16**). No evidence indicating the preferential splitting of internucleotide bonds involving any particular purine or pyrimidine base has been noted. Ribonuclease II is however, very sensitive to the macromolecular structure of the polyribonucleotide subtrate (**7,15**). Thus, the enzyme appears to be specific for single-stranded polyribonucleotides: Helical forms are not hydrolyzed, nor do they inhibit the hydrolysis of single-stranded chains.

Ribonuclease II does not appear to hydrolyze short-chain oligoribonucleotides (chain length less than about 8) and these materials accumulate as resistant end products of polyribonucleotide hydrolysis (**1,7**).

Mechanism of Action

The action of Ribonuclease II on polyribonucleotides appears to be primarily, if not exclusively, exonucleolytic. The products of hydrolysis are 5'-nucleoside monophosphates as well as a small amount of resistant oligonucleotide material (see above). The relative amount of oligonucleotide material will, of course, depend on the average chain length of the polyribonucleotide substrate. Enzyme prepared from *E. coli* ribosomes as described above is known to contain a small amount of endonuclease activity (**1**). This activity was detected by studying the sedimentation properties of phage R-17 RNA before and after enzyme treatment. Samples of enzyme prepared by the other procedure have not been tested with this very sensitive test.

REFERENCES

1. SPAHR, P. F. 1964. J. Biol. Chem. *239:* 3716.
2. SPAHR, P. F., and B. R. HOLLINGWORTH. 1961. J. Biol. Chem. *236:* 823.
3. BRAY, G. A. 1960. Anal. Biochem. *1:* 279.
4. SINGER, M. F., L. A. HEPPEL, G. W. RUSHIZKY, and H. A. SOBER. 1962. Biochim. Biophys. Acta. *61:* 474.
5. LOWRY, O. H., N. J. ROSEBROUGH, A. L. FARR, and R. J. RANDALL. 1951. J. Biol. Chem. *193:* 265.
6. LAYNE, E. 1957. *In* Methods in enzymology, S. P. Colowick and N. Kaplan, eds. Academic Press, New York. Vol. III, p. 448.
7. SINGER, M. F., and G. TOLBERT. 1965. Biochemistry. *4:* 1319.
8. CHAMBERLIN, M., and P. BERG. 1962. Proc. Natl. Acad. Sci. U.S. *48:* 81.
9. TORRIANI, A. 1960. Biochim. Biophys. Acta. *38:* 460.
10. NEU, H. C., and L. A. HEPPEL. 1964. Biochem. Biophys. Res. Commun. *17:* 215.
11. LITTAUER, U. Z., and A. KORNBERG. 1957. J. Biol. Chem. *226:* 1077.
12. WILLIAMS, F. R., and M. GRUNBERG-MANAGO. 1964. Biochim Biophys. Acta. *89:* 66.
13. ANRAKU, Y. 1964. J. Biol. Chem. *239:* 3412.
14. TISSIERES, A., and J. D. WATSON. 1962. Proc. Natl. Acad. Sci. U.S. *48:* 1061.
15. SINGER, M. F., and G. TOLBERT. 1964. Science. *145:* 593.
16. SPAHR, P. F., and D. SCHLESSINGER. 1963. J. Biol. Chem. *238:* PC2251.

Exonuclease I (Phosphodiesterase) (1) from

Escherichia coli

I. R. LEHMAN
DEPARTMENT OF BIOCHEMISTRY
STANFORD UNIVERSITY SCHOOL OF MEDICINE
STANFORD, CALIFORNIA

Reagents

1. The reaction mixture (total volume 0.3 ml) contains

   0.067 M glycine buffer, pH 9.5
   6.7 mM $MgCl_2$
   1.0 mM β-mercaptoethanol
   20 mμmoles of P^{32}-labeled *E. coli* DNA-nucleotide (approximately 2 to 5×10^6 cpm/μmole) denatured by heating for 10 min at 100 C, then chilling rapidly (2)
   Enzyme, diluted in a solution composed of Tris buffer, 0.05 M, pH 8.0; 0.25 M ammonium sulfate, and crystalline bovine plasma albumin (Armour Laboratories), 1 mg/ml

2. 3.5% $HClO_4$
   "Carrier," salmon sperm DNA, 2.5 mg/ml

Procedure

This assay measures the formation of acid-soluble products from heat-denatured P^{32}-labeled DNA.

After incubation at 37 C for 30 min, the reaction is stopped by the addition of 0.2 ml "carrier" DNA and 0.5 ml of cold $HClO_4$. After 5 min at 0 C, the resulting precipitate is removed by centrifugation at $10,000 \times g$ for 3 min. A sample of the supernatant fluid (0.2–0.5 ml) is pipetted into a planchet and after the addition of 1 or 2 drops of 1 N KOH, the solution is evaporated to dryness and the radioactivity is determined.

The supernatant fluids obtained from control incubations (enzyme omitted) usually contain 0.05 to 0.1% of the added radioactivity and this value is subtracted from each sample. A unit of enzymatic activity is defined as the amount causing the production of 10 mμmoles of acid-soluble P^{32} in 30 min. The specific activity is expressed as units per milligram of protein. With both crude extracts of E. coli and the purified enzyme, the radioactivity made acid soluble is proportional to the enzyme concentration at levels of 0.05 to 0.25 unit. The pH optimum is from 9.2 to 9.8 (in glycine buffer). The purified enzyme has an absolute requirement for Mg^{2+}; there is no detectable activity in its absence. Mn^{2+} cannot replace Mg^{2+}.

ISOLATION PROCEDURE

Unless otherwise indicated, all operations are carried out at 0–4 C. All centrifugations are at $15,000 \times g$ for 10 min.

Preparation of Extracts

E. coli strain B is grown in a medium containing 1.1% K_2HPO_4, 0.85% KH_2PO_4, 0.6% Difco yeast extract, and 1% glucose, and harvested in late log phase. The cells are frozen and stored at −20 C until used. Partially thawed cells (450 g wet weight) are mixed with 300 ml of glycylglycine buffer, 0.05 M, pH 7.0 in a large Waring Blendor (5-liter capacity) equipped with a cooling jacket and connected to a Variac. Slow stirring is begun. After 5 min, 1350 g of acid-washed glass beads (Superbrite, average diameter 200 μ, Minnesota Mining and Manufacturing Company) are gradually added to the suspension. When the mixture appears homogeneous, stirring is increased to approximately one-third of maximal speed. After 20 min an additional 1200 ml of the same buffer are added and the homogenization is continued for 10 min at reduced speed to prevent excessive foaming. During the period of homogenization, the temperature should not be permitted to rise above 12 C. The beads are then allowed to settle out and the broken cell suspension is decanted and saved. An additional 800 ml of buffer are added to the glass beads and the residual broken cells are extracted by a 10-min homogenization at slow speed. The beads are again allowed to settle out, and the supernatant fluid is decanted and combined with the first supernatant fluid to give a final volume of approximately 2000 ml (Fraction I-P). This fraction may be stored at 0 C for at least 2 weeks without loss of activity.

The next three steps in the purification are those employed in the isolation of DNA polymerase from E. coli (3). Exonuclease I is readily recovered in good yield from an ammonium sulfate fraction normally discarded in the course of polymerase purification (see Table 1).

TABLE 1. *Purification of Exonuclease I from* E. coli

Fraction	Protein (mg/ml)	Specific Activity (units/mg of protein)	Total Units ($\times 10^{-6}$)
From polymerase purification:			
I–P. Blendor fraction	15.9	10.7	6.8
II–P. Streptomycin eluate	11.8	29.4	3.5
III–P. Autolyzed streptomycin eluate	1.6	230	3.7
IV–P. Ammonium sulfate	16.0	215	3.4
V. Refractionated ammonium sulfate	12.4	730	1.5
VI. Pooled DEAE-cellulose	0.5	5950	0.95
VII. Pooled hydroxylapatite	0.15	14,700	0.60
VIII. Concentrated hydroxylapatite	9.2	12,500	0.46

Streptomycin Precipitation

To 10 liters of extract are added 10 liters of Tris Cl buffer, 0.05 M, pH 7.5, containing 1 mM EDTA; then with constant stirring, 1440 ml of 5% streptomycin sulfate are added over a 45-min period.[†] After 10 min, the suspension is centrifuged and the supernatant fluid is dis-

[†] The amount of streptomycin sulfate required to precipitate the nucleic acids and the DNA polymerase (as well as exonuclease I) varies from one preparation of E. coli extract to another. Therefore, a trial precipitation on a small scale is required to determine the optimal amount of streptomycin sulfate. It has also been observed on several occasions that the 5% streptomycin solution was less effective in precipitating DNA and the enzymes after storage for 7 to 10 days at 4 C. For this reason, the streptomycin sulfate solution should be prepared just before its addition to Fraction I-P.

carded. The thick, sticky precipitate is transferred to a beaker and 1000 ml of potassium phosphate buffer, 0.05 M, pH 7.4 are added. The precipitate is suspended by slow mechanical stirring for approximately 12 hr and the final volume is adjusted to 2500 ml by the addition of the same buffer (Fraction II-P). Fraction II-P is stored at 0 C until sufficient quantities are obtained for the subsequent procedures. There is no detectable loss of activity after storage for 1 month.

Autolysis

Eleven liters of Fraction II-P are made 3 mM in $MgCl_2$ by the addition of 65 ml of 0.5 M $MgCl_2$. The suspension is incubated at 30 C for 7 to 12 hr, until 95% of the ultraviolet absorbing material at 260 mμ is rendered acid soluble.† The autolysate is then chilled to 0 C and the protein precipitate that settled out during the digestion is removed by centrifugation in a Spinco continuous-flow refrigerated centrifuge at 28,000 × g at a rate of 120–130 ml/min. The supernatant fraction (Fraction III-P) is stored at 0 C; no loss in activity occurs over a 1-week period.

Ammonium Sulfate Fractionation

To 10 liters of Fraction III-P are added 50 ml of 0.2 M EDTA and 50 ml of 0.2 M glutathione. Over a 60-min period, 3 kg of ammonium sulfate are added with stirring, and after 30 min the precipitate that forms is removed by centrifugation. The precipitate is dissolved in 1.1 liters of potassium phosphate buffer, 0.02 M, pH 7.2 (Fraction IV-P). To the supernatant fluid an additional 1.15 kg of ammonium sulfate are added with stirring over a 60-min period. After 30 min, the precipitate is collected by centrifugation. This precipitate, which is dissolved in 1.1 liters of potassium phosphate buffer, 0.02 M, pH 7.2, represents the DNA polymerase fraction and may be processed further as described by Richardson et al. (3).

Ammonium Sulfate Refractionation

To 1 liter of Fraction IV-P are added with stirring 140 g of ammonium sulfate.‡ After standing for 10 min, the precipitate is collected

---

† At intervals of 1 hr, 1-ml portions are removed and centrifuged, and the optical density of the supernatant fluid after suitable dilution in Tris-HCl buffer, 0.05 M, pH 7.4, is determined at 260 mμ; a portion of the supernatant fluid is precipitated with an equal volume of cold 1 N perchloric acid and the optical density of the acid-soluble fraction is determined.

‡ Different batches of Fraction IV-P contain variable amounts of residual ammonium sulfate. It is therefore necessary to carry out a small-scale ammonium sulfate refractionation for each batch in order to determine the level of ammonium sulfate required for optimal purification.

by centrifugation and suspended in 150 ml of potassium phosphate buffer, 0.02 M, pH 7.4. The insoluble residue is removed by centrifugation. The volume at this point is 170 ml (Fraction V). Fractions IV-P and V have been stored at −20 C for as long as 2 years without loss of activity.

DEAE-Cellulose Chromatography

A column of DEAE-cellulose (Brown and Company, Type 40), 12 cm × 2.2 cm, is prepared and washed with 1000 ml of potassium phosphate buffer, 0.02 M, pH 7.4, containing 1 mM β-mercaptoethanol. Fraction V (40 ml), previously dialyzed against 4 liters of this buffer for 12–15 hr, is added to the column at the rate of 30 ml/hr and washed into the column with 10 ml of equilibration buffer. A linear gradient of elution is applied with 0.1 and 0.5 M potassium phosphate, pH 7.4 (containing 1 mM β-mercaptoethanol) as limiting concentrations; 200 ml of each buffer is used and the flow rate is maintained at 60 ml/hr. The peak of enzymatic activity appears approximately midway through the gradient. The best purification and most reproducible fractionation have been obtained under these conditions. Attempts to scale up the DEAE-cellulose chromatography by employing larger columns or by processing larger amounts of protein on a column of the same size have invariably led to reduced yields and fractions of lower specific activity. Four separate DEAE-cellulose chromatograms are therefore required to process the 170 ml of Fraction V. The column eluates containing enzyme of specific activity of 4500 or greater are pooled (320 ml) and stored at 0 C (Fraction VI). No loss in activity has been observed over a 1-month period under these conditions.†

Hydroxylapatite Chromatography

A column of hydroxylapatite (4) (Hypatite −C, Clarkson Chemical Co., Williamsport, Pa.), 15 cm × 2.2 cm, is equilibrated with 1500 ml of potassium phosphate buffer, 0.05 M, pH 5.5, containing 1 mM β-mercaptoethanol. Fraction VI (200 ml) is dialyzed for 6 hr against 18 liters of the phosphate buffer used for column equilibration. The dialyzed Fraction VI is applied to the column at the rate of 45 ml/hr and washed into the column with 10 ml of the equilibration buffer. A linear gradient of elution is applied with 0.05 and 0.25 M potassium phosphate, pH 6.5 (containing 1 mM β-mercaptoethanol) as limiting concentrations; 250 ml of each buffer is used, and the flow

† Fraction VI may be concentrated by precipitation with ammonium sulfate in the following way: To 320 ml are added 112 g of ammonium sulfate with stirring. After standing for 20 min, the suspension is centrifuged for 60 min. The resulting precipitate is taken up in 15 ml of Tris buffer, 0.05 M, pH 7.5. The small amount of insoluble residue is removed by centrifugation.

rate is maintained at 72 ml/hr. The peak of activity appears approximately midway through the gradient. The specific activity of the enzyme fractions throughout the entire peak of activity is constant with a value of 14,000–15,000. Two hydroxylapatite chromatograms are required to process the 320 ml of Fraction VI. The column eluates are pooled (275 ml) and stored at 0 C (Fraction VII). This fraction is stable under these conditions for a 1-week period.

Concentration of Hydroxyapatite Fraction

To 270 ml of Fraction VII are added 96 g of ammonium sulfate with stirring. After standing for 20 min, the suspension is centrifuged for 60 min. The resulting precipitate is taken up in 3.8 ml of Tris Cl buffer, 0.05 M, pH 7.5. A small amount of insoluble residue is removed by centrifugation (Fraction VIII).

Comments

The enzyme preparation obtained by this procedure, although purified about 1400-fold (Table 1) appears to be physically inhomogeneous. In the ultracentrifuge the preparation revealed one minor and two major boundaries. Electrophoreses in starch gels at pH 8.8 (Tris-citrate buffer) produced four bands, two major and two minor. Only one of the major bands possessed enzymatic activity.

Fraction VI, when concentrated by precipitation with ammonium sulfate, has retained essentially all of its activity upon storage at −12 C for periods as long as 2 years, even after repeated freezing and thawing. On the other hand, the more highly purified Fraction VIII is far less stable and loses approximately 50% of its activity within 1 month when stored at either 0 or −12 C.

Fraction VI has been found to be generally adequate as a reagent for quantitative digestion of denatured DNA to mononucleotides and for the detection and selective removal of single-stranded DNA in mixtures of single- and double-stranded DNAs. Chromatography of Fraction VI on hydroxylapatite (yielding Fraction VII) does, however, remove the traces of endonuclease activity present in Fraction VI.

PROPERTIES OF ENZYME

Contamination with Other Enzymes

Fraction VIII of exonuclease I is essentially free of the other three deoxyribonucleases thus far identified in E. coli. The only exception appears to be exonuclease III (the DNA phosphatase-exonuclease), which is present to the extent of 0.003% of exonuclease I.

Both Fractions VI and VIII are free of detectable 5'-nucleotidase activity (less than 0.01% of the exonuclease I activity) when measured under conditions optimal for exonuclease I.

Fraction VIII has only very slight activity on polyribonucleotides. Incubation of 25 μg of P^{32}-labeled tobacco mosaic virus RNA (approximately 80 mμmoles of phosphorus) with 100 units of enzyme for 1 hr under standard assay conditions, resulted in the conversion of 5.4% of the P^{32} to an acid-soluble form. When 1000 units of enzyme were added, 53.3% of the P^{32} became acid soluble. On the other hand, exonuclease I is unable to attack sRNA. When sRNA from E. coli (0.85 μmole of phosphorus) was incubated with 150 units of exonuclease I under standard assay conditions for 3 hr, there was no loss in acceptor activity when the treated RNA was subsequently tested as an acceptor of methionine in the reaction catalyzed by methionyl-RNA synthetase (5). An assay of this kind is an extremely sensitive measure of ribonuclease activity, since removal of the terminal adenosine residue or a single endonucleolytic break in the RNA would be sufficient to destroy completely its amino acid acceptor activity. Since a low, but significant, level of activity can be observed with RNA from tobacco mosaic virus, which probably exists as a random coil in solution, the resistance of sRNA to attack by exonuclease I may be related to its ordered conformation.

Ribonucleotide residues which have been incorporated into DNA by the action of DNA polymerase from E. coli under the conditions described by Berg et al. (6) are susceptible to exonuclease I once the DNA has been denatured. These are attacked at about one-fourth the rate found with the corresponding deoxyribonucleotide linkages.

Specificity

With Fraction VIII, native DNA is degraded at a rate 40,000 times less than the rate at which heat-denatured DNA is attacked. Since hydrolysis ceases after 0.5–3.0% of the DNA (depending upon the DNA preparation) has been converted to mononucleotides, this low rate with native DNA is probably due to the action of exonuclease I on single-stranded regions within the DNA molecules used. Fraction VIII of exonuclease I would therefore appear to be totally specific for single-stranded or denatured DNA. In the case of Fraction VI, native DNA is attacked at a rate about 10,000 times less than that observed with denatured DNA. The somewhat greater rate of attack on native DNA found with Fraction VI is most probably attributable to the presence of a low level of endonuclease.

An interesting exception to the stringent requirement of exonuclease I for single-stranded DNA is the dAT copolymer (7), which can be degraded quantitatively at rates ranging from 0.6 to 10% of that found with denatured DNA depending upon the particular dAT preparation examined. This effect may have its basis in the relatively low temperature at which the adenine-thymine hydrogen bond pair dissociates. Thus, given a dAT preparation with frayed, non-hydrogen-bonded ends (the degree of fraying may vary from one preparation to the next), hydrolysis can begin at these ends, and with successive cleavage of phosphodiester bonds, the two strands of the molecule can dissociate forming non-hydrogen-bonded stretches susceptible to further enzymatic attack.

Hydrolysis of a single-stranded polydeoxyribonucleotide by exonuclease I proceeds in a stepwise manner beginning at the 3'-hydroxyl end of the chain producing deoxyribonucleoside 5'-monophosphates. A free 3'-hydroxyl group is indispensable for enzymatic activity so that circular DNAs (8) and polydeoxyribonucleotides with 3'-phosphoryl or 3'-O-acetyl groups are completely resistant to attack. Exonuclease I is unable to cleave dinucleotides so that the last two residues at the 5'-terminus of the chain appear either as a dinucleoside monophosphate or a dinucleoside diphosphate, depending upon the presence or absence of a 5'-phosphoryl group.

The V_{max} for the hydrolysis of oligodeoxyribonucleotides with 3 to 6 residues is significantly greater than that found for denatured DNA, but the apparent K_m values are about 10^6-fold greater for the small oligonucleotides than for denatured DNA.

In contrast to the other exonucleases thus far examined [for example, venom phosphodiesterase (9,10)], exonuclease I is able to degrade denatured T-even bacteriophage DNAs bearing glucosylated hydroxymethylcytosine residues quantitatively to their constituent mononucleotides (11).

REFERENCES

1. LEHMAN, I. R., and A. L. NUSSBAUM. 1964. J. Biol. Chem. *239:* 2628.
2. LEHMAN, I. R. 1960. J. Biol. Chem. *235:* 1479.
3. RICHARDSON, C. C., C. L. SCHILDKRAUT, H. V. APOSHIAN, and A. KORNBERG. 1964. J. Biol. Chem. *239:* 222.
4. TISELIUS, A., S. HJERTEN, and O. LEVIN. 1956. Arch. Biochem. Biophys. *65:* 132.
5. BERG, P., F. H. BERGMANN, E. J. OFENGAND, and M. DIECKMANN. 1961. J. Biol. Chem. *236:* 1726.
6. BERG, P., H. FANCHER, and M. J. CHAMBERLIN. 1963. *In* H. Vogel, editor, Symposium on informational macromolecules. Academic Press, New York. p. 467.

7. SCHACHMAN, H. K., J. ADLER, C. M. RADDING, I. R. LEHMAN, and A. KORNBERG. 1960. J. Biol. Chem. *235:* 3242.

8. FIERS, W., and R. L. SINSHEIMER. 1962. J. Mol. Biol. *5:* 408.

9. SINSHEIMER, R. L. 1954. Science. *120:* 551.

10. VOLKIN, E. 1954. J. Am. Chem. Soc. *76:* 5892.

11. LEHMAN, I. R., and E. A. PRATT. 1960. J. Biol. Chem. *235:* 3254.

Exonuclease III from

Escherichia coli

CHARLES C. RICHARDSON
DEPARTMENT OF BIOLOGICAL CHEMISTRY
HARVARD MEDICAL SCHOOL
BOSTON, MASSACHUSETTS

ASSAY

Exonuclease III (The DNA† phosphatase-exonuclease (1,2) from *Escherichia coli*) hydrolyzes phosphomono- or diester bridges of DNA between the phosphate and the 3'-hydroxyl group. Given a 3'-phosphoryl terminus on DNA, as shown in Fig. 1, the enzyme releases inorganic phosphate and then proceeds as an exonuclease with the stepwise release of 5'-mononucleotides. The enzyme may be assayed by measuring either the phosphatase or the exonuclease activity. The former activity readily distinguishes exonuclease III from other known

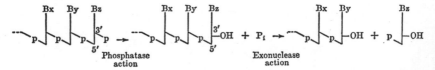

Fig. 1. The sequential action of exonuclease III on a DNA chain terminated by nucleotides containing the bases Bx, By, and Bz. (Reproduced from J. Biol. Chem., Ref. 1.)

† The following abbreviations have been used in this chapter: DNA, RNA: deoxyribonucleic acid, ribonucleic acid; dAMP, dTMP, dCMP, dGMP: deoxyadenosine monophosphate, deoxythymidine monophosphate, deoxycytidine monophosphate, deoxyguanosine monophosphate; dAT copolymer: copolymer of deoxyadenylate and deoxythymidylate; rAU copolymer: copolymer of adenylate and uridylate.

nucleases, and provides a unique assay for its identification during fractionation procedures. The less time consuming exonuclease assay may be used in the later stages of purification.

ASSAY OF THE PHOSPHATASE ACTIVITY

Reagents

1. The reaction mixture (total volume 0.3 ml) contains

   P^{32}-labeled 3'-phosphoryl terminated DNA, 50 mμmoles of DNA-phosphorus (for preparation see below)
   0.07 M potassium phosphate buffer, pH 7.0
   0.01 M $MgCl_2$
   0.01 M 2-mercaptoethanol
   enzyme, 0.04 to 0.4 phosphatase units in a volume of 0.02 ml

2. Calf thymus DNA, 2.5 mg/ml
3. 0.7 N trichloroacetic acid
4. Norit-carrier solution consisting of bovine serum albumin, 5 mg/ml, 0.025 M sodium pyrophosphate, and 0.025 M potassium phosphate buffer, pH 7.0
5. Norit suspension, 20% packed volume

   3'-Phosphoryl-terminated DNA, the substrate for the phosphatase activity, is prepared by partially digesting P^{32}-labeled native DNA with micrococcal nuclease (1). This enzyme hydrolyzes phosphodiester bonds of DNA to produce oligonucleotides terminated at one end by a 3'-phosphoryl group (3–6). The incubation mixture (20 ml) consists of 0.05 M glycine buffer, pH 9.2, 0.01 M $CaCl_2$, 20 μmoles of P^{32}-labeled DNA (approximately 2×10^7 CPM per μmole of DNA-phosphorus) and 74 units of micrococcal nuclease (a unit of enzyme is the amount catalyzing the production of 10 mμmoles of acid-soluble DNA nucleotide in 30 min). The reaction mixture is incubated at 37 C until approximately 30% of the radioactivity becomes acid soluble (1). The reaction mixture is then chilled and dialyzed against 100 volumes of 1 M KCl for 12 hr at 4 C to remove the dialyzable oligonucleotides. The dialysis procedure is repeated three times and the mixture is finally dialyzed against 0.02 M KCl. The extensively dialyzed solution represents the 3'-phosphoryl-terminated DNA and is acid precipitable to the extent of 97%. The solution is stored at −20 C.

Procedure

   The phosphatase assay measures the formation of acid-soluble, Norit-nonadsorbable products arising from P^{32}-labeled 3'-phosphoryl-terminated DNA and has been routinely used during purification of the enzyme.

After 30 min of incubation at 37 C, the reaction is stopped by the addition of 0.20 ml of a cold solution of calf thymus DNA (2.5 mg/ml) and 0.50 ml of cold 0.7 N trichloroacetic acid. After 5 min at 0 C, the resulting precipitate is removed by centrifugation for 5 min at 12,000 × g, and 0.50 ml of the supernatant fluid is pipetted into a tube containing 0.75 ml of H_2O, 0.15 ml of Norit-carrier solution (reagent 4) and 0.20 ml of a Norit suspension (reagent 5), all at 0 C. The mixture is shaken for 1 min; after 5 min at 0 C the Norit is removed by centrifugation, and the supernatant fluid is quantitatively transferred to a tube containing 0.20 ml of a Norit suspension (reagent 5). After treating the mixture as described above, 1.0 ml of the supernatant fluid is pipetted into a planchet, and 1 drop of 3 N KOH is added to the sample; the solution is taken to dryness and the radioactivity is measured in a gas flow counter.

A control reaction mixture without enzyme is incubated and treated as described above. The supernatant fluids obtained from the control incubations contain from 0.01 to 0.07% of the added radioactivity; this value is subtracted from each sample. A unit of phosphatase activity is defined as the amount catalyzing the production of 1.0 mμmole of acid-soluble, Norit-nonadsorbable P^{32} in 30 min. The radioactivity produced is proportional to the enzyme concentration at levels of 0.04 to 0.40 units of enzyme.

ASSAY OF THE EXONUCLEASE ACTIVITY

Reagents

1. The reaction mixture (total volume 0.3 ml) contains

   P^{32}-labeled native *E. coli* DNA, 50 mμmoles of DNA-phosphorus
   0.07 M Tris-HCl buffer, pH 8.0
   0.7 mM $MgCl_2$
   0.01 M 2-mercaptoethanol
   enzyme, 0.1 to 2.0 exonuclease units in a volume of 0.02 ml

2. Calf thymus DNA, 2.5 mg/ml
3. 1 N perchloric acid

Procedure

The exonuclease assay measures the conversion of a P^{32}-labeled native DNA to acid-soluble products. The simplicity of the procedure provides a rapid assay of the enzyme during the latter stages of purification. The exonuclease assay has been successfully used during DEAE-cellulose and phosphocellulose column chromatography where the enzyme is relatively free of contaminating nucleases.

After 30 min of incubation at 37 C, the reaction is stopped by the addition of 0.20 ml of a cold solution of calf thymus DNA (reagent 2) and 0.50 ml of cold 1 N perchloric acid. After 5 min at 0 C, the resulting precipitate is removed by centrifugation for 5 min at $12,000 \times g$; 0.2 ml of the supernatant fluid is pipetted into a planchet, and 1 drop of 1 N KOH is added to the fraction. The solution is taken to dryness, and the radioactivity is measured in a gas flow counter.

The supernatant fluids obtained from control incubations lacking enzyme contain 0.3–0.5% of the added radioactivity; the value obtained is subtracted from each sample. A unit of exonuclease activity is defined as the amount catalyzing the production of 1.0 mμmole of acid-soluble P^{32} in 30 min. The radioactivity produced is proportional to the enzyme concentration at levels of 0.1 to 2.0 units of enzyme.

Enzyme Dilutions

Dilutions of the enzyme for either the phosphatase or exonuclease assay are made by diluting into a solution composed of 0.05 M Tris buffer, pH 7.4, bovine plasma albumin, 0.5 mg/ml, and 0.01 M 2-mercaptoethanol. Samples of the diluted enzyme solutions are added to the reaction mixtures within 15 min of dilution.

ISOLATION PROCEDURE

Unless otherwise stated, all operations are carried out at 0–4 C. All centrifugations are performed at $15,000 \times g$ for 10 min. The purification procedure and the results of a typical preparation are summarized in Table 1.

I. Growth of Cells and Preparation of Extracts

E. coli strain B is grown in a medium containing 1.1% K$_2$HPO$_4$, 0.85% KH$_2$PO$_4$, 0.6% Difco yeast extract, and 1% glucose; the cells are harvested during the late exponential phase of growth. Cells stored at −20 C show no loss of activity for 6 months. The activity of exonuclease III is highest during the exponential phase of cell growth. The activity may be as much as tenfold lower in cells during stationary phase (7).

Partially thawed cells (450 g wet weight) are mixed with 300 ml of

TABLE 1. *Purification of Exonuclease III from E. coli*

Fraction and Step	Protein (mg/ml)	Phosphatase Activity		Exonuclease Activity	
		Total Units ($\times 10^{-4}$)	Specific Activity (units/mg)	Total Units ($\times 10^{-4}$)	Specific Activity (units/mg)
I. Extract	18.5	176	36	61	12
II. Streptomycin	5.9	160	54	52	17
III. Acetone	10.9	112	103	45	40
IV. DEAE-cellulose	0.15	60	2,380	19	745
V. Phosphocellulose	0.03	30	48,600	—	—
VI. Phosphocellulose concentrate	0.4	26	48,800	9	16,300

glycylglycine buffer, 0.05 M, pH 7.0, in a large Waring Blendor (5-liter capacity) equipped with a cooling jacket and connected to a variable transformer. After 5 min of slow stirring, 1350 g of acid-washed glass beads (Superbrite, average diameter 200 μ, Minnesota Mining and Manufacturing Company) are slowly added to the suspension. When the mixture appears homogeneous, stirring is increased to one-third of maximal speed. After 20 min an additional 1200 ml of the same buffer are added, and the mixing is continued for 10 min at reduced speed to prevent excessive foaming. During the homogenization procedure the temperature is kept below 12 C. The beads are allowed to settle out and the broken cell suspension is decanted and saved. An additional 800 ml of buffer is added to the glass beads, and the residual broken cells are extracted by a 10-min homogenization at slow speed. The beads are again allowed to settle out, and the supernatant fluid is decanted and combined with the first supernatant fluid. The combined supernatant fluids are centrifuged and the supernatant fluid (2000 ml) is saved. This fraction (Fraction I) may be stored at 0 C for 2 weeks without loss of activity.

II. Streptomycin Precipitation

To 2500 ml of Fraction I are added 2500 ml of Tris-HCl buffer, 0.05 M, pH 7.5, containing 0.001 M EDTA. With constant stirring 360 ml of a 5% streptomycin sulfate solution are added over a 45-min period. After 10 min, the suspension is centrifuged and the supernatant fluid is collected (Fraction II). The streptomycin supernatant fluid may be stored at -20 C for 6 months without loss of activity. Due to variations resulting from the use of different extracts, it is advisable to carry out a trial fractionation for the streptomycin step.

III. Acetone Fractionation

To 5000 ml of Fraction II, made 0.001 M with glutathione, are added, with constant stirring, 325 ml of acetone over a 45-min period. Stirring is continued for 10 min and the suspension is centrifuged; the supernatant fluid is saved. To the supernatant fluid an additional 1425 ml of acetone are added, with stirring, over a 90-min period. The suspension is stirred for 10 min and then centrifuged. The precipitate is dissolved in 1000 ml of potassium phosphate buffer, 0.01 M, pH 7.5, containing 0.001 M 2-mercaptoethanol (Fraction III). All procedures in the acetone fractionation are carried out at 0 C. The amount of acetone required to precipitate the enzyme varies from one preparation to another. Therefore, a trial precipitation on a small scale is required to determine the optimal amounts of acetone.

IV. DEAE-Cellulose Fractionation

A column of DEAE-cellulose (85 cm^2 × 18 cm) is prepared and washed with approximately 5 liters of potassium phosphate buffer, 0.10 M, pH 7.5. When the pH of the eluate is that of the washing solution, the column is equilibrated with 10 liters of potassium phosphate buffer, 0.01 M, pH 7.5, containing 0.01 M 2-mercaptoethanol. Fraction III (1000 ml) is applied to the column at the rate of 1000 ml/hr. The adsorbent is then washed with 800 ml of the equilibrating buffer. A linear gradient of elution is applied, with 0.01 and 0.16 M potassium phosphate buffer, pH 7.5, as limiting concentrations. The total volume of the gradient is 13,000 ml, and 0.01 M 2-mercaptoethanol is present throughout the gradient. The flow rate is adjusted to 2000 ml/hr, and 200-ml fractions are collected. Approximately 80% of the activity is eluted in a peak between 4.0 and 5.5 resin bed volumes of effluent. The fractions that contain enzyme of specific activity greater than 1600 units/mg of protein (approximately 50% of the activity applied to the column) are pooled. This solution (1800 ml) is dialyzed for 8 hr against 15 volumes of potassium phosphate buffer, 0.02 M, pH 6.5, containing 0.01 M 2-mercaptoethanol (Fraction IV).

V. Phosphocellulose Fractionation

A column of phosphocellulose (25 cm^2 × 14 cm) is prepared and washed with 10 liters of potassium phosphate buffer, 0.02 M, pH 6.5, containing 0.01 M 2-mercaptoethanol. The dialyzed DEAE-cellulose fraction (1800 ml) is applied to the column at a rate of 1500 ml/hr, and the adsorbent is washed with 1250 ml of potassium phosphate buffer, 0.02 M, pH 6.5, containing 0.01 M 2-mercaptoethanol. A linear gradient of elution is applied with 0.02 and 0.28 M potassium phosphate buffer at pH 6.5 as limiting concentrations. The total volume of the gradient is 4300 ml, and 0.01 M 2-mercaptoethanol is present throughout the gradient. The flow rate is adjusted to 750 ml/hr and 25-ml fractions are collected. Of the applied activity, 85% is eluted in a peak between 6.2 and 7.2 resin bed volumes of effluent. The peak fractions containing enzyme of specific activity ranging from 44,000 to 59,000 units per mg of protein (50% of the activity applied to the column) are pooled (Fraction V).

VI. Concentration of Phosphocellulose Fraction

The pooled phosphocellulose fraction (166 ml) is reduced in volume by pressure dialysis against 4 liters of potassium phosphate buffer, 0.10

M, pH 7.4, containing 0.005 M reduced glutathione. A 30-cm length of Visking size 8 dialysis tubing is filled with the enzyme solution. With one end open to the atmosphere, by means of a glass tube passed through a rubber stopper, the tubing is placed in a 4-liter suction flask containing buffer. A vacuum is applied to the flask by means of a water suction pump, and after approximately 20 hr the solution can be reduced to 10 to 15 ml. As the dialysis tubing will not contain the total volume to be concentrated, it is necessary to add additional enzyme solution as the volume decreases. Approximately 10 to 15% of the activity is lost during concentration.

The phosphocellulose fraction represents a 1300-fold purification over the starting extract and contains 15% of the initial activity. The concentrated phosphocellulose fraction (Fraction VI) has been stored at 0 C in the presence of 0.01 M 2-mercaptoethanol for 6 months with a 10% loss of activity. Fraction VI may be further dialyzed against potassium phosphate buffer, 0.01 M, pH 7.5, containing 0.005 M reduced glutathione to assure removal of 2-mercaptoethanol and may be frozen at −20 C. The frozen enzyme has been stable (less than 10% loss of activity) for 6 months.

PROPERTIES OF THE ENZYME

Contamination with Other Enzymes

The other known *E. coli* nucleases are not detectable in Fraction VI. Absence of activity (less than 10 units per mg of protein) on pTpTpTpTpT rules out the presence of exonucleases I (8) and II (9); endonuclease I (10) is judged to be absent by the lack of inhibition by RNA or the specific antiserum with native DNA as substrate. The kinetics of inactivation of the genetic activity of *Bacillus subtilis* DNA also indicate the absence of endonuclease (11). There is no detectable DNA polymerase activity. Absence of activity on nucleoside 3'- and 5'-monophosphates and 3'- and 5'-phosphoryl terminated deoxyribonucleotides (see Table 2) rules out the presence of 5'-nucleotidase and the conventional phosphomonoesterase.

Fraction VI will catalyze the release of acid-soluble radioactivity from P^{32}-labeled *E. coli* ribosomal RNA at a rate 2% of that seen with native DNA. However, the following results suggest that this activity is due to a contamination with *E. coli* ribonuclease (12) and is not a property of exonuclease III. (a) The hydrolysis of RNA is inhibited by Mg^{2+}, (b) the acid-soluble products of the hydrolysis of RNA are oligonucleotides, and (c) no 5'-mononucleotides are formed.

Phosphatase and Exonuclease Activities Are Part of a Single Enzyme

Several lines of evidence suggest that the phosphatase and the exonuclease activities reside on the same protein molecule, reflecting the ability of the enzyme to cleave a 3'-phosphoryl linkage whether it is involved in a mono- or a diester linkage. (a) During the course of purification the ratio of the two activities remains essentially constant (Table 1). (b) The rates of release of Pi and 5'-mononucleotides are identical when measured under similar reaction conditions. (c) Requirements for optimal activity are similar for both the phosphatase and the exonuclease. (d) Both activities are inhibited by $ZnCl_2$ and *p*-chloromercuribenzoate. (e) The two activities follow identical heat inactivation curves.

Properties of the Phosphatase

SPECIFICITY.   Table 2 summarizes the specificity of the phosphatase. The phosphatase will quantitatively release inorganic orthophosphate from 3'-phosphoryl terminated deoxyribonucleic acid. The enzyme prefers double-stranded DNA, attacking heat-denatured 3'-phosphoryl-terminated DNA at a reduced rate. Both 5'-phosphoryl-terminated DNA and 3'-phosphoryl-terminated ribonucleic acid are

TABLE 2.   *Specificity of the Phosphatase Activity*

Compound	Relative Activity[a]
3'-Phosphoryl-terminated DNA	100[b]
Heat-denatured 3'-phosphoryl-terminated DNA	48[c]
3'-Phosphoryl-terminated RNA	<0.1
5'-Phosphoryl-terminated DNA	<0.3
TpTpTp	<0.3
3'-dAMP, dTMP, dCMP, dGMP (mixture)	<0.1
5'-dAMP, dTMP	<0.3
p-Nitrophenyl phosphate	<2.0

[a] The rates of hydrolysis of these compounds were measured in the standard reaction mixture as previously described (1) using Fraction VI of the enzyme.

[b] Represents a turnover number of 1600 mμmoles of P_i released per minute per mg of Fraction VI; activity on other compounds is expressed relative to this.

[c] Enzyme proportionality was obtained only up to the release of 0.20 mμmole of P_i.

inactive as substrates. Unlike *E. coli* alkaline phosphatase (13), exonuclease III is unable to act on 3'- or 5'-deoxymononucleotides or on deoxyoligonucleotides of short chain length.

The ability of the phosphatase to remove the 3'-phosphoryl end groups of high molecular weight oligonucleotides makes this enzyme a useful reagent for identifying such end groups and for studying their effect on other enzymatic reactions. The variable priming capacities of DNA preparations for *E. coli* DNA polymerase have been, in part, attributed to the presence of inhibitory 3'-phosphoryl termini as judged by the phosphatase activity of exonuclease III (11,14). The study of the specificity of exonuclease I from *E. coli* has been facilitated by the ability of exonuclease III to catalyze the hydrolysis of 3'-phosphoryl end groups (15). The phosphatase activity can be used to identify the type of phosphodiester bond cleavages catalyzed by endonucleases (1).

REACTION REQUIREMENTS. The optimal pH range for the purified enzyme is 6.8 to 7.4 in potassium phosphate buffer. At pH 6.0 and 7.8 the activity is 70 and 62% of the optimum. Mg^{2+} is required for maximal activity. Under the conditions of the assay the optimal Mg^{2+} concentration is 1×10^{-2} M. At 6.6×10^{-3} M and 3×10^{-2} M, 63 and 80%, respectively, of maximal activity is observed. Mn^{2+}, at an optimal concentration of 1×10^{-2} M, can partially replace Mg^{2+} (59% of the activity obtained with Mg^{2+}). In order to obtain sustained activity during incubations longer than 30 min the presence of 2-mercaptoethanol at a concentration of 0.01 M is required. In the absence of this compound complete loss of activity occurs after approximately 60 min of incubation.

Properties of the Exonuclease

SPECIFICITY. Table 3 summarizes the specificity of the exonuclease. The enzyme preferentially attacks double-stranded DNA, degrading it to mononucleotides to an extent of 45–50% (see below). The enzyme is unable to hydrolyze single-stranded short oligonucleotides, ribosomal ribonucleic acid, or the double-stranded adenylate-uridylate copolymer. DNAs containing glucosylated hydroxymethylcytosine, isolated from T-even bacteriophage, are not effectively hydrolyzed by the purified enzyme.

PRODUCTS OF THE REACTION. Exonuclease III initiates a stepwise hydrolysis at the 3'-hydroxyl terminus of a native DNA. The acid-soluble products have been identified as 5'-mononucleotides. As shown in Table 3 the enzyme is unable to hydrolyze native DNA beyond an extent of 50%. The exonuclease, initiating its attack from

TABLE 3. *Specificity of the Exonuclease Activity*

Compounds	Relative Activity[a]	Extent[b] (% Total)
dAT copolymer	100[c]	92
Native *E. coli* DNA	88	44 (40)[d]
Native *B. subtilis* DNA	150	40
Native T7 DNA	99	48
Native T2 DNA	1.7	
Heat-denatured *E. coli* DNA	25	18 (3)[d]
Ribosomal RNA	<0.1	
rAU copolymer	<0.1	
pTpTpTpTpT	<0.4	

a The rates of hydrolysis of these compounds were measured in the standard reaction mixture as previously described (2) using Fraction VI of the enzyme.

b The amount (extent) of radioactivity made acid soluble is recorded as the percentage of total radioactivity present in the reaction mixture.

c Represents a turnover number of 1370 mμmoles of nucleotide released per minute per mg of Fraction VI; activity on other compounds is expressed relative to this.

d The numbers in parentheses represent the *extent* of hydrolysis at 45 C rather than at 37 C. The higher temperature has been used to decrease nonspecific hydrogen bonding.

both 3'-hydroxyl ends of the double-stranded molecule, would be expected to degrade DNA to a limit of 50%. At this point all of the residual DNA should be single stranded and would be expected to be resistant to further attack. This model is supported by (a) the identification of the residual DNA as predominantly single-stranded DNA of high molecular weight; (b) the complete hydrolysis of the double-stranded dAT copolymer, and (c) electron micrographs of the acid-insoluble product at varying extents of hydrolysis (11).

The preference of exonuclease III for double-stranded DNA makes it possible to carry out a stepwise degradation of a native DNA. Exonuclease III has been used to prepare partially single-stranded DNA templates for the study of the mechanism of DNA polymerase action (11). These partially single-stranded DNA molecules have also been used to examine the specificity of an endonuclease from *Neurospora crassa*, specific for polynucleotides lacking an ordered structure (16). The effect of the stepwise removal of nucleotides by exonuclease III on the genetic activity of *B. subtilis* DNA (11) and phage λ DNA (17) has been investigated.

REACTION REQUIREMENTS. The optimal pH range for the exonuclease is 7.7 to 8.4 in Tris buffer. Mg^{2+} is required for maximal activity. Under the conditions of the assay the optimal Mg^{2+} concentration is 7×10^{-4} M, Mn^{2+} is about equally as effective as Mg^{2+} in a range of 2 to 7×10^{-4} M. The exonuclease activity has the same requirements for 2-mercaptoethanol as does the phosphatase activity.

REFERENCES

1. RICHARDSON, C. C., and A. KORNBERG. 1964. J. Biol. Chem. *239:* 242.
2. RICHARDSON, C. C., I. R. LEHMAN, and A. KORNBERG. 1964. J. Biol. Chem. *239:* 251.
3. CUNNINGHAM, L., B. W. CATLIN, and M. J. PRIVAT DE GARILHE. 1956. J. Am. Chem. Soc. *78:* 4642.
4. CUNNINGHAM, L. 1958. J. Am. Chem. Soc. *80:* 2546.
5. PRIVAT DE GARILHE, M., L. CUNNINGHAM, U. R. LAURILA, and M. LASKOWSKI. 1957. J. Biol. Chem. *224:* 751.
6. ALEXANDER, M., L. A. HEPPEL, and J. HURWITZ. 1961. J. Biol. Chem. *236:* 3014.
7. SHORTMAN, K., and I. R. LEHMAN. 1964. J. Biol. Chem. *239:* 2964.
8. LEHMAN, I. R. 1960. J. Biol. Chem. *235:* 1479.
9. LEHMAN, I. R., and C. C. RICHARDSON. 1964. J. Biol. Chem. *239:* 233.
10. LEHMAN, I. R., G. G. ROUSSOS, and E. A. PRATT. 1962. J. Biol. Chem. *237:* 819.
11. RICHARDSON, C. C., R. B. INMAN, and A. KORNBERG. 1964. J. Mol. Biol. *9:* 46.
12. SPAHR, P. F., and B. R. HOLLINGSWORTH. 1961. J. Biol. Chem. *236:* 823.
13. GAREN, A., and C. LEVINTHAL. 1960. Biochem. Biophys. Acta. *38:* 470.
14. RICHARDSON, C. C., C. L. SCHILDKRAUT, and A. KORNBERG. 1964. Cold Spring Harbor Symp. Quant. Biol. *28:* 9.
15. LEHMAN, I. R., and A. L. NUSSBAUM. 1964. J. Biol. Chem. *239:* 2628.
16. LINN, S., and I. R. LEHMAN. 1965. J. Biol. Chem. *240:* 1294.
17. STRACK, H. B., and A. D. KAISER. 1965. J. Mol. Biol. *12:* 36.

5. Phosphomonoesterases

Alkaline Phosphatase from

Escherichia coli

A. TORRIANI

DEPARTMENT OF BIOLOGY

MASSACHUSETTS INSTITUTE OF TECHNOLOGY

CAMBRIDGE, MASSACHUSETTS

ASSAY

$$p\text{-Nitrophenylphosphate} \overset{OH^-}{\rightleftharpoons} p\text{-Nitrophenol} + \text{Orthophosphate}$$

The assay consists of the colorimetric determination of free p-nitrophenol (NP) cleaved by enzymic hydrolysis from p-nitrophenyl-phosphate (NPP). The reaction is performed at its optimum pH (in Tris-HCl buffer:8.2) and at a temperature between 25 and 37 C (Q_{10} 27–37 C = 1.5) (I).

Addition of inorganic orthophosphate (P_i) as K_2HPO_4 inhibits the enzyme activity almost completely (more than 95% at 1 M).

Addition of NaF does not interfere with the activity of alkaline phosphatase, but inhibits almost completely (85% at 0.01 M) (2) the activity of acid phosphatase.

At enzyme saturation with substrate, the optical absorption of the

224

NP liberated is proportional to the concentration of the enzyme and to the time of incubation.

The number of μmoles of substrate hydrolyzed per unit time can be calculated from the absorbency of NP liberated, whose molecular extinction coefficient at 410 mμ and pH 8.2 is 1.62×10^4.

Procedure

METHOD 1. A "quick method" may be used when dealing with very active preparations (e.g., 0.06 to 0.006 μmoles of NPP hydrolyzed per minute and per ml of enzyme).

The reaction mixture (total volume 1 ml) contains the substrate (0.0066 moles of NPP dissolved in 0.6 M Tris-HCl buffer at pH 8.2) and the enzyme. In a spectrophotometric cuvette (light pathway 10 mm, volume 1 ml), 0.9 ml of the substrate is prewarmed at the chosen temperature. 0.1 ml of enzyme is added at time zero and the reaction is followed directly by measuring the increase of absorption at 410 mμ due to the accumulation of free NP liberated.

METHOD 2. An alternative way, useful when large numbers of samples are analyzed, consists of performing the enzymic reaction in test tubes incubated in a constant temperature bath for a fixed period of time. The reaction is stopped by addition of K_2HPO_4 (0.1 M final concentration). The absorption at 410 mμ of each sample is read against a suitable blank without enzyme.

Under these conditions an amount of enzyme, which produces an increase in optical density of 1.0 in 20 secs at 37 C, liberates NP linearly with time for at least 10 min.

METHOD 3. This method is preferable when dealing with small amounts of enzyme for which long incubation is required (assays up to 72 hr have been run successfully). Double strength reagents are used: NPP 0.0135 moles in Tris-HCl buffer, 1.2 M at pH 8.2. Addition of NaF, 0.01 M, is recommended to prevent interfering hydrolysis of NPP by contaminating acid phosphatase.

One volume of reagent is mixed with one volume of enzyme and incubated at 37 C. When a visible increase of color (yellow at this pH) is reached, the sample is quickly cooled in an ice bath and the absorption is read against a suitable blank.

In the presence of NaF the reaction cannot be stopped by addition of K_2HPO_4, because a precipitate is formed, but because the enzymic reaction is slow it will not proceed appreciably at 0 C.

ENZYME PRODUCTION

Strains

E. coli wild type (K_{10}, ML, W, B) is an alkaline phosphatase producer, but due to end-product repression, the enzyme is not synthesized when orthophosphates are present in the growth medium (2,3). Constitutive mutants have been isolated (C_4, C_6, C_4F_1, etc.) (4,5). In their case, the presence of inorganic phosphate is irrelevant for enzyme synthesis. Alkaline phosphatase negative mutants are also frequent.

Repressible, constitutive, and negative clones may be easily distinguished by the following procedure. Two types of agar plates (a and b), which differ only by the amount of P_i, are used.

Use Medium "121" as described in Growth of Cells (medium) with the omission of Bacto-Peptone and add

Difco Special Agar (Noble)	3 g%
Glucose	0.2 g%
KH_2PO_4	0.09 g% for plates type (a)

or

KH_2PO_4	0.9 g% for plates type (b)

The culture to be tested is diluted in order to spread 200–300 colonies per plate. After incubation (48 hr at 37 C) the colonies reach an easily visible size and the plates are sprayed with a solution of NPP (15 mg/ml Tris-HCl buffer, 1 M, pH 8.2).

On plates (a): Repressible and constitutive colonies will turn yellow in a few seconds. Negative colonies will turn yellow in 20 min to a few hours only.

On plates (b): Constitutive colonies will turn yellow in few seconds. Repressible and negative colonies will turn yellow in 20 min to few hours only.

Stock cultures are maintained as agar stabs at room temperature for over two years.

Stabs medium:	Difco nutrient broth	8 g
	Difco Bacto agar	7 g
	H_2O	1 liter

sterilized and distributed in small vials (5 ml)—2.5 ml per vial—closed with sterile corks coated with paraffin.

Growth of Cells

MEDIUM FOR BATCH CULTURES: "121 PEPTONE"

Tris (Sigma "121")	0.12 M
NaCl	0.08 M
KCl	0.02 M
NH_4SO_4	0.02 M
$MgCl_2$	0.001 M
$CaCl_2$	2×10^{-4} M
$ZnCl_2$	4×10^{-6} M
Bacto-peptone Difco	0.5%
$FeCl_3$	2×10^{-6} M
pH adjusted to 7.4 with HCl	

Sterilize at 15 psi pressure.

As C source, 5 ml of a solution of glucose (40% in H_2O sterilized separately) is added per liter of medium. Supplements are sterilized and added separately when required. This medium contains limiting amounts of orthophosphate ($3\mu g$/ml of P_i, as contaminant of the Bacto-peptone Difco) and it is suitable for the formation of alkaline phophatase from bacteria either repressible or constitutive.

Rejuvenate the stock culture by transferring it from the stab to a freshly made agar slant of the same medium and incubate at 37 C overnight.

INOCULUM. Few (5–10) loops of the fresh agar slant culture are transferred to a volume of "121 peptone medium" corresponding to $\frac{1}{50}$ of the large batch to be inoculated. The culture is grown overnight at 37 C with strong aeration obtained by shaking in a large (1:10 v/v) flask or by bubbling air through a cotton filter.

BATCH CULTURE. The inoculum is added to the large batch of medium "121 peptone." The culture is allowed to grow overnight at 37 C with strong aeration. The aeration is obtained either in a rotating cylinder (Biogen) or by violent air bubbling through cotton filters into large (15-liter) vessels. After 15–20 hr of incubation, the culture reaches a cell density of 5–7×10^8 bacteria/ml, deduced from turbidity reading in a spectrophotometer (at 540 mμ, 10 mm cuvette, using a Beckman DU the OD should be ca. 0.5–0.7).

The cells are harvested by centrifugation at 4 C in a continuous flow centrifuge (e.g., Sharples) or in an angle centrifuge (Servall) at $6000 \times g$ for 20 min.

ENZYME ISOLATION

Purification

EXTRACTION OF THE ENZYME FROM THE CELLS. Three methods that take advantage of some of the specific properties of the alkaline phosphatase in order to separate the enzyme from most of the other components of the cells in a single step of purification have been described.

Method A. Heat Shock.   The enzyme is quite stable to heat denaturation (1) particularly in the presence of Mg^{2+} and is released from heat-shocked cells.

The bacterial pellet is suspended in Tris-HCl buffer, 0.1 M, pH 7.4, with $MgSO_4$ or $MgCl_2$, 0.01 M, at ca. 2×10^{10} cells/ml. This suspension is equilibrated at 82 C for 15 min, then cooled at 4 C and dialyzed against the same buffer for 20 hr at 4 C. The dialysate is then centrifuged at 20,000 rev/min in a Spinco 20 for 20 min. 90% of the original enzymic activity is liberated in the supernatant fluid.

The small amount of enzyme trapped in the pellet is extracted by three washings and centrifugations with a small volume (50 ml) of 0.1 M Tris-HCl buffer, pH 7.4. This method is useful when dealing with a heat-stable wild type enzyme and when EDTA (used in the following methods) should be avoided.

Method B. Spheroplast Formation.   Upon formation of spheroplasts by treatment of *E. coli* cells with lysozyme and EDTA (6), almost all the phosphatase is released from the cells. This property, first described by Malamy and Horecker (7,8), has been adapted for the purpose of enzyme purification (9,10).

The bacterial pellet is resuspended in 0.1 M Tris-HCl buffer, pH 8.0. The cells are subsequently spun down at $9000 \times g$ for 20 min at 4 C and thoroughly resuspended to ca. 2×10^{11} cells/ml in a solution of sucrose, 0.5 M, in 0.03 M Tris-HCl buffer at pH 8.0. Crystalline lysozyme ($100\mu g$/ml) is added to the suspension standing at room temperature (24 C) and 2 min later EDTA is also added (0.001 M final concentration); swirl gently and let sit for 10 min. Then add $MgSO_4$ (0.01 M final concentration) to stop the lysozyme-EDTA action and to stabilize the spheroplasts (11). After 20 min, the spheroplasts are spun down at $12,000 \times g$ for 20 min at 4 C. The supernatant fluid contains 90–95% of the original enzyme.

Method C. Osmotic Shock.   It has been found that alkaline phosphatase is released from *E. coli* cells even in the absence of lysozyme by EDTA treatment alone in the "cold water wash" described by Neu and Heppel (12,13).

The bacterial pellet suspended in Tris-HCl buffer, 0.01 M, at pH 7.7 is washed three times† with the same buffer and finally resuspended (1 g in 20 ml) with a solution of 0.5 M sucrose‡ in Tris buffer, 0.03 M, pH 8.0, containing EDTA, 5×10^{-4} M. The suspension is gently swirled for 10 min at 23 C in a 2-liter flask. The cells, carefully separated from the sucrose solution by centrifuging 10 min at 13,000 $\times g$, are then resuspended in the same volume of water at 3 C: "osmotic shock." After 10 min of gentle swirling at 3 C, the cells are centrifuged 10 min at 13,000 $\times g$; 70–90% of the total alkaline phosphatase originally contained in the cells is now in the supernatant fluid ("cold water wash"), whereas only 5–10% of the other cellular proteins are released (12,13). The enzyme is already 40% pure and only 13–14 bands of proteins are shown in starch gel electrophoresis (13). The enzyme solution is now adjusted to pH 8 by adding Tris buffer for 0.01 M and $MgSO_4$ for 0.01 M.

HEAT STEP. The crude extract of the enzyme prepared with one of the three methods described above is dialyzed exhaustively against 0.01 M Tris-HCl buffer, pH 7.4, and 0.01 M $MgSO_4$. The dialyzed preparation is kept at 80 C in a water bath for 15 min. Most of the contaminating proteins are temperature sensitive and become insoluble. The supernatant fluid is filtered through a Whatman filter paper No. 1. The "heat step" should be avoided when dealing with heat-sensitive enzyme (e.g., altered by mutation). The "heat step" should then be replaced by a second DEAE fractionation after fractionation by DEAE-cellulose column.

CONCENTRATION. Concentration by precipitation with $(NH_4)_2$-SO_4. Enough salt for 85–90% saturation is added to the preparation. The precipitate is dissolved in a small (1/50) volume of 0.01 M Tris-HCl buffer, pH 7.4, with 0.01 M $MgSO_4$ and dialyzed against the same buffer.

FRACTIONATION BY DEAE-CELLULOSE COLUMN. The enzyme must be concentrated in a fairly small volume before the column fractionation, because it is important to obtain sharp narrow bands and good resolution in order to separate the phosphatase from the

---

† Neu and Heppel (personal communication) pointed out that this step is important. *E. coli* washed once will release only 60% of the enzyme during the osmotic shock.

‡ N. Nossal (personal communication) has recently found that sucrose can successfully be substituted by 0.4 M NaCl.

ribonuclease [as they run very close together (L. A. Heppel, personal communication)]. The column (2.5-cm diameter and 10 cm high) is packed under 8-lb pressure with a suspension of DEAE (ca. 33 mg/ml) equilibrated with 0.01 M Tris-HCl buffer, pH 7.4, with $MgSO_4$, 0.01 M. The packed column is washed with the same buffer and the enzyme solution is applied. When the entire preparation is adsorbed, the column is washed again, with buffer (50 ml). Elution is carried out with a linearly increasing concentration of NaCl from 0 to 0.2 M in 0.01 M Tris-HCl and 0.01 M $MgSO_4$, pH 7.4. The eluting solution is passed through the column at a rate of about 0.5–1 ml/min and collected in separate tubes (ca. 4–5 ml/tube) on a fraction collector.

The phosphatase activity is eluted from the column with 0.125 M NaCl (9). The fractions that contain the bulk (80–90%) of the enzyme are pooled and if necessary concentrated by lyophylization to 10 ml. At this step, the enzyme is 95% pure, as judged by its specific activity and its behavior on starch gel electrophoresis (10).

From this step on, the procedure is essentially the one described by Malamy and Horecker (9) and modified by Neu and Heppel (13) and Heppel and Brockman (14).

$(NH_4)_2SO_4$ PRECIPITATION. The enzyme solution is adjusted to pH 8 with NaOH and cooled to 0 C. A saturated solution of $(NH_4)_2SO_4$ at 0 C is added dropwise until incipient turbidity appears (at ca. 61% saturation).

CRYSTALLIZATION. The crystallization is started by slowly (16 hr) warming the suspension from 0 to 22 C (9) and is completed in several (10 or more) days at room temperature.

RECRYSTALLIZATION. The crystalline precipitate is centrifuged (in a clinical centrifuge at room temperature), dissolved in a solution of $(NH_4)_2SO_4$, 50% saturated at 4 C and pH 8.0, and recrystallized by repeating the $(NH_4)_2SO_4$ precipitation and crystallization. The steps of purification are summarized in Table 1.

PROPERTIES OF THE ENZYME

Contamination with Other Enzymes

In some instances it is essential to have a phosphomonoesterase free from diesterases and nucleases. Some of these enzymes are released together with alkaline phosphatase in the process of making the spheroplasts: "external enzymes" (Table 2). Others are released

TABLE 1. *Purification of Alkaline Phosphatase from*
E. coli **(1,9,10,12–14)**

	% Recovery of Enzyme	Units[a] (per mg of protein)	Degree of Purity (%)
Cells disrupted by sonication	100		
Extraction from the cells:			
(A) by heat shock	90		
(B) by spheroplast formation	90–100		30
(C) by osmotic shock	70– 90	450–540	35–40
Heat step (optional): Dialyzed crude extract, heat 15 min at 82 C, filter through Whatman No. 1	100	1450	80–90
Concentration by $(NH_4)_2SO_4$ 85–90% saturation. Dialysis	100		
DEAE cellulose column, eluted with NaCl, 0.125 M	90–100	1480	85–97
$(NH_4)_2SO_4$ precipitation to 61% saturation at 4 C, pH 8.0			
Crystallization by slow warming from 0 to 22 C		1500	99–100
Recrystallization, 2 previous steps repeated			

[a] 1 unit of activity produces a change of optical density of 1.0/min at 420 mμ, pH 8.2, and 37 C.

only if the cells undergo some lysis: "internal enzymes" (Table 2). After the methods of extraction described none or very little lysis should occur. An easy control of lysis is to measure the level of one of the "internal enzymes" during the extraction of alkaline phosphatase. No more than 5–10% of the total activity per cell for each of these enzymes is supposed to be released by the extraction procedure.

The crystalline phosphatase is practically free of ribosomal ribonuclease and phosphodiesterase even by the most sensitive test, e.g., the loss of acceptor activity of sRNA for C^{14}-amino acides [H. C. Neu as reported by Malamy and Horecker (8)].

Molecular Size

Alkaline phosphatase (molecular weight 80,000) (1) is composed of two identical subunits (23). Treatment of the enzyme at pH 2.3–3.5

TABLE 2. *Separation of Enzymes by Extraction
of Alkaline Phosphatase of* E. coli

Enzymes	Percent of Total Cellular-Enzyme[a] Extracted by		References
	"Osmotic Shock"	"Spheroplast Formation"	
External Enzymes[b]			
Alkaline phosphatase	88	85–100	12,7,8
Latent ribonuclease	1.5	71	11,12
RNA inhibited deoxyribonuclease	3	51	12,15,16
5′ nucleotidase	80	80–100	15,12
Acid phosphatase	95	80	15,2,17
Cyclic phosphodiesterase	100	100	12,18,19
Internal Enzymes[c]			
DNA polymerase	0.53	0	12
β-Galactosidase	5–10	0.5–0.7	7,12
Glucose-6-phosphate dehydrogenase	5–10		7
Glutamic dehydrogenase	5–10		7
Polynucleotide phosphorylase	5–10		12
RNA phosphodiesterase	5–10		12,20–22
Inorganic pyrophosphatase	0.56	7.0	12
Leucine aminopeptidase	5–10		12

[a] Total cellular enzymes measured after breaking of the cells by sonic treatment.

[b] "External enzymes": released by the extraction procedure together with the alkaline phosphatase.

[c] "Internal enzymes": enzymes kept inside the protoplasm during extraction.

at 0 C results in loss of enzymic activity and separation of the two subunits (10,24,25). The sedimentation coefficient of the purified enzyme is 6.77 (1,26). The acid-treated material sediments with an S_{20} of 2.6 (26). The process is fully reversible: Dimerization is a bimolecular reaction dependent on pH, temperature, and Zn^{2+} concentration (24,25).

Other Properties

The enzyme in its native state appears to be a tightly folded globular molecule. It is resistant to proteolysis by trypsin and chymotrypsin (10). In the presence of 10^{-2} M Mg^{2+}, the enzyme is stable at 85 C for at least 30 min (1,10). Enzymatic activity persists even in presence of 6 M urea or in presence of thioglycollic acid. Combined treatment

TABLE 3. *Substrates and Inhibitors of Alkaline Phosphatase of* E. coli

	Relative Reaction Velocity[a]	Inhibitor Constant $K_i/K_m{}^b$ at 25 C	References
p-Nitrophenylphosphate (NPP)	1.0		1,2,16,33
Na-β-glycerol phosphate	0.9	4.2	1,2,33
Glucose-6-phosphate	0.7		2,16
Glucose-1-phosphate	0.9	5.3	1,2,16
Fructose-1,6-phosphate	0.6		2
Adenosine-2′-phosphate	1.0		31
Adenosine-3′-phosphate	1.0		1,16,33
Adenosine-5′-phosphate (AMP)	0.8	7.8	1,2,16,33
Cytidine-2′ and 3′-phosphate	1.1		33
Cytidine-5′-phosphate	0.8	1	1,33
Guanosine-2′ and 3′-phosphate	0.9		33
Guanosine-5′-phosphate	0.9	3.8	1,33
Inosine-5′-phosphate	0.9		33
Uridine-2′ and 3′-phosphate	1.0		33
Uridine-5′-phosphate	0.8	3.7	1,16,33
Thymidine-5′-phosphate	0.9		33
Ribose-5′-phosphate	0.7		16
Deoxy AMP	1.1		33
Deoxy CMP	0.9		33
Deoxy GMP	1.1		33
UDP	1.0		16
Riboflavine-5′-phosphate	0.7		1
L-histidinol-phosphate	0.9		1
Bis (p-nitro-phenylphosphate)	0		2,33
Terminal P_i removed from			
pUpU			16
pApApApU, etc.			16
pApA			16
pApApA up to 10			16

[a] Enzyme activity measured by release of orthophosphate. Substrate concentration used: 0.01–0.001 M.

[b] NPP concentration 0.001 M.

with thioglycollic acid and 6 M urea leads to reduction of disulfide bonds and separation into subunits of MW 40,000. This process (as well as the acid treatment mentioned) is reversible and the reduced enzyme can be reactivated under oxidizing conditions (10).

The native enzyme contains two atoms of Zn^{2+} per molecule (27) and two phosphate ions (28).

The purified enzyme can be resolved by electrophoresis in starch gel into a number of extremely closely related proteins separable on the basis of their charges (29), but all controlled by a single genetic cistron (30). Each band has a specific activity very close to the one of the pure enzyme.

The isoelectric point of the purified enzyme was estimated to be 4.5 (1).

The turnover number calculated for a molecular weight of 80,000 is 2700 molecules of NPP hydrolyzed per molecule of enzyme per minute at 25 C.

Substrates and Inhibitors (see Table 3)

All the monosubstituted phosphate linkages are hydrolyzed by the enzyme. The pure enzyme does not hydrolyze phosphodiesters and causes no loss of amino acid acceptor activity of sRNA (31–33).

Heppel *et al.* (16) find that the Lineweather–Burk plot gives two intersecting lines. Measurements with dilute substrate yield K_m of the order of 10^{-5} (for instance, 1.4×10^{-5} for NPP and 3.3×10^{-5} for AMP). However, when the substrate is present in relatively high concentration a higher set of values of K_m are obtained (of the order of 10^{-3}).

REFERENCES

1. GAREN, A., and C. LEVINTHAL. 1960. Biochim. Biophys. Acta. *38:* 470.
2. TORRIANI, A. 1960. Biochim. Biophys. Acta. *38:* 460.
3. HORIUCHI, T., S. HORIUCHI, and D. MIZUNO. 1959. Nature. *183:* 1529.
4. ECHOLS, H., A. GAREN, S. GAREN, and A. TORRIANI. 1961. J. Mol. Biol. *3:* 425.
5. TORRIANI, A., and F. ROTHMAN. 1961. J. Bact. *81:* 835.
6. REPASKE, R. 1958. Biochim. Biophys. Acta. *30:* 225.
7. MALAMY, M. H., and B. L. HORECKER. 1961. Biochem. Biophys. Res. Comm. *5:* 104.
8. MALAMY, M. H., and B. L. HORECKER. 1964. Biochemistry. *3:* 1889.
9. MALAMY, M. H., and B. L. HORECKER. 1964. Biochemistry. *3:* 1893.
10. LEVINTHAL, C., E. R. SIGNER, and K. FETHEROLF. 1962. Proc. Natl. Acad. Sci., U.S. *48:* 1230.
11. NEU, H. C., and L. A. HEPPEL. 1964. J. Biol. Chem. *239:* 3893.
12. NEU, H. C., and L. A. HEPPEL. 1964. Biochem. Biophys. Res. Comm. *17:* 215.
13. NEU, H. C., and L. A. HEPPEL. Unpublished.
14. HEPPEL, L. A., and R. W. BROCKMAN. Personal communication.
15. NEU, H. C., and L. A. HEPPEL. 1964. Biochem. Biophys. Res. Comm. *14:* 109.

16. HEPPEL, L. A., D. R. HARKNESS, and R. J. HILMOE. 1962. J. Biol. Chem. *237:* 841.
17. ROGERS, D., and F. J. REITHEL. 1960. Arch. Biochem and Biophys. *89:* 97.
18. ANRAKU, Y. 1964. J. Biol. Chem. *239:* 3412.
19. ANRAKU, Y. 1964. J. Biol. Chem. *239:* 3420.
20. SPAHR, P. F., and B. R. HOLLINGWORTH. 1961. J. Biol. Chem. *236:* 823.
21. SINGER, M. F., and G. TOLBERT. 1964. Science. *145:* 593.
22. SINGER, M. F., and G. TOLBERT. 1965. Biochemistry. *4:* 1319.
23. ROTHMAN, F., and R. BYRNE. 1963. J. Mol. Biol. *6:* 330.
24. SCHLESINGER, M. J., and C. LEVINTHAL. 1963. J. Mol. Biol. *7:* 1.
25. SCHLESINGER, M. J., A. TORRIANI, and C. LEVINTHAL. 1963. Cold Spring Harbor Symp. Quant. Biol. *28:* 539.
26. MALAMY, M. H. 1963. Ph.D. thesis, N.Y. University.
27. PLOCKE, D. G., C. LEVINTHAL, and B. L. VALLEE. 1962. Biochemistry. *1:* 373.
28. SCHWARTZ, G. H., and F. LIPMANN. 1961. Proc. Natl. Acad. Sci., U.S. *47:* 1996.
29. BACH, M. L., E. R. SIGNER, C. LEVINTHAL, and I. W. SIZER. 1961. Fed. Proc. *20:* 255.
30. GAREN, A., and S. GAREN. 1963. J. Mol. Biol. *7:* 13.
31. HARKNESS, D. R., and R. J. HILMOE. 1962. Biochem. Biophys. Res. Comm. *9:* 393.
32. NEU, H. C., and L. A. HEPPEL. 1964. J. Biol. Chem. *239:* 2927.
33. HORIUCHI, S. 1959. Jap. J. Med. Sci. Biol. *12:* 429.

Spleen Acid Phosphomonoesterase (1)

GIORGIO BERNARDI

CENTER FOR RESEARCH IN MACROMOLECULES

STRASBOURG, FRANCE

A very highly purified acid phosphomonoesterase has been prepared from hog spleen by Chersi, Bernardi, and Bernardi (1). The enzyme is obtained as a by-product during the preparation of acid deoxyribonuclease.

Spleen acid phosphomonoesterase is very similar in both its physical and enzymological properties to acid prostatic phosphomonoesterase (2).

ASSAY

Reaction

$$p\text{-Nitrophenyl phosphate} \longrightarrow p\text{-Nitrophenol} + \text{Phosphate}$$

The phosphomonoesterase activity is assayed by measuring the liberation of p-nitrophenol from p-nitrophenyl phosphate.

Reagents

1. The reaction mixture (total volume 1.1 ml) contains
    a. 1 μmole of p-nitrophenyl phosphate, disodium salt
       150 μmoles of acetate buffer, pH 5.0
       10 μmoles of EDTA
    b. Enzyme—this is diluted, if necessary, with 0.15 M acetate buffer + 0.01 M EDTA, pH 5.0, containing 0.05% Armour bovine serum albumin.
2. 2 N $(NH_4)OH$

Procedure

After 10 min of incubation at 37 C, the reaction is stopped by adding 0.2 ml of 2 N $(NH_4)OH$. The absorption at 400 mμ is measured and a suitable blank is subtracted from the reading. The concentration of liberated p-nitrophenol is calculated from the corrected reading taking an $E_{400} = 12,000$ for p-nitrophenol (3). One activity unit is defined as the amount of enzyme that catalyzes the liberation of 1 μmole of p-nitrophenol per minute under the above conditions. Assays are performed using enzyme concentrations to obtain OD_{400} readings not higher than 5.0. Under these conditions a linear relationship is obtained between enzyme concentration and p-nitrophenol liberation. The specific activity is calculated by dividing the activity by the OD_{280} of the enzyme solution.

CHROMATOGRAPHIC PURIFICATION

The starting material is crude spleen nuclease II (p. 105). If acidification to pH 2.5 is omitted, and the fraction precipitated between 0.3 and 0.6 saturation (20 C) of $(NH_4)_2SO_4$ is collected, a much higher acid phosphomonoesterase activity is found (Table 2, p. 147). Most of this activity belongs, however, to a different acid phosphomonoesterase, which is not retained by hydroxyapatite equilibrated with 0.05 M phosphate buffer pH 6.8. The chromatographic purification is patterned on Procedure C described for spleen acid deoxyribonuclease (p. 113) and summarized in Table 1.

STEP 1. DEAE-SEPHADEX A-50 (FIG. 1). This step has been described (p. 113). Acid phosphomonoesterase activity is not retained by the column equilibrated with 0.05 M phosphate buffer, pH 6.8.

A second minor activity peak, belonging to a different acid phosphomonoesterase is eluted by 0.5 M phosphate buffer, pH 6.8.

STEP 2. HYDROXYAPATITE (FIG. 2). This step has been described (p. 113). Acid phosphomonoesterase is eluted by a 0.05–0.5 M linear gradient of phosphate buffer, pH 6.8, at a molarity of about 0.25.

The second peak of acid phosphomonoesterase activity was not investigated further (see, however, step 2 in the purification of acid ribonuclease, p. 40).

STEP 3. SEPHADEX G-100 (FIG. 3). The acid phosphomonoesterase activity from the previous step is loaded on a Sephadex G-100 column equilibrated with 0.1 M acetate buffer, pH 5.6. All the activity is eluted before the main protein peak.

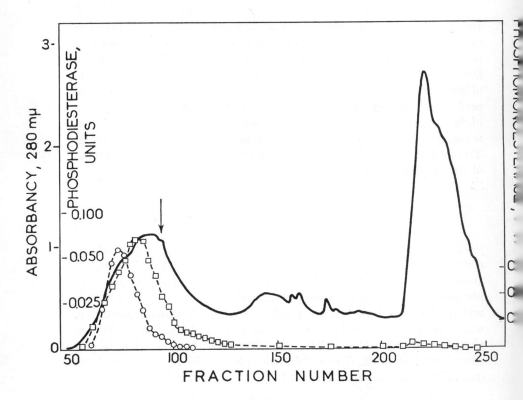

Fig. 1. Chromatography on DEAE-Sephadex A-50 of crude spleen nuclease II (see also p. 112) (Step 1). 330 ml of preparation HS 9 (OD_{280} = 10.3; OD_{260} = 6.9) were loaded on a 8- × 80-cm column of DEAE-Sephadex A-50 equilibrated with 0.05 M phosphate buffer, pH 6.8. This buffer was also used to elute the first protein peak. 0.5 M phosphate buffer, pH 6.8, was loaded at the fraction indicated by the arrow. 24-ml fractions were collected. The continuous line indicates the absorption at 280 mμ. Squares indicate the acid phosphomonoesterase activity (right-hand scale); circles, the phosphodiesterase activity, which is due to nucleoside polyphosphatase (left-hand inner scale). Acid deoxyribonuclease, cytochrome c, acid and basic ribonuclease were also assayed; the results are shown on pp. 39 and 112.

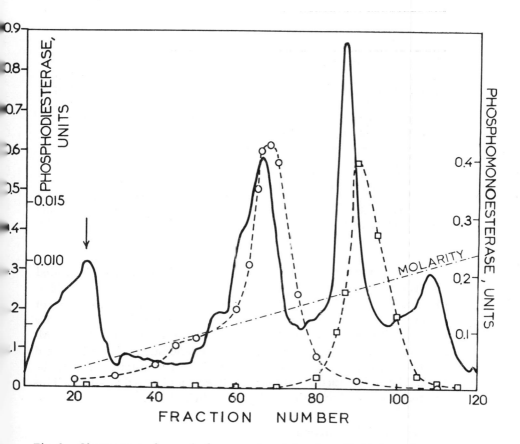

Fig. 2. Chromatography on hydroxyapatite of fractions 50–65 from Step 1. 370 ml (OD$_{280}$ = 1.48) were loaded on a 2- × 40-cm column of hydroxyapatite equilibrated with 0.05 M phosphate buffer, pH 6.8. A molarity gradient (0.05–0.5) was started at the fraction indicated by the arrow (at fraction 120 M = 0.35). 24-ml fractions were collected. The continuous line indicates the absorption at 280 mμ. Squares indicate the acid phosphomonoesterase activity (right-hand outer scale); circles, the phosphodiesterase activity, which is due to nucleoside polyphosphatase (left-hand inner scale). Acid deoxyribonuclease, acid and basic ribonuclease, and cytochrome c were also assayed (see Fig. 4, p. 114).

TABLE 1.   *Chromatographic Purification of Spleen Acid Phosphomonoesterase[a]*

	Volume (ml)	Total OD_{280}	Total Units	Specific Activity
Crude spleen nuclease II				0.048[b]
Step 1. DEAE-Sephadex[c]	160	950	1,090	1.15
Step 2. Hydroxyapatite	120	170	834	4.86
Step 3. Sephadex G-100	130	10	544	54.4
Step 4. CM-Sephadex	65	1	256	256
CM-Sephadex	12	0.45	128	280

[a] All values reported refer to the fractions that were processed further, or to the final product. The side fractions of the activity peaks were processed separately.

[b] This value was found for preparation HS 11.

[c] This product was formed by the phosphomonoesterase-rich fractions obtained from the first peak of the DEAE-Sephadex and from the subsequent hydroxyapatite chromatography (Steps 1 and 2 of Procedure C in the acid deoxyribonuclease purification).

STEP 4. CM-SEPHADEX C-50 (FIG. 4).   The activity is loaded on a CM-Sephadex C-50 column equilibrated with 0.1 M acetate buffer, pH 5.6. The activity is eluted by a molarity gradient, 0.1–0.3 M of acetate buffer at a molarity of about 0.26. The active fractions are diluted with one volume of water and rechromatographed on CM-Sephadex C-50 as above (Fig. 5). Phosphomonoesterase is again eluted at about 0.26 M acetate; the specific activity is constant through the peak. The active fractions are pooled, frozen, and stored at −60 C. This product is referred to as the final product in Table 1.

Properties of the Enzyme

PHYSICAL PROPERTIES.   A sedimentation constant equal to 5.6 was determined when the acid phosphomonoesterase activity was centrifuged in a sucrose gradient as described by Bernardi and Griffé (4), using cytochrome c or acid deoxyribonuclease as reference proteins.

PURITY.   The following possible contaminating activities were assayed in the final product: acid deoxyribonuclease, acid ribonuclease, exonuclease, and phosphodiesterase; this latter activity was determined using Ca [bis(p-nitrophenyl) phosphate]$_2$ in 0.15 M acetate buffer + 0.01 M EDTA, pH 5.0, and in 0.25 M succinate buffer, pH 6.5. In every case 0.1 ml of the final solution was used and digestions were carried out for

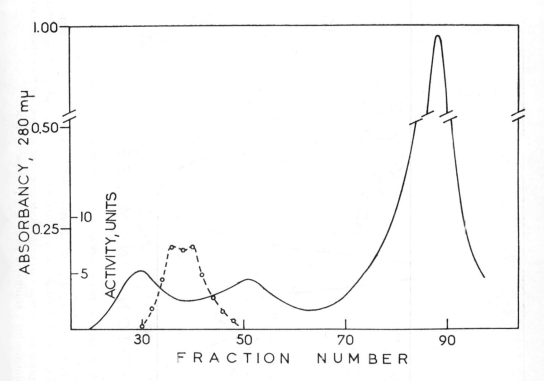

Fig. 3. Gel filtration on Sephadex G-100 of acid phosphomonoesterase–rich fractions from a hydroxyapatite chromatography. 120 ml (OD$_{280}$ = 1.40) were loaded on a 4- $\times$ 95-cm column of Sephadex G-100 equilibrated with 0.1 M acetate buffer, pH 5.6; the same solvent was used to elute the protein from the column. 13-ml fractions were collected. The continuous line indicates the absorption at 2.80 mμ. Circles indicate the acid phosphomonoesterase activity (left-hand inner scale). Fractions 34–42 were processed further.

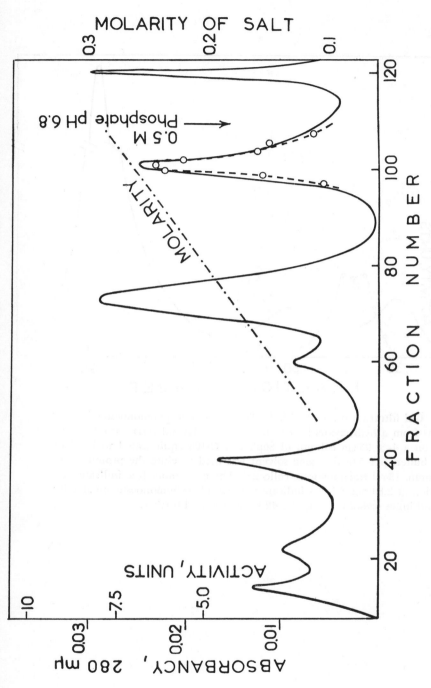

Fig. 4. Chromatography on CM-Sephadex C-50 of the acid phosphomonoesterase fraction from Sephadex G-100. 130 ml (OD$_{280}$ = 0.080) were loaded on a 2 × 38-cm CM-Sephadex C-50 column equilibrated with a 0.1 M acetate buffer, pH 5.6. A molarity gradient (0.1–0.3) of acetate buffer was started at the fraction indicated with an arrow (right-hand ordinate). 0.5 M phosphate buffer, pH 6.8, was loaded at the fraction indicated by the arrow. 5-ml fractions were collected. The continuous line indicates the absorption at 280 mμ. Circles indicate the acid phosphomonoesterase activity (left-hand inner scale). Fractions 97–109 were diluted with 1 volume of water and processed further.

242

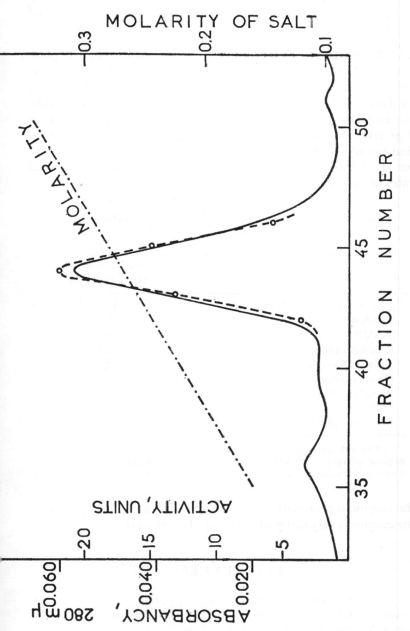

Fig. 5. Rechromatography on CM-Sephadex C-50 of the acid phosphomonoesterase fraction. 130 ml were loaded on a 0.9- × 16-cm column of CM-Sephadex C-50 equilibrated with 0.125 M acetate buffer, pH 5.6. A molarity gradient (0.125–0.5) of acetate buffer was used to elute the enzyme (right-hand scale). 3.2-ml fractions were collected. The continuous line indicates the absorption at 280 mμ. Circles indicate the acid phosphomonoesterase activity (left-hand inner scale).

2 hr at 37 C. No contaminating activities were detected. When using a 1:100 dilution of the same enzyme solution, the liberation of 0.058 μmoles of p-nitrophenol from p-nitrophenyl phosphate was obtained in 10 min.

ENZYMOLOGICAL PROPERTIES. With p-nitrophenyl phosphate as the substrate, at $\mu = 0.1$ between pH 2.0 and 6.0 the pH-activity curve shows a very broad optimum between pH 3.0 and 5.0. The activity falls much more rapidly on the acid than on the basic side. Cysteine and versene do not exert any relevant effect on the enzyme at a 0.01 M level. Magnesium is very slightly inhibitory. L(+) tartaric acid, but not D(−) tartaric acid, F⁻, Cu^{2+}, and Mo^{6+} are powerful inhibitors at a 0.001 M level. The relative rates of hydrolysis of several substrates are given in Table 2.

TABLE 2.   *Relative Rate of Hydrolysis of Several Substrates by Spleen Acid Phosphomonoesterase*

Substrates[a]	Relative Rate of Hydrolysis (%)
p-Nitrophenyl phosphate	100
2′-3′-AMP	96
5′-AMP	63
Riboflavinphosphate	29
Thiaminphosphate	21
Phosphothreonine	6
Phosphoserine	4
ATP	0
Bis(p-nitrophenyl) phosphate	0

[a] The substrate concentration was 1.5 mM. The liberation of inorganic phosphate at 37 C was determined at different incubation times, and the initial rates were used.

The enzyme is competitively inhibited by inorganic phosphate. The enzyme is very easily adsorbed by glass surfaces.

REFERENCES

1. CHERSI, A., A. BERNARDI, and G. BERNARDI. In preparation.
2. SCHMIDT, G. 1961. *In* P. D. BOYER, H. LARDY, and K. MYRBACK, editors. The enzymes. Academic Press, New York. Vol. V, p. 37.
3. RAZZELL, W. E., and H. G. KHORANA. 1961. J. Biol. Chem. *236:* 1144.
4. BERNARDI, G., and M. GRIFFÉ. 1964. Biochemistry. *3:* 1419.

Polynucleotide Phosphorylase

MAXINE F. SINGER

NATIONAL INSTITUTE OF ARTHRITIS

AND METABOLIC DISEASES

NATIONAL INSTITUTES OF HEALTH

BETHESDA, MARYLAND

ASSAY

$$(AMP)_n + n\ P_i^{32} \xrightarrow{\quad Mg^{2+} \quad} n\ ADP^{32}$$

Principle

This assay measures the formation of P^{32}-labeled ADP from the phosphorolytic cleavage of polyadenylic acid (poly A) in the presence of P_i^{32}. Although polynucleotide phosphorylase catalyzes several other reactions, which are also applicable to the assay of the enzyme (1), the phosphorolysis of polyribonucleotides, and in particular, of poly A, has been the method of choice in recent years. Poly A is preferred over the other homopolymers primarily because it is readily available commercially and at reasonable prices.† After the reaction is carried out the ADP^{32} must be separated from the excess P_i^{32}; several methods are useful. Grunberg-Manago has favored a modification of the procedure of Berenblum and Chain (2–4). Singer has generally relied on the

† Miles Chemical Company, Clifton, New Jersey; or Calbiochem, Los Angeles, California.

adsorption of the nucleotide onto charcoal to separate it from P_i^{32} (5); the procedure is based on a method described by Littauer and Kornberg (6). Both procedures are convenient and reliable. The charcoal method will be described in detail here.

Reagents

1. Tris buffer, pH 8.2, chloride salt, 1 M
2. $MgCl_2$, 0.1 M
3. $K_2HP^{32}O_4$, 0.1 M (containing from 50–150 $\times$ 10^5 cpm/ml)†
4. 0.01 M EDTA
5. Polyadenylic acid,‡ 10 μmoles of mononucleotide equivalent/ml
6. Bovine serum albumin, 10 mg/ml
7. A suspension containing one part of a 10% (weight by weight) aqueous suspension of acid-washed Norite A (Pfanstiehl Laboratories, Inc., Waukegan, Illinois) in 10 parts of 2.5% $HClO_4$

Procedure

The incubation mixture contains 0.01 ml Tris, 0.005 ml $MgCl_2$, 0.01 ml K_2HPO_4, 0.01 ml polymer, 0.01 ml EDTA, 0.003 to 0.02 units of enzyme, and H_2O to a final volume of 0.1 ml. With purified fractions, 0.01 ml of bovine serum albumin is included in the assay. After 15 min at 37 C, the tube is placed in ice and 1 ml of cold perchloric acid-charcoal mixture is added. After mixing, the tubes are allowed to remain in ice for 10 min with occasional shaking. The contents of the tubes are washed directly onto a suitable filter in a filtration apparatus (Millipore Type 4A, pore size, 45 μ; disk diameter, 25 mm) and washed three times, with suction, each time with about 15 ml of cold, distilled H_2O. The filters are placed (charcoal side down) on planchets and dried for a few minutes under an infrared lamp. The planchets are counted in a suitable counter. A blank, without enzyme, is run with each set of assays and its value is subtracted from each sample.

† The P^{32} obtained from Oak Ridge National Laboratory must be extensively purified before use in order to obtain blank values of less than 1% of the counts. The following procedure is satisfactory (7,8): From 1 to 5 millicuries of P^{32} are ashed in a Kjeldahl flask with 0.02 ml of 10% $Mg(NO_3)_2$ in alcohol (9). After cooling, 0.2 ml of H_2O and 0.02 ml of $Mg(NO_3)_2$ are added and the ashing is repeated. After cooling, 2 ml of 1 N HCl are added and the mixture is boiled gently for 10 min. The mixture is transferred to a centrifuge tube using about 15 ml of H_2O. 200 μmoles each of $MgCl_2$ and K_2HPO_4 are added and then 10 ml of 5 N NH_4OH. The suspension is centrifuged and the precipitate is washed twice with 5 ml of 1.5 M NH_4OH. The precipitate is then dissolved in about 5 ml of H_2O, using a minimum of 1 N HCl. The precipitation is repeated twice more. The final solution is passed through a column of Dowex 50, H^+ to remove Mg^{2+}, and the specific radioactivity is determined.

‡ It is advisable to dialyze the commercial polymer against 1 mM EDTA and then against H_2O before use in the assay. It should be noted that various polymer preparations are hydrolyzed at different rates. Therefore comparisons of assays with different substrates are not reliable.

From the specific radioactivity of the inorganic P^{32}, the μmoles of nucleoside diphosphate are calculated. The error in counting resulting from self-absorption is below 10% and is ignored. One unit of activity in this phosphorolysis assay is equivalent to the incorporation of 1 μmole of P_i^{32} into nucleoside diphosphate per 15 min. Specific enzyme activity is defined as units per mg of protein. Under the conditions described, the extent of phosphorolysis is proportional to time of incubation. Except with the crudest fractions, it is also proportional to enzyme concentration: it has been suggested (3) that a ten-fold increase in the concentration of poly A in the assay affords somewhat more satisfactory results (see Table 1). In addition, with highly purified fractions, crystalline bovine serum albumin is generally included in the assay mixtures. A concentration of from 0.05 to 0.10 mg/ml has proven satisfactory.

Sources of Purified Enzyme

Reproducible procedures for the preparation of highly purified polynucleotide phosphorylase from *Escherichia coli* (3,10), *Micrococcus lysodeikticus* (5,11), and *Azotobacter vinelandii* (10) are available and are described below. Another published method for the extensive purification of enzyme from *Azotobacter vinelandii* has not proved reproducible, even in the hands of the original workers (7,12–14). In general, it is not necessary to carry out any of the procedures in its entirety in order to obtain enzyme suitable for the preparation of polymers. Indeed, in the case of the *M. lysodeikticus* enzyme, the primer† requirement of the highly purified enzyme (11,15) makes it quite unsuitable for the routine preparation of polymers. In each of the preparations described below, the step at which enzyme useful for polymer synthesis is obtained is indicated. Such enzyme can also be prepared by carrying the procedure of Ochoa and co-workers (12,13,16) through the protamine fractionation step. In addition, alternative methods of purification, leading to enzyme that is adequate for polymer preparation, have also been described (6,17).

PURIFICATION FROM *E. COLI* (3,10)

Growth of Cells

Escherichia coli, strain B, is grown in a medium containing the following, per liter: 100 μmoles of sodium-potassium phosphate buffer, pH 7.4; 2 g of $(NH_4)_2SO_4$; 0.1 g of $MgSO_4$; 2 g of glucose (sterilized

---

† In this discussion of polynucleotide phosphorylase, the term "primer" is used to indicate a polyribonucleotide chain that serves as a starting point for chain proliferation. It does not mean a template.

separately); 5 mg of $FeSO_4$; and 20 g of peptone. A 16-hr culture is used to inoculate media; the volume of inoculum is approximately 2% of the volume of fresh media and the initial absorption of fresh media, after inoculation, is about 0.150 at 420 mμ. The cells are grown at 37 C with aeration, and are harvested at the end of the exponential phase of growth (absorption at 420 mμ equal to 2.2) by centrifugation in a Sharples centrifuge. The cells are stored at -20 C. The yield of cells is approximately 3 g (wet weight)/liter.

Extraction of Cells

All steps are carried out between 0 and 3 C. The cells are ground with 2 g of alumina per g of cells and the mixture is then suspended in 2 ml of Tris buffer, pH 8, 0.02 M, per g of cells. The suspension is stirred for 30 min at 4 C. The mixture is then centrifuged for 1 hr at 14,000 × g. The supernatant fluid is decanted and the precipitate is then washed once with the same buffer. The washing is combined with the original supernatant fluid and the combined fluids are dialyzed overnight against 30 liters of 0.02 M Tris buffer, pH 7.4. The resulting crude extract is Fraction I.

Purification

Unless indicated otherwise, all operations are carried out below 4 C. Protein is determined by the procedure of Warburg and Christian (18). Addition of all reagents to enzyme solutions is dropwise with efficient mechanical stirring. In between the various steps the fractions may be stored in ice for not more than 24 hr, except for the $(NH_4)_2SO_4$ II fraction (Fraction IV), which may be stored for several days. The enzyme should not be frozen before the preparation is completed. The results of this procedure are summarized in Table 1. Fraction V is suitable for the preparation of polymers.

FIRST AMMONIUM SULFATE FRACTIONATION. Fraction I is diluted with 0.02 M Tris, pH 7.4, to yield a concentration of from 20 to 30 mg of protein/ml. Then 14.4 g of solid $(NH_4)_2SO_4$ is added per 100 ml of enzyme solution. After one additional hour of stirring the precipitate is removed by centrifugation at 14,000 × g for 1 hr. The supernatant fluid is treated with 30.1 g of $(NH_4)_2SO_4$ per 100 ml of initial solution; the suspension is allowed to equilibrate for 30 min and the precipitate is collected by centrifugation at 14,000 × g for 1.5 hr. The supernatant fluid is decanted with care and the partially viscous precipitate is dissolved in 0.02 M Tris, pH 7.4, using one-quarter the volume of Fraction I originally used. The pH of the solution is adjusted to 7.4 with 0.5 N KOH (Fraction II).

TABLE 1. *Purification of Polynucleotide Phosphorylase from E. coli. (400 g wet) (3,10)*

Fraction	Total Protein (mg)[a]	280/260	Total Units[b]	S.A.[b]
I. Crude extract	67,800	0.6	10,865	0.16
II. $(NH_4)_2SO_4$ I	38,800	0.53	10,865	0.28
III. Protamine Sup.	12,560	1.34	4,648	0.37
IV. $(NH_4)_2SO_4$ II	3,674	1.69	6,338	1.7
V. DEAE-Sephadex	345	1.5	5,575	16
VI. DEAE-cellulose	160	1.3	2,550	16
VII. G-200	15.4	1.3	2,038	132
VIII. Sucrose gradient	2.5	1.3	498	199

[a] Protein determined by the procedure of Warburg and Christian (18).

[b] The assay used to evaluate these fractions differs somewhat from the standard assay described in this article (3). The most important differences are in the concentrations of poly A and of $MgCl_2$ which are 10 and 7.5 mM, respectively (3). The data in this table have been recalculated from that of the original report (3) so that a unit of enzyme is equivalent to that defined in this article, namely, 1 μmole ADP produced per 15 min.

PROTAMINE SULFATE PRECIPITATION. A 1% suspension of protamine sulfate is prepared 24 hr in advance and is adjusted to pH 7 before use. For each 100 ml of Fraction II, 160 ml of the protamine solution is added.† After 30 min the mixture is dialyzed against 10 liters of 0.01 M Tris, pH 7.4; the dialysis is continued for 18 hr, and the dialysis fluid is changed 2 times. The precipitate is removed by centrifuging at 14,000 × g for 10 minutes. The supernatant fluid is Fraction III.

SECOND AMMONIUM SULFATE FRACTIONATION. Fraction III is treated with solid $(NH_4)_2SO_4$ in the manner described above to give the following fractions: 0–34, 34–45, and 45–55% saturation with $(NH_4)_2SO_4$ [100% saturation with $(NH_4)_2SO_4$ is equivalent to the addition of 70 g of $(NH_4)_2SO_4$ per 100 ml of solution at 0 C]. When the protein recovered in Fraction III is approximately 20–30% of the protein in the original crude extract, the bulk of the activity is recovered between 34 and 45% saturation with $(NH_4)_2SO_4$. During the fractionation, the pH is maintained at pH 7.35 by the addition of 0.5 N KOH. The precipitate is dissolved in 0.02 M Tris (pH 7.4) and dialyzed overnight against the same buffer (Fraction IV).

† Particularly because of the differences in quality of commercially available protamine sulfate, it is preferable to make a few preliminary tests in order to determine the exact amount of protamine to be added in any given preparation.

CHROMATOGRAPHY ON DEAE-SEPHADEX. The column is prepared in the following way: 25 g of coarse mesh, DEAE-Sephadex, A-50 is suspended in 4 liters of H_2O and allowed to swell overnight. It is then washed, on a Büchner funnel, with 4 liters of each of the following: 1.0 M KH_2PO_4; 1.0 M K_2HPO_4; 0.1 M KCl; and 0.1 M Tris, pH 8.1. The material is then washed with 15–20 2-liter portions of distilled H_2O and finally suspended in 0.05 M Tris, pH 7.6. A column (3 cm × 55 cm for the preparation described in Table 1) is prepared, and then cooled to 4 C. In general 1 ml of column volume is required per mg of protein and the ratio of column diameter to column height must be 1:15 to 1:20. Fraction IV is adsorbed onto the column, and enzyme is eluted with 0.4 M Tris buffer, pH 7.8, at a rate of 50 ml/hr. The elution gives a large protein peak followed by a shoulder, which contains the activity. Suitable fractions are pooled and concentrated either by dialyzing against saturated $(NH_4)_2SO_4$ and finally dissolving in a small volume of 0.1 M Tris, pH 8.1, or by passage through a DEAE-cellulose column (Fraction V).

DEAE-CELLULOSE CHROMATOGRAPHY. DEAE-Cellulose (10–15 g, 200–600 mesh) is washed on a Büchner funnel with 2 liters of each of the following: 1 M K_2HPO_4; 1 M KH_2PO_4; 1 M KCl; 1 M Tris, pH 8.1; and 0.01 M Tris, pH 7.4. A column (1 cm × 4 cm is suitable for the preparation given in Table 1) is packed under a pressure of about 1 kg/cm². The column is washed with 0.01 M Tris, pH 7.4, and left overnight at 4 C to stabilize. Fraction V is dialyzed for 2 hr against 0.02 M Tris, pH 7.6, before being absorbed onto the column and the latter is then eluted with 1 M Tris, pH 8.1. Five 10-ml fractions are collected. The fraction containing enzyme of the highest specific activity is Fraction VI.

SEPHADEX G-200 COLUMN. One hundred grams of Sephadex G-200 (140–200 mesh) is suspended in 4 liters of distilled H_2O and allowed to swell overnight. The material is then washed several times with distilled water and then with 0.01 M Tris, pH 8.1. For 50 mg of protein a column 3 cm × 55 cm is prepared. The column must be long and the sample at most 0.02 column volume. The sample is carefully absorbed onto the top of the column, which is then eluted with 0.1 M Tris, pH 8.1. The enzyme is found in the first large protein peak (Fraction VII).

SUCROSE GRADIENT CENTRIFUGATION. A gradient of from 5–20% sucrose, in 0.1 M Tris buffer, pH 8, is prepared (19). Samples of Fraction VII are centrifuged for 5–6 hr at top speed in a swinging bucket rotor (Spinco SW-39), and 10-drop fractions are collected (19). Two major protein peaks are obtained; enzyme activity is associated with the slower sedimenting peak. The fractions corresponding to the middle of the peak are pooled and dialyzed first against 0.1 M Tris, pH 8, and then against a saturated solution of $(NH_4)_2SO_4$, in order to concentrate the enzyme (Fraction VIII).

Storage of Purified Enzyme

Enzymatic activity is stable for 1 week at 4 C in Tris buffer at pH values from 8.1 to 9.7. Stock enzyme is routinely stored at −20 C.

PURIFICATION FROM *A. VINELANDII* (10)†

Growth of Cells

The cells are grown as described by Ochoa and co-workers (13) and are lyophilized, without washing, and stored at −20 C until use.

Preparation of Extracts

An acetone powder is prepared by mixing 100 g of lyophilized bacteria with 800 ml of acetone in a mixer such as a Waring Blendor for 90 sec. The suspension is filtered through Whatman No. 1 paper on a Büchner funnel and the precipitate resuspended in 400 ml of acetone. After treatment for 30 sec in the mixer the suspension is filtered. The powder is spread out on filter paper and allowed to dry for 1 hr at room temperature.

The acetone powder (6 g lots) is ground at 4 C in a mortar for 15 min with an equal weight of alumina. Each batch is suspended in 60 ml of 0.15 M KCl and several batches may then be pooled. The suspension is stirred for 1 hr, centrifuged for 1 hr at 15,000 × g and the supernatant fluid saved and kept cold. The precipitate is washed with one quarter of the initial volume of 0.15 M KCl. The combined supernatant fluids constitute the crude extract: It is dialyzed overnight against 0.03 M succinate, pH 6.3, containing 0.5 mM cysteine (Fraction I).

Purification

The results of a typical fractionation are shown in Table 2 (10). Unless stated otherwise, all operations are carried out between 0 and

† *A. vinelandii,* No. 9104 in the sixth edition (1958) of the American Type Culture Collection, Washington, D.C.

TABLE 2. *Purification of Polynucleotide Phosphorylase*
from Azotobacter Vinelandii (**10**)

Fraction	Description	Total Protein[a] (mg)	280/260	Total Units[c]	S.A.[c] (u/mg)	Percent Yield
	Preparation A					
I	Crude extract[b]	34,000	0.5	22,440	0.66	
II	$(NH_4)_2SO_4$ I (34–46)[b]	12,300	0.63	27,675	2.25	120
III	$Ca_3(PO_4)_2$ Gel (A_2E_1)	634	0.55	14,475	22.8	64
IV	$(NH_4)_2SO_4$ II (42–55)	157	0.93	12,364	78.7	55
V	DEAE-Sephadex	31	0.95	6,202	194	28
VI	DEAE-Cellulose	6	0.96	2,165	361	10
VII	$(NH_4)_2SO_4$ III	5	1.0	1,978	396	9
	Preparation B[d]					
IV	$(NH_4)_2SO_4$ II (42–55)	800	1.2	4,250	5.3	100
V	DEAE-Sephadex	59	1.4	2,538	43	60
VI	DEAE-Cellulose	29	1.3	2,325	80	57
VII	$(NH_4)_2SO_4$ III	25	1.3	2,675	107	62
VIII	G-200 Sephadex	5.6	1.1	1,250	223	30

[a] Protein determined by the procedure of Warburg and Christian (**18**).

[b] The assay used to evaluate these fractions (**3**) differs somewhat from the standard assay described in this article. The most important differences are in the concentrations of poly A and of $MgCl_2$, which are 10 and 7.5 mM, respectively (**3**).

[c] The data in this table have been recalculated from that of the original report (**10**) so that a unit of enzyme is equivalent to that defined in this article, namely, 1 μmole of ADP produced per 15 min. It should be pointed out that bovine serum albumin was not used in these assays.

[d] These data represent a summary of the later steps in a separate purification. The total units in Fraction IV are arbitrarily set at 100% yield.

4 C. Addition of all reagents is made with efficient mechanical stirring. Protein is determined by the procedure of Warburg and Christian (**18**). Fraction IV, the result of the second $(NH_4)_2SO_4$ fractionation, is suitable for the synthesis of polyribonucleotides.

FIRST $(NH_4)_2SO_4$ FRACTIONATION.† Fraction I is diluted to about 15 mg of protein per ml and 238 mg of solid $(NH_4)_2SO_4$ per ml of solution are slowly added (34% saturation). The suspension is

† As in the case of the *E. coli* purification, a saturated solution of $(NH_4)_2SO_4$ at 0 C is defined here as equivalent to the addition of 70 g of $(NH_4)_2SO_4$ per 100 ml of solution.

stirred for an additional 30 min and centrifuged for 45 min at 15,000 × g. The supernatant fluid is similarly brought to 46% saturation with the addition of 84 mg of solid $(NH_4)_2SO_4$ per ml of initial Fraction I and the supernatant fluid is discarded. The precipitate is suspended in 0.03 M phosphate, pH 6.3, containing 5mM cysteine and is then dialyzed overnight against the same buffer (Fraction II).

Ca_3PO_4 GEL. Fraction II is diluted to 10 mg of protein/ml and adjusted to pH 5.6 by adding acetate buffer at pH 5.2. For every 100 mg of protein, 32 mg of Ca_3PO_4 gel are added. Addition is very slow and is made with the tip of the pipette submerged under the surface of the solution, while the mixture itself is vigorously stirred. The mixture is stirred continuously for another 30 min. The gel (A_1) is separated by centrifugation and the supernatant fluid is treated, successively, in identical fashion, with 2 additional portions of gel, yielding gels A_2 and A_3. The gels are then eluted with 0.1 M phosphate buffer, pH 6.0; the gel is carefully crushed before addition of the eluting fluid, and the mixture is stirred for 30 min. The eluates are recovered by centrifugation yielding eluates A_1E_1, A_2E_1, and A_3E_1. Each portion of gel is then eluted, in similar fashion, with 0.01 M phosphate buffer, pH 7.4; this elution with pH 7.4 buffer is repeated. Thus eluates A_1E_2, A_1E_3, A_2E_2, A_2E_3, etc., are obtained. The quantitative nature of both the absorption and elution steps vary according to the state of the crude extract, the quality of the gel, and the care taken during the operations. Each of the eluates must be assayed since the bulk of the enzyme may be found in any of several fractions. In the original experiments (10), enzymatic activity was found mainly in either eluate A_2E_1 or A_3E_1 (Table 2). The eluate containing a good yield of enzyme activity with a high specific activity is dialyzed for 2 hr against 0.01 M phosphate buffer, pH 7.6 (Fraction III).

SECOND $(NH_4)_2SO_4$ FRACTIONATION. A solution saturated† with $(NH_4)_2SO_4$ at 4 C is prepared, adjusted to pH 7.4, and made 5 mM in β-mercaptoethanol. For each 100 ml of Fraction III, 72.2 ml of $(NH_4)_2SO_4$ solution is added (42% saturation); the tip of the pipette should be under the surface of the enzyme solution, and the flow rate is from 2 to 3 ml/min. The suspension is then mixed for an additional 30 min and the supernatant fluid is collected by centrifugation. To the supernatant fluid 49 ml of $(NH_4)_2SO_4$ solution are added for each 100 ml of Fraction III originally used (55% saturation). The

† As in the case of the *E. coli* purification, a saturated solution of $(NH_4)_2SO_4$ at 0 C is defined here is equivalent to the addition of 70 g of $(NH_4)_2SO_4$ per 100 ml of solution.

precipitate is collected. It is often useful to collect an additional precipitate; 10.5 ml of $(NH_4)_2SO_4$ solution may then be added per 100 ml of Fraction III (57% saturation). The bulk of the activity is usually recovered in the fraction collected between 42 and 55% saturation and is taken up in 0.01 M Tris, pH 7.6 (Fraction IV). At this stage the enzyme is stable and can be stored. Fraction IV is an excellent source of enzyme for the preparation of polyribonucleotides.

DEAE-SEPHADEX CHROMATOGRAPHY. A column of A-50 DEAE-Sephadex is prepared (1 ml for each 1–2 mg of protein), equilibrated with 0.1 M Tris buffer, pH 8.1, and stabilized at 4 C overnight. Fraction IV is made 0.1 M in Tris buffer, pH 8, and is absorbed onto the column; the column is then rinsed with a little of the same buffer. The column is then eluted with 1 column volume of 0.2 M Tris, pH 8.1; 30–40% of the protein but none of the enzyme is thereby eluted. Further elution is with a linear gradient between 0.3 and 0.7 M in Tris, pH 8; each solution is 350 ml. The flow rate is 1 drop/8 sec and 5-ml fractions are collected. The enzyme activity appears at tube number 61. Tubes 70 to 110 are pooled and dialyzed against 0.02 M Tris, pH 8.1 (Fraction V).

DEAE CHROMATOGRAPHY. Fraction V is absorbed onto a DEAE column equilibrated with 0.02 M Tris, pH 8.1. The enzyme is then eluted with 0.4 M Tris, pH 8.1; 5-ml fractions are collected. Tubes 3, 4, and 5 contain enzyme of the highest specific activity and are pooled (Fraction VI).

THIRD $(NH_4)_2SO_4$ FRACTIONATION. Fraction VI is dialyzed for 2 hr against 0.01 M Tris, pH 8. The dialysis fluid is then changed to saturated $(NH_4)_2SO_4$ containing 5 mM β-mercaptoethanol in order to concentrate the enzyme. Dialysis is carried out for 4 hr during which time the tube must be submerged in the solution. The resulting precipitate is recovered by centrifugation and dissolved in 0.01 M Tris, pH 8. The solution is dialyzed overnight against the same buffer. Generally 85% of the activity is recovered (Fraction VII).

SEPHADEX G-200. A further purification can be obtained by passing Fraction VII over a column of Sephadex G-200. A column 2.1 cm × 50 cm is suitable for 22 mg of protein: The column is equilibrated with 0.1 M Tris, pH 8. The enzyme solution (Fraction VII) is passed through the column and elution is effected with 0.1 M Tris, pH 8. The maximum flow rate is used (generally about 10 ml/hr). Four-milliliter fractions are collected; two major protein peaks are eluted and the enzyme activity is in the first peak (Fraction VIII).

PURIFICATION FROM *M. LYSODEIKTICUS*
(5,11,17)

Growth of Cells (17)†

Acetone-dried cells, which may be stored indefinitely at −20 C, are used in this preparation. Such dried cells may be obtained from the Miles Chemical Corporation, Takamine Division, Clifton, New Jersey. Cultures of *M. lysodeikticus* (American Type Culture Collection, No. 4698) are maintained on 2% agar slants containing the following: 1% yeast extract, 2% glucose, 0.87% K_2HPO_4, and 1% of a salt solution, which contains 4% $MgSO_4 \cdot 7H_2O$, 0.2% NaCl, 0.2% $FeSO_4 \cdot 7H_2O$, and 0.16% $MnSO_4$. The pH of the medium is brought to approximately pH 8.0 with 1 N KOH before the 2% agar is added. Sterilization time should be limited to 15 min of autoclaving at 15 lb/sq in. pressure. Several transfers should be made until the growth rate is maximal, i.e., nearly complete in 24 hr at room temperature. The cells can be stored on the agar slants in the deep freeze for periods up to 1 yr without loss of viability or of capacity for rapid growth rate.

The first step in the large scale production of the cells is the preparation of a 24-hr submerged culture in a series of Erlenmeyer flasks, each containing 90 ml of liquid medium prepared as follows. (Six such flasks are required for every 5-gallon carboy to be inoculated.) Forty-five milliliters of a solution containing 2% yeast extract, 0.85% $NaHCO_3$, and 2% of the above salt solution are placed in each 250-ml wide-mouthed Erlenmeyer flask to be used. The flasks are plugged with cotton and autoclaved for 15 min at 15 lb pressure. After cooling, 45 ml of a similarly sterilized solution of 4% glucose is added aseptically. The cells from a 24-hr agar slant are suspended in sterile water or in a portion of the above liquid media and transferred to the shake flasks (1 slant for 5 flasks). The cultures are agitated on a rotatory shaker for 24 hr at room temperature, at the end of which time the growth should be luxuriant.

Into a 5-gallon Pyrex carboy are added 16 liters of tap water, 136 g of $NaHCO_3$, 160 g of yeast extract, and 160 ml of the above salt solution. The surface of the medium is sprayed with Dow-Corning anti-foam A spray. A 1-liter beaker serves to cover the opening and neck of the bottle. The contents are sterilized, either by autoclaving at 15 lb

---

† The description of the growth of the cells is taken from the book by Steiner and Beers (17), pages 374–375, and is reproduced with the kind permission of the publisher.

pressure for 1 hr or by bringing the contents to a boil on two successive days. After cooling, a sterilized solution containing 320 g of glucose in 400 ml of water is added aseptically. The contents of approximately 6 Erlenmeyer shake flasks are added after the homogeneity of the culture in each has been checked by microscopic examination. As a general rule, however, the characteristic odor of these cultures can be used as an index of their purity. The medium is then aerated vigorously with a suitable cotton-filtered aeration system for 24 to 48 hr at room temperature. The pH of the culture should not fall below 7 and preferably not below 8.0. A low pH indicates contamination by yeast or by a spore-forming bacillus. The cells are harvested with a Sharples centrifuge or some other continuous centrifuge equipment. The yield of cells should be approximately 3.5 g/liter, based on dry weight of the cells. The cells are washed once with distilled water and then suspended in ice cold acetone. The suspension is filtered on a Büchner funnel and the cells are washed twice with acetone.

Preparation of Extract

A suspension of 40 g of dried cells, in 400 ml of 0.5% NaCl, is adjusted to pH 8.0 with approximately 20 ml of unbuffered 0.5 M tris (hydroxymethyl) aminomethane. The suspension is brought to 37 C and 100 mg of crystalline lysozyme (Worthington Biochemical Corporation) dissolved in 4 ml of H_2O is added and the suspension mixed well. A stop watch is started at the time of lysozyme addition. Lysis is allowed to proceed at 37 C, with intermittent stirring. After about 5 min, the suspension will be somewhat darker in color, and by 10 min it will set (like rennin-treated milk), becoming very viscous. From 1 to 2 min after setting, the formation of curds is visible as the suspension is stirred. The mixture is immediately placed in an ice-water bath; 200 ml of cold, saturated $(NH_4)_2SO_4$ is added and the mixture rapidly stirred. If lysis is allowed to continue too long, the extract will contain a large quantity of nucleic acid. Because it is sometimes difficult to determine the proper stopping point, the following rule of thumb may be convenient: Add the $(NH_4)_2SO_4$ one and one-half minutes after the suspension reaches its most viscous stage. Additional characteristics of the suspension at the time the $(NH_4)_2SO_4$ should be added include a glistening texture and a failure of the cell debris to adhere to the sides of the vessel. The suspension is centrifuged for 15 min at $20,000 \times g$. A clear, yellow-brown supernatant is obtained (Fraction I). The volume of Fraction I (410–440 ml) is a good indication of the success of the lysis step. Because of the critical nature of the lysis procedure, it is not practical to work up larger batches of cells, or several batches simultaneously. However, several lots of Fraction I may be worked up in one day and combined at this point. The next step in the preparation should be carried out on the same day. In order to assay Fraction I, a small sample is dialyzed against cold distilled water until free of $(NH_4)_2SO_4$.

Purification

The results of a typical fractionation are shown in Table 3 (5,11). Unless stated otherwise, all operations are carried out between 0 and 4 C and addition of all reagents to enzyme solutions is made with efficient mechanical stirring. Protein is determined by the procedure

TABLE 3. *Purification of Polynucleotide Phosphorylase from* M. lysodeikticus

Fraction	Description	Protein[a] (mg/ml)	Specific Activity (units/mg)	Total Units	280/260
I	Crude extract	2.1	0.18	440	0.75
II	$(NH_4)_2SO_4$ (30–65%)	21.0	0.38	529	1.07
III	$(NH_4)_2SO_4$ (43–57%)	19.2	0.64	403	1.41
IV	Protamine eluate				
V	Protamine eluate (dialyzed)	8.1	1.5	401	1.39
VI	$(NH_4)_2SO_4$ (40–60%, pH 6.3)	14.4	1.9	258	1.54
VII	Zinc-Sephadex	0.26	32	199	1.72
VIII	DEAE-Cellulose:				
	Peak fraction	0.14	48.3	42	1.61
	Total recovered			185	

[a] Protein is determined by the method of Lowry and co-workers (20).

of Lowry and co-workers (20). Fraction VI, the result of $(NH_4)_2SO_4$ fractionation at pH 6.3, is suitable for the synthesis of polyribonucleotides. It is stable for years if stored at −20 C.

PRECIPITATION BY $(NH_4)_2SO_4$. Fraction I, which is 30% saturated with $(NH_4)_2SO_4$, is brought to 65% saturation by the addition of 21.7 g of solid $(NH_4)_2SO_4$ per 100 ml. After stirring for 20 additional min, the precipitate is collected by centrifugation at 20,000 × g for 15 min and dissolved in a minimum amount of 0.1 M Tris buffer, pH 8.1. This solution is dialyzed against distilled H_2O until free of $(NH_4)_2SO_4$; the water is changed every hour and 4–5 hr is usually sufficient (Fraction II). A 280:260 ratio of about 1.0 indicates proper lysis. Fraction II may be stored briefly at 4 C, or for longer periods, at −20 C.

SECOND $(NH_4)_2SO_4$ FRACTIONATION. Fraction II is diluted to 10 mg of protein/ml, and simultaneously made 0.1 M in Tris buffer, pH 8.1. The solution is brought to 43% saturation with $(NH_4)_2SO_4$ by the addition of 24.4 g of solid $(NH_4)_2SO_4$ per 100 ml. The supernatant fluid is collected by centrifugation at 20,000 × g for 15 min, and 8.7 g of solid $(NH_4)_2SO_4$ is added per 100 ml to obtain 57% saturation. The precipitate is collected by centrifugation and dissolved in 0.1 M Tris, pH 8.1 (about 10–15 ml of buffer for each 40 g of original cells). The solution is dialyzed against 0.1 M Tris, pH 8.1, containing 1 mM EDTA for 3 to 4 hr; the dialysis fluid is changed every hour (Fraction III). Fraction III may be stored frozen.

PROTAMINE STEP. Fraction III is routinely diluted to 4.3 mg of protein/ml. The procedure described here (5,11) has been successful repeatedly, with a given batch of protamine sulfate (Nutritional Biochemicals Corporation). However, other batches of protamine sulfate have given different results. An alternate procedure is therefore included. This alternate procedure appeared satisfactory† when tested with five different preparations of protamine sulfate obtained from both Nutritional Biochemicals Corporation and Sigma Chemical Company. The most detailed studies were carried out with a preparation of protamine sulfate, Grade I, from Sigma Chemical Company.

The originally published procedure is as follows: With the aid of efficient stirring, 14.4 ml of a 0.5% protamine sulfate solution per 100 ml of diluted Fraction III are added dropwise. After stirring for 1 hr, the suspension is centrifuged for 10 min at 7000 × g and the supernatant fluid discarded. The precipitate is eluted with 20 ml of 0.5 M Tris, pH 8.1, per 100 ml of diluted starting material. Care is taken to disperse the sticky precipitate, and the mixture is kept for 1 hr, with stirring. The supernatant fluid (Fraction IV) is collected by centrifugation and dialyzed in 15-ml batches for 2.5 hr against 100 volumes of 0.01 M Tris, pH 8.1–1 mM β-mercaptoethanol. The dialysis fluid is changed after 1 hour. Any precipitate that forms is removed by centrifugation. This fraction (Fraction V) may be stored frozen.

For the alternative procedure, 5 ml of a 0.5% protamine sulfate solution are added to each 100 ml of diluted Fraction III. The suspension is allowed to stir for 30 min and is then centrifuged for 10 min at 7000 × g. The supernatant fluid contains the enzyme activity and is dialyzed for 2.5 hr against 0.01 M Tris, pH 8.1, containing 10^{-3} M β-mercaptoethanol. The dialysis fluid is changed after 1 hr. This material is then treated as described below for Fraction V.

† R. E. Thach and M. F. Singer, unpublished experiments.

$(NH_4)_2SO_4$ FRACTIONATION AT pH 6.3. Fraction V is adjusted to pH 6.3 with 1 M acetic acid. Internal electrodes are used. The solution is then brought to 40% saturation with $(NH_4)_2SO_4$ by the addition of 22.6 g of solid salt per 100 ml. After stirring for 10 min, the supernatant fluid is collected by centrifugation for 10 min at 10,000 × g. The supernatant fluid (pH maintained at 6.3) is made 60% saturated with $(NH_4)_2SO_4$ by the addition of 12 g of solid salt per 100 ml, and the precipitate is collected as above. It is dissolved in 0.2 of the volume of Fraction V of 0.5 M Tris, pH 8.1, and dialyzed for 2.5 hr against 200 volumes of 0.01 M Tris, pH 8.1–0.001 M β-mercaptoethanol 1–0.001 M EDTA. The dialysis fluid is changed every hour. The enzyme solution (Fraction VI) may be stored frozen for several years. It is stable for at least 2 weeks at 4 C.

Fraction VI has been used routinely for the preparation of polymers. Polymerization reactions should be run at pH 9.

ZINC-SEPHADEX. Fraction VI is diluted to 10 mg of protein/ml with cold distilled water. Small samples, usually 0.1 ml, are treated with varying amounts of 0.1 M $ZnCl_2$ (from 0.03 to 0.2 volumes), the precipitates removed, and the activity and protein concentration of the supernatant fluids determined. It is essential to perform this preliminary experiment as various preparations behave somewhat differently. The condition giving the best purification and yield is then applied to the main portion of diluted Fraction VI. Generally, from 0.1 to 0.15 volumes of 0.1 M $ZnCl_2$ have been optimal. In the preparation described here, 0.11 volume of 0.1 M $ZnCl_2$ is used. Thus, 1.45 ml of 0.1 M $ZnCl_2$ is added, dropwise, with mechanical stirring to 13.2 ml of diluted Fraction VI. The mixture is stirred for an additional 15 min and centrifuged for 10 min at 10,000 × g. The supernatant fluid (13.3 ml) is passed through a column of Sephadex G-75† equilibrated with 0.01 M Tris buffer, pH 8.2, 0.001 M EDTA, 0.001 M β-mercaptoethanol, and 0.25 M NaCl. A column containing 40 g of G-75 Sephadex (total volume approximately 420 ml, void volume, 130 ml) was used in the preparation described here. The column can be used repeatedly. It is washed with several column volumes of the above buffer mixture just before and after each use. The activity appears at the void volume. The specific activity of the various fractions is determined and those

---

† Sephadex is washed three times with absolute alcohol and allowed to dry over silica gel and paraffin, under reduced pressure. It is then suspended in H_2O and allowed to settle for 5 min; the supernatant fluid is discarded. This procedure is repeated until the supernatant fluid is clear. The Sephadex is washed three times with 1 mM EDTA, and a column poured. The column is equilibrated with 0.05 M NaCl and the void volume determined with hemoglobin. The column is then washed with the buffer required for the preparation.

of highest specific activity are pooled (Fraction VII). A yellow color generally accompanies activity at this step.

DEAE-CELLULOSE CHROMATOGRAPHY. Fraction VII (38 ml) is diluted threefold (final volume, 114 ml) with 0.01 M Tris, pH 8.2, 0.001 M EDTA, and 0.001 M β-mercaptoethanol. This enzyme solution is passed slowly through a column (2.8 cm^2 × 7.2 cm) of DEAE-cellulose (Brown and Company) that was previously equilibrated with 0.01 M Tris-HCl, pH 8.2, 0.001 M β-mercaptoethanol, and 0.001 M MgCl$_2$ (mixer solution). Then two 5-ml portions of the mixer solution are used to wash the last bit of enzyme solution onto the column. A 5-ml head of the mixer solution is applied, and a nonlinear gradient elution started. The mixer flask contains 250 ml of mixer solution, and the reservoir contains 250 ml of the same solution made 0.5 M in NaCl. Fractions of approximately 5 ml are collected, and the flow rate is approximately 3.3 ml/min. Approximately 93% of the units placed on the column are recovered in the fractions between 180 and 248 ml of effluent. The yellow color that accompanies polynucleotide phosphorylase in the earlier steps is almost completely lost on this chromatography. Thus, the ratio of absorbancy at 404 mμ to that at 280 mμ is 0.51 at a cumulative volume of 173 ml, and 0.11 at a cumulative volume of 208 ml. The specific activities of the peak fractions ranged from 30 to 48. The specific activity and recovery in the peak tube are given in Table 3.

CONCENTRATION OF DEAE-CELLULOSE ELUATE. Fraction VIII may be concentrated in the following way: It is diluted twofold with the mixer solution (above) and readsorbed onto a small DEAE-cellulose column. The enzyme is then eluted with the mixer solution containing 0.4 M NaCl. A 10- to 20-fold concentration is easily obtained.

Storage

The purified enzyme, either directly off the DEAE column, or concentrated, can be stored for several years at −20 C.

PROPERTIES OF ENZYME ISOLATED FROM THE VARIOUS SOURCES

The properties of these enzymes have been described in detail in recent review articles (1,21,22,23). Therefore, only brief mention of certain properties relevant to enzyme preparation will be made here.

Contamination with Other Enzymes

Enzymes prepared from *E. coli* and *A. vinelandii* in the manner described above were tested and found to be essentially free of the following activities: ribonuclease, phosphatase and ribonucleoside diphosphate kinases (3,10). Similarly, preparations of *M. lysodeikticus* enzyme (Fraction VIII, Table 3) are essentially free of myokinase and ribonuclease activity (11).

Molecular Weight

The molecular weight of the *E. coli, A. vinelandii,* and *M. lysodeikticus* enzyme is of the order of 200,000 (3,10,11).

Dependence on Oligonucleotides

Highly purified *M. lysodeikticus* enzyme requires an oligonucleotide primer† for the polymerization of nucleoside diphosphate (5,11). These oligonucleotides must have a free, terminal 3'-hydroxyl group in order to be effective. Polymerization proceeds by the addition of nucleoside monophosphate groups to the 3'-hydroxyl of the terminal residue of the growing chain. It has recently been shown that essentially every polymer chain contains the oligonucleotide primer molecule at the starting position (24). Thus, it appears that little or no *de novo* chain initiation occurs.

With *E. coli* or *A. vinelandii* enzyme prepared as described above no oligonucleotide primer requirement is apparent under optimal conditions for polymerization (3,10). Furthermore, with the *E. coli* enzyme it has been shown that new poly A chains are synthesized without the intervention of possible polyribonucleotide contaminating the enzyme preparation. With these *E. coli* fractions, it is possible to induce a lag phase by various treatments (3). These lags can be eliminated by oligonucleotides; oligonucleotides with a free 3'-hydroxyl group or with a monophosphate ester at the 3'-hydroxyl group both serve to eliminate the lag (3).

REFERENCES

1. GRUNBERG-MANAGO, M. 1961. *In* The enzymes, P. D. Boyer, H. Lardy, and K. Myrback, eds. Academic Press, New York. 2nd ed., Vol. 5, p. 257.

† In this discussion of polynucleotide phosphorylase, the term "primer" is used to indicate a polyribonucleotide chain that serves as a starting point for chain proliferation. It does not mean a template.

2. GRUNBERG-MANAGO, M., P. J. ORTIZ, and S. OCHOA. 1956. Biochim. Biophys. Acta. *20:* 269.

3. WILLIAMS, F. R., and M. GRUNBERG-MANAGO. 1964. Biochim. Biophys. Acta. *89:* 66.

4. BERENBLUM, E., and E. CHAIN. 1938. Biochem. J. *32:* 295.

5. SINGER, M. F., and J. K. GUSS. 1962. J. Biol. Chem. *237:* 182.

6. LITTAUER, U. Z., and A. KORNBERG. 1957. J. Biol. Chem. *226:* 1077.

7. SINGER, M. F. Unpublished.

8. RACKER, E. Personal communication.

9. AMES, B. N., and D. T. DUBIN. 1960. J. Biol. Chem. *235:* 769.

10. THANG, D. C. In preparation.

11. SINGER, M. F., and B. M. O'BRIEN. 1963. J. Biol. Chem. *238:* 328.

12. OCHOA, S., and S. MII. 1961. J. Biol. Chem. *236:* 3303.

13. OCHOA, S., J. S. KRAKOW, and C. BASILIO. 1963. *In* Methods in enzymology, S. P. Colowick and N. O. Kaplan, eds. Academic Press, New York. Vol. VI, p. 3.

14. GRUNBERG-MANAGO, M. Personal communication.

15. SINGER, M. F. 1963. J. Biol. Chem. *238:* 336.

16. OCHOA, S. Personal communication.

17. STEINER, R. F., and R. F. BEERS, JR. 1961. *In* Polynucleotides, Elsevier Publishing Company, Amsterdam.

18. WARBURG, O., and W. CHRISTIAN. 1941. Biochem. Z. *310:* 384.

19. MARTIN, R. G., and B. N. AMES. 1961. J. Biol. Chem. *236:* 1372.

20. LOWRY, O. H., N. J. ROSEBROUGH, A. L. FARR, and R. J. RANDALL. 1951. J. Biol. Chem. *193:* 265.

21. GRUNBERG-MANAGO, M. 1962. Ann. Rev. Biochem. *31:* 301.

22. KHORANA, H. G. 1960. *In* The nucleic acids, E. Chargaff and J. N. Davidson, eds., Academic Press, New York. Vol. III, p. 105.

23. GRUNBERG-MANAGO, M. 1963. *In* Progress in nucleic acid research, J. N. Davidson and W. E. Cohn, eds. Academic Press, New York. Vol. I.

24. THACH, R. E. 1963. Thesis, Harvard University.

DNA Polymerase from

Escherichia coli

CHARLES C. RICHARDSON

DEPARTMENT OF BIOLOGICAL CHEMISTRY

HARVARD MEDICAL SCHOOL

BOSTON, MASSACHUSETTS

ASSAY

DNA† polymerase purified from *Escherichia coli* (1) catalyzes the synthesis of deoxyribonucleic acid when the triphosphates of the four deoxyribonucleosides commonly found in DNA are incubated with a primer DNA. The reaction may be formulated thus:

$$
\begin{matrix} n \ \text{dAPPP} \\ n \ \text{dGPPP} \\ n \ \text{dCPPP} \\ n \ \text{dTPPP} \end{matrix} + \text{DNA} \rightleftharpoons \text{DNA} - \begin{bmatrix} \text{dAP} \\ \text{dGP} \\ \text{dCP} \\ \text{dTP} \end{bmatrix}_n + 4(n)\text{PP}
$$

Two assays (2) are used to follow the purification of polymerase: a thymus DNA-primed assay, used in the early stages of purification (Fractions I through VI, Table 1) and a dAT-primed assay, used in the subsequent purification steps. Both assays measure the conversion

† The following abbreviations have been used in this chapter: DNA, RNA: deoxyribonucleic acid, ribonucleic acid; dAT, a copolymer of deoxyadenylate and deoxythymidylate; dGdC, polymer consisting of homopolymers of deoxyguanyl-ate and deoxycytidylate; dATP or dAPPP, deoxyadenosine triphosphate; dTTP or dTPPP, deoxythymidine triphosphate; dGTP or dGPPP, deoxyguanosine triphosphate; dCTP or dCPPP, deoxycytidine triphosphate; PP, pyrophosphate.

of radioactively labeled deoxyribonucleoside triphosphates into an acid-insoluble product.

Reagents

"ACTIVATED" THYMUS DNA-PRIMED ASSAY

1. The reaction mixture (total volume 0.3 ml) contains

> 0.07 M glycine buffer, pH 9.2
> 7 mM $MgCl_2$
> 1 mM 2-mercaptoethanol
> dTTP, dCTP, and dGTP, 10 mμmoles of each
> P^{32}-labeled dATP† (approximately 3×10^6 cpm/μmole), 10 mμ-moles
> "Activated" calf thymus DNA, 40 mμmoles of DNA-phosphorus (for preparation, see below)
> Enzyme, 0.02–0.15 units in a volume of 0.02 ml

2. 1 N perchloric acid

"Activated" thymus DNA (3) is prepared by partially degrading calf thymus DNA with pancreatic deoxyribonuclease. The reaction mixture (10 ml) consists of 0.05 M Tris buffer, pH 7.5, 0.005 M $MgCl_2$, 2.5 mg of thymus DNA, 5 mg of bovine serum albumin, and 5×10^{-3} μg of crystalline pancreatic deoxyribonuclease. After incubation for 15 min at 37 C, the solution is heated for 5 min at 80 C and then immediately cooled in an ice bath. The solution is stored at −20 C.

dAT-PRIMED ASSAY

1. The reaction mixture (total volume 0.3 ml) contains

> 0.07 M potassium phosphate buffer, pH 7.4
> 7 mM Mg Cl_2
> 1 mM 2-mercaptoethanol
> dTTP, 10 mμmoles
> P^{32}-labeled dATP (approximately 3×10^6 cpm/μmole), 10 mμ-moles
> dAT copolymer (4), 6 mμmoles of DNA-phosphorus
> Enzyme, 0.02–0.15 unit in a volume of 0.02 ml

2. 1 N perchloric acid

Procedure

In both the thymus DNA-primed and the dAT-primed assay the reaction mixture is incubated for 30 min at 37 C. The reaction is

---

† P32-, C14-, or H3-labeled dATP, dCTP, dGTP, or dTTP may be used in the reaction mixture with identical results.

stopped by chilling and the addition of 0.5 ml of cold 1 N perchloric acid. After 5 min at 0 C, 2.5 ml of cold water are added. A glass filter (Whatman GF/C glass paper, 2.4-cm diameter) is placed on the wire mesh of a stainless steel filter assembly and the mixture is filtered with the aid of suction. The paper is washed with three 3-ml portions of cold water, transferred to a planchet, dried, and counted in a gas-flow counter. When H^3- or C^{14}-labeled deoxyribonucleoside triphosphates are used, the filter paper is transferred to a scintillation vial and dried. The filter is covered with 10 ml of a scintillator solution consisting of 4 g of 2,5-diphenyloxazole (PPO) and 50 mg of 1,4-bis-2-(4-methyl-5-phenyloxazolyl)-benzene (dimethyl POPOP) per liter of toluene and counted in a liquid-scintillation counter.

A control reaction mixture without enzyme is incubated and treated as described above. For either assay the control incubations contain 0.1–0.3% of the added radioactivity. A more time-consuming centrifuge assay has been described (1) in which control incubation mixtures containing less than 0.1% of the total radioactivity are obtained. The latter procedure is useful when carrying out assays that contain radioactive substrate of specific activity greater than that described above.

A unit of polymerase activity is defined as the amount catalyzing the incorporation of 10 mμmoles of total nucleotide into an acid-insoluble product during the standard period of incubation. Thus, the radioactivity incorporated in the thymus-primed assay is corrected to give the total nucleotide incorporation based on a guanosine and cytidine content of 43%; the radioactivity incorporated in the dAT-primed assay is multiplied by 2. The amount of radioactivity made acid insoluble is proportional to the amount of enzyme added from 0.02 to 0.15 unit of enzyme.

Enzyme Dilutions

Dilutions of enzyme for assay are made by addition to a solution composed of 0.05 M Tris buffer, pH 7.5, 0.1 M ammonium sulfate, 0.01 M 2-mercaptoethanol, and bovine plasma albumin, 1 mg/ml. Samples of the dilute enzyme solution are added to the reaction mixtures within 15 min of dilution.

Assay of Enzyme Fractions During Purification; Change in Priming Activity of Native DNA as a Result of Purification of Polymerase

During the purification of polymerase, an apparent decrease in activity is encountered when native DNA is used as primer (2). The priming activity of native thymus DNA decreases by approximately 50, 86, and 97% when assayed with Fractions IV, VII, and IX, respectively. Through the ethanol fractionation (Step VI) this decrease in priming capacity can be circumvented by the limited pretreatment of the DNA with pancreatic deoxyribonuclease ("activated" DNA), an endonuclease which cleaves the phosphodiester bond to produce 3'-hydroxyl and 5'-phosphoryl termini. Therefore, the "activated" thymus DNA-primed assay is used in the early purification procedures (Fractions I through VI, Table 1). As the purification of the enzyme proceeds, the ability of "activated" DNA to direct DNA synthesis also decreases. The substitution of the dAT copolymer as primer gives the expected recovery of enzymatic activity at each stage of purification and is used in the subsequent purification steps for this reason. Because of the susceptibility of the dAT polymer to the nucleases present in Fractions I through IV, poor proportionality is obtained and the "activated" thymus DNA-primed assay is used for the early purification steps.

The progressive decrease in the priming capacity of DNA during the course of purification of polymerase is largely due to the removal of endonuclease I (5) and exonuclease III (6,7). Endonuclease I produces 3'-hydroxyl and 5'-phosphoryl end groups on DNA, and these groups have been shown to enhance the rate of DNA synthesis by the purified enzyme (8). Exonuclease III, removed from polymerase during chromatography on hydroxylapatite (Step IX), activates the primer both by removing inhibitory 3'-phosphoryl end groups from the primer and by producing single-stranded termini on the primer (8). The single-stranded regions of these molecules can be copied by polymerase at a more rapid rate than native, helical DNA (9).

ISOLATION PROCEDURE (2)

Unless otherwise stated, all operations are carried out at 0–4 C. All centrifugations are performed at 15,000 × g for 10 min. The pH of each buffer is determined at room temperature and at a concentration of 0.05 M. The purification procedure and results of a typical preparation are summarized in Table 1.

Growth of Cells and Preparation of Extracts

E. coli strain B is grown in a medium containing 1.1% K_2HPO_4, 0.85% KH_2PO_4, 0.6% Difco yeast extract, and 1% glucose; the cells are harvested during the late exponential phase of growth. Cells stored at −20 C show no loss of activity for 6 months. Cells grown and har-

TABLE 1. *Purification of DNA polymerase from E. coli (2)*[a]

Fraction No. and Step	Units[b] ($\times 10^{-4}$)	Protein (mg/ml)	Specific Activity (units/mg)	Yield (%)
I. Extract	297	20.0	3.8	100
II. Streptomycin	139	7.3	18.5	47
III. Autolysis	119	1.6	73.2	40
IV. Ammonium sulfate	106	5.0	148.0	36
V. Acid precipitation	100	3.5	200.0	33
VI. Ethanol	91	4.4	590.0	30
VI. Ethanol	301	4.4	2,030	30
VII. DEAE-cellulose	227	5.5	7,600	23
VIII. Phosphocellulose	140	0.25	19,000	14
IX. Hydroxylapatite	129	0.25	18,800	13

[a] The purification procedure and results of a typical preparation. The preparation summarized in Table 1 was carried out on an 8.8-kg batch. Steps I through IV may be carried out on a smaller scale, and the fractions stored until sufficient quantities are accumulated (see the text).

[b] The assay utilizing "activated" calf thymus DNA is routinely used for assaying Fractions I to VI. The dAT-primed assay is used for the subsequent purification (Fractions VI to IX). The activity of Fraction VI has been measured in both assays.

vested commercially have been used successfully for the isolation of the enzyme.

Partially thawed cells (450 g wet weight) are mixed with 300 ml of glycylglycine buffer, 0.05 M, pH 7.0, in a large Waring Blendor (5-liter capacity) equipped with a cooling jacket and connected to a variable transformer. After 5 min of slow stirring 1350 g of acid-washed glass beads (Superbrite, average diameter 200 μ, Minnesota Mining and Manufacturing Company) are slowly added to the suspension. When the mixture appears homogeneous, stirring is increased to one-third of maximal speed. After 20 min, an additional 1200 ml of the same buffer is added, and the mixing is continued for 10 min at reduced speed to prevent excessive foaming. During the homogenization procedure the temperature is kept below 12 C. The beads are allowed to settle out and the broken cell suspension is decanted and saved. An additional 800 ml of buffer is added to the glass beads and the residual broken cells are extracted by a 10-min homogenization at slow speed. The beads are again allowed to settle out, and the supernatant fluid is decanted and combined with the first supernatant fluid. The combined supernatants are then centrifuged and the supernatant fluid

(2000 ml) is saved. This fraction (Fraction I) may be stored at 0 C for 2 weeks without loss of activity.

Streptomycin Precipitation

To 10 liters of extract (Fraction I) are added 10 liters of Tris buffer, 0.05 M, pH 7.5, containing 0.001 M EDTA; then, with constant stirring, 1440 ml of a 5% streptomycin sulfate solution are added over a 45-min period. After 10 min, the suspension is centrifuged and the supernatant fluid is discarded. The thick, sticky precipitate is transferred to a beaker and 1000 ml of potassium phosphate buffer, 0.05 M, pH 7.4, are added. The precipitate is suspended by slow mechanical stirring for approximately 12 hr, and the final volume is adjusted to 2500 ml by the addition of the same buffer. Fraction II is stored at 0 C until sufficient quantities are obtained for the subsequent procedures. The fraction may be stored for 1 month without detectable loss of activity.

Autolysis

Eleven liters of Fraction II are adjusted to 0.003 M in $MgCl_2$ by the addition of 65 ml of 0.5 M $MgCl_2$. The suspension is incubated at 30 C for 7–12 hr, until 95% of the ultraviolet-absorbing material at 260 mμ is rendered acid soluble. The assay consists of removing 1-ml samples of the incubation mixture at intervals of 1 hr, centrifuging, and determining the optical density of the supernatant fluid at 260 mμ, after a suitable dilution in 0.05 M Tris buffer, pH 7.4. A portion of the supernatant fluid is precipitated with an equal volume of cold 1 N perchloric acid and the optical density of the acid-soluble fraction is determined after centrifugation. When the digestion is completed the autolysate is chilled to 0 C; the protein precipitate that settled out during the digestion is removed by centrifugation. The supernatant fluid (Fraction III) is stored at 0 C, and is stable for at least 1 week. During the several hours of nucleic acid digestion at 30 C, there is less than 10% loss in enzymatic activity. However, if the incubation is allowed to continue beyond the complete acid solubilization of the nucleic acid, there is a further loss in enzymatic activity to the extent of 10% in 60 min.

Ammonium Sulfate Fractionation

To 10 liters of Fraction III are added 50 ml of 0.2 M glutathione and 50 ml of 0.2 M EDTA. Over a 60-min period, 3 kg of ammonium sulfate are added with stirring, and after 30 min at 4 C, the precipitate is removed by centrifugation. To the supernatant fluid an additional

1.15 kg of ammonium sulfate is added, with stirring, over a 60-min period and, after 30 min at 4 C, the precipitate that forms is collected by centrifugation. This precipitate is dissolved in 1.1 liters of potassium phosphate buffer, 0.02 M, pH 7.2 (Fraction IV). Fraction IV may be stored for 3 years at −20 C without loss of activity.

Acid Precipitation

Fraction IV (1.1 liters) is dialyzed for 12 hr against 35 liters of sodium acetate buffer, pH 5.55 (the pH is determined at 25 C at an ionic strength of 0.08), ionic strength 0.08, and the resulting precipitate is removed by centrifugation. The supernatant fluid (Fraction V) is immediately subjected to ethanol fractionation.

Ethanol Fractionation

To 1.1 liters of Fraction V are added, with constant stirring, 46 ml of 100% ethanol (−20 C) from a burette over a 60-min period. The temperature of the solution is not allowed to rise above −1 C after the addition of approximately 10 ml of ethanol. After 10 min at 0 C, the precipitate is removed by centrifugation at 0 C. To the supernatant fluid are added, with stirring, 110 ml of 100% ethanol (−20 C) from a burette over a 60-min period. The temperature of the solution is gradually decreased until the final temperature is −4 C. The solution is permitted to warm to 0 C, and after sitting for 10 min at 0 C the precipitate is collected by centrifugation at 0 C and dissolved in 350 ml of 0.02 M K_2HPO_4 containing 0.01 M 2-mercaptoethanol (Fraction VI).

DEAE-cellulose Fractionation

A column of DEAE-cellulose (16 cm^2 × 10 cm) is prepared and washed with approximately 5 liters of 0.02 M K_2HPO_4 containing 0.01 M 2-mercaptoethanol and 0.002 M sodium EDTA, followed by equilibration with 0.02 M K_2HPO_4 containing 0.01 M 2-mercaptoethanol. The 350 ml of Fraction VI (1.5 g of protein) are applied to the column at the rate of 250 ml/hr. The adsorbent is then washed with 160 ml of 0.02 M K_2HPO_4 containing 0.01 M 2-mercaptoethanol. The protein is eluted at a flow rate of 250 ml/hr with potassium phosphate buffers, pH 6.5, containing 0.01 M 2-mercaptoethanol as follows; 160 ml of 0.05 M, 160 ml of 0.1 M, and finally 160 ml of 0.2 M. The 0.2 M eluate is collected in 10-ml fractions. Approximately 70% of the enzyme applied to the adsorbent is obtained in the 0.2 M eluate. The fractions that contain enzyme of specific activity greater than 5000 units/mg of protein (approximately 60% of that applied to the adsorbent) are pooled (Fraction VII).

Phosphocellulose Chromatography

A column of phosphocellulose (15 cm² × 21 cm) is prepared and washed with 5 liters of potassium phosphate buffer, 0.02 M, pH 6.5, containing 0.01 M 2-mercaptoethanol. With the same buffer, 50 ml of Fraction VII (275 mg of protein) are diluted to 500 ml and applied to the column with pressure at the rate of 500 ml/hr. The adsorbent is washed with 160 ml of the above buffer. A linear gradient of elution is applied with 0.02 M and 0.3 M potassium phosphate at pH 6.5 as the limiting concentrations. The total volume of the gradient is 1500 ml, and 0.01 M 2-mercaptoethanol is present throughout the gradient. The flow rate is 180 ml/hr, and 20-ml fractions are collected. Of the applied activity, 75% is eluted in a peak between 2.7 and 3.8 resin bed volumes of effluent (0.17 to 0.25 M potassium phosphate). The peak fractions containing enzyme of specific activity ranging from 14,000 to 18,000 units/mg of protein (65% of that applied to the adsorbent) are pooled (Fraction VIII). The elution of protein is followed spectrophotometrically at 280 mμ, which permits a rapid identification of the enzyme peak, since the polymerase activity is contained in the only major protein peak in this region of the chromatogram.

Hydroxylapatite Chromatography

A column of hydroxylapatite (1 cm² × 10 cm) is prepared and washed with 350 ml of potassium phosphate buffer, 0.02 M, pH 6.5, containing 0.01 M 2-mercaptoethanol. Fraction VIII (20 ml containing 5 mg of protein) is dialyzed against 2 liters of the same buffer and applied to the adsorbent with pressure at a rate of 20 ml/hr. The adsorbent is washed with 12 ml of potassium phosphate buffer, 0.05 M, pH 6.5, containing 0.01 M 2-mercaptoethanol. A linear gradient of elution is applied with 0.05 M and 0.3 M potassium phosphate, pH 6.5, as limiting concentrations. The total volume of the gradient is 130 ml, and 0.01 M 2-mercaptoethanol is present throughout the gradient. The flow rate is maintained at approximately 5 ml/hr and 2-ml fractions are collected. Of the activity applied to the adsorbent, approximately 90% is eluted in a single, sharp peak between 8.0 and 9.4 resin bed volumes (0.20 to 0.25 M potassium phosphate). The elution of protein may be followed spectrophotometrically at 280 mμ. The specific activity of the enzyme is constant across the peak. The fractions of the entire peak are pooled (Fraction IX) and stored at 0 C in an ice bath. At a concentration of 0.3 mg/mm, the hydroxylapatite enzyme, stored at 0 C for 1 year, retained 75% of its initial activity. Chromatography on hydroxylapatite of from 5 to 100 mg of protein may be carried out by increasing the resin bed volume (column height kept constant) and gradient volume proportionately.

Concentration of Hydroxylapatite Fraction

The pooled hydroxylapatite fractions may be reduced in volume by pressure dialysis against 4 liters of potassium phosphate buffer, 0.10 M, pH 7.0, containing 0.01 M 2-mercaptoethanol. A 30-cm length of Visking size 8 dialysis tubing is filled with the enzyme solution. With one end open to the atmosphere, by means of a glass tube passed through a rubber stopper, the tubing is placed in a 4-liter suction flask containing buffer. A vacuum is applied to the flask by means of a water suction pump, and after approximately 20 hr the solution can be reduced to a volume of 1–5 ml. Additional enzyme solution may be added to the dialysis tubing as the volume decreases. Approximately 10% of the activity is lost during concentration of the enzyme.

The concentrated enzyme may be stored at 0 C in an ice bath or it may be dialyzed against potassium phosphate buffer, 0.10 M, pH 7.0, containing 0.01 M glutathione and then frozen at −20 C. In either case the enzyme has been found to retain 80% of its activity after 1 year.

PROPERTIES OF THE ENZYME

Physical Properties of the Enzyme

The purified enzyme (Fraction IX) appears to be a homogeneous protein by chromatography on hydroxylapatite, by sedimentation analysis, and by starch gel electrophoresis. Attempts to further purify the enzyme have not resulted in any change in the specific activity. The ratio of absorbance at 280 mμ to that at 260 mμ is 1.6 and suggests that less than 0.3% (by weight) nucleic acid is present. The amino acid composition of the enzyme is similar to that of the total protein of E. coli. The molecular weight of the purified protein is 1×10^5 (2).

Exonuclease Activity in the Purified Polymerase Preparation

A nuclease activity (exonuclease II) (2,10) is present throughout the purification procedure at a constant ratio to polymerase. There is no separation of the two activities during either phophocellulose or hydroxylapatite chromatography. Attempts to purify either enzyme activity further have not altered the ratio of the two activities. Both activities are inactivated at the same rate by heat and with urea.

The nuclease carries out an exonucleolytic attack on native and denatured DNA, hydrolyzing it quantitatively to deoxyribonucleoside 5'-phosphates. The initial site of attack is at the 3'-hydroxyl end of a polydeoxyribonucleotide chain; the enzyme is unable to initiate hydrolysis at a 5'-phosphoryl or 5'-hydroxyl terminus, nor can it degrade oligonucleotides bearing 3'-phosphomonoester groups.

When the polymerase and exonuclease activities are measured under optimal conditions for each, the ratio of the rate of nucleotide incorporation by polymerase to the rate of hydrolysis by the exonuclease is 2.8; at pH 7.4 the ratio is increased to 6.0 and at pH 7.0 to 10. Thus, the nuclease, exhibiting its optimal activity at pH 9.0, hydrolyzes DNA at a very slow rate in the neutral pH range where polymerase activity is maximal. In addition, nucleotides removed by exonuclease action during the course of polymerization would be expected to be replaced without residual effects provided the supply of deoxyribonucleoside triphosphates remains sufficient.

Contamination with Other Enzymes

The purified enzyme (Fraction IX) appears to be free of endonuclease as judged by the following criteria: (a) The kinetics of inactivation of the transforming activity of DNA from *Bacillus subtilis* (2,9) and (b) studies on the effect of polymerase on the genetic activity of phage λ DNA (11) indicate the absence of endonuclease. (c) The cyclic deoxythymidine trinucleotide is insusceptible to attack by the enzyme (10). There is no detectable exonuclease I (12) or exonuclease III (6) activity in Fraction IX when each is measured under optimal conditions. Fraction IX contains no detectable ribonuclease activity as measured by the formation of acid-soluble products from radioactively labeled ribosomal RNA, or as measured by the amino acid acceptor activity of sRNA from *E. coli* after incubation with polymerase. The enzyme preparation has no measurable amounts of nucleotidase activity.

Reaction Requirements

EFFECT OF pH AND DIVALENT METALS. Maximal activity is obtained at pH 7.4 in potassium phosphate or Tris-HCl buffer with either native DNA or the synthetic dAT copolymer as primer. The purified enzyme requires added Mg^{2+}. In the absence of $MgCl_2$ there is no detectable activity. The optimal Mg^{2+} concentration at pH 7.4

in potassium phosphate buffer under the conditions of the standard assay is 7×10^{-3} M. Mn^{2+} can partially fulfill the metal requirement.

REQUIREMENT FOR DEOXYRIBONUCLEOSIDE TRIPHOSPHATES. Maximal incorporation of deoxyribonucleotides into DNA (thymus primed assay) depends on the presence of the deoxyribonucleoside triphosphates of adenine, thymine, cytosine, and guanine (13). In the absence of one or more of these substrates in the standard reaction mixture there is no measurable incorporation. In the dAT-primed assay only the presence of dATP and dTTP are required. However, using highly labeled substrates the addition of only one of the deoxyribonucleotides onto DNA, in the absence of the other three deoxyribonucleoside triphosphates, can be demonstrated (see p. 274, "The Limited Reaction"). Several pyrimidine and purine analogs may be substituted for the natural bases and are incorporated enzymatically into DNA (14). In each case a given analog substitutes specifically for the base it resembles with respect to the hydrogen-bonding properties required in the DNA structure proposed by Watson and Crick.

REQUIREMENT FOR DNA PRIMER. There is no detectable nucleotide incorporation under the conditions of the standard assay without added DNA. In the standard assay 40 mμmoles of native DNA or 6 mμmoles of dAT polymer produce the maximal rate of incorporation with a given amount of enzyme. The purified polymerase utilizes heat-denatured and native DNA at approximately equal rates under the conditions of the standard assay (2). However, at reduced temperatures (20 C) native DNA is not an effective primer, in contrast to heat-denatured or partially single-stranded DNA primers (9).

Synthetic deoxyribo-oligonucleotides of short-chain length can also serve as primers for DNA polymerase. Oligonucleotides with sequences of from 6 to 14 alternating deoxyadenylate and deoxythymidylate residues prime the synthesis of the high molecular weight dAT copolymer (15). By using mixtures of synthetic deoxyribo-oligonucleotides of specified composition and sequence it is possible to synthesize (a) the homopolymers, polydeoxyadenylate and polydeoxythymidylate, and (b) a polymer containing alternating deoxyadenylate and deoxyguanylate units in one strand and alternating deoxycytidylate and deoxythymidylate units in the complementary strand (16).

An interesting property of DNA polymerase is its ability to utilize the homopolymers of riboadenylate and ribouridylate as primer (17). When it is provided with dATP and dTTP the enzyme catalyzes the synthesis of the homopolymers of deoxyadenylate and deoxythymidylate.

Net Synthesis of DNA with Polymerase

Polymerase is capable of catalyzing the synthesis of DNA in excess of the primer initially present. However, as a result of the removal of endonuclease and exonuclease III, synthesis occurs at a much slower rate with fraction IX than with less purified fractions. It is possible to obtain the product of a fivefold net synthesis of a native DNA where 85% of the primer remains undegraded (2). There is a slow degradation of the primer, presumably by exonuclease II associated with polymerase, during the long incubations necessary to obtain extensive synthesis.

The product of extensive replication of a helical DNA can be readily dissociated from the primer by denaturing treatments. The chemical and physical characteristics of the enzymatic product synthesized from a helical DNA resemble those of the native DNA in all but two respects (18); (a) an unusual capacity to resume a helical conformation after denaturing treatments; and (b) the appearance of a branched structure as seen in the electron microscope. By contrast, the repair of a partially single-stranded DNA results in the synthesis of DNA, which appears to have all the physical properties of naturally occurring DNA (9).

Addition of a Single Deoxyribonucleotide to the End of a Primer Chain; the Limited Reaction

Although the presence of all four deoxyribonucleoside triphosphates is required for extensive synthesis, a small but significant incorporation of single deoxyribonucleotides can be demonstrated. The addition of one or a very few molecules of a single deoxyribonucleotide has been shown to occur at the 3'-hydroxyl terminus of the DNA primer, forming a 3',5'-phosphodiester bond (19). With a natural DNA as the primer, the incorporation occurs with any of the four deoxyribonucleoside triphosphates, whereas with the dAT polymer as primer, incorporation occurs only with dATP or dTTP (20).

The ability of polymerase to add one or a very few molecules of a deoxyribonucleotide to the 3'-hydroxyl terminus of a DNA molecule enables a selective labeling of the molecule. Such DNA molecules are useful substrates for the study of the specificity of nucleases (7, 10,12).

Incorporation of Ribonucleotides into a DNA Polymer

In the presence of Mg^{2+}, the divalent cation normally used in the polymerase reaction mixture, the enzyme utilizes the deoxyanalogues of the nucleoside triphosphates exclusively. However, in the presence of Mn^{2+}, DNA polymerase will readily utilize ribonucleoside triphosphate counterparts (21). The mixed polymers produced contain ribo- and deoxyribonucleotides in the same chain. When rCTP replaces dGTP the reaction proceeds at approximately 60% the rate found with all four deoxyribonucleoside triphosphates; rCTP and rATP are less effective as substitutes for dCTP and dATP. rUTP does not support appreciable rates of incorporation when added in place of dTTP. Two or three of the deoxyribonucleoside triphosphates may be replaced simultaneously by the corresponding ribo analogs, but the rates of incorporation are lower and the extents of incorporation are markedly decreased. The base composition and the dinucleotide frequency of the synthesized polymers are indistinguishable from that of the DNA used to prime the synthesis. The ability of DNA polymerase to incorporate ribonucleotides into a mixed polymer has been used for sequence analysis of bases in DNA (21), for studying the action of nucleases on polymers containing ribo- and deoxyribonucleotides (6,7,10,22), and for studying the mechanism of chain extension by polymerase (9).

De Novo Synthesis of dAT and dGdC Polymers

In the absence of added primer, DNA polymerase catalyzes the synthesis of the dAT copolymer, containing alternating deoxyadenylate and deoxythymidylate units, with dATP and dTTP as substrates (4). In contrast to the primed reactions, synthesis is observed only after a lag period of several hours. A second, similar reaction occurs without added primer in the presence of dGTP and dCTP; after a lag period of several hours the synthesis of homopolymers of deoxyguanylate and deoxycytidylate is observed (23). The lag period can be eliminated by the addition of the appropriate synthetic polymer to the reaction mixture.

Fraction IX carries out synthesis de novo of dAT, but the lag period is extended over that observed with less purified fractions. Fraction IX is unable to effectively catalyze de novo or primed synthesis of dGdC polymer unless endonuclease is added to the reaction mixture (2).

Reversal of Reaction

DNA polymerase catalyzes a pyrophosphorolytic cleavage of DNA (13). The reversal of the synthetic reaction has been demonstrated by cleavage of E. coli DNA by inorganic pyrophosphate, yielding the four deoxyribonucleoside triphosphates in proper molar proportions (2).

REFERENCES

1. LEHMAN, I. R., M. S. BESSMAN, E. S. SIMMS, and A. KORNBERG. 1958. J. Biol. Chem. *233:* 163.
2. RICHARDSON, C. C., C. L. SCHILDKRAUT, H. V. APOSHIAN, and A. KORNBERG. 1964. J. Biol. Chem. *239:* 22.
3. APOSHIAN, H. V., and A. KORNBERG. 1962. J. Biol. Chem. *237:* 519.
4. SCHACHMAN, H. K., J. ADLER, C. M. RADDING, I. R. LEHMAN, and A. KORNBERG. 1960. J. Biol. Chem. *235:* 3242.
5. LEHMAN, I. R., G. G. ROUSSOS, and E. A. PRATT. 1962. J. Biol. Chem. *237:* 819.
6. RICHARDSON, C. C., and A. KORNBERG. 1964. J. Biol. Chem. *239:* 242.
7. RICHARDSON, C. C., I. R. LEHMAN, and A. KORNBERG. 1964. J. Biol. Chem. *239:* 251.
8. RICHARDSON, C. C., C. L. SCHILDKRAUT, and A. KORNBERG. 1963. Cold Spring Harbor Symp. Quant. Biol. *28:* 9.
9. RICHARDSON, C. C., R. B. INMAN, and A. KORNBERG. 1964. J. Mol. Biol. *9:* 46.
10. LEHMAN, I. R., and C. C. RICHARDSON. 1964. J. Biol. Chem. *239:* 233.
11. STRACK, H. B., and A. D. KAISER. 1965. J. Mol. Biol. *12:* 36.
12. LEHMAN, I. R. 1960. J. Biol. Chem. *235:* 1479.
13. BESSMAN, M. J., I. R. LEHMAN, E. S. SIMMS, and A. KORNBERG. 1958. J. Biol. Chem. *233:* 171.
14. BESSMAN, M. J., I. R. LEHMAN, J. ADLER, S. B. ZIMMERMAN, E. S. SIMMS, and A. KORNBERG. 1958. Proc. Natl. Acad. Sci. U.S. *44:* 633.
15. KORNBERG, A., L. L. BERTSCH, J. F. JACKSON, and H. G. KHORANA. 1964. Proc. Natl. Acad. Sci. U.S. *51:* 315.
16. BYRD, C., E. OHTSUKA, M. W. MOON, and H. G. KHORANA. 1965. Proc. Natl. Acad. Sci. U.S. *53:* 79.
17. LEE-HUANG, S., and L. CAVALLIERI. 1964. Proc. Natl. Acad. Sci., U.S. *51:* 1022.
18. SCHILDKRAUT, C. L., C. C. RICHARDSON, and A. KORNBERG. 1964. J. Mol. Biol. *9:* 24.
19. ADLER, J., I. R. LEHMAN, M. J. BESSMAN, E. S. SIMMS, and A. KORNBERG. 1958. Proc. Natl. Acad. Sci., U.S. *44:* 641.
20. KORNBERG, A. 1961. Enzymatic synthesis of DNA, Ciba lectures in microbial biochemistry. John Wiley, New York.
21. BERG, P., H. FANCHER, and M. CHAMBERLIN. 1963. *In* H. Vogel, V. Bryson, and J. O. Lampen, editors, Symposium on informational macromolecules. Academic Press, New York. p. 467.
22. LEHMAN, I. R., and A. L. NUSSBAUM. 1964. J. Biol. Chem. *239:* 2628.
23. RADDING, C. M., J. JOSSE, and A. KORNBERG. 1962. J. Biol. Chem. *237:* 2869.

DNA Polymerase from

T2-Infected

Escherichia coli

H. VASKEN APOSHIAN

DEPARTMENT OF MICROBIOLOGY

TUFTS UNIVERSITY SCHOOL OF MEDICINE

BOSTON, MASSACHUSETTS

ASSAY

$$\begin{bmatrix} \text{dTP PP} \\ \text{dGP*PP} \\ \text{dAP PP} \\ \text{dHMCP PP} \end{bmatrix} + \text{DNA} \longrightarrow \text{DNA} - \begin{bmatrix} \text{dTP} \\ \text{dGP*} \\ \text{dAP} \\ \text{dHMCP} \end{bmatrix} + 4(n)\,\text{PP}$$

Reagents

1. The reaction mixture (total volume 0.3 ml) contains

   0.07 M Tris buffer, pH 8.6

   0.007 M $MgCl_2$

   0.01 M 2-mercaptoethanol

   3×10^{-5} M of each of the following: dHMCTP, dATP, dTTP and C^{14} dGTP (1×10^6 cpm/μmole) or dGTP-αP^{32}

   7×10^{-6} M sodium versenate, pH 6.8

   Heated salmon sperm DNA, 60 mμmoles of DNA-phosphorus. (A solution of salmon sperm DNA, 1 μmole DNA-phosphorus per ml of Tris-HCl buffer 0.02 M, pH 7.5, and 0.02 M NaCl is heated for 15 min at 100 C and quickly cooled in ice water.)

277

2. 0.10 M GTP

3. 7% perchloric acid (PCA)

Procedure

This assay measures the conversion of C^{14}- or P^{32}-labeled deoxynucleoside triphosphates into an acid-insoluble product and was used to follow enzymic activity during the purification procedure.

After 30 min at 37 C, the reaction mixture is cooled in an ice bucket and 0.01 ml of 0.10 M GTP is added. This is followed by the addition of 0.50 ml of cold 7% PCA and 3 ml of cold water. The mixture is stirred and filtered through a GF/C Whatman Glass Filter paper (2.4-cm diameter). The tube and filter are washed three times with 4 ml of cold water. If a P^{32}-labeled deoxynucleoside triphosphate is used, the filter paper is placed on a planchet, dried under an infrared lamp, and counted. Alternatively, the filter may be dried and then counted in a scintillation counter, especially if a C^{14}- or H^3-labeled substrate is used. A blank without enzyme is run with each set of assays and its value subtracted from each sample. One unit is defined as the amount catalyzing the incorporation of 10 mμmoles of the labeled deoxynucleotide into the acid-insoluble product during the 30-min incubation period. Enzyme specific activity is expressed as units of enzyme per milligram of protein.

The radioactivity made acid insoluble is proportional to the amount of enzyme added.

Enzyme dilutions are made in 0.05 M Tris buffer, pH 7.5, containing 0.01 M 2-mercaptoethanol and bovine serum albumin (1 mg/ml). Fractions of the diluted enzyme solutions are added to the reaction mixture immediately after dilution and are then discarded.

During the early stages of the purification and especially if crude extracts are being assayed it is necessary to use deoxyhydroxymethyl-cytidine triphosphate (dHMCTP) instead of dCTP in the assay mixture because of the presence of phage-induced dCTPase.

ISOLATION PROCEDURE

Growth of T2 phage-Infected *E. coli* B

The phage-infected cells are grown and harvested as described by Dr. S. Zimmerman, this volume, page 307. In the fractionation procedures to be described, the temperature was maintained near 0 C except where noted, and centrifugations were at 14,000 × g for 20 min. The procedure is summarized in Table 1.

Preparation of Extract

The extract is prepared by mixing 45 g of frozen cells, 150 g of glass beads (Superbrite No. 100), and 50 ml of a buffer solution (A) containing glycylglycine (0.05 M, pH 7.0), Sodium Versenate (0.002 M), and reduced glutathione (0.002 M) for ten 2-min periods in a 1-quart glass Waring Blendor at two-thirds of maximal speed. The container and its contents are chilled between mixing periods by immersion in an ice water bath until the temperature of the suspension is below 10 C. After the last mixing period, 140 ml of Buffer A are added, and mixing is continued at one-fifth of maximal speed for 10 min. The glass beads are allowed to settle for 3 min, the supernatant fluid is decanted, and the beads are briefly washed with 100 ml of Buffer A. The supernatant and wash fluids are combined and centrifuged, and the resulting supernatant fluid is collected. The procedure is repeated with an additional 45 g of cells, and the supernatant fluids from these two batches are combined to give 500 ml of Fraction I.

Streptomycin Precipitation

To 500 ml of Fraction I are added 420 ml of Buffer A and then, with stirring during a 10-min period, 276 ml of streptomycin sulfate (5% solution). Stirring is continued for an additional 20 min. The precipitate, collected after centrifugation, is homogenized in a Waring Blendor at one-fifth of maximal speed for 30 min with 230 ml of a buffer solution (B) containing potassium phosphate (0.05 M, pH 7.4), Sodium Versenate (0.002 M), and reduced glutathione (0.002 M). This suspension is mixed with 596 ml of Buffer B and 840 ml of a solution containing Sodium Versenate (0.002 M) and reduced glutathione (0.002 M) to produce Fraction II.

TABLE 1. *Purification of DNA Polymerase from*
T2-Infected E. coli

Fraction	Protein (mg/ml)	Specific Activity (units/mg)	Total Units
I. Cell extract	15.8	2.6	20,850
II. Streptomycin	2.18	3.9	14,280
III. Protamine	0.30	32.7	6,272
IV. Ammonium sulfate	4.08	52.2	5,325
V. Dialysis	3.57	44.8	4,000
VI. DEAE-cellulose	0.12	366	1,866
VII. Phosphocellulose	0.058	1576	1,554

Protamine Precipitation and Elution

To 1680 ml of Fraction II are added, with stirring, 210 ml of a 1% protamine sulfate solution. The addition requires 4 min. The suspension is divided into two equal parts, which are treated as separate batches. After centrifugation, the supernatant fluid is discarded, and the precipitate is transferred to a Waring Blendor with 200 ml of potassium phosphate buffer (0.10 M, pH 7.0) containing Sodium Versenate (0.002 M) and reduced glutathione (0.002 M), and homogenized at one-fifth of maximal speed for 10 min. An additional 140 ml of this buffer is added, and the mixing is continued for another 5 min. After centrifugation, the supernatant fluid is collected. The supernatant fluids from both batches are combined (Fraction III).

Ammonium Sulfate Fractionation

To 640 ml of Fraction III are added, with stirring, 131 g of ammonium sulfate. After 15 min, the precipitate is removed by centrifugation. To the supernatant fluid an additional 95 g of ammonium sulfate are added, and after 15 min the precipitate is collected by centrifugation and dissolved in 25 ml of potassium phosphate buffer (0.025 M, pH 7.4) containing Sodium Versenate (0.002 M) and reduced glutathione (0.002 M) to yield Fraction IV.

Dialysis

20 ml of Fraction IV is dialyzed for 4 hr against K_2HPO_4 (0.02 M) containing 2-mercaptoethanol (0.01 M), and the dialysate (Fraction V) is immediately used for the preparation of Fraction VI.

DEAE-Cellulose Chromatography

A column of DEAE-cellulose (11 cm × 1.1 cm) is prepared and equilibrated with K_2HPO_4 (0.02 M) containing 2-mercaptoethanol (0.01 M). Fraction V (20 ml) is passed through the column at the rate of 36 ml/hr. The column is then washed with 10 ml of the K_2HPO_4-mercaptoethanol solution. A constant gradient, the limits of which are 0.02 and 0.30 M potassium phosphate buffer, pH 6.5, is applied. The buffers contained mercaptoethanol (0.01 M), and 150 ml of each buffer are used. Fractions are collected at 12-min intervals. Elution of 63% of the activity occurred between 8.4 and 14.8 resin-bed volumes of effluent. The peak fraction is eluted in approximately 0.09 M phosphate. The peak fractions having specific activities of 172 to 564 are combined to yield 34 ml of Fraction VI.

Phosphocellulose Chromatography

A column of phosphocellulose (10 cm × 0.6 cm) is prepared and washed with potassium phosphate buffer (0.02 M, pH 6.5) containing 2-mercaptoethanol (0.01 M), until the pH of the effluent was 6.5. Fraction VI (5.0 ml) is passed through the column at a rate of 0.3 ml/min. The following potassium phosphate buffers (pH 6.5) containing 2-mercaptoethanol (0.01 M) are used as stepwise eluents: 3 ml of 0.05 M, 6 ml of 0.10 M, 6 ml of 0.15 M, 8 ml of 0.20 M, 2 ml of 0.50 M, and finally, 2 ml of 0.50 M. Approximately 83–99% of the enzyme activity applied to the phosphocellulose column is in the last eluate fraction.

Comments

A summary of a typical preparation is shown in Table 1. The specific activity of Fraction VII has varied from 1000 to 2200 depending on the particular lot of infected cells used as the source of the enzyme.

PROPERTIES OF THE ENZYME

Features Distinguishing *E. coli* and T2 DNA Polymerase

The incubation of *E. Coli* polymerase with rabbit antiserum prepared against purified *E. coli* polymerase results in virtually complete inhibition of the enzyme activity. Equivalent amounts of antiserum to *coli* polymerase do not inhibit T2 polymerase. Conversely, rabbit antiserum prepared against T2 polymerase inhibits T2 polymerase but does not inhibit *E. coli* polymerase. Such antiserum can be used to inhibit the appropriate DNA polymerase activity in crude extracts of T2-infected cells.

Levels of *p*-chloromercuribenzoate (1.7×10^{-4} M), which inhibit T2 DNA polymerase almost completely, inhibit the *E. coli* DNA polymerase only 27%.

The two DNA polymerases have difference requirements as to the source and conformation of the DNA template.

Finally, the two DNA polymerases can be separated by chromatography on a phosphocellulose column.

Deoxyribonuclease Activities of T2 Polymerase Fractions

The last two fractions in the purification of the T2 DNA polymerase were assayed for endonuclease I (2) and exonuclease I activities

(3) as described by Lehman. The ratios of polymerase to endonuclease ($m\mu$moles nucleotides rendered acid insoluble:$m\mu$moles rendered acid soluble) of Fractions VI and VII were 46 and 220, respectively. The polymerase-exonuclease I ratios of Fractions VI and VII were 27 and 26, respectively. The endonucleolytic and phosphodiesterase activities were measured on native and heated *E. coli* DNA, respectively.

Requirements for Reaction

The omission of a single one of the four deoxynucleoside triphosphates or of DNA or $MgCl_2$ reduced the reaction to undetectable levels. The purified enzyme was about half as active when 2-mercaptoethanol was omitted and was unaffected by the absence of sodium versenate. Replacing $MgCl_2$ by $MnCl_2$ reduced the incorporation 90%.

Specificity

With T2 polymerase, as is the case with the DNA polymerase of *E. coli,* analogues of the naturally occurring bases serve as substitutes in a manner dictated by the hydrogen-bonding relationships of adenine to thymine and of guanine to cytosine (Table 2).

DNAs isolated from *E. coli,* bacteriophage T2, and animal tissues supported only 5–10% of the polymerase activity when compared with these same DNAs when they had been heated (Table 3).

TABLE 2. *Specificity of T2 DNA Polymerase for Deoxynucleoside Triphosphates*

Analogue (used in form of deoxynucleoside triphosphate)	Deoxynucleoside Triphosphate Replaced by Analogue			
	dTTP	dATP	dCTP	dGTP
	(% of control value)			
5-Bromouracil	100	<2	<2	<2
5-Fluorouracil	9	<2	<2	<2
5-Bromocytosine	<2	<2	104	<2
5-Fluorocytosine	<2	<2	67	<2
5-Hydroxymethylcytosine	<2	<2	98	<2

Note: Control values were measured as radioactive deoxynucleotide incorporated into DNA in the presence of dTTP, or dATP, dCTP, and dGTP, but in the absence of the analogue.

The rates were measured in the standard reaction mixtures except incubation was for 60 min.

Fraction VII was used as the source of the enzyme.

TABLE 3. *Relative Effectiveness of Various DNA Primers for T2 DNA Polymerase*

Source of DNA	Priming Activity	
	Heated DNA	Native DNA
Salmon sperm	100	5
dG-dC homopolymer	58	
Calf thymus	20	0.7
Salmon liver	15	4
dAT copolymer	11	
E. coli	10	0.3
T2 Bacteriophage	8	0.8
"Activated" calf thymus	1	

Note: The rates were measured in the standard reaction mixture and Fraction VII was used as the source of the enzyme.

REFERENCES

1. APOSHIAN, H. V., and A. KORNBERG. 1962. J. Biol. Chem. 237: 519.
2. LEHMAN, I. R., G. ROUSSOS, and E. A. PRATT. 1962. J. Biol. Chem. 237: 819.
3. LEHMAN, I. R. 1960. J. Biol. Chem. 235: 1479.

Preparation of Deoxynucleotide Polymerizing Enzymes from Calf Thymus Gland

F. J. BOLLUM

BIOLOGY DIVISION

OAK RIDGE NATIONAL LABORATORY

OAK RIDGE, TENNESSEE

Calf thymus gland is a source of two separate deoxynucleotidyl transferases: DNA polymerase and a terminal deoxynucleotidyl transferase. Both enzymes are conveniently isolated from the same preparative process since separation of the two polymerizing activities is the final purification step (1).

ASSAY

I. DNA polymerase (*Replicative*-deoxynucleotidyl transferase).

C^{14}-dATP
dCTP   + Denatured DNA $\longrightarrow$ Native C^{14}-DNA + PP_i
dGTP   template
dTTP

Research sponsored by the U.S. Atomic Energy Commission under contract with the Union Carbide Corporation.

II. *Terminal*-deoxynucleotidyl transferase.

$$n\text{C}^{14}\text{-dATP} + \text{d(pTpTpT)} \xrightarrow[\text{initiator}]{} \text{d(pTpTpT(pA)}_n) + n\text{PP}_i$$

Reagents

I. DNA Polymerase

a. The reaction mixtures (total volume 0.25 ml) contain

40 mM potassium phosphate, pH 7.0

8 mM $MgCl_2$

1 mM 2-mercaptoethanol

0.1 mM C^{14}-dATP (approximately 8×10^6 cpm/μmole)

0.1 mM dGTP

0.1 mM dCTP

0.1 mM dTTP

50 μg of calf thymus DNA (heated 5 min in a boiling water bath and cooled rapidly in ice)

Enzyme

b. One inch Whatman No. 1 filter paper disks

c. Disk washing reagents are

1. Cold 5% trichloracetic acid containing 1% $Na_4P_2O_7 \cdot 10\ H_2O$
2. Cold 5% trichloroacetic acid
3. 95% ethanol
4. Anhydrous diethylether (U.S.P.)

II. Terminal Transferase

a. The reaction mixtures (total volume 0.25 ml) contain

40 mM sodium cacodylate, pH 6.8

8 mM $MgCl_2$

1 mM C^{14}-dATP (approximately 8×10^5 cpm/μmole)

0.01 mM d(pTpTpT), that is 0.03 mM oligodeoxynucleotide phosphate

b. One inch Whatman No. 1 filter paper disks

c. Disk washing reagents as for DNA polymerase

Procedure

The assay described measures the conversion of C^{14}-deoxynucleoside triphosphate (acid soluble) to C^{14}-deoxypolynucleotide (acid insoluble) and is applicable at any stage of purification. Tritium or P^{32}-labeled deoxynucleoside triphosphates are also useful. It should be noted that the DNA polymerase reaction mixtures contain only one labeled triphosphate and all four are incorporated in proportion to the base composition of the denatured DNA template used. To obtain total nucleotide incorporation for calf thymus DNA template, multiply C^{14}-dATP incorporation by 3.4.

Other methods of assay, useful after partial purification, are

1. Measurement of pyrophosphate formation.
2. Measurement of hypochromicity due to polymer formation.

The enzyme reactions are started by addition of the enzyme fraction. Samples taken with a 50-μliter Lang-Levy pipet at 15 min and 30 min are immediately applied to the properly numbered filter paper disk held in a forceps. The disks are all collected in a single beaker containing washing reagent 1. For every disk collected (equal to the number of samples incubated times the number of time points taken) a volume of 10-ml reagent 1 is used. Disks are routinely accumulated for up to 2 hr of incubation when required. If longer time points are desired, they are usually accumulated in a separate beaker.

The disks are washed by swirling the beaker and pouring off the wash liquid after 10–15 min in each reagent. Wash disks twice in reagent 2, twice in reagent 3, and twice in reagent 4. Transfer disks to paper towels to air dry and arrange in numerical order. Place disks in scintillation vials when air dry and add 5 ml of 0.4% POP, 0.01% POPOP in absolute toluene (0.4% BBOT may be used with equal efficiency). Count in a scintillation counter. Scintillation vials may be reused since they are not contaminated. If C^{14} or P^{32} deoxynucleoside triphosphates are used, the disks may be counted directly in a suitable thin-window Geiger counter.

One unit of enzyme activity is defined as the incorporation of one millimicromole of labeled nucleotide in 1 hr. Specific activity is calculated as units of enzyme per milligram of protein. Protein is measured using a biuret reagent (2), or absorbancy at 280 millimicrons.

PURIFICATION PROCEDURE

Adsorbents

Whatman phosphocellulose P-1 floc, 7 meq/g, is obtained from H. Reeve Angel Co., Clifton, N.J. Two and one-half kg of this material is washed by decantation with successive 80-liter washes of 0.1 N HCl in 50% ETOH, H_2O until neutral, 0.1–0.2 N NaOH, 10^{-3}M EDTA, and finally H_2O until neutral. The washed phosphocellulose is then transferred to a plastic column (24-cm diameter × 76 cm) and equi-

librated with the appropriate phosphate buffer. About 300 g of phosphocellulose is removed and used to prepare a column (8.7-cm
diameter × 35 cm) for the second adsorption step; the remainder is
left in the column and used in the first batch adsorption step. After
each use the phosphocellulose is removed from the columns and regenerated by an alkaline cycle.

DEAE-Cellulose ($N,$-N-diethylaminoethyl cellulose, Eastman Organic Chemicals, exchange capacity 0.9 meq/g) is batch washed with
0.1 N NaOH in 50% ETOH, H_2O until neutral, 0.1–0.2 N HCl, and
then H_2O until neutral. The DEAE-Cl is then suspended in 0.2 M
phosphate buffer and equilibrated to pH 7.2 in a plastic column. An
8.7-cm diameter × 40-cm column of DEAE is used in the enzyme
preparation. After use, DEAE-cellulose is regenerated by an alkaline
cycle.

Brushite is prepared in 40-liter batches and converted to hydroxylapatite in 4-liter portions exactly as described by Levin (3). Hydroxylapatite prepared in this fashion, i.e., allowing a settling time of exactly
5 min after each heating, gave unrestricted flow rates of at least 1 ml
per cm^2 per minute. Using this material the analytical and preparative
column runs usually required less than 36 hr. Glass columns with
coarse frits covered with a 5-mm layer of glass beads are used for
hydroxylapatite chromatography. The hydroxylapatite is transferred
to the column as a slurry, allowed to settle, washed with one column
volume of 0.05 M potassium phosphate, pH 7.5, containing 0.01 M
Na_3 citrate, and then equilibrated with 0.05 M pH 7.5 buffer containing 10^{-3} M mercaptoethanol. An 8-cm diameter × 24-cm column is
required. Before use, the column should be checked for channeling by
observing uniform movement of a phenol red band through the column. After use, 2 to 3 column volumes of 0.5 M K_2HPO_4 removes residual protein and the column is reused after equilibration.

Sephadex G-100 (Pharmacia, Rochester, Minn.) is allowed to swell
in distilled water overnight and fines are removed by decantation.
Washed Sephadex G-100 is packed into a column 2.5 cm in diameter
and 80 cm long and equilibrated with 0.1 M potassium phosphate at
pH 7.2.

PREPARATION OF CRUDE EXTRACT. Calf thymus glands
are packed in ice at the slaughterhouse and transported to the laboratory. All subsequent operations are performed in a cold room or in
refrigerated centrifuges at 0–4 C.

After extraneous tissues and fat are removed, 30 kg of thymus gland
is passed through an electric meat grinder fitted with a fine face plate
($\frac{1}{16}$- or $\frac{5}{64}$-in. holes). The minced tissue is collected directly in a 55-

gallon polyethylene mixing tank that contains 150 liters of cold extracting solution. The extracting solution consists of 150 liters of deionized water, 6.24 moles of NaCl, 1.19 moles of KH_2PO_4, and 5.06 moles of K_2HPO_4, final pH 7.3–7.4. Minced tissue and extracting solution are mixed gently ($\frac{1}{4}$-HP Lightin Mixer, one 7-in. propeller, about 100 rev/min) for 1 hr. The amount of sedimentable solid is then estimated by centrifuging a 10-ml sample for 3 min in the International clinical centrifuge, and the total volume of mixture is adjusted to contain 20–22% solids by adding extracting solution. The mixture of minced tissue and extracting solution is then pumped through an automatic pilot plant de-sludger centrifuge (Model SAOOH205, manufactured by Westphalia Separator Ag., Germany, sold in the U.S.A. by Sharples Corp.) at 2 liters/min with a flexible tube pump (Sigma Motor, Middleport, New York, Model 6SH). The turbid crude extract (about 140 liters, 11–14 mg of protein/ml) thus obtained is adjusted to pH 6.5 by careful addition of 10% acetic acid (2–3 liters is required) and allowed to settle overnight. After the pH adjustment, a precipitate forms by slow aggregation, and removal of this material is essential for subsequent column operations. The overnight precipitate is resuspended with the mixer, and the suspension is passed through the Westphalia centrifuge at 0.5 liter/min for final clarification (yield about 135 liters, 10–11 mg of protein/ml).

ADSORPTION ONTO PHOSPHOCELLULOSE.   Phosphocellulose slurry (equivalent to about 1.5 kg of dry material) previously equilibrated to pH 6.5 with 0.05 M phosphate buffer is removed from the equilibration column (see "Adsorbents," above) and added as a wet paste directly to the 135 liters of crude extract. The pH is readjusted to 6.5 if necessary. The suspension is mixed slowly but thoroughly for 30–45 min.

In large-scale runs it is essential that the degree of enzyme adsorption be tested on a sample filtered through a coarse glass frit to remove phosphocellulose. If less than 85–90% of the enzyme has adsorbed, more phosphocellulose should be added. In our experience 1 kg is usually sufficient and 2 kg is always sufficient. The amount of protein adsorbed is generally not detectable by loss of biuret-reactive material from the supernatant solution, but protein adsorption can be detected by the watermelon red color of the phosphocellulose and disappearance of polymerizing activity.

When a satisfactory degree of activity is adsorbed the phosphocellulose is allowed to settle for 30 min and then the supernatant solution is siphoned off and discarded. The phosphocellulose slurry, containing 85–95% of the enzyme activity, is now washed by decantation two times with 80 liters of 0.05 M phosphate buffer, pH 6.5, 10^{-3} M mercaptoethanol, and is then transferred with a plastic scoop back to the large column (24-cm diameter) that now should contain a 10- to 15-cm pad of fresh phosphocellulose (any extra phosphocellulose not used in the batch adsorption is removed). After washing this column with 40 liters of 0.1 M phosphate buffer, pH 7.2, the polymerizing enzymes are eluted with 40 liters of 0.2 M phosphate buffer at pH 7.2 and 2-liter fractions are collected. The fractions are assayed for DNA polymerase activity and the active fractions thus obtained (12–15 liters, about 2 mg of protein/ml, $A_{280}/A_{260} = 1.0$–1.2) are pooled and passed directly through a DEAE column (8.7 cm × 40 cm), equilibrated with 0.2 M phosphate, pH 7.2, as previously described (4). DEAE-treated enzyme solution (15–18 liters, about 1.7 mg of protein/ml, $A_{280}/A_{260} \geqslant 1.7$) is diluted to 0.05 M phosphate by continuous dilution with 0.001 M mercaptoethanol as it is loaded onto a phosphocellulose column (8.7 cm × 35 cm) equilibrated with 0.05 M phosphate buffer, pH 7.2.

Continuous dilution is carried out as follows: A tank 34 cm in diameter containing the enzyme fraction to be diluted and another tank 55 cm in diameter containing an equal depth of the diluent (0.001 M mercaptoethanol) are connected to the top of a 1-liter aspirator bottle arranged to permit magnetic stirring of the contents. The outlet of the aspirator bottle is connected to the input of the phosphocellulose column. As the two tanks drain through the mixing chamber a dilution factor equal to the radius² of tank 2 (diluent) + radius² of tank 1/radius² of tank 1 (enzyme) takes place. This process avoids an appreciable loss of activity that we have observed in diluted enyme solutions during the rather prolonged loading period (24–48 hr) required.

After washes of 0.05 M (10 liters) and 0.1 M (4 liters) phosphate buffer, pH 7.2., the polymerizing enzymes are eluted from the column by 0.2 M buffer and 200-ml fractions are collected. It is desirable to assay fractions for DNA polymerase and terminal transferase at this stage since a partial separation may occur.

AMMONIUM SULFATE FRACTIONATION. All the active fractions of the 0.2 M eluate (regardless of any DNA polymerase and terminal transferase separation) from the second phosphocellulose column are pooled and concentrated by precipitation with solid $(NH_4)_2SO_4$ between 30% and 55% saturation. The precipitate is collected by centrifugation and dissolved in 0.05 M phosphate, pH 7.5, containing 10^{-3} M mercaptoethanol (45–50 mg of protein/ml, 100 ml).

HYDROXYLAPATITE CHROMATOGRAPHY. The $(NH_4)_2SO_4$ fraction is diluted to 1 liter with 0.05 M phosphate, pH 7.5, just prior

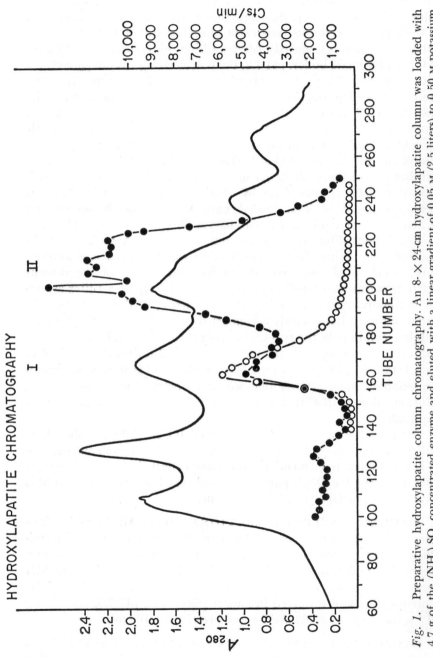

Fig. 1. Preparative hydroxylapatite column chromatography. An 8- × 24-cm hydroxylapatite column was loaded with 4.7 g of the $(NH_4)_2SO_4$ concentrated enzyme and eluted with a linear gradient of 0.05 M (2.5 liters) to 0.50 M potassium phosphate, pH 7.5. Solid line is A_{280}; black circles, DNA polymerase activity; white circles, terminal transferase activity.

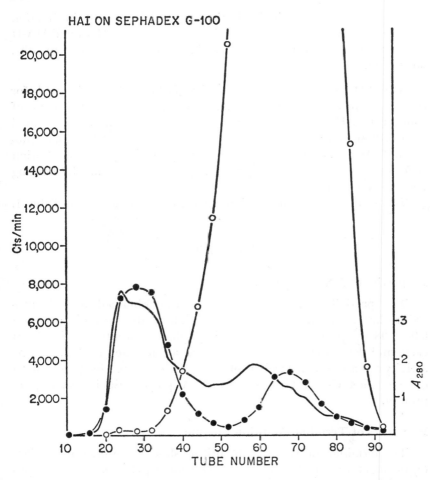

Fig. 2. Preparative gel-filtration of terminal transferase. A 2.5- × 100-cm Sephadex G-100 column was equilibrated with 0.1 M potassium phosphate (pH 7.2) and loaded with about 15 ml of concentrated hydroxylapatite fraction I (about 0.4 g of protein). Solid line is A_{280}; black circles, DNA polymerase; white circles, terminal transferase.

to loading onto the hydroxylapatite column (8 cm × 23 cm) equilibrated with the same buffer. After washing with 100 ml of 0.05 M phosphate buffer, pH 7.5, the column is eluted with a linear potassium phosphate gradient (0.05–0.5 M, 2.5 liters each). As shown in Fig. 1, separation of terminal and replicative deoxynucleotidyl transferases is achieved, and each of these enzyme fractions is free of the traces of phosphodiesterase and deoxyribonuclease activity that elute early in the gradient. The terminal addition enzyme is present in fraction HA-I and DNA polymerase in Fraction HA-II. Pooled HA-I and HA-II are concentrated by addition of solid ammonium sulfate to 70% saturation.

GEL FILTRATION. A Sephadex G-100 column is used for further purification of the terminal transferase enzyme. Fifteen ml of concentrated HA-I is loaded onto the Sephadex column equilibrated with 0.10 M phosphate buffer, pH 7.2, containing 0.001 M mercaptoethanol. As shown in Fig. 2, DNA-polymerase and terminal-addition enzymes are separated by this procedure; eluting at 1.1 and 1.7 holding volumes, respectively.

The results of this purification scheme are summarized in Table 1.

RESULTS

Properties of DNA Polymerase

The partially purified DNA polymerase obtained by this procedure has an optimum pH of 7.0, optimum Mg^{2+} concentration is 0.04–0.08 M, optimum nucleoside triphosphate concentration is 0.1 μM each, and denatured DNA is required as a template (5). The enzyme activity has a molecular weight of 1.1×10^5, estimated by gel filtration on Sephadex G-200. Calf thymus DNA polymerase is not a pure protein.

Properties of Terminal-Addition Enzyme

The terminal-addition enzyme utilizes short chain oligonucleotides (6) or denatured DNA as initiators. Optimum pH is 6.7–7.0 and optimum Mg^{2+} concentration 0.02–0.08 M. In Mg^{2+}-activated polymerizations catalyzed by the enzyme at its present state of purity, the substrate saturation curve is different from the various deoxyribonucleoside triphosphate substrates. dGTP, dTTP, and dCTP show saturation at 0.1 mM, whereas dATP polymerization date is maximal at 1.0–2.0 mM (7). The enzyme activity has a molecular weight of 3.7×10^4 by gel filtration on Sephadex G-200.

DISCUSSION

The large-scale purification process described was developed primarily for DNA polymerase and is the result of considerable experience (25 preparations). Each step has been tested separately, usually with bet-

TABLE 1. *Purification of DNA Polymerase*

Fraction	Total Units[a] ($\times 10^{-5}$)	Recovery (%)	Total Protein (g)	DNA Polymerase Specific Activity (dCTP units/mg)	Terminal Transferase Specific Activity (dATP units/mg)
Crude	17	100	1060	1.6	
Phosphocellulose-1	14	82	19.5	73.8	
Phosphocellulose-2	8.1	58	8.8	91.2	
$(NH_4)_2SO_4$ (35–55%)	4.6	27	4.5	102.2	
Hydroxylapatite II (concentrated)	2.4	14	0.99	250	
Hydroxylapatite I (concentrated)			0.46		
G-100 (concentrated)			0.12		15×10^3

[a] 1 unit = one mµ mole of labeled substrate per hour; for approximate total nucleotide incorporation multiply by 3.4 in the DNA polymerase column.

ter purity and yields than that reported in Table 1. The incorporation of any analytical purification into a large-scale process usually involves compromises in both technique and nicety. In developing the present process, we have selected for high yields in the initial stages since rather large amounts of enzyme are involved and small percentage losses are large on the absolute scale. Thus, considerably greater specific activities may be obtained by selecting narrow fractions or by more gradual elution of columns if the resultant losses in total activity can be tolerated. We have taken major activity fractions in all stages. If the preparation is run on a $\frac{1}{10}$ scale to obtain hydroxylapatite fraction II for analytical experiments, it might be profitable to carry out a more gradual elution of the second phosphocellulose column, cut narrower $(NH_4)_2SO_4$ fractions, and select only the best fractions from hydroxylapatite for concentration. We do not recommend reducing the slope of the phosphate gradient on hydroxylapatite.

The phosphocellulose step is unquestionably the most useful step in this purification process with greater than 50-fold purification and 10-fold concentration of DNA polymerase routinely achieved. The DEAE column simply removes residual nucleic acid and the second phosphocellulose column effects (in our process) another 10-fold concentration to allow $(NH_4)_2SO_4$ fractionation on a reasonable volume. Purification does not exceed two- to threefold in the latter two stages. The hydroxylapatite step was originally run at pH 7.2–7.3 to effect final separation of traces of deoxyribonuclease and phosphodiesterase activity from DNA polymerase. When carried out at pH 7.5, removal of degradative enzymes and separation of the DNA polymerase from terminal-addition enzyme results.

Gel filtration (G-100) of the terminal transferase removes considerable inactive protein from the hydroxylapatite concentrate to produce an enzyme preparation useful for polymer synthesis (7). G-100 filtration of the DNA polymerase fraction from hydroxylapatite is recommended where complete freedom from terminal-addition activity is required. The hydroxylapatite fraction is sufficient for the most analytical work. Gel filtration of DNA polymerase on G-200 has resulted in major losses of enzyme activity in our experience.

The terminal-addition reaction on oligodeoxyribonucleotide initiators was first thought to be a minor activity of DNA polymerase (8). When the terminal transferase enzyme is separated from DNA polymerase, total activity increases and the enzyme has somewhat different substrate specificity and saturation curves. This phenomenon presents certain difficulties in the analysis of this enzyme activity and prohibits any statement about the degree of purification obtained (Table 1). The possibility that the terminal transferase may be related to or a derivative of the DNA polymerase has not been critically explored.

REFERENCES

1. YONEDA, M., and F. J. BOLLUM. 1964. J. Biol. Chem. *240:* 3385.
2. GORNALL, A. G., C. J. BARDAWILL, and M. M. DAVID. 1949. J. Biol. Chem. *177:* 751.
3. LEVIN, O. 1962. *In* S. P. Colowick and N. O. Kaplan, editors, Methods in enzymology. Academic Press, New York. Vol. V, p. 27.
4. BOLLUM, F. J. 1960. J. Biol. Chem. *235:* 2399.
5. BOLLUM, F. J. 1959. J. Biol. Chem. *234:* 2733.
6. BOLLUM, F. J. 1962. J. Biol. Chem. *237:* 1945.
7. BOLLUM, F. J., E. GROENIGER, and M. YONEDA. 1964. Proc. Natl. Acad. Sci., U.S. *51:* 853.
8. BOLLUM, F. J. 1960. J. Biol. Chem. *235:* PC18.

Filter Paper Disk Techniques
for Assaying Radioactive
Macromolecules

F. J. BOLLUM
BIOLOGY DIVISION
OAK RIDGE NATIONAL LABORATORY
OAK RIDGE, TENNESSEE

INTRODUCTION

The biochemist desiring to work in purification of nucleic acid related enzymes, in coding properties of polynucleotides, or other general analyses of macromolecular substances, often faces the problem of processing hundreds of samples through complicated washing procedures in an attempt to remove extraneous substances before the final analysis for radioactivity. Suitable chemical washing procedures can usually be devised, but applying these washing procedures to a large number of samples on an individual basis results in an extremely tedious and time-consuming endeavor. Pathologists and histologists have faced a somewhat similar problem for many years and have solved this problem by developing batch washing procedures. In order to apply this philosophy to biochemical procedures, it is necessary to develop a means whereby the biochemical samples can be treated in the batch fashion that the pathologist and histologist uses.

Research sponsored by the U.S. Atomic Energy Commission under contract with the Union Carbide Corporation.

A general method for working up radioactive polymer samples, therefore, requires only that an inert carrier material be used for each sample and that this "carried" sample can then be subjected to the required selective extraction procedures. A suitable process was developed and used for assaying the numerous enzyme fractions obtained during a DNA polymerase purification and analysis (1,2) and has become a technique of general use in this Laboratory. The method consists simply of numbering a series of Whatman No. 1 (or No. 3) cellulose disks (1-in. in diameter) and then applying the impure radioactive sample, such as an aliquot of a reaction mixture, to the properly numbered disk. The enzyme reaction is stopped by placing the filter paper disk in a large beaker of trichloroacetic acid. A large number of such disks can be accumulated in a convenient washing vessel and all the samples, for example all of the time points in a multitube kinetic experiment or density gradient run, can be accumulated and subsequently processed simultaneously through the several reagents necessary for extraction of extraneous material. After extraneous materials, for example radioactive precursors, are removed from the radioactive product, the washing reagents that may interfere with the analysis of the radioactive product are removed by suitable solvents and residual water is removed by drying—either with solvents or air or oven drying. The radioactivity of the sample embedded within the fibers of the cellulose filter paper disk can now be determined without interference from radioactivity contamination by extraneous material and free from a large variety of quenching materials, such as salt and sucrose. The radioactivity of the sample can then be analyzed for the various types of isotopes that it may contain, either by scintillation techniques or by a straightforward Geiger counting procedure, depending upon the isotope and detailed nature of the analysis required. The process is very simple and the time required for washing is independent of the number of samples involved. The approximate efficiencies for counting in a Packard Scintillation Counter with the disk lying under 5 ml of 0.4% PPO, 0.01% POPOP, or 0.4% BBOT are P^{32}, 100%; C^{14}, 50%; and H^3, 1–5%. The low efficiency of H^3 analysis is thought to be due to the short range of the H^3 beta particle. Because of the low cost and high specific activity of the H^3-labeled compounds now available, efficiency is usually not a critical consideration in this analysis. What follows is a description of specific modifications of this disk procedure useful for a number of enzymatic polymerizations and depolymerizations that use radioactive substrates to measure the radioactive product. Some recipes for use with techniques that involve fractionation of radioactive polymers and some crude assay procedures for deoxyribonuclease, ribonuclease, and exonuclease assays are also included.

SPECIFIC PROCEDURES

Procedure A. DNA Polymerase, Terminal Deoxynucleotidyl Transferase, Polynucleotide Phosphorylase, and RNA Polymerase

Collect disks in 5% trichloroacetic acid containing 1% $Na_4P_2O_7 \cdot 10\ H_2O$. Wash two times in 5% trichloroacetic acid; two times in 95% ethanol; two times in diethyl ether. Air dry.

Procedure B. Protein Synthesis (3)

Collect disks in 10% trichloroacetic acid. Wash two times in 5% trichloroacetic acid. Heat to 90 C for 15 min in 5% trichloroacetic acid. Wash with 5% trichloroacetic acid. Wash two times with ethanol ether (1:1 at 37 C). Wash two times with diethyl ether. Air dry the disks.

Procedure C. Aminoacyl-sRNA Synthesis (4,5)

Collect disks in 5% trichloroacetic acid. Wash three times for 7 min with 5% trichloroacetic acid. Wash two times for 10 min with Hokins reagent at 37 C (Hokins reagent is made up as follows: 4 pints of absolute ethanol, 1.6 ml of 10 N NaOH, 120 ml of glacial acetic acid). Wash one time for 10 min with equal parts of diethyl ether and Hokins reagent. Wash two times with diethyl ether. Air dry the disks.

Procedure D. Biosynthetic Polypeptides (6)

Disks from reaction mixtures containing polyuridylate to stimulate polyphenylalanine synthesis may be collected in 10% trichloroacetic acid and worked up exactly as described for protein synthesis.

Disks from reaction mixtures containing polyadenylate to test formation of polylysine may be worked up as follows:

Collect disks in tungstate-trichloroacetic reagent made up as follows: Adjust pH of 1 liter of 5% trichloroacetic acid to pH 2.0 with 10 N NaOH. Dissolve 2.5 g of $Na_2WO_4 \cdot 2\ H_2O$ in the pH 2.0, trichloroacetic acid. Readjust pH of the clear solution to pH 2.0 with 5% trichloroacetic. Wash two times in tungstate-trichloroacetic reagent. Hydrolyze 15 min at 90 C in 5% trichloroacetic acid. Wash two times for 10 min with 5% trichloroacetic. Wash two times with ethanol and two times with diethyl ether. Air dry.

ASSAY FOR MACROMOLECULAR DEGRADATIVE ENZYMES (RIBONUCLEASE, PHOSPHODIESTERASE, EXONUCLEASE, AND ENDONUCLEASE)

To use the disk assay for degradation of macromolecular substances, it is desirable to have radioactive substrates; for example, radioactive protein, radioactive RNA, or radioactive DNA. Assays for nucleic acid degradative enzymes are preformed by collecting disks in 5% trichloroacetic acid and washing up as described in Procedure A. In this procedure, one measures the decrease in radioactive polymer on the disk. Assay for protein degradation can be worked up directly as described in Procedure A or B.

Exonuclease assays are readily performed using this disk procedure, but it should be noted that the disk assay for endonuclease-type activities is not particularly sensitive since larger oligonucleotides would remain insoluble in the washing reagents and, therefore, would not score as a loss of acid insoluble material. The procedure is, however, useful for rough surveys for major endonuclease activities in chromatographic fractions. A more sensitive assay for endonuclease using cellulose nitrate filters has been described by Geiduschek and Daniels (7).

ASSAY FOR RADIOACTIVE POLYMERS IN DENSITY GRADIENTS, COLUMN CHROMATOGRAMS, AND COUNTER CURRENT FRACTIONS

Separation of macromolecules in density gradients, on columns, and by counter-current procedures often necessitates analysis of a large number of fractions that contain the necessary ions and solvents required for the separation. These materials may result in quenching in scintillation counters or may contribute to self-adsorption. Any series of fractions containing radioactive polymers may be collected on disks and washed up to effect the removal of quenching materials, such as sucrose, cesium chloride, high concentrations of salt, and a variety of solvents. For nucleic acids the general washing procedure A above is a useful first approximation (2,8,9).

The disk assay for radioactive polymers, as described above, has a variety of possibilities and the essential feature is the batch washing of a large number of samples; for example, Cherayil and Bock (10) have proceeded even further and have isolated fractionated transfer RNA and run reaction mixtures directly on filter paper disks, resulting in no intermediate work-up from column fractionation to analysis. The disks are worked up according to the methods described above. The batch-washing idea can also be applied to DEAE disks, and this approach has been used by Mead for assaying for oligodeoxynucleotide transferase activity (11). They also provide a useful assay for endonuclease activities (12). DEAE disks have also been used by Furlong (13) and Breitman (14) for assaying for thymidine kinase. Other possibilities are obvious, such as the use of charcoal impregnated or ion-exchange impregnated cellulose disks for other separations of this type.

REFERENCES

1. BOLLUM, F. J. 1959. J. Biol. Chem. *234:* 2733.
2. BOLLUM, F. J. 1963. Cold Spring Harbor Symp. Quant. Biol. *28:* 21.
3. MANS, R. J., and G. D. NOVELLI. 1961. Arch. Biochem. Biophys. *94:* 48.
4. BARNETT, W. E., and K. B. JACOBSON. 1964. Proc. Natl. Acad. Sci. U.S. *51:* 642. Barnett, W. E. Unpublished.
5. NISHIMURA, S., and G. D. NOVELLI. 1964. Biochim. Biophys. Acta. *80:* 574.
6. NISHIMURA, S., and G. D. NOVELLI. 1965. Proc. Natl. Acad. Sci. U.S. *53:* 178.
7. GEIDUSCHEK, E. P., and A. DANIELS. 1965. Anal. Biochem. *11:* 133.
8. MESELSON, M., M. NOMURA, S. BRENNER, C. DAVERN, and D. SCHLESSINGER. 1964. J. Mol. Biol. *9:* 696.
9. NOMURA, M., K. MATSUBARA, K. OKAMOTO, and R. FUJIMURA. 1962. J. Mol. Biol. *5:* 535.
10. CHERAYIL, J. D., and R. M. BOCK. 1964. Federation Proc. *23:* 477.
11. MEAD, C. G. 1964. Proc. Natl. Acad. Sci. U.S. *52:* 1482.
12. MEAD, C. G. Unpublished.
13. FURLONG, N. B. 1963. Anal. Biochem. *5:* 515.
14. BREITMAN, T. R. 1963. Biochim. Biophys. Acta. *67:* 153.

DNA Methylase from

Escherichia coli (**1**)

MARVIN GOLD AND JERARD HURWITZ
ALBERT EINSTEIN COLLEGE OF MEDICINE
YESHIVA UNIVERSITY
BRONX, NEW YORK

ASSAY

DNA + S-adenosylmethionine (C^{14}-methyl-labeled) $\longrightarrow$
$\qquad\qquad\qquad\qquad$ C^{14}H$_3$-DNA + S-adenosylhomocysteine

Reagents

1. The reaction mixture (total volume 0.25 ml) contains

0.1 M Tris buffer, pH 8.0
0.016 M 2-mercaptoethanol
0.04 mM C^{14}-CH$_3$-labeled S-adenosylmethionine (2 to 4 × 10^7 cpm per
μmole)
0.4 mM DNA (in terms of nucleotide residues). For routine assays, DNA
isolated from either *Micrococcus lysodeikticus* or *Mycobacteria phlei*
may be used.
Enzyme

2. 7% perchloric acid
0.5% bovine plasma albumin
0.1 M sodium pyrophosphate
2% perchloric acid containing 0.002 M sodium pyrophosphate
0.2 M NH$_4$OH

Procedure

The assay is based on the incorporation of radioactivity into an acid-insoluble product.

After 30 min of incubation at 37 C, the reaction is stopped and the DNA precipitated with 0.4 ml of ice-cold perchloric acid. Bovine plasma albumin (0.05 ml) is added as a carrier to facilitate complete precipitation and sodium pyrophosphate (0.1 ml) to prevent the nonspecific binding of unreacted S-adenosylmethionine. After 2 min at 0 C with occasional shaking, the suspensions are centrifuged for 1 min at 15,000 × g and the supernatants discarded. The pellets are then finely suspended in the 2% perchloric acid with a tight fitting glass pestle and the suspensions centrifuged as above. This procedure is repeated once more and the pellets dissolved with 1.5 ml of ammonium hydroxide. The solutions are decanted into metal planchets, dried under an infrared lamp and counted in a windowless gas-flow counter. A blank without enzyme or DNA is included and its value subtracted from each sample; these blank values are routinely less than 1 $\mu\mu$mole of C^{14}-methyl group incorporated.

One unit of DNA methylase activity is defined as that amount catalyzing the incorporation of 1 mμmole of methyl group in 30 min. Specific activity is defined as units per milligram of protein. Under the conditions described, and using *M. lysodeikticus* DNA, the rate of methylation is proportional to enzyme concentration up to 1 unit. The rate is also proportional to time of incubation until a fixed yield is attained (see below).

ISOLATION PROCEDURE

Growth of Cells

Escherichia coli strain W was grown and harvested as previously described (2). All subsequent operations are carried out at 0–5 C, and all solutions should contain 0.005 M 2-mercaptoethanol and 0.001 M EDTA.

Crude Extract

Frozen *E. coli,* strain W (200 g), is ground with 400 g of Alumina A-301 (Alcoa) in a prechilled mortar kept in an ice bath. When the loose consistency of the mixture indicates that cell breakage is complete, it is stirred with 400 ml of 0.05 M triethanolamine buffer, pH 8.8, containing 0.01 M $MgCl_2$. The suspension is centrifuged for 20 min at

12,000 × g, and the pellet is re-extracted with 300 ml of the same buffer and centrifuged. The two supernatant solutions are combined and centrifuged for 2 hr at 30,000 rev/min in the No. 30 rotor of the Spinco preparative ultracentrifuge. The supernatant solution (crude extract, 660 ml) is stored in the refrigerator overnight.

Alumina Cγ Gel Eluate

To 650 ml of the crude extract are added 260 ml of alumina Cγ gel (17.9 mg of solids per ml), and the suspension is mixed. After 20 min, the gel is removed by centrifugation at 5000 × g for 10 min and the supernatant solution is discarded. The gel is washed by homogenization with 325 ml of 0.05 M potassium phosphate buffer, pH 7.5. After 10 min, the suspension is centrifuged at 5000 × g for 10 min and the supernatant fluid is discarded. This procedure is repeated twice more. The DNA-methylating activity is then eluted from the gel by homogenization in 225 ml of 0.5 M potassium phosphate buffer, pH 7.5, and centrifugation at 5000 × g for 10 min. The pellet is re-extracted with 0.5 M potassium phosphate buffer, and the two supernatant solutions are combined to give the alumina Cγ gel eluate (450 ml).

Calcium Phosphate Gel Eluate

The alumina Cγ gel eluate is diluted with water to a volume of 4500 ml, and 450 ml of calcium phosphate gel (12.1 mg of solids per ml) are added with stirring. After 30 min, the suspension is centrifuged and the supernatant fluid is discarded. The gel is washed by homogenization with 1 liter of 0.1 M potassium phosphate buffer, pH 6.5, and centrifuged. The supernatant solution is discarded and the gel is washed once more with 500 ml of the same buffer. The activity is then' eluted from the gel with two homogenizations with 100-ml portions of 0.5 M potassium β,β-dimethylglutarate buffer, pH 7.5. These two washings are combined (calcium phosphate gel eluate).

Ammonium Sulfate I

The combined eluates are immediately further fractionated with ammonium sulfate. To the calcium phosphate gel eluate (194 ml), 104 ml of saturated ammonium sulfate solution (prepared at room temperature and having a pH of 7.4 after 100-fold dilution) are added. After 30 min, the suspension is centrifuged for 15 min at 30,000 rev/min in the No. 30 rotor of the Spinco Model L ultracentrifuge, and the pellet is discarded. The supernatant fluid is brought to 65% saturation by the addition of 55.2 g of solid ammonium sulfate. After 30 min, the suspension is centrifuged and the supernatant solution is discarded. The pellet is dissolved in 0.02 M potassium phosphate buffer, pH 7.5, to give ammonium sulfate Fraction I (volume, 10.6 ml).

Phosphocellulose Chromatography

Phosphocellulose is suspended in water and the fines are removed. The phosphocellulose is then poured as a slurry into a column 2.5 cm in diameter and packed by pressure to a height of 20 cm. The column is washed with 0.02 M potassium phosphate buffer, pH 7.5, until the pH of the effluent is 7.5. Ammonium sulfate Fraction I is dialyzed against 1 liter of the same buffer for 40 min after which time the dialysis fluid is replaced with 1 liter of fresh buffer, and the dialysis is continued for an additional 45 min. The volume of ammonium sulfate Fraction I increases to 13 ml, and the slight precipitate that formed inside the dialysis bag is not removed.

The dialyzed fraction is applied to the top of the column, which is then washed successively with the following potassium phosphate buffers, pH 7.5: 50 ml of 0.02 M, 100 ml of 0.1 M, 150 ml of 0.2 M, and 150 ml of 0.5 M. The flow rate is approximately 5 ml/min and 25-ml fractions are collected. Most of the enzymatic activity eluted from the column appears in the third 0.5 M fraction, and this is retained for further purification (phosphocellulose eluate, 25 ml).

Ammonium Sulfate II

Solid ammonium sulfate (9 g) is added to the phosphocellulose fraction (25 ml), and after 15 min, the suspension is centrifuged for 10 min at 40,000 rev/min in the No. 40 rotor of the Spinco Model L ultra-centrifuge. The pellet is then successively extracted by homogenization in ammonium sulfate solutions of various concentrations containing 0.05 M potassium phosphate buffer, pH 7.5, as follows: 10 ml of 60% saturated, 10 ml of 50%, and 1.5 ml of 30%. After each extraction, the suspension is allowed to stand for 10 min before it is centrifuged. Over 95% of the enzymatic activity is found in the last fraction (ammonium sulfate II, 1.5 ml).

A summary of the purification is given in Table 1. The activity has been purified approximately 400-fold with a yield of 15%.

Properties of the Enzyme

PURITY. The final preparation still contains small amounts of the tRNA methylases (3). Deoxyribonuclease activity can be detected only by the destruction of biologically active DNA.

TABLE 1.   *Purification of DNA Methylase Activity*[a]

Enzyme Fraction	Total Units	Protein (mg/ml)	Specific Activity (units/mg of protein)
Crude extract	1980	13.4	0.22
Alumina Cγ gel eluate	1710	2.8	1.36
Calcium phosphate gel eluate	1240	0.53	12.0
Ammonium sulfate I	1000	4.5	22.2
Phosphocellulose eluate	655	0.44	59
Ammonium sulfate II	300	2.3	87

[a] Assayed with *M. lysodeikticus* DNA.

REQUIREMENTS.   The reaction does not require the presence of divalent metal ions and in fact can be assayed in the presence of relatively high concentrations (0.02 M) of EDTA. In crude extracts the presence of EDTA enhances the activity. If 2-mercaptoethanol is omitted from the reaction mixture, the activity of the enzyme is decreased by 90%. The requirement for S-adenosylmethionine cannot be met by other methyl donors (1) and S-adenosylethionine is inactive. S-adenosylhomocysteine is a potent inhibitor of the reaction.

Most DNA preparations from viral, bacterial, plant, or animal sources can serve as methyl group acceptors (4–6). Mononucleotides, RNA, or synthetic polydeoxynucleotides of known base sequence are inactive.

PRODUCTS.   In most DNA preparations, the sites of methylation are cytosine and adenine yielding moieties of 5-methylcytosine and 6-methylaminopurine, respectively. The products are identified routinely by standard methods of base analysis.

NATURE OF REACTION.   With any given DNA, the reaction proceeds until a finite number of methyl groups have been incorporated. The addition of further excess enzyme at this point is without effect, and the reactions appear to be irreversible. The yield of methylation appears to be a characteristic of the DNA and can reach levels as high as 2 to 5% of the total nucleotide residues with such DNAs as *Mb. phlei, M. lysodeikticus* and *Pseudomona aeruginosa*. The relative amount of 5-methylcytosine and 6-methylaminopurine formed is also a characteristic of any given DNA. Both of the above properties appear to be independent of base composition.

Although DNA partially degraded by nucleases or sonic oscillation can serve as an acceptor, heat-denatured DNA is inactive (6). DNA isolated from the same strain as the enzyme is also inactive (4,5).

OTHER SOURCES. The enzyme may be purified from other strains of *E. coli* by the procedure given above. It should be noted that K12 strains contain activity for both cytosine and adenine, whereas B strains can form only 6-methylaminopurine (7).

After infection with certain bacteriophage, the activity of DNA methylase in cell extracts increases markedly (8) and can be purified by a slight modification of the above procedure.

STABILITY. Except for the calcium phosphate gel eluate, all enzyme fractions can be stored at 0–5 C for several days without significant loss of activity. The ammonium sulfate fractions are unstable during prolonged dialysis.

REFERENCES

1. GOLD, M., and J. HURWITZ. 1964. J. Biol. Chem. *239:* 3858.
2. FURTH, J. J., J. HURWITZ, R. KRUG, and M. ALEXANDER. 1961. J. Biol. Chem. *236:* 3317.
3. HURWITZ, J., M. GOLD, and M. ANDERS. 1964. J. Biol. Chem. *239:* 3462.
4. GOLD, M., J. HURWITZ, and M. ANDERS. 1963. Biochem. Biophys. Res. Commun. *11:* 107.
5. GOLD, M., and J. HURWITZ. 1963. Cold Spring Harbor Symp. Quant. Biol. *28:* 149.
6. GOLD, M., J. HURWITZ, and M. ANDERS. 1963. Proc. Natl. Acad. Sci., U.S. *50:* 164.
7. GOLD, M., and J. HURWITZ. 1964. J. Biol. Chem. *239:* 3866.
8. GOLD, M., R. HAUSMANN, U. MAITRA, and J. HURWITZ. 1964. Proc. Natl. Acad. Sci., U.S. *52:* 292.

DNA-Glucosylating Enzymes of T2-, T4-, and T6-Infected

Escherichia coli

STEVEN B. ZIMMERMAN

NATIONAL INSTITUTE OF ARTHRITIS
AND METABOLIC DISEASES
NATIONAL INSTITUTES OF HEALTH
BETHESDA, MARYLAND

T2-, T4-, AND T6-HMC-α-GLUCOSYL TRANSFERASES

Assay

$$\text{UDP-glucose} + \text{HMC-DNA} \rightleftharpoons \alpha\text{-glucosyl-HMC-DNA} + \text{UDP}$$

Reagents

1. The reaction mixture (total volume 0.20 ml) contains

    0.1 M Tris (Cl⁻) buffer, pH 7.5
    0.04 M 2-mercaptoethanol
    0.01 M $(NH_4)_2SO_4$
    0.03 mM C^{14}-glucose-labeled UDP-glucose (approximately 2×10^6 cpm/μmole)

307

0.075 mM (in nucleotide equivalents) synthetic 5-hydroxymethyl-cytosine (HMC)-containing DNA†,‡

Enzyme from dilutions in cold 0.05 M Tris (Cl⁻) buffer, pH 7.5, containing 1 mg/ml of crystallized bovine plasma albumin and 0.01 M 2-mercaptoethanol

2. Other reagents used are

2.5 mg/ml of calf thymus DNA (1)
1 N $HClO_4$
1 N acetic acid
0.2 N NaOH
2 N NH_4OH

Procedure

This assay (2) measures formation of an acid-insoluble product from C^{14}-glucose-labeled UDP-glucose in the presence of a suitable acceptor DNA, and is used to follow enzymatic activity during the purification procedure.

After 15 min incubation at 30 C, the mixtures are placed on ice and the DNA precipitated and washed as follows: First, 0.2 ml of cold thymus DNA solution (2.5 mg/ml) is stirred in, followed by 0.5 ml of cold 1 N $HClO_4$ and 4 ml of cold water. After centrifugation for 5 min at 9000 × g, the supernatant fluid is discarded and the precipitate dissolved in 0.3 ml of 0.2 N NaOH, reprecipitated with 0.3 ml of cold 1 N $HClO_4$, diluted with 4 ml of cold water, and centrifuged again. The precipitate is washed by suspension in 2 ml of cold 1 N acetic acid and centrifuged. This acetic acid wash removes residual $HClO_4$, allowing greater precision in C^{14} measurement. The precipitate is dissolved and washed into a planchet with three 0.4-ml portions of 2 N NH_4OH. The planchet is dried and the radioactivity is measured with a gas flow counter. Control assays, performed either in the absence of enzyme or without incubation, measure 5 cpm or less.

† The abbreviations used are 5-hydroxymethylcytosine, HMC, and the disodium salt of ethylenediaminetetraacetic acid, EDTA.

‡ Synthetic HMC-DNA is prepared with highly purified DNA polymerase from *E. coli* in reaction mixtures containing dHMCTP, dGTP, dATP, dTTP, and primer DNA. (Lehman, I. R., *et al.* 1958. Proc. Natl. Acad. Sci., U.S. *44:* 1191.) Primer DNA from a variety of sources (e.g., calf thymus, T2) yields DNA products with similar behavior in the assay. Since the T4- and T6-HMC-α-glucosyl transferases glucosylate natural T2 DNA (Kornberg, S. R., *et al.* 1961. J. Biol Chem. *236:* 1487), an assay for these two enzymes might be devised using this more easily available DNA. Other possible acceptors for the HMC-α-glucosyl transferases are the glucose-deficient DNAs from host-modified T-even phages (Hattman, S., and T. Fukasawa. 1963. Proc. Natl. Acad. Sci. U.S. *50:* 297; Shedlovsky, A., and S. Brenner. 1963. *ibid. 50:* 300).

The acid-insoluble product may alternatively be collected on glass filter paper. The filter procedure (3) is more rapid, but less precise than that described above.

One unit of enzyme is defined as the amount that transfers 1 μmole of glucose in 1 hr under the conditions described. The amount of reaction is proportional to both enzyme concentration and time of incubation up to 0.4 mμmole of glucose incorporated. Specific enzyme activity is defined as units per mg of protein. Protein is determined by the method of Lowry *et al.* (4); enzyme fractions containing interfering materials such as streptomycin or 2-mercaptoethanol are first precipitated in the cold with trichloroacetic acid (10% final concentration).

Isolation Procedure

The purification procedures for the HMC-α-glucosyl transferases from T2-, T4-, and T6-infected cells are similar. A detailed procedure is given below for the enzyme from T2-infected cells (2). Modifications follow for purification of the HMC-α-glucosyl transferases from T6- or T4-infected cells (2,3). The chromatography on XE-64 and DEAE-cellulose was carried out on scales suited to the amounts of fractions available; the scales indicated should be useful for the amounts indicated regardless of whether the transferase is from T2-, T4-, or T6-infected cells. Similarly, it is expected that the T6-transferase will fractionate on DEAE-cellulose in a manner similar to that described for the other two enzymes. Results of the isolation procedures are summarized in Table 1.

Except where specified, all procedures are carried out at 0–5 C and the centrifugations are at 12,000 $\times$ g.

T2-HMC-α-glucosyl Transferase

GROWTH AND INFECTION OF CELLS. *E. coli* B or *E. coli* B/1,5 is grown at 37 C with vigorous aeration in a M-9 medium (5) modified to contain per liter: KH_2PO_4, 3 g; Na_2HPO_4, 6 g; NH_4Cl, 1 g; $MgSO_4 \cdot 7 H_2O$, 0.49 g; glucose, 5 g; and $FeSO_4 \cdot 7 H_2O$, 0.5 mg. The glucose and $MgSO_4$ are autoclaved as separate solutions. With good aeration, logarithmic growth continues to 4–5 $\times$ 10^9 cells/ml with a generation time of about 50 min. Large-scale cultures may be grown in a 50- or 100-liter "Biogen" (American Sterilizer Company) filled to half capacity with medium and receiving maximal aeration. The medium is inoculated with 1/15 volume of fresh fully grown culture in the same medium. When the cells reach late logarithmic phase, 2–4 $\times$ 10^9

TABLE 1. *Purification of HMC-α-Glucosyl Transferases from T2-, T4-, and T6-infected E. coli*

Fraction	T2-α-Transferase			T4-α-Transferase			T6-α-Transferase		
	Protein (mg/ml)	Specific Activity (units/mg)	Yield of Activity (%)	Protein (mg/ml)	Specific Activity (units/mg)	Yield of Activity (%)	Protein (mg/ml)	Specific Activity (units/mg)	Yield of activity (%)
I. Extract	20	0.10	100	25	0.30	100	28	0.10	100
II. Streptomycin	3.0	0.17	68	3.2	0.59	82	3.3	0.19	79
III. Ammonium sulfate	21	0.41	63	28	0.70	63	17	0.31	70
IV. XE-64	11.8[a]	18.4	38	0.18	65	61	6.4[a]	15.9	22
V. DEAE-cellulose	0.28	63	14	0.42	185	37			

[a] After concentration with ammonium sulfate.

cells/ml depending on conditions of aeration, T2r+ is added at an input ratio of 3–5 phage/cell. Bacteriophages T2r+, T4r+, and T6r+ are grown and purified according to Herriott and Barlow (6). After phage addition, aeration is continued for 15 min at 37 C and the culture is immediately chilled to 0–5 C and harvested by centrifugation. Because of the fragility of the infected cells, the packed cells are not washed before storage at −12 C. In the original large-scale preparations, chloramphenicol (50 mg/liter) was added to the infected culture immediately before chilling, to prevent cell lysis. This addition is not obligatory (3), but seems of value when handling large volumes of culture where the chilling and centrifugation are relatively slow. The yield of cells is 2.0–2.5 g wet weight per liter of cells infected at 2×10^9 cells/ml. Cells may be stored frozen for at least several months without changes in activity.

PREPARATION OF EXTRACT. T2-infected cells (50 g), 150 g of glass beads (Superbrite No. 100, Minnesota Mining and Manufacturing Company), and 50 ml of a solution (Buffer A) containing 0.05 M glycylglycine buffer, pH 7.0, 0.002 M EDTA, and 0.002 M reduced glutathione are mixed at two-thirds of maximal speed for ten 2-min periods in a 1-quart glass Waring Blendor. The container is immersed in an ice water bath between mixing periods until the temperature of the contents is below 10 C. After the last mixing period, 140 ml of Buffer A are added and mixed for 10 min at one-fifth of maximal speed. The glass beads are allowed to settle for 3 min, the supernatant fluid is decanted, and the beads are briefly washed with 100 ml of Buffer A. The supernatant fluid and wash are combined, and after centrifugation for 30 min the supernatant fluid (250 ml) is collected. This procedure is repeated on additional 50-g portions of infected cells (Fraction I).

STREPTOMYCIN PRECIPITATION OF INACTIVE MATERIALS. Fraction I (500 ml) is diluted with Buffer A to 10 mg of protein/ml. A volume of 5% streptomycin sulfate equal to 0.3 that of the diluted extract is added with stirring over a 10-min period. After the mixture is stirred for an additional 20 min, the supernatant fluid is collected after centrifugation for 20 min (Fraction II).

AMMONIUM SULFATE FRACTIONATION. To 2620 ml of pooled Fraction II are added 2570 ml of alkaline saturated ammonium sulfate† over a 10-min period with stirring. After an additional 5 min of stirring, the suspension is centrifuged 10 min, and the pellet is discarded. The volume of the supernatant solution is determined, and

† Saturated at 5 C and adjusted with NH₄OH to pH 8.0 to 8.1 (measured at room temperature after tenfold dilution).

solid ammonium sulfate (0.148 g/ml) is added with stirring. After the salt is dissolved, stirring is continued for 5 min, and the insoluble material is collected by centrifugation. The pellet is redissolved in a minimal volume of Buffer A (Fraction III).

XE-64 CHROMATOGRAPHY. A column (15 cm^2 × 30 cm) of XE-64 resin† is equilibrated with 0.10 M sodium phosphate buffer, pH 6.55, containing 0.002 M EDTA and 0.01 M 2-mercaptoethanol. Pooled Fraction III preparations (475 ml) are dialyzed against 40 volumes of 0.02 M sodium phosphate buffer, pH 6.08, containing 0.002 M EDTA and 0.01 M 2-mercaptoethanol, for 5 hr, and a small amount of insoluble material that forms is removed by centrifugation for 10 min. The dialyzed preparation is passed through the column at a rate of 18 ml/hr and finally washed into the resin at the same flow rate with 20 ml of the dialysis buffer. About 90% of the protein applied is not retarded by the column. During the loading period, the input solution occasionally becomes turbid and forms a thin, dense, white layer over the resin bed. This layer is cautiously disrupted with a stirring rod before the elution is started. A constant gradient‡ of elution from 0 to 0.3 M NaCl is applied, both limiting solutions containing 0.01 M sodium phosphate buffer, pH 6.55, 0.002 M EDTA, and 0.01 M 2-mercaptoethanol. The total gradient volume is 2.4 liters. Fractions of 17 ml are collected at a flow rate of 90 ml/hr. The activity is eluted as a symmetrical peak in the middle third of the gradient. The total recovery of the added activity is 74%. Fractions of highest specific activity are pooled. The activity is concentrated by precipitation with ammonium sulfate with 90–100% yield as follows. The pooled fractions are stirred with ammonium sulfate (0.6 g/ml) for 40 min, and then centrifuged for 30 min. The pellet is thoroughly drained, resuspended in one-half of the original volume of 85% saturated (at 5 C) ammonium sulfate, and centrifuged as before. The washed precipitate is dissolved in 1/50 of the original volume in 0.05 M Tris buffer, pH 7.5, containing 0.002 M EDTA and 0.004 M reduced glutathione. Insoluble material is removed by centrifugation for 10 min at 5000 × g (Fraction IV).

DEAE-CELLULOSE CHROMATOGRAPHY. Fraction IV (5 ml) is dialyzed for 2 hr against 100 volumes of 0.02 M potassium buffer, pH 8.1, containing 0.01 M 2-mercaptoethanol and 0.002 M EDTA. A col-

† Amberlite XE-64 (Rohm and Haas Company) is processed and adjusted to pH 6.55 according to Hirs, C. H. W., *et al.* 1953. J. Biol Chem. *200:* 493.

‡ A constant or "linear" gradient is obtained from two open reservoirs of equal cross-sectional area. Initially, the reservoirs contain equal volumes of the two limiting solutions of the gradient. The more concentrated solution flows into the second reservoir containing the more dilute solution as the latter, being continuously stirred, flows into the column.

umn (1 cm² × 18 cm) of DEAE-cellulose† is equilibrated with a solution of the same composition used for dialysis. The dialyzed Fraction IV is passed through the column at a flow rate of 30 ml/hr and washed into the column at the same flow rate with 9 ml of the equilibrating solution. A constant gradient‡ of elution from 0.02 M NaCl to 0.17 M NaCl is applied, both limiting solutions containing 0.02 M potassium phosphate buffer, pH 8.1, 0.01 M 2-mercaptoethanol, and 0.002 M EDTA. The total gradient volume is 260 ml. Fractions of 5 ml are collected at a flow rate of 36 ml/hr. A peak of protein and activity is eluted at the midpoint of the gradient. Fractions of highest specific activity are pooled (Fraction V).

COMMENTS. Fractions I, II, III, and IV are stable for at least 3 months at −15 C. Fraction V lost 50% of its activity after storage for 3 weeks at 0 C (unfrozen).§

T4-HMC-α-glucosyl Transferase

GROWTH AND INFECTION OF CELLS. T4r+ is used to infect *E. coli* as described above for T2r+ except L-tryptophan (50 mg/liter) is added immediately before the phage.

PREPARATION OF EXTRACT; STREPTOMYCIN PRECIPITATION OF INACTIVE MATERIALS. These are done as described above for the enzyme from T2-infected cells (Fractions I and II, respectively).

AMMONIUM SULFATE FRACTIONATION. To 1400 ml of Fraction II, an equal volume of alkaline-saturated ammonium sulfate‖ is added, with stirring, over a 10-min period. After an additional 10 min of stirring, the suspension is centrifuged for 15 min and the supernatant fluid is collected. Solid ammonium sulfate (0.212 g/ml) is added with stirring over a 10-min interval, and the suspension is stirred an additional 10 min. After centrifugation for 20 min, the supernatant fluid is discarded and the pellet dissolved in 110 ml of a solution containing

† DEAE-cellulose is suspended in 0.25 N NaOH for 15 min at room temperature, and then exhaustively washed with water and buffer, both before use and to regenerate used materials.

‡ A constant or "linear" gradient is obtained from two open reservoirs of equal cross-sectional area. Initially, the reservoirs contain equal volumes of the two limiting solutions of the gradient. The more concentrated solution flows into the second reservoir containing the more dilute solution as the latter, being continuously stirred, flows into the column.

§ Fractions containing 2-mercaptoethanol lose large amounts of activity upon freezing and thawing, and should be stored at 0 C (unfrozen).

‖ Saturated at 5 C and adjusted with NH₄OH to pH 8.0 to 8.1 (measured at room temperature after tenfold dilution).

0.05 M glycylglycine buffer, pH 7.0, 0.002 M EDTA, and 0.002 M reduced glutathione (Fraction III).

XE-64 CHROMATOGRAPHY. An XE-64 column† (5 cm² × 27 cm) is equilibrated, and Fraction III (65 ml) is dialyzed and centrifuged as in the corresponding steps for the T2-enzyme above. The column is loaded at a rate of flow of 3.5 ml/hr and washed into the resin at the same flow rate with 4 ml of the dialysis buffer. A constant gradient‡ of elution from 0 to 0.6 M NaCl is then applied to the column, both limiting solutions containing 0.10 M sodium phosphate buffer, pH 6.55, 0.002 M EDTA, and 0.01 M mercaptoethanol. The total gradient volume is 1.5 liters; the flow rate is 15 ml/hr. Fractions of 8 ml are collected. The enzyme is eluted in the first third of the gradient with a recovery of 100%; the T4-HMC-β-glucosyl transferase (see below) is eluted in the middle third of the gradient with a recovery of 87%. The two enzymes are clearly separated from one another and occur as symmetrical peaks after 90% of the protein has already passed through the column. The fractions with highest T4-HMC-α-glucosyl transferase are pooled (90 ml, Fraction IV).

DEAE-CELLULOSE CHROMATOGRAPHY. A DEAE-cellulose§ column (0.25 cm² × 18 cm) is equilibrated as described above for the enzyme from T2-infected cells. Fraction IV (60 ml) is dialyzed for 5 hr against 100 volumes of the same solution used for equilibrating the column. The dialyzed preparation is then passed through the column at a rate of 3 ml/hr and washed into the resin at the same flow rate with 3 ml of the dialysis solution. Chromatography is carried out as described for the T2-transferase above, with a total gradient volume of 70 ml. Fractions of 1.5 ml are collected at a flow rate of 6 ml/hr. The enzyme is recovered in the middle third of the gradient as a symmetrical peak of constant specific activity (Fraction V) with a recovery of 81% of the activity applied to the column.

COMMENTS. Fractions I, II, and III are stable for at least 2 months at −15 C. Fraction IV is stable for 2 months if kept at 0 C (unfrozen); under the same conditions, Fraction V lost 40% of its activity.‖

† Amberlite XE-64 (Rohm and Haas Company) is processed and adjusted to pH 6.55 according to Hirs, C. H. W., et al. 1953. J. Biol. Chem. 200: 493.

‡ A constant or "linear" gradient is obtained from two open reservoirs of equal cross-sectional area. Initially, the reservoirs contain equal volumes of the two limiting solutions of the gradient. The more concentrated solution flows into the second reservoir containing the more dilute solution as the latter, being continuously stirred, flows into the column.

§ DEAE-cellulose is suspended in 0.25 N NaOH for 15 min at room temperature, and then exhaustively washed with water and buffer, both before use and to regenerate used materials.

‖ Fractions containing 2-mercaptoethanol lose large amounts of activity upon freezing and thawing, and should be stored at 0 C (unfrozen).

T6-HMC-α-Glucosyl Transferase

GROWTH AND INFECTION OF CELLS. T6r+ is used to infect *E. coli* as described above for T2r+ except L-tryptophan (20 mg/liter) is added immediately before the phage.

PREPARATION OF EXTRACT; STREPTOMYCIN PRECIPITATION OF INACTIVE MATERIALS; AMMONIUM SULFATE PRECIPITATION. These are done as described above for the T2-HMC-α-glucosyl transferase (Fractions I, II, and III, respectively).

XE-64 CHROMATOGRAPHY. The protocol for chromatography on XE-64 is similar to that described above for the enzyme of T2-infected cells, but is carried out on a reduced scale. Fraction III (64 ml) is dialyzed and applied to an XE-64† column (3.8 cm² × 30 cm). The total volume of the gradient of elution is 440 ml. The fraction volume is 4 ml. The rate of flow during loading and elution are 4 ml and 22 ml/hr, respectively. The total recovery of the added activity is 70%. The activity is concentrated with 50% recovery by ammonium sulfate precipitation (without the 85% saturated ammonium sulfate wash, but otherwise as described above for the T2-HMC-α-glucosyl transferase) (Fraction IV).

COMMENTS. Fraction IV loses 45% of its activity after storage for 3 months at −15 C. This loss might be avoided by including the 85% saturated ammonium sulfate wash described above in the T2-HMC-α-glucosyl transferase isolation. The wash removes traces of 2-mercaptoethanol.‡

T4-HMC-β-GLUCOSYL TRANSFERASE

Assay

$$\text{UDP-glucose} + \text{HMC-DNA} \rightleftharpoons \beta\text{-glucosyl-HMC-DNA} + \text{UDP}$$

Reagents

1. The reaction mixture (total volume 0.20 ml) contains

   0.1 M potassium phosphate buffer, pH 7.8
   0.05 mM C¹⁴-glucose-labeled UDP-glucose (approximately 2×10^6 cpm/μmole)

---

† Amberlite XE-64 (Rohm and Haas Company) is processed and adjusted to pH 6.55 according to Hirs, C. H. W., *et al.* 1953. J. Biol. Chem. *200*: 493.
‡ Fractions containing 2-mercaptoethanol lose large amounts of activity upon freezing and thawing, and should be stored at 0 C (unfrozen).

0.06 mM (in nucleotide equivalents) T2 DNA (7)

0.025 M MgCl

Enzyme from dilutions in cold 0.05 M potassium phosphate buffer, pH 7.8, containing 1 mg/ml of crystallized bovine plasma albumin

Note: To avoid formation of a precipitate, the assay mixtures are made up cold, and the $MgCl_2$ and enzyme are added last.

2. Other reagents used are

2.5 mg/ml of calf thymus DNA (1)

10% trichloroacetic acid

1 N $HClO_4$

1 N Acetic acid

0.2 N NaOH

2 N NH_4OH

Procedure

The assay principle and procedure, definitions of the enzyme unit and specific activity, and the range of proportionality are as described previously for the HMC-α-glucosyl transferases. In the first acid precipitation, 10% trichloroacetic acid is substituted for the 1 N $HClO_4$ to avoid a $KClO_4$ precipitate.

Isolation Procedure

Two procedures are available to isolate the T4-HMC-β-glucosyl transferase (3). The first is described below and allows purification of both the HMC-α- and HMC-β-glucosyl transferases from the same T4-infected cells. The second (see reference 3) applies only to the purification of the T4-HMC-β-glucosyl transferase; the second scheme gives higher yields and greater purification in the early steps, thus reducing the scale of subsequent chromatographic steps. The final specific activity achieved by either scheme is the same.

Procedures are carried out at 0–5 C. Centrifugations are at 12,000 $\times$ g.

The first five steps are the same as those described previously for purification of T4-HMC-α-glucosyl transferase. The XE-64 fractions in Step V containing the highest specific activity for the HMC-β-glucosyl transferase are pooled (50 ml, Fraction IV).

CM-CELLULOSE CHROMATOGRAPHY.   A column (0.25 cm² $\times$ 22 cm) of CM-cellulose, processed according to Peterson and Sober (8), is equilibrated with 0.01 M potassium phosphate buffer, pH 6.03. Fraction IV, 50 ml, is dialyzed for 5 hr against 80 volumes of the same solution used to equilibrate the column. The dialyzed solution is passed through the column at a rate of 2 ml/hr and washed into the resin with 3 ml of the dialyzing solution at the same flow rate. A constant gradient† from 0.02 to 0.40 M potassium phosphate buffer, pH 6.47 at 0.05 M, is then applied to the column. The total gradient volume is 100 ml; fractions of 2 ml are collected at a flow rate of 8 ml/hr. The enzyme is recovered in the middle third of the gradient as a skewed peak of changing specific activity. The total recovery of activity from the column is 65%, one-half of which is present in fractions of maximal specific activity (Fraction V).

COMMENTS. The results of this procedure are summarized in Table 2. All the fractions are stable for at least 4 months when kept at 0 C (unfrozen). Fractions I, II, and III can be frozen without loss of activity. Fractions IV and V lose 30–80% of their activity after a single freezing and thawing.

TABLE 2.   *Purification of HMC-β-Glucosyl Transferase from T4-Infected E. Coli*

Fraction	Protein (mg/ml)	Specific Activity (units/mg)	Yield of Activity %
I. Extract	25	0.20	100
II. Streptomycin	3.2	0.25	53
III. Ammonium sulfate	28	0.29	40
IV. XE-64	0.07	95	27
V. CM-cellulose	0.11	260	9

T6-GLUCOSYL-HMC-β-GLUCOSYL TRANSFERASE

Assay

UDP-glucose + glucosyl-HMC-DNA ⇌ diglucosyl-HMC-DNA + UDP

Reagents

1. The reaction mixture (total volume 0.20 ml) contains

0.1 M Tris (Cl⁻) buffer, pH 7.5
0.04 M 2-mercaptoethanol

† A constant or "linear" gradient is obtained from two open reservoirs of equal cross-sectional area. Initially, the reservoirs contain equal volumes of the two limiting solutions of the gradient. The more concentrated solution flows into the second reservoir containing the more dilute solution as the latter, being continuously stirred, flows into the column.

0.025 M $MgCl_2$

0.05 mM C^{14}-glucose-labeled UDP-glucose (approximately 2×10^6 cpm/μmole)

0.08 mM (in nucleotide equivalents) T4 DNA (prepared as described for T2 DNA in reference 7)

Enzyme from dilutions in 0.02 M Tris (Cl^-) buffer, pH 7.5, containing 0.001 M 2-mercaptoethanol

2. Other reagents used are

2.5 mg/ml of calf thymus DNA (1)

1 N $HClO_4$

1 N Acetic acid

0.2 N NaOH

2 N NH_4OH

Procedure (9)

The assay principle and procedure, and the definition of the enzyme unit are the same as described above for the HMC-α-glucosyl transferases.

Isolation Procedure

All steps are carried out at 0–5.† Centrifugations are for 15 min at 12,000 $\times$ g.

GROWTH AND INFECTION OF CELLS.   See T6-HMC-α-glucosyl transferase described before.

PREPARATION OF EXTRACT.   T6r$^+$-infected cells (12 g) suspended in 54 ml of 0.05 M glycylglycine buffer, pH 7.0, are treated for 20 min in a 10-kc Raytheon sonic oscillator and the supernatant fluid (Fraction I) collected by centrifugation.

STREPTOMYCIN PRECIPITATION OF INACTIVE MATERIALS.   Extract (28 ml) is diluted to a protein concentration of 10 mg/ml with 50 ml of the same buffer and 0.8 ml of 1 M 2-mercaptoethanol. The diluted extract is treated with 0.3 volume of a 5% streptomycin sulfate solution. After 15 min, the supernatant fluid is collected by centrifugation (Fraction II).

DEAE-CELLULOSE CHROMATOGRAPHY.   A column of DEAE-cellulose‡ (4 cm^2 $\times$ 20 cm) is equilibrated with 0.02 M potassium

---

† Fractions containing 2-mercaptoethanol lose large amounts of activity upon freezing and thawing, and should be stored at 0 C (unfrozen).

‡ DEAE-cellulose is suspended in 0.25 N NaOH for 15 min at room temperature, and then exhaustively washed with water and buffer, both before use and to regenerate used materials.

phosphate buffer, pH 8.0, containing 0.01 M 2-mercaptoethanol. This buffer mixture is added in equal volume to Fraction II (97 ml), which is then adjusted to pH 8.0 with 0.1 N NaOH by dropwise addition with good stirring and applied to the column. The column is washed with 70 ml of the buffer mixture and a constant gradient† (280 ml total volume) is applied from 0.08 M to 0.32 M NaCl, both solutions containing 0.01 M 2-mercaptoethanol and 0.02 M potassium phosphate buffer, pH 8.0. The flow rate for all operations is about 180 ml/hr. Fractions of 6 ml are collected. One-third of the activity is not held by the column; the remainder appears between 57 and 80 ml of eluent (Fraction III). None is found in the fractions (115 to 126 ml of eluent) where the HMC-α-glucosyl transferase is eluted. The enzyme may be dialyzed before use against 0.05 M Tris buffer, pH 7.5, containing 0.02 M reduced glutathione.

COMMENTS. This procedure was derived in the course of an earlier procedure (9) for the T6-HMC-α-glucosyl transferase. The yield is only 20% for a fourfold purification (Table 3); however, the preparation is largely freed of nucleic acid and is well separated from the T6-HMC-α-glucosyl transferase.

TABLE 3. *Purification of Glucosyl-HMC-β-Glucosyl Transferase from T6-Infected E. coli*

Fraction	Protein (mg/ml)	Specific Activity (units/mg)	Yield of Activity (%)
I. Extract	28	0.1	100
II. Streptomycin	3.2	0.1	35
III. DEAE-cellulose	0.6	0.4	21

PROPERTIES OF THE ENZYMES

Distribution

DNA-glucosylating activity has been found in cells infected with those bacteriophages containing HMC in their DNA, i.e., T2, T4, T6, and hybrids of T2 and T4 (9,10). Noninfected cells or cells infected

† A constant or "linear" gradient is obtained from two open reservoirs of equal cross-sectional area. Initially, the reservoirs contain equal volumes of the two limiting solutions of the gradient. The more concentrated solution flows into the second reservoir containing the more dilute solution as the latter, being continuously stirred, flows into the column.

with a cytosine-containing phage, T5, do not contain this activity (11). The kinetics of transferase synthesis following infection are similar for those enzymes examined (T2-HMC-α-, T4-HMC-α- or -β-glucosyl transferases), activity first being detectable about 4 min after infection and then increasing up to about 15 min (11,9).

The transferases known for T2-, T4-, or T6- infections produce *in vitro* all the HMC-derivatives characteristic of the DNA of these phages (9), with the exception of a means of forming diglucosyl-HMC residues in T2-infected cells. Hybrids of T2 and T4 induce transferases compatible with the HMC-derivatives in the DNA of the hybrids (10). Mutants of T2 or T6 that do not induce HMC-α-glucosyl transferase activity have been described (12).

pH Optima

The T2- and T4-HMC-α-glucosyl transferases have a similar pH optimum for activity, pH 7.5–8.0 in 0.1 M Tris (Cl$^-$) buffer. The T6-HMC-α-glucosyl transferase optimum is pH 8.0–8.3 in the same buffer (2,3). The optimum for the T4-HMC-β-glucosyl transferase is 7.5–8.5 in 0.1 M potassium phosphate or Ammediol (Cl$^-$) buffers (3).

Effects of Ions, Sulfhydryl Compounds, and Other Reagents

The HMC-α-glucosyl transferases from T2-, T4-, and T6-infected cells grossly share the following properties (2,3,9): They require the presence of sulfhydryl compounds to maintain activity. They are inhibited by phosphate; substitution of phosphate buffer at the same pH as the assay buffer (Tris) reduces activity two- to fivefold. They are inhibited by Mg^{2+}; addition of 0.025 M MgCl$_2$ to the assay reduces activity to $\leq 15\%$. Their activity is not affected by EDTA (0.01 M in the assay). When assayed with synthetic DNA as acceptor, these enzymes are stimulated two- to threefold by spermine or ammonium sulfate (10^{-4} M or 0.01 M, respectively, for maximal effect). Other salts or polyamines tested were less effective; this effect was not seen with a natural DNA as glucosyl acceptor.

The T4-HMC-β-glucosyl transferase shows no requirement for protective sulfhydryl reagents; p-hydroxymercuribenzoate (10^{-3} M) has no effect on its activity. The cation requirement of this enzyme is complex. In phosphate buffer, there is about a fivefold stimulation by MgCl$_2$ (0.025 M); larger amounts of KCl, K$_2$SO$_4$, or NaCl give partial stimulation. In Ammediol or Tris buffers, there is an absolute requirement for a divalent cation, 0.025 M MgCl$_2$ or CaCl$_2$ giving maximal stimulation. Tris is an inhibitor of this enzyme, whereas Ammediol is not, although chemically very similar (3,9).

The T6-glucosyl-HMC-β-glucosyl transferase is dependent on protective sulfhydryl reagents. This enzyme has similar activity in phosphate or Tris buffers of the same pH. It is stimulated tenfold by 0.025 M $MgCl_2$ and completely inhibited by 0.01 M EDTA (9).

Reversal and Equilibrium Constant of the Reaction

In the presence of large amounts of UDP and enzyme, a slow deglucosylation of DNA has been observed with all the monoglucosyl-forming transferases (2,3). The reversal of the reaction is specifically dependent on UDP. DNA glucosylated either *in vivo* or *in vitro* is a substrate for the reverse reaction.

The equilibrium constant of the reaction of the T2-HMC-α-glucosyl transferase strongly favors glucosylation (2). Limiting values for forward and reverse reactions indicate $K_{eq} = $ (glucosyl-HMC) (UDP)/ (HMC) (UDP-glucose) = 200–2000.

K_m for DNA and UDP-Glucose

The K_m for DNA of the HMC-α- or HMC-β-glucosyl transferases are similar (ca. 3×10^{-5} M in nucleotide equivalents). The K_m for UDP-glucose of HMC-α-glucosyl transferases of T2-, T4-, and T6-infections are significantly different (3.6×10^{-5} M, 0.7×10^{-5} M, and 1.5×10^{-5} M, respectively). The K_m for UDP-glucose of the T4-HMC-β-glucosyl transferase is strongly influenced by specific salt effects, but falls in the range covered by the other enzymes (2,3).

Specificity for DNA Acceptor

The transferases from a given phage infection do not further glucosylate the DNA of that phage. The enzymes induced by a given phage, will however, add further glucose to the DNA of other of the T-even phage DNAs in several cases (9). Synthetic DNAs containing HMC-residues, including dGdHMC, are acceptors for all the mono-glucosyl-forming transferases (3,9).

It is uncertain what determines which HMC residues are glucosylated by a given enzyme. The involvement of primary structure of the DNA is suggested by the limited number of the possible HMC-containing base sequences, that bear glucosyl-moieties after *in vivo* (13) or *in vitro* (14) glucosylation. However, HMC residues, which were α-glucosylated *in vivo*, can accept β-glucosyl groups *in vitro*, and formerly β-substituted HMC residues can accept α-glucosyl groups (3). An influence of secondary or tertiary structure of the DNA on glucosylation specificity has been proposed (3) to account for this result. Consistent with this hypothesis is the reduction in rate or extent of glucosylation with several transferases when the acceptor DNA is heat denatured (2,3).

Deoxyribonuclease Contamination

Deoxyribonuclease activity is undetectable in purified preparations (Fractions IV or V above) of the T2- or T6-HMC-α-glucosyl transferases under the conditions used to assay their glucosylating activity (pH 7.5, no Mg^{2+} added). Under conditions optimal for two of the deoxyribo- nucleases in *E. coli,* the T2-induced enzyme (Fraction V) has low but significant activity (2).

REFERENCES

1. KAY, E. R. M., N. S. SIMMONS, and A. L. DOUNCE. 1952. J. Am. Chem. Soc. *74:* 1724.
2. ZIMMERMAN, S. B., S. R. KORNBERG, and A. KORNBERG. 1962. J. Biol. Chem. *237:* 512.
3. JOSSE, J., and A. KORNBERG. 1962. J. Biol. Chem. *237:* 1968.
4. LOWRY, O. H., N. J. ROSEBROUGH, A. L. FARR, and R. J. RANDALL. 1951. J. Biol. Chem. *193:* 265.
5. ANDERSON, E. H. 1946. Proc. Natl. Acad. Sci., U.S. *32:* 120.
6. HERRIOTT, R. M., and J. L. BARLOW. 1952–1953. J. Gen. Physiol. *36:* 17.
7. LEHMAN, I. R. 1960. J. Biol. Chem. *235:* 1479.
8. PETERSON, E. A., and H. A. SOBER. 1956. J. Am. Chem. Soc. *78:* 751.
9. KORNBERG, S. R., S. B. ZIMMERMAN, and A. KORNBERG. 1961. J. Biol. Chem. *236:* 1487.
10. PRATT, E. A., S. KUNO, and I. R. LEHMAN. 1963. Biochim. Biophys. Acta. *68:* 108.
11. KORNBERG, A., S. B. ZIMMERMAN, S. R. KORNBERG, and J. JOSSE. 1959. Proc. Natl. Acad. Sci., U.S. *45:* 772.
12. REVEL, H. R., S. HATTMAN, and S. E. LURIA. 1965. Biochem. Biophys. Res. Commun. *18:* 545.
13. BURTON, K., M. R. LUNT, G. B. PETERSEN, and J. C. SIEBKE. 1963. Cold Spring Harbor Symp. Quant. Biol. *28:* 27.
14. DE WAARD, A., M. M. VROEGOP, and C. M. M. WIENTJES. 1964. 6th Intl. Cong. Biochem., Abstracts, III: 228.

DNA-Dependent RNA

Polymerase (EC 2.7.7.6)

WOLFRAM ZILLIG, ECKART FUCHS,

AND ROBERT MILLETTE

MAX PLANCK INSTITUTE FOR BIOCHEMISTRY

MUNICH, WEST GERMANY

Methods for the preparation of this enzyme from *Escherichia coli* have been published by Hurwitz (1) and by Chamberlin and Berg (2). The procedure described here is based on the relatively high sedimentation coefficient of the enzyme particle and avoids the protamine sulfate precipitation step of the above authors. It is designed to obtain maximum yields of the intact polymerase molecule.

ASSAY

$$\begin{matrix} n \text{ ARPPP} \\ n \text{ GRPPP} \\ n \text{ CRPPP} \\ n \text{ URPPP} \end{matrix} + \text{DNA} \rightleftarrows \text{DNA} + \begin{bmatrix} \text{ARP} \\ \text{GRP} \\ \text{CRP} \\ \text{URP} \end{bmatrix}_n + 4(n)\text{PP}$$

Reagents

In a total volume of 0.5 ml

0.03 M Tris acetate, pH 7.9

0.13 M Ammonium chloride

0.03 M Magnesium acetate

0.001 M each of Guanosine-5'-triphosphate, cytidine-5'-triphosphate, uridine-5'-triphosphate (or adenosine-5'-triphosphate)

0.0005 M Adenosine-5'-triphosphate-8-C^{14} (or UTP-C^{14}) specific activity 0.3 c/mole

Thanks are due to Prof. A. Butenandt and to the Deutsche Forschungsgemeinschaft for generous support of this work. One of the authors (R. M.) was supported by a Public Health Service fellowship (I-F2-GM-19, 333–01) from the National Institute of General Medical Sciences. We are also grateful to H. Döderlein for valuable technical assistance and to Dr. P. H. Hofschneider and Miss A. Preuss for the electron microscopy.

0.01 M Phosphoenolpyruvate; Pyruvate kinase 20 μg/ml; DNA (from
bacteriophage T4 or calf thymus) 100 μg/ml; Enzyme, 2–20 units/ml
All solutions are adjusted to pH 7.9; incubation is carried out at 37 C
for 10 min.

Procedure

The assay measures the incorporation of labeled nucleotide residues
into acid-insoluble RNA. After incubation, the reaction mixture is
diluted with 1.0 ml of ice water. When the amount of protein in the
enzyme preparation is low (less than 200 μg), 250 μg of casein carrier
is added with the water. The product is precipitated by the addition of
1.5 ml of ice-cold 10% TCA. The precipitates are collected on membrane filters (MF 50, 25-mm Membranfiltergesellschaft, Goettingen),
washed 4 times each with about 5 ml of 5% TCA, dried, and then
counted in a thin window gas flow counter.

One unit of enzyme is the amount that, in excess of DNA, incorporates 1 mμmole of ATP in 10 min at 37 C, under the conditions described.

ISOLATION PROCEDURE

The purification procedure consists of successive differential centrifugation steps, the separation of the enzyme from nucleic acid by
chromatography on DEAE-cellulose using a salt gradient, ammonium
sulfate precipitation followed by sucrose gradient centrifugation and,
if desired, sucrose gradient electrophoresis. Concentration of the enzyme is achieved by ultracentrifugation.

STEP I. PREPARATION OF CRUDE EXTRACT. *E. coli* K$_{12}$
are grown at 37 C with vigorous aeration in 15-1 bottles to a concentration of 10^9 cells/ml (end of logarithmic growth phase). Fraser medium
is used (3) modified by replacement of the casamino acids with the same
amount of peptone (Merck) and addition of 5% glucose. The cells are
harvested by pouring onto an excess of ice and collected by centrifugation at 37,000 rev/min in a Cepa continuous flow centrifuge (C. Padberg,
Lahr, Germany). The bacterial sediment is washed twice by suspension
in TMA buffer (0.01 M Tris acetate pH 7.5, 0.022 M NH$_4$Cl, 0.01 M
magnesium acetate, 0.001 M β-mercaptoethanol) and centrifugation for
10 min in a Servall centrifuge, SS34 rotor, at 15,000 rev/min. The
bacterial sediment is stored in a deep freeze at −20 C.

400 g of the washed bacteria are suspended in 600 ml of TMA
buffer and homogenized in 90-ml portions in the presence of 135 ml of
glass beads (measured dry, diam. 0.1 mm). Homogenization is performed by shaking at 80 cycles/sec for 2 min, at 0–4 C, in a 200-ml

stainless steel beaker of a vibrational homogenizer (Otto Bühler, Tuebingen, Germany) (4). The extract is separated from the glass beads by mild suction on a sintered glass funnel and the beads are washed with a total of 300 ml of TMA buffer. The washings are combined with the original filtrate and the bacterial debris is removed by centrifugation in the Spinco Type 30 rotor for 40 min at 30,000 rev/min.

STEP 2. PREPARATION OF DNA-PROTEIN FRACTION. The crude extract is centrifuged in the Spinco 30 rotor for 20 hr at 30,000 rev/min and the supernatant liquid is discarded. The sediment consists of two layers. The upper layer (DNA and protein, containing the enzyme) is easily removed from the lower layer (ribosomes) with a spatula. The combined upper layers are resuspended in a final volume of 400 ml of TMA by gentle homogenization.

STEP 3. CHROMATOGRAPHY ON DEAE-CELLULOSE. 140 g of DEAE-cellulose (Serva, Heidelberg, Germany), 0.68 meq/g, is washed alternately two times with 0.1 M KOH, water, and 0.1 M HCl, and finally with 0.1 M KOH. It is then washed with water until the effluent is neutral and equilibrated with an excess of TMA buffer. The TMA-washed DEAE-cellulose is added as a de-aerated slurry to the "DNA-protein fraction" and slowly stirred for 15 min. The excess liquid is removed by suction on a sintered glass funnel (not to complete dryness). To elute a large part of the contaminating protein the DEAE-cellulose is then washed 3 times with 300 ml of TMA buffer containing 0.15 M NH_4Cl and is finally suspended in 300 ml of this same buffer and de-aerated by suction.

A glass column (5 cm × 35 cm) is packed with DEAE-cellulose, equilibrated with TMA buffer containing 0.15 M NH_4Cl, up to a height of 3–5 cm. The suspension of DEAE-cellulose to which the enzyme has been adsorbed is poured on top of this cushion and packed with a pressure of 0.35 kg/cm². The adsorbed proteins and nucleic acids are then eluted from the packed column by a gradient of 0.15–0.5 M NH_4Cl in TMA buffer, using a closed mixing vessel originally containing 1 liter of 0.15 M NH_4Cl in TMA. The flow rate should be about 100 ml/hr. The extinction of the effluent at 254 mμ is recorded with an LKB-Uvicord. Fractions of 10–20 ml are collected and, in the falling part of the protein peak, assayed for enzyme activity (see Fig. 1).

The elution of proteins may be followed with the Lowry reaction (5). The enzyme peak appears before nucleic acids are eluted and sometimes a second smaller peak of enzyme activity is observed under the DNA peak.

The elution from DEAE column is a critical step in the enzyme preparation. The usual yields vary from 20–70%. The higher yields are obtained when an excess of DEAE-cellulose over the given amount

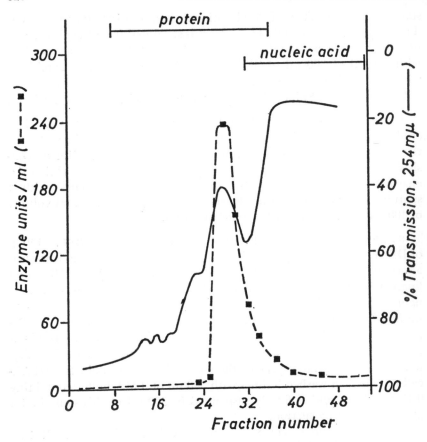

Fig. 1. Chromatography of the "DNA-protein-fraction" on DEAE-cellulose. Percent transmission curve was taken from a LKB-Uvicord recording of the eluate using a 3-mm cell. Fraction size ranged from 20 ml at the start to about 10 ml. Chromatography was performed as described in the text.

is avoided and the pH in the gradient is well controlled (between pH 7.3 and 7.5).

STEP 4. AMMONIUM SULFATE FRACTIONATION. The enzyme-containing fractions from the DEAE column are combined and adjusted if necessary, by the addition of TMA buffer, to a concentration of 5–10 mg of protein/ml (total, about 250 mg). Then ice-cold saturated ammonium sulfate solution in TMA (pH 7.5) is added to a concentration of 40% by volume. After standing 30 min at 0 C the precipitate is removed by centrifugation for 10 min at 15,000 rev/min in the SS34 rotor of the Servall centrifuge. The supernatant fluid is brought to 50% ammonium sulfate saturation in the same way. The precipitate is again collected after standing 30 min at 0 C, by centrifugation as above; after complete decantation of the supernatant fluid, the precipitate is dissolved in about 30 ml of TMA buffer. The enzyme particles are collected by centrifugation for 5 hr at 50,000 rev/min in the Spinco 50 rotor. The sediment is dissolved in 6 ml of TMA buffer.

The ultracentrifugation is the second critical step in the preparation of the enzyme. At high gravitational fields (for example 302,000 × g at 60,000 rev/min in the 60 rotor of the Christ† ultracentrifuge for 4 hr) and also after longer centrifugation times in the Spinco 50 rotor the enzyme-containing pellet becomes difficult to dissolve and much of the activity may be lost.

STEP 5. SUCROSE GRADIENT CENTRIFUGATION. Six Spinco SW25 tubes are each filled with 28 ml of a linear sucrose gradient ranging from 30 to 10% (w/v) sucrose in TMA buffer. The gradients are each layered with 1 ml of the concentrated ammonium sulfate fraction and centrifuged in SW25 rotors for 20 hr at 25,000 rev/min. Fractions are collected from the bottom of the tubes, while the extinction at 254 mμ is followed by a LKB-Uvicord (Fig. 2). Usually there is a small heavy peak without enzyme activity immediately above the bottom of the tube followed by a high middle peak containing all of the enzyme activity (sometimes with a small amount of a yellow impurity in its lighter edge) and finally a smaller light protein peak. Enzyme activity closely follows the protein content in the fractions of the middle peak. The enzyme-containing fractions are combined and the enzyme particles are collected, after twofold dilution with TMA buffer, by centrifugation for 7 hr, at 50,000 rev/min in the Spinco 50 rotor. For most purposes (enzymological work, etc.) this enzyme preparation is sufficiently pure. With the ribonuclease test that has been applied in this work, no nucleases can be detected.

STEP 6. SUCROSE GRADIENT ELECTROPHORESIS. For chemical studies the enzyme after sucrose gradient centrifugation is usually not sufficiently pure. Further purification may be achieved by sucrose gradient electrophoresis. The apparatus (H. Technik/A. Hölzel, Munich, Germany) consists of a Plexiglas column, 2.5 cm × 35 cm, which is surrounded by a cooling jacket and closed at the bottom by a semipermeable membrane (cellophane) and ends at the top and at the bottom in electrode vessels (see Fig. 3). An outlet at the bottom of the column is connected to a plastic capillary, which ends about 8 cm from the lower end of the column. First a layer of 50% (w/v) sucrose (Mann Research Labs.) in half-concentrated TMA buffer is filled in to about 1 cm above the end of the capillary. Then the column is filled to the top with a linear gradient of 40–0% (w/v) sucrose in half-concentrated

† Martin Christ, Osterode, Harz, Germany.

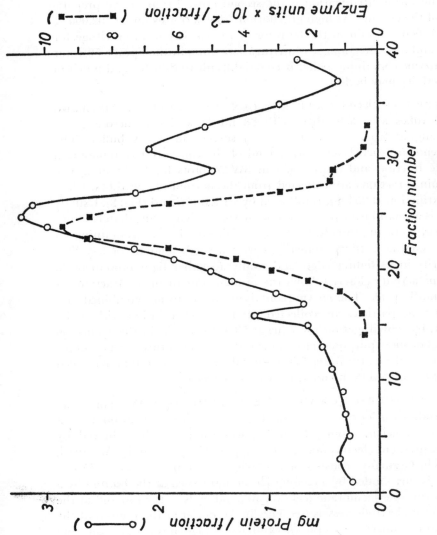

Fig. 2. Sucrose gradient centrifugation of the ammonium sulfate fraction. 48 mg of protein in 1.8 ml of TMA was applied to a 10–30% w/v gradient and fractionated as described. Fraction size 0.77 ml.

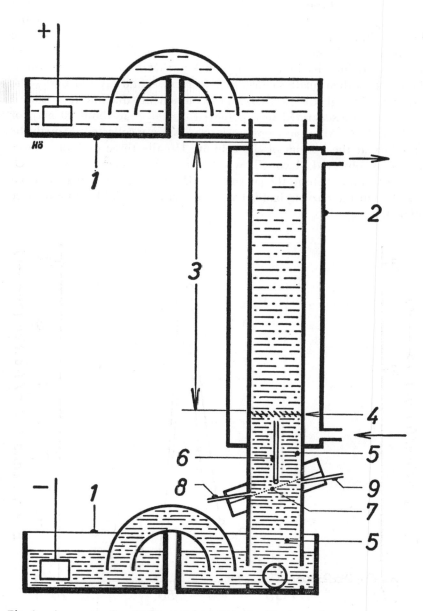

Fig. 3. Apparatus for gradient electrophoresis. (1) electrode vessels, (2) cooling jacket, (3) 40–0% sucrose gradient in TMA buffer, (4) enzyme sample layer, (5) 50% sucrose in TMA, (6) capillary for layering sample and collecting fractions, (7) dialysis membrane, (8) capillary for adding 50% sucrose, and (9) capillary for removing air from beneath membrane.

TMA buffer. Through the capillary the boundary between the 50 and the 40% sucrose is sharpened by removal of about 10 ml of the sucrose buffer filling. The concentrated enzyme fraction from the sucrose gradient centrifugation step is diluted by the addition of 2 volumes of water to reduce its ionic strength below that of the electrophoresis buffer. It is then made to 45% w/v in sucrose, and layered under the gradient through the capillary. The components that migrate toward the anode are separated in a potential of 600 v (at about 20 ma) for 20 hr at 2.5 C. After electrophoresis, fractions are collected through the capillary at the bottom of the column. Usually three or four components are observed. Two yellow peaks (usually present in only small amounts) move behind the enzyme band. A further component moving faster than the enzyme band may be present in variable amounts (see Fig. 4).

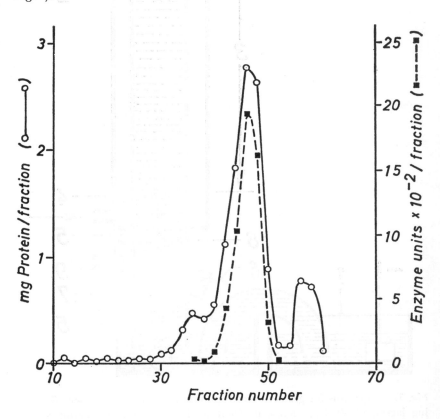

Fig. 4. Sucrose gradient electrophoresis. 34 mg of protein from a sucrose gradient centrifugation was applied in 2 ml of ½ concentrated TMA buffer containing 45% w/v sucrose. Electrophoresis was run 23½ hr; fraction size 1.5 ml, other conditions described in text.

TABLE 1. *Summary of the Purification*

Fraction	Total units	Total mg of protein	Specific Activity (units/mg)	% Recovery	Purification
1. Homogenate	243,000	60,300	4.0	100	1
2. Crude extract (-debris)	261,000	28,100	9.3	107	2.3
3. DNA-Protein fraction	185,000	8,580	21.6	76	5.6
4. DEAE fraction	75,400	740	102	31	26
5. 40–50% ammonium sulfate precipitate	50,300	299	168	21	42
6. Sucrose gradient fraction	38,900	153	254	16	63
7. Sucrose gradient electrophoresis fraction	31,600	55	574	13	145

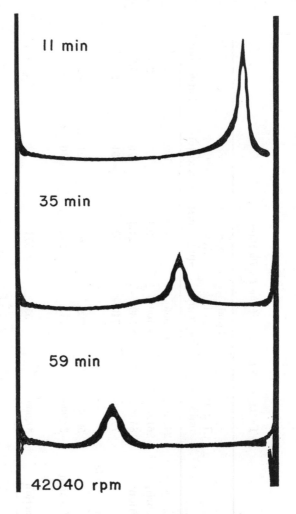

Fig. 5. Ultracentrifugal analysis of RNA-polymerase from sucrose gradient centrifugation. Enzyme concentration was 8 mg/ml in TMA buffer. Centrifugation was at 42,040 rev/min at 15.1 C. Photographs were taken 11, 35, and 59 min after the start of the run.

The best separation is obtained at pH 6.1, where the enzymatically inactive components are clearly separated from the enzyme activity peak. However under this condition the polymerase is quite unstable. We recommend using pH 7, where the faster yellow band is still present in the trailing edge of the enzyme, but where the product is quite stable. After a twofold dilution in TMA buffer the enzyme is collected by centrifugation for 7 hr at 50,000 rev/min in the Spinco 50 rotor. A summary of the purification steps is given in Table 1.

PROPERTIES OF THE RNA POLYMERASE

Physical Properties

The *sedimentation coefficient* of the purified enzyme, $s_{20,w\,(c\to 0)}$, is 23.7 S. The sedimentation velocity is almost independent of concentration. Assuming $f/f_0 = 1$ a *molecular weight* of 5.8×10^5 has been calculated. From Fig. 5 it is apparent, that the enzyme from sucrose gradient centrifugation behaves as a homogenous material with not more than 15% of a faster sedimenting impurity. The enzyme from sucrose gradient electrophoresis appears almost pure moving as a single component in both the electrophoresis and the ultracentrifuge (see page 332). From the mobilities at various pH values an approximate isoelectric point of pH 4 has been extrapolated.

Electronmicrographs of enzyme preparations negatively stained with phosphotungstic acid (28) or uranyl acetate (29) show enzyme particles mainly in two orientations (Fig. 6). One appears to be a vertical view showing six spherical subunits surrounding a central hole. The diameter is about 125 Å. The other, apparently a side view, shows a channel surrounded by material that sometimes shows a substructure perpendicular to the direction of the channel. The length of these particles is about 95 Å. A tentative model, in which six cylindrical subunits surround a hollow core in a hexagonal array forming a short hollow cylinder, is shown in Fig. 7. By assuming a partial specific volume of 0.74 and from the dimensions of the particles on the basis of the tentative model, a theoretical molecular weight of 6.2×10^5 has been calculated.

The enzyme particle disaggregates into subunits upon dialysis against 0.01 M sodium carbonate buffer at pH 10. The end product sediments with an $s_{20,w}$ of 3.1 S. An intermediate product has a sedimentation coefficient of 13 S. The 3.1 S subunits do not reaggregate in TMA buffer at pH 7.5.

A different disaggregation process, which was observed previously by Richardson (15), occurs at high ionic strength. In 0.5 M NaCl or NH_4Cl in TMA buffer at pH 7.5 we find that the enzyme particle is entirely dissociated into subunits that sediment with an $s_{20,w}$ of 12 S. Even in 0.15 M NH_4Cl in TMA about 90% of the particles are already disaggregated. This process is entirely reversible.

In addition to these subunits an active 18 S particle and two active components sedimenting with 32 and 39 S have been observed in gradient centrifugation runs. In electron microscopy the faster sedi-

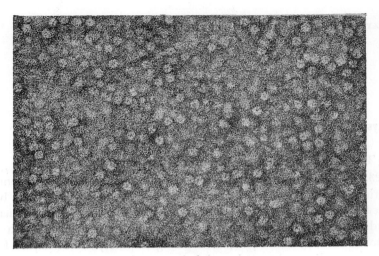

(a)

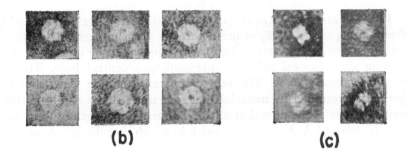

(b)   (c)

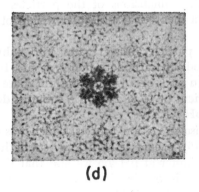

(d)

Fig. 6. Electronmicrographs of the RNA-polymerase particles: (a) negatively stained with phosphotungstic acid according to Horne and Brenner (**28**), × 160,000; (b) and (c) negatively stained with uranyl acetate by the method of Bradley (**29**) showing end views (b) and side views (c) of the particles × 400,000; (d) end view of a polymerase particle negatively stained (PTA) × 800,000. The print was exposed six times, rotating each time through 60° in order to confirm the sixfold symmetry of the particle (**30**).

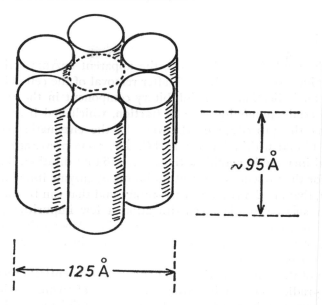

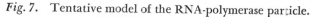

Fig. 7. Tentative model of the RNA-polymerase particle.

menting particles appear as head to tail aggregates (along the axis of the central channel) of 24 S molecules.

By assuming an $f/f_0 = 1$, the following estimates of molecular weights have been calculated for the subunits: 3.1 S, 0.27×10^5; 12 S, 2×10^5; 18 S, 4×10^5; 32 S, 9×10^5; 39 S, 12×10^5.

Chemical Properties

No nucleic acid has been detected with the Dische method (DNA) and the orcinol procedure (RNA). Therefore, the enzyme preparation contains less than 1% DNA and less than 0.6% RNA. However in our most purified preparations the ratio

$$\frac{A_{280\,m\mu}}{A_{260\,m\mu}} = 1.25$$

which would not exclude the presence of a small amount of a nucleic acid component or derivative.

In starch gel electrophoresis in 0.02 M ammonium formate + 6 M urea, pH 3.8, after staining with Amidoschwarz 10 B, two major components and possibly six minor components are visible, indicating that the enzyme consists of different protein subunits. Reduction with mercaptoethanol does not change the pattern.

Impurities

In the crude bacterial extract, the apparent enzyme activity consistently increases (up to 1.7-fold) after removal of the cell debris. This may be an indication of an inhibitory component in the cell debris.

In a crude ammonium sulfate fraction, which had been prepared following the procedure of Hurwitz (1), the enzymatic activity increased 14-fold within 4 weeks at 0 C. The same preparation showed a 12-fold increase in specific activity after 16-fold dilution. This again speaks for the presence of potent inhibitors of enzyme function, in this fraction, that are destroyed during storage and that can be diluted out.

After sucrose gradient centrifugation a few impurities (10–20%) may still be present in the enzyme preparation. Among these is a small amount of a yellow fraction, which sediments in the lighter, trailing edge of the enzyme peak.

Two of the contaminating components can be entirely removed by sucrose gradient electrophoresis at pH 7. One of them, moving about 1.3-fold faster to the anode than the enzyme, exhibits a Tyndall effect, is colorless, and sediments in the analytical ultracentrifuge with a sedimentation coefficient of 24 S. In electronmicrographs, it closely resembles the enzyme particle. However, in starch gel electrophoresis (in 6 M urea, 0.02 M ammonium formate, pH 3.8) it yields an entirely different pattern of protein bands. An antiserum against this component neither precipitates nor inactivates the enzyme. Therefore it is clear that this fast protein is unrelated to the polymerase. The other impurity, a yellow protein, sediments at 20 S and migrates slower than the enzyme band in electrophoresis. A second minor yellow component migrates under the trailing edge of the enzyme peak. Judged by its electrophoretic and sedimentation behavior the "electrophoresis enzyme" may be considered pure.

During the purification procedure, successive removal of nuclease activity is accomplished. After sucrose gradient centrifugation, no ribonuclease activity (as measured by the decrease in acid-insoluble RNA) can be observed in the enzyme preparation. The test procedure is as follows: After a 10-min RNA synthesis period (conditions described above), the reaction is stopped by the addition of actinomycin C_3 (0.1 μmole/ml) and the fate of the synthesized radioactive RNA is followed by precipitation with TCA after various times of further incubation. The average chain length of the newly synthesized RNA molecules, after the synthesis reaction reaches a plateau, is 500–1000 nucleotide residues. This again speaks for a lack of ribonuclease activity in this preparation.

No deoxyribonuclease activity has been detected by measuring the increase in acid-soluble nucleotides after incubation of DNA with the enzyme obtained from sucrose gradient centrifugation. Also, there is no loss of template activity and viscosity of DNA preincubated for 1 hr at 37 C with an excess of polymerase.

Stability of the Enzyme

Before sucrose gradient centrifugation, the enzyme is quite stable. For example, after standing 40 days at 0 C, only about 20% of the activity was lost. After gradient centrifugation the stability has decreased (20% loss in 20 days at 0 C). A further stability loss is observed after gradient electrophoresis. However, the enzyme can be stabilized and/or reactivated by high salt concentrations. For example, a partially inactivated enzyme showed a 40% increase in activity when incubated at 4 C for 1 hr in 1 N NH_4Cl. Ultracentrifuge studies indicated that at least part of this effect is due to the disaggregation of higher enzyme aggregates, which form upon prolonged standing at low ionic strength.

The enzyme is inactivated by shaking or bubbling with air, either due to surface denaturation or to oxidation. Mercaptoethanol at low concentrations (0.001 M) has little effect on the enzyme activity, whereas at high concentrations (0.02 M) it leads to fast and complete inactivation. In 0.01 M versene half of the activity was lost within 12 hr. Low ionic strength and pH (below pH 6.5) also lead to enzyme inactivation.

Polymerase activity is entirely lost upon lyophilization. However, the enzyme may be frozen and thawed without significant reduction of activity. The stability in the frozen state (−25 C), however, is not higher than at 0 C. No loss of enzyme activity is observed within 30 min at 37 C.

Function of the Enzyme

The enzyme particles prepared by the described procedure have the same enzymological properties as those described in earlier publications (1,2,6–11). Single-stranded and double-stranded DNA serve as templates. With double-stranded DNA, the kinetics are of the type described and interpreted by Bremer and Konrad (6); with single-stranded DNA, hybrids of the RNA product and the DNA are formed, which then function as semiconserved templates for a longer time period (7,12,13). RNA of phage M12 does not exert a significant template action. With double-stranded DNA, a 15-fold net synthesis over the amount of DNA template has been observed. The pH optimum of the polymerase reaction is 7.9. With a temperature increase from 27 to 37 C, the reaction rate rises slightly more than twofold. In the kinetics one sees a short lag phase (0.75 min at 37 C, 4 min at 20 C), which does not disappear when the enzyme and the DNA are pre-incubated without substrates.

Most of the enzyme in the crude extract is bound to DNA (14,8). The purified enzyme forms a stable complex with DNA, as shown by electron microscopy (8) and by gradient electrophoresis (14) or gradient centrifugation (15).

With high amounts of Mg^{2+} ions (above 0.01 M) the same or higher reaction rates are obtained as with a mixture of Mg^{2+} and Mn^{2+} (0.004 M each) when using T4 DNA as template.

An increase in ionic strength exerts a twofold effect. As described above, the enzyme dissociates and as a result does not bind to DNA. When no RNA strand has been initiated, the polymerase is removed from the DNA (15).

Once the enzyme molecules have initiated RNA synthesis, both the rate and amount of RNA synthesis are stimulated (approximately two-fold) by an increase in salt concentration (e.g., from 0.004 M to 0.13 M NH_4Cl in the presence of 0.03 M Mg acetate). Such molecules remain bound to the DNA and continue synthesis even after the ionic strength has been raised to 0.65. The optimal concentrations of NH_4Cl and Mg acetate have been included in the enzyme assay.

Polyanions (RNA, heparin, polyvinylsulfate) inhibit the enzyme by competition with the template (7). Actinomycin inhibits RNA synthesis on double- and on single-stranded DNA (7,16,17), whereas proflavin inhibits only on a double-stranded template (7).

By hybridization experiments with separated strands of phage DNAs, it has been shown that transcription *in vivo* is an asymmetric process in which only one strand of the DNA template is copied by the polymerase (18,19). Subsequently with similar techniques it has been found that the RNA polymerase also copies bacteriophage DNAs asymmetrically *in vitro* (20–24).

From pulse-labeling experiments it appears that synthesis of the RNA strand proceeds from the 5′ toward the 3′ end (25). Since the direction of translation is most likely the same as that of transcription (26), the above observation is supported by experiments, which indicate that the direction of translation is also from the 5′ toward the 3′ end of the messenger RNA (27).

REFERENCES

1. FURTH, J. J., J. HURWITZ, and M. ANDERS. 1962. J. Biol. Chem. *237:* 2611.
2. CHAMBERLIN, M., and P. BERG. 1962. Proc. Nat. Acad. Sci. U.S. *48:* 81.
3. FRASER, D., and E. A. JERREL. 1953. J. Biol. Chem. *205:* 291.

4. ZILLIG, W., and H. HOELZEL. 1958. Z. Physiol. Chem. *312:* 140.
5. LOWRY, O. H., N. J. ROSEBROUGH, A. L. FARR, and R. J. RANDALL. 1951. J. Biol. Chem. *193:* 265.
6. BREMER, H., and M. W. KONRAD. 1964. Proc. Nat. Acad. Sci. U.S. *51:* 801.
7. DOERFLER, W., W. ZILLIG, E. FUCHS, and M. ALBERS. 1962. Z. Physiol. Chem. *330:* 96.
8. FUCHS, E., W. ZILLIG, P. H. HOFSCHNEIDER, and A. PREUSS. 1964. J. Mol. Biol. *10:* 546.
9. HURWITZ, J., and J. T. AUGUST. 1963. Progress in nucleic acid research. Academic Press, New York. Vol. 1, p. 59.
10. NAKAMOTO, T., C. F. FOX, and S. B. WEISS. 1964. J. Biol. Chem. *239:* 167.
11. STEVENS, A., and J. HENRY. 1964. J. Biol. Chem. *239:* 196.
12. CHAMBERLIN, M., and P. BERG. 1964. J. Mol. Biol. *8:* 297.
13. SINSHEIMER, R. L., and M. LAWRENCE. 1964. J. Mol. Biol. *8:* 289.
14. KADOYA, M., H. MITSUI, Y. TAKAGI, E. OTAKA, H. SUZUKI, and S. OSAWA. 1964. Biochim. Biophys. Acta. *91:* 36.
15. RICHARDSON, J. P. In preparation.
16. HURWITZ, J., J. J. FURTH, M. MALAMY, and M. ALEXANDER. 1962. Proc. Nat. Acad. Sci. U.S. *48:* 1222.
17. HARTMANN, G., U. COY, and G. KNIESE. 1963. Z. Physiol. Chem. *330:* 227.
18. MARMUR, J., and C. M. GREENSPAN. 1963. Science. *142:* 387.
19. TOCCHINI-VALENTINI, G. P., M. STODOLSKY, A. AURISICCHIO, M. T. SARNAT, F. GRAZIOSI, S. B. WEISS, and E. P. GEIDUSCHEK. 1963. Proc. Nat. Acad. Sci. U.S. *50:* 935.
20. HAYASHI, M., M. N. HAYASHI, and S. SPIEGELMAN. 1963. Proc. Nat. Acad. Sci. U.S. *50:* 664.
21. HAYASHI, M., M. N. HAYASHI, and S. SPIEGELMAN. 1964. Proc. Nat. Acad. Sci. U.S. *51:* 351.
22. GEIDUSCHEK, E. P., G. P. TOCCHINI-VALENTINI, and M. T. SARNAT. 1964. Proc. Nat. Acad. Sci. U.S. *52:* 486.
23. GREEN, M. H. 1965. Proc. Nat. Acad. Sci. U.S. *52:* 1388.
24. LURIA, S. E. 1965. Biochem. Biophys. Res. Comm. *18:* 735.
25. BREMER, H., M. W. KONRAD, K. GAINES, and G. S. STENT. 1965. J. Mol. Biol. *13:* 540.
26. ZILLIG, W., P. TRAUB, and P. PALM. 1964. Sixth international congress of biochemistry. Internat. Congr. Biochem. New York.
27. OCHOA, S. 1965. Second meeting of the Federation of European Biochemical Societies. Vienna.
28. HORNE, R. W., and S. BRENNER. 1958. Fourth international congress of electronmicroscopy. Sec. II, p. 625. Springer-Verlag, Berlin.
29. BRADLEY, D. E. 1965. J. Gen. Microbiol. *38:* 395.
30. MARKHAM, R., S. FREY, and G. J. HILLS. 1963. Virology. *20:* 88.

RNA Synthetase from

Phage MS2-Infected

Escherichia coli (1)

CHARLES WEISSMANN, PIET BORST, AND

SEVERO OCHOA

DEPARTMENT OF BIOCHEMISTRY

NEW YORK UNIVERSITY SCHOOL OF MEDICINE

NEW YORK, NEW YORK

INTRODUCTION

It has been shown in several laboratories (1–6) that infection of susceptible cells with RNA-containing animal, bacterial, and plant viruses leads to the formation of RNA-synthesizing enzymes not previously present in the host cell. Three partially purified preparations of such enzymes have been obtained from *Escherichia coli* infected with RNA phages.

1. From *E. coli* Hfr 3000 infected with phage MS2 "RNA synthetase" was purified about 20-fold (1). This enzyme has been shown to synthesize almost exclusively MS2 RNA of the "plus"† or parental type (7).
2. From *E. coli* K 38 (nonpermissive), infected with the amber mutant f2 su-11, "RNA-dependent RNA polymerase" was purified about 100-fold. The enzyme requires added RNA as a template and synthesizes a strand complementary to it (8,9).

† "Plus" strands are defined as viral RNA strands of the parental type as opposed to "minus" strands, which have the complementary base sequence.

3. From *E. coli* infected with MS2 "RNA replicase" has been purified, which is specifically primed by MS2 RNA. The nature of the RNA formed by this enzyme was not described (5).

The possible role of these enzymes in the replication of viral RNA is discussed elsewhere (10).

Materials

Materials were obtained from the following sources: Crystalline pyruvate kinase and phosphoenolpyruvate (sodium salt), C. F. Boehringer and Sons, Mannheim, Germany; pancreatic deoxyribonuclease I and pancreatic ribonuclease A, Worthington Biochemical Corporation; C^{14}-labeled ribonucleoside triphosphates, Schwarz Bioresearch, Inc.; nonlabeled ribonucleoside triphosphates, Pabst Laboratories; Millipore filters and Pyrex Filter Holder, Millipore Co.; Liquifluor, Nuclear-Chicago; Superbrite glass beads, type 100–5005, Minnesota Mining and Manufacturing Co.

ASSAY

Principle

The incorporation of radioactive nucleotides from acid-soluble ribonucleoside triphosphates into acid-insoluble RNA is measured. The composition of the assay medium precludes incorporation of radioactivity by DNA-primed RNA nucleotidyl transferase (RNA polymerase), poly A polymerase, polynucleotide phosphorylase, and the enzyme catalyzing the addition of cytidylic and adenylic acid residues to partially degraded sRNA (11).

Reagents

1. The assay mixture (total volume 0.2 ml) contains

    0.1 M Tris-HCl buffer, pH 7.2
    7.5 mM $MgCl_2$
    2.5 mM $MnCl_2$ (when added)
    10 mM mercaptoethylamine
    5 mM phosphoenolpyruvate, sodium salt
    175 μg/ml of pyruvate kinase
    125 μg/ml of pancreatic deoxyribonuclease I
    0.25 mM C^{14}-labeled UTP
    0.25 mM GTP
    0.25 mM ATP
    0.25 mM CTP
    Enzyme

A fourfold concentrated stock solution, containing all components except the radioactive triphosphate, the Mn^{2+}, and the enzyme can be stored frozen.

2. 8% sodium pyrophosphate, pH 7
   6% trichloroacetic acid (TCA)

Procedure

The reaction mixture is incubated for 5 min at 37 C and then chilled in an ice bath. 0.05 ml of 8% pyrophosphate solution and 3 ml of chilled 6% trichloroacetic acid are added. After 10–30 min at 0 C the precipitate is filtered off on an acid-soaked Millipore filter (pore size 0.45 μ, disk diameter 25 mm; or 47 mm, when heavy precipitates are obtained, as in the case of crude extracts) with use of a Millipore Pyrex Filter Holder. The filter is washed with three 10-ml portions of chilled 6% TCA. If the radioactivity is to be determined on an end-window or gas-flow counter, the filter is glued to a planchet with rubber cement, the precipitate facing upward, and dried under an infra-red lamp. For scintillation counting, 25-mm filters are pierced through the edge by a glass needle and inserted in an upright position into a vial. 47-mm filters are simply rolled into the vials. After drying overnight at 60–65 C, Liquifluor, diluted 1:25 with toluene, is added as scintillator.

A blank is prepared by incubating the enzyme-containing reaction mixture without the radioactive triphosphate, cooling, and adding in rapid succession, with mixing, the radioactive triphosphate, pyrophosphate, and trichloroacetic acid. The blank is subtracted from the corresponding experimental values. The blank values depend on the amount and the nature of the protein in the assay and also on the purity of the radioactive nucleoside triphosphate. One unit of enzyme activity under these assay conditions corresponds to the incorporation of 1 mμmole of C^{14}-labeled UTP into acid-insoluble material per minute. Specific enzyme activity is defined as units per milligram of protein. Protein was determined by a modified biuret method (12). Incorporation is approximately linear with time for 5 min and proportional to the amount of enzyme. However, when crude extracts are used, proportionality holds only if not more than 0.5 mg of protein is added per assay.

ISOLATION PROCEDURE

Phage-Infected Cells

Frozen, MS2-infected cells are prepared as described in "Double-Stranded MS2 RNA from MS2-Infected *E. coli*" (page 498). All operations are performed at 0–5 C. Centrifugations are carried out in the

SS34 rotor of the Servall refrigerated centrifuge, Model RC2; g values are given as g maximal. pH values are determined with a precooled Radiometer glass electrode (Type G2026) and a Beckman pH-meter model G, at 0 C. The purification procedure should be carried out rapidly and without interruptions to insure optimal results. This can be accomplished in a period of 6–7 hr.

Step 1. Extraction

40–50 g of frozen, MS2-infected cells are enveloped in cellophane wrap and reduced to small pieces by pounding with a mallet, without allowing the cells to thaw. The material is placed in the 400-ml bowl of a Servall Omni-Mixer together with 20 ml of standard buffer (10 mM Tris-HCl, pH 8; 1 mM Na_3 EDTA; 3 mM $MgCl_2$; 5 mM mercaptoethylamine) and 150 g (dry weight) of Superbrite glass beads (previously washed with standard buffer and not dried). The mixture is homogenized at low speed in an ice bath until the cells are thawed and a smooth paste is obtained. Homogenization is then continued in an ethanol-ice bath at -5 C with the powerstat set at 45 (maximum $= 100$), for a total of 15 min. The contents of the container are inspected every 5 min to make sure that the paste is neither freezing near the walls of the container nor warming up above 4 C. 0.1 ml of a solution of 10 mg/ml of deoxyribonuclease and 130 ml of standard buffer are added and mixed with the homogenate and the glass beads are allowed to settle for 1 min. The supernatant fluid is decanted and the beads are washed with two further 25-ml portions of standard buffer. The supernatant fluid is combined with the washings and distributed into eight 40-ml tubes. After centrifuging for 30 min at 27,000 $\times$ g (15,000 rev/min), the supernatant fluid is carefully decanted and placed in a 500-ml beaker packed in ice. The solution is stirred by a magnetically driven stirring bar and 0.2 M sodium acetate buffer (pH 5.0 at 20 C) is added slowly until pH 6.5 is reached. This requires about 10–15 ml of acetate buffer. The volume of the solution is determined. It contains about 7–10 mg/ml of protein and its absorbance at 260 mμ is about 130–150/ml.

Step 2. First Mg Fractionation

$MgCl_2$, 1.0 M, is added to the Step 1 preparation with rapid stirring, to a final concentration of 0.035 M. The opalescent solution is distributed into eight 40-ml tubes and kept at 0 C. 5 min after the $MgCl_2$ addition, the preparation is centrifuged for 20 min at 30,000 $\times$ g (16,000 rev/min). The supernatant fluid is completely drawn off and discarded and the pellets are transferred quantitatively to a hand-operated Potter-Elvehjem homogenizer (A. H. Thomas tissue grinder, 55-ml working capacity). They are brought into solution by gently homogenizing with Tris-EDTA buffer (0.02 M Tris-HCl, 0.002 M EDTA, adjusted to pH 8.2 at 20 C). A total of 90 ml is used to dissolve the pellets and rinse all tubes and the homogenizer. The pH of the solution, which should now be 7.6–7.9, is measured and adjusted to this value if necessary, with 0.2 M sodium acetate buffer, pH 5.0, or 1.0 M Tris-HCl buffer, pH 8. The solution is centrifuged for 20 min at 30,000 × g to remove a substantial amount of insoluble material. The supernatant fluid is carefully drawn off with a pipette and its volume is determined.

Step 3. Second Mg Fractionation

To the Step 2 preparation, $\frac{1}{10}$ of its volume of 1 M $MgCl_2$ is added. After 5 min the turbid solution is centrifuged for 20 min at 30,000 × g and the supernatant fluid is discarded. The glassy pellet is dissolved as described above, using 70 ml of Tris-EDTA buffer. Insoluble material is removed by centrifuging for 20 min at 31,000 × g. The supernatant fluid is carefully decanted and its volume determined.

Step 4. Ammonium Sulfate Fractionation

To the Step 3 preparation is added, with stirring, $\frac{1}{10}$ of its volume of 1 M $MgCl_2$. After 5 min, finely powdered ammonium sulfate is added to 20% saturation (0.106 g/ml). The resulting precipitate is immediately collected by centrifuging for 20 min at 34,800 × g (17,000 rev/min). The clear, glassy pellet is dissolved using a 5-ml hand-operated Potter-Elvehjem homogenizer, in a total volume of 10 ml of Tris-HCl buffer, pH 7.2. The preparation is immediately frozen in small portions and stored at −12 C. It contains about 2.5–3.0 mg/ml of protein and the absorbance at 260 mμ is 105–125/ml.

A summary of a typical preparation is shown in Table 1.

PROPERTIES OF THE ENZYME AND ITS PRODUCT

The enzyme (Step 4) loses 10–20% of its activity on freezing and thawing; it loses activity at the rate of 5–10% per week on storage at −12 C. Addition of 0.5 mM $MnSO_4$ to the standard assay mixture from which $MnSO_4$ has been omitted gives a 5–25% stimulation of nucleotide incorporation; 2.5 mM $MnSO_4$ gives 3–19% inhibition and higher concentrations give progressively increasing inhibition. Variation of the Mg^{2+} concentration between 2 and 32 mM has no significant effect on enzyme activity, whereas 0.025 M EDTA, pH 7.0, causes a complete inhibition. Addition of actinomycin D (20 μg/ml) or proflavin (75 μg/ml) does not affect the activity of the enzyme. The activity of the Step 4 preparation is the same whether in the presence or absence of 0.1 M

TABLE 1. *Partial Purification of RNA Synthetase of MS2-Infected* E. coli[a]

Step	Units[b]	Specific Activity[c]	Yield	RNA[d] (mg/mg of protein)	"Minus" strands[e] (µg/mg protein)
Extract	122(93–238)	0.05(0.04–0.09)	100	0.6(0.5–0.7)	5
1st Mg fractionation	96(85–158)	0.28(0.26–0.53)	80(56–95)	0.8(0.7–0.9)	16.5
2nd Mg fractionation	61(38–97)	0.56(0.36–0.80)	49(26–54)	1.2(1.1–1.3)	—
$(NH_4)_2SO_4$ fractionation	38(17–50)	1.02(0.67–1.30)	23(18–32)	1.8(1.6–2.0)	96

[a] 42–47 g of bacteria were processed in one run. The values given represent the median (and range) of 5 separate preparations, with bacteria from 2 different vat runs, except for the values in the last column which were obtained in one experiment only.

[b] mµmoles of UTP-C[14] incorporated/min. Values recalculated for 50 g of starting material.

[c] Units/mg of protein.

[d] Assuming that all absorbancy at 260 mµ is RNA with an extinction coefficient of 25.0 mg⁻¹ ml⁻¹.

[e] Assayed through reannealing with P[32]-labeled MS2 RNA (1). Most of the "minus" strands are part of a double helix.

orthophosphate, indicating that polynucleotide phosphorylase does not contribute to the incorporation of nucleotides under the conditions of the synthetase assay, although its presence can be detected under appropriate conditions. DNA-dependent RNA nucleotidyl transferase is absent from the Step 4 preparation [less than 5% of the synthetase activity (1)].

Neither the crude enzyme nor the Step 4 preparation requires an exogenous primer or template for activity. As shown in Table 1, the Step 4 enzyme is enriched in regard to MS2 "minus" strands, most of which are in a double-stranded form. This material is presumed to be the template (1). When supplied with radioactive nucleoside triphosphates, RNA synthetase (Step 4) incorporates all four nucleotides at about the same rate into RNA. As revealed by an isotope dilution test about 93% of the radioactive product consists of MS2 "plus" strands and 7% of MS2 "minus" strands. Within the limits of error of the method the product is thus entirely virus specific. A substantial part of the product is in a double-stranded form. The isolated double-stranded RNA (which contains about 85% of the radioactivity in the "plus" strand) is indistinguishable from the double-stranded MS2 RNA (replicative form) prepared from MS2-infected *E. coli* (cf. page 498).

REFERENCES

1. WEISSMANN, C., P. BORST, R. H. BURDON, M. A. BILLETER, and S. OCHOA. 1964. Proc. Nat. Acad. Sci. U.S. *51:* 890.
2. BALTIMORE, D., and R. M. FRANKLIN. 1962. Biochem. Biophys. Res. Comm. *9:* 388.
3. WEISSMANN, C., L. SIMON, and S. OCHOA. 1963. Proc. Nat. Acad. Sci. U.S. *49:* 407.
4. AUGUST, J. T., S. COOPER, L. SHAPIRO, and N. D. ZINDER. 1963. Synthesis and structure of macromolecules. Cold Spring Harbor Symp. Quant. Biol. *28:* 95.
5. HARUNA, I., K. NOZU, Y. OHTAKA, and S. SPIEGELMAN. 1963. Proc. Nat. Acad. Sci. U.S. *50:* 905.
6. ASTIER-MANIFACIER, S., and P. CORNUET. 1965. Biochem. Biophys. Res. Comm. *18:* 283.
7. WEISSMANN, C. 1965. Proc. Nat. Acad. Sci. U.S. *54:* 202.
8. AUGUST, J. T., L. SHAPIRO, and L. EOYANG. 1965. J. Mol. Biol. *11:* 257.
9. SHAPIRO, L., and J. T. AUGUST. 1965. J. Mol. Biol. *11:* 272.
10. OCHOA, S., C. WEISSMANN, P. BORST, R. H. BURDON, and M. BILLETER. 1964. Federation Proc. *23:* 1258.
11. WEISSMANN, C., L. SIMON, P. BORST, and S. OCHOA. 1963. Synthesis and structure of macromolecules. Cold Spring Harbor Symp. Quant. Biol. *28:* 99.
12. MOKRASH, L. C., and R. W. MCGILVERY. 1956. J. Biol. Chem. *221:* 909.

tRNA-CMP-AMP-

Pyrophosphorylase from

Escherichia coli (**1**)

JERARD HURWITZ
ALBERT EINSTEIN COLLEGE OF MEDICINE
YESHIVA UNIVERSITY
BRONX, NEW YORK

J. J. FURTH
DEPARTMENT OF PATHOLOGY
UNIVERSITY OF PENNSYLVANIA SCHOOL OF
   MEDICINE
PHILADELPHIA, PENNSYLVANIA

ASSAY

$$2CTP + C^{14}\text{-}ATP + tRNA \longrightarrow$$
$$tRNA\text{-}CMP\text{-}CMP\text{-}C^{14}\text{-}AMP + 3PP_i$$

Reagents

The reaction mixture (0.5 ml) contains

50 mM Tris buffer, pH 8.4
8 mM $MgCl_2$,
2 mM mercaptoethanol

0.1 mM C^{14}-CTP or ATP
300 mμmoles of ribonucleotides as tRNA
Enzyme

Procedures

THE ASSAY MEASURES THE INCORPORATION OF ACID-SOLUBLE LABELED ATP OR CTP INTO AN ACID-INSOLUBLE FORM. After incubation at 38 C for 20 min, 0.2 ml of 7% $HClO_4$ and 1.5 mg of bovine serum albumin are added. The albumin serves as a carrier precipitate. The precipitate is collected by centrifugation at approximately 10,000 × g in an International PR2 refrigerated centrifuge with multispeed attachment. The supernatant solution is discarded, and the precipitate is washed twice by resuspension in 3 ml of 1% $HClO_4$ and recentrifuged. The residue is dissolved in 1.5 ml of 0.2 M NH_4OH, the solution is dried on metal planchets, and the radioactivity is measured. No correction is made for self-absorption. Incubation mixtures, from which the enzyme is omitted or added after perchloric acid, serve as controls. A unit of enzyme is defined as that amount of activity leading to the conversion of 1 mμmole of radioactive ribonucleotide into an acid-insoluble form under these conditions. The rate of incorporation of AMP or CMP is proportional to enzyme and to time of incubation. The pH optimum of the reaction is approximately 8.4. At pH 6.8 and pH 10, the reaction is about one-half as rapid.

PREPARATION OF SOLUBLE RNA. Low molecular weight yeast RNA is prepared by the following procedure, which is a modification of that described by Monier *et al.* (2). All operations are carried out at 2–3 C unless otherwise stated. Baker's yeast (200 g) is suspended in 400 ml of water and 400 ml of phenol-water (80:20, volume per volume) were added. The slurry is mixed vigorously for 1 hr. The suspension is then centrifuged for 8 min at approximately 10,000 × g. The aqueous layer is withdrawn and to it 0.1 volume of 20% potassium acetate buffer, pH 5.1, and 2 volumes of 95% ethanol are added. After 30 min, the precipitate containing RNA is collected by centrifugation, and suspended in 25 ml of 0.02 M Tris buffer, pH 7.6. The residual phenol is removed by extraction with four 12.5-ml portions of ether at 25 C. The solution is treated with 0.1 volume of potassium acetate buffer, pH 5.1, and 2 volumes of ethanol; the RNA is collected by centrifugation and dissolved in 20 ml of 0.02 M Tris buffer, pH 7.6. The RNA solution is then dialyzed for 16 hr against 500 ml of 0.02 M Tris buffer, pH 7.6. The preparation at this stage has 100 optical density units per ml when examined at 260 mμ and shows a 280:260 ratio of 0.5. The solution contains 6.6 μmoles of orcinol-reacting material (3) per ml (uncorrected for the lack of detection of pyrimidine nucleotides). This preparation, under the conditions described above, is a good acceptor of AMP, but accepts CMP poorly or not at all. It becomes a CMP acceptor when the solution (10 ml) is incubated for 20 min at 38 C with 370 units of venom phosphodiesterase (4) in the presence of 0.045 M glycylglycine buffer, pH 8.6, and 0.005 M MgCl$_2$. The modified product is precipitated with 1 ml of 7% HClO$_4$, washed twice with 2-ml portions of 1% HClO$_4$, and dissolved by the addition of 7 ml of 0.11 M Tris buffer, pH 7.6. This treatment is analogous to that done by Preiss et al. (5) with E. coli tRNA.

ISOLATION PROCEDURE

Growth of Cells

E. coli W is grown on the following medium: K$_2$HPO$_4$, 0.1%; KH$_2$PO$_4$, 0.3%; sodium citrate, 0.05%; MgSO$_4$, 0.0098%; glucose, 0.5%; and Difco yeast extract, 0.1%. Cultures are grown with vigorous aeration and harvested during late exponential growth. The cells are washed with a solution containing 0.5% NaCl and 0.5% KCl (300 ml/ 100 g of packed wet cells) and stored at -10 C.

Purification of tRNA Adenylate (Cytidylate) Pyrophosphorylase

PREPARATION OF EXTRACTS. Eighty grams of E. coli W (frozen packed cells) are thawed and stirred with 50 ml of 0.01 M Tris buffer, pH 7.5, containing 0.01 M MgCl$_2$. This mixture is then added to 200 g of glass beads (Minnesota Mining and Manufacturing Company, Grade 100) in a Waring Blendor previously cooled to -10 C. The suspension is homogenized for 15 min between 0 and 5 C, treated with 200 ml of a solution containing 0.01 M Tris buffer, pH 7.5, and 0.01 M MgCl$_2$, and homogenized for 10 min longer. The glass beads are allowed to settle and the supernatant suspension is decanted. Subsequent operations are performed at 2–3 C. The combined extracts are centrifuged for 2 hr in a Spinco Model L ultracentrifuge at 105,000 $\times$ g, yielding approximately 300 ml of crude extract, which is then dialyzed for 16 hr against 10 liters of 10^{-4} M 2-mercaptoethanol.

STREPTOMYCIN AND DEOXYRIBONUCLEASE TREATMENT AND AMMONIUM SULFATE PRECIPITATION. To 250 ml of dialyzed extract, 12.5 ml of a fresh 5% streptomycin sulfate solution are added and the mixture is allowed to stand for 20 min with occasional stirring. The resulting precipitate is collected by centrifugation, suspended in 25 ml of 0.05 M potassium phosphate buffer, pH 7.5, and homogenized in a glass tube fitted with a Teflon pestle. The mixture is centrifuged at 10,000 × g for 10 min and the supernatant material is collected (streptomycin sulfate eluate). The eluate solution is made 0.0035 M with respect to $MgCl_2$, and 0.85 μg of pancreatic deoxyribonuclease is added per ml of enzyme solution. The mixture is incubated for 15 min at 38 C and then centrifuged to remove insoluble material. To 20 ml of the deoxyribonuclease treated solution, 7.22 g of solid $(NH_4)_2SO_4$ are added (to 60% saturation). After 10 min at 2 C, the resulting precipitate is collected by centrifugation and dissolved in 5 ml of water (ammonium sulfate Fraction I).

DEAE-CELLULOSE CHROMATOGRAPHY. This solution is then dialyzed for 16 hr against 2 liters of 0.03 M Tris buffer, pH 8.4, containing 10^{-4} M 2-mercaptoethanol. The dialyzed ammonium sulfate fraction (5 ml) is passed through a DEAE-cellulose column 3.4 cm × 4.9 cm². (The DEAE-cellulose is prewashed with 30 ml of water and 30 ml of 0.1 M Tris buffer, pH 8.4.) Protein is eluted successively with 30 ml of 0.1 M, 30 ml of 0.2 M, 120 ml of 0.25 M, and 60 ml of 0.5 M Tris buffer, pH 8.4, and 30-ml fractions are collected. The bulk of the enzyme activity is eluted with 0.2 M Tris buffer. Each of the column fractions is assayed for AMP-incorporating activity, and those fractions that show a fourfold or greater purification are combined (DEAE-cellulose eluate).

AMMONIUM SULFATE FRACTIONATION. The DEAE-cellulose eluate fractions are concentrated with ammonium sulfate as follows: to

TABLE 1. *Purification of RNA-AMP (CMP) Pyrophosphorylase*

Enzyme Fraction	AMP Incorporation (total units)	Specific Activity[a] (units/mg of protein)
Crude extract	5040	9.0
Streptomycin sulfate eluate	4160[b]	42.5
Ammonium sulfate Fraction I	4000[b]	76
DEAE-cellulose eluates	2980[b]	1700
Ammonium sulfate Fraction II	2220[b]	1010

[a] Protein is measured by the method of Lowry et al. (6).

[b] At each step in the purification, fractions are removed. The total units in this column are adjusted to indicate the yield that would have been obtained if the entire fraction had been used in the subsequent step.

110 ml of the combined DEAE-cellulose eluates, 71.5 g of solid ammonium sulfate are added (to 95% saturation) and after 1 hr the mixture is centrifuged in a Spinco Model L centrifuge for 30 min at $105,000 \times g$. The small precipitate is dissolved in 2.4 ml of 0.05 M Tris buffer, pH 8.4 (ammonium sulfate Fraction II). The results of a typical enzyme preparation are summarized in Table 1.

Properties of the Purified Enzyme

CONTAMINATION WITH OTHER ENZYMES. The final preparation contains no detectable polynucleotide phosphorylase, inorganic pyrophosphatase, or DNA-dependent RNA polymerase. Cleavage of $\beta\gamma$-P^{32}-ATP yielding P_i^{32} could be detected; also present are amino acid tRNA synthetases for leucine and valine.

STABILITY OF THE PURIFIED ENZYME. The DEAE-cellulose eluates show essentially no loss in enzyme activity after storage at either 2 or -10 C for 4 months. There is a gradual loss of activity after repeated freezing and thawing.

SPECIFICITY

Nucleotide requirement. The enzyme fractions incorporate both CMP and AMP, and the ratio of the activity with each nucleotide remains constant over the entire range of purification. Loss of AMP-incorporating activity on heating is accompanied by identical loss of CMP-incorporating activity. When the ammonium sulfate Fraction II is heated at 50 C for 6 min, 68% of AMP- and 61% of the CMP-incorporating activity remain. After the fraction is heated for 24 min at 50 C, 16% of the AMP- and 18% of the CMP-incorporating activity remain.

The final enzyme preparation is specific for CTP or ATP and does not incorporate detectable amounts of UMP or GMP when their corresponding triphosphate derivatives are used. ITP, CTP (or ATP), UTP, and GTP are without effect on the incorporation of C^{14}-ATP (or CTP).

Polynucleotide Requirement. For AMP incorporation, the requirement for RNA is satisfied by tRNA isolated from yeast and liver, whereas *E. coli* tRNA is a poor acceptor. None of these tRNA preparations will accept detectable amounts of CMP. The latter nucleotide is incorporated into tRNA after such preparations are briefly treated with an exonuclease such as venom phosphodiesterase. After this treatment, the three different tRNA preparations behave similarly in their ability to incorporate CMP and AMP. No other RNA preparation is active as an acceptor for CMP and AMP. The list of RNA preparations tested includes the following: *E. coli* ribosomal, TMV, TYMV, and synthetic polynucleotide made with polynucleotide phosphorylase.

NATURE OF ADDITION OF NUCLEOTIDES TO RNA. Alkaline degradation of the product of the reaction indicates that CMP and AMP are added at the end of RNA chains that bear an unsubstituted 3′-hydroxyl group. After alkaline degradation of yeast RNA labeled with C^{14}-AMP, 95% of the radioactivity is recovered as adenosine. Similar results are obtained with *E. coli* tRNA (5). This indicates that a single AMP residue is added to the terminal end of the RNA chain. When C^{14}-CMP is incorporated into *E. coli* tRNA, the radioactivity, after alkaline degradation, is equally distributed between cytidine and the 2′(3′)-CMP mixture. This suggests that CMP is incorporated in a specific dinucleotide sequence—pCpC. With yeast RNA, however, an unequal distribution of radioactivity from C^{14}-CMP is observed: 81% of the C^{14} is recovered as cytidine, and 19% is found as 2′(3′)-CMP.

SUPPORT FOR THE TRINUCLEOTIDE SEQUENCE. pCpCpA in *E. coli* RNA is obtained by determining the effect of AMP incorporation on the distribution of C^{14} from CMP after alkaline degradation. After incubation with C^{14}-CTP alone, 51% of the radioactivity is found in cytidine and 49% in CMP. However, if ATP is also present in the reaction mixture, 93% of the radioactivity is recovered as CMP and only 7% as cytidine. Incorporation of AMP, therefore, leads to the disappearance of the terminal cytidylate residue (isolated as cytidine) and the simultaneous appearance of a new internal CMP residue.

REFERENCES

1. FURTH, J. J., J. HURWITZ, R. KRUG, and M. ALEXANDER. 1961. J. Biol. Chem. *236:* 3317.
2. MONIER, R., M. L. STEPHENSON, and P. C. ZAMECNIK. 1960. Biochim. Biophys. Acta. *43:* 1.
3. MEJBAUM, W. 1939. Z. Physiol. Chem. *258:* 117.
4. KOERNER, J. F., and R. L. SINSHEIMER. 1957. J. Biol. Chem. *228:* 1049.
5. PREISS, J., M. DIECHMANN, and P. BERG. 1961. J. Biol. Chem. *236:* 1748.
6. LOWRY, O. H., N. J. ROSEBROUGH, A. L. FARR, and R. J. RANDALL. 1951. J. Biol. Chem. *143:* 265.

tRNA ... pCpCpA Pyrophosphorylase of Rat Liver [ATP(CTP) : RNA Nucleotidyl Transferase] (1)

URIEL Z. LITTAUER AND VIOLET DANIEL
BIOCHEMISTRY SECTION
WEIZMANN INSTITUTE OF SCIENCE
REHOVOTH, ISRAEL

ASSAY

$$\text{tRNA} \ldots \text{pX} + 2\text{CTP} + \text{ATP} \rightleftharpoons$$
$$\text{tRNA} \ldots \text{pXpCpCpA} + 3\text{PP}_i \quad (1)$$

Reagents

1. The reaction mixture (total volume 0.45 ml) contains

   20 μmoles of glycine buffer, pH 9.5
   2.0 μmoles of $MgCl_2$
   0.25 μmole of ATP-8-C^{14} (or CTP-2-C^{14}) (approximately 2.5×10^5 cpm/μmole)
   5.0 μmoles of phosphoenolpyruvate
   2.0 μg of pyruvate kinase
   0.2–0.5 mg of "incubated" rat liver tRNA
   Enzyme

353

The incorporation of CMP-C[14] is measured under the same conditions as described for AMP using CTP-2-C[14] and "pyrophosphorolyzed" tRNA.

2. "Incubated" rat liver tRNA is prepared according to Hecht *et al.* (2).

The "pH 5 fraction" prepared from the $105,000 \times g$ supernatant fraction of rat liver homogenate (see below) is incubated for 60 min at 37 C in the presence of 0.01 M Tris buffer, pH 7.4. To 100 ml of the incubated "pH 5 fraction" 0.1 ml of 0.1 M EDTA solution, pH 8.0, is added. The suspension is mixed with one volume of 75% freshly redistilled phenol and stirred for 1 hr at 20 C. The suspension is chilled and then centrigued at $10,000 \times g$ for 3 min at 0 C.

The aqueous phase is removed and allowed to stand. The phenol phase is mixed with 50 ml of 10^{-4} M EDTA and after 5 min at 20 C, chilled and the aqueous phase separated by centrifugation. The aqueous supernatant solutions containing the RNA are combined and centrifuged for 20 min at $10,000 \times g$ and 0 C. RNA is precipitated from the supernatant fluid by addition of 2 volumes of cold 96% ethanol containing 2% potassium acetate. After 30 min at -15 C the precipitate is removed by centrifugation for 10 mins ($10,000 \times g$ at 0 C) and the precipitate is dissolved in 0.01 M Tris buffer, pH 7.4, containing 10^{-4} M EDTA. Small amounts of insoluble material are removed by centrifugation (20 min at $10,000 \times g$). The RNA is again precipitated with two volumes of ethanol containing 2% potassium acetate, washed with cold 95% ethanol, dissolved in 0.01 M Tris buffer, pH 7.4, dialyzed against 10^{-3} M sodium chloride solution, and then lyophilized. To remove heavy-metal contamination the dialysis bags, before use, were soaked for several days in cold EDTA solution (0.01 M, pH 8.0), which was changed several times. The bags were then washed with water (1,3).

3. "Pyrophosphorolyzed" rat liver tRNA.

The "pH 5 fraction" of rat liver homogenerate is incubated for 60 min at 37 C in the presence of 6mM inorganic pyrophosphate, 6mM MgCl$_2$, and 40 mM Tris buffer, pH 7.6. After the incubation, 0.2 N acetic acid is added to pH 5.1, and the precipitate formed is collected by centrifugation and dissolved in 0.01 M Tris buffer, pH 7.6. The incubation in the presence of pyrophosphate and MgCl$_2$ is repeated and the reaction terminated by adjusting the pH to 5.1. The precipitate is dissolved in 0.01 M Tris buffer, pH 7.6, containing 10^{-4} M EDTA, and the RNA is isolated by the phenol-water procedure describe above.

4. 5% and 1% HClO$_4$.

Procedure

The enzyme activity is measured by the incorporation of ATP-8-C^{14} or CTP-2-C^{14} into an acid-insoluble precipitate.

After 5 min of incubation at 37 C the reaction is stopped by immersing the tube in an ice bath. 0.5 ml of cold 5% $HClO_4$ are then added and the precipitate filtered through a Millipore filter (pore size, 0.45 μ; disc diameter, 25 mm), washed with suction three times, each time with 5 ml of cold 1% $HClO_4$. The filters are finally glued to aluminium planchets, dried, and counted. A reaction mixture, incubated at 0 C, serves as control and its value is subtracted from each sample. One unit of enzyme is defined as the amount catalyzing the incorporation of 1 μmole of ATP in 1 hr at 37 C, and the specific enzyme activity is expressed as enzyme units per mg of protein. Under the conditions described, the rate of nucleotide incorporation is proportional to enzyme concentration (0.003 to 0.04 unit of enzyme) and to the time of incubation (up to 10 min). The pH optimum for AMP incorporation is from 9 to 9.5. The control values (reaction mixture incubated at 0 C) for the crude 105,000 $\times$ g supernatant fluid and the pH 5 fraction are significantly high. Reduction of background counts can be achieved merely by using a different assay (1).

ISOLATION PROCEDURE

Preparation of Crude Extract

Three-month-old albino rats are killed by cervical fracture; the livers are quickly excised and placed in 0.34 M sucrose solution at 0 C. All subsequent purification steps are carried out at 0–4 C. 170 g of liver are minced with scissors, washed repeatedly with 0.34 M sucrose, and homogenized with 2.3 volumes of 0.34 M sucrose in a Teflon-glass homogenizer. The homogenization is performed at high speed, taking care to prevent foaming and heating. The homogenate is centrifuged at 10,000 $\times$ g for 10 min to remove cell debris and the supernatant fluid is filtered through cheese cloth to remove fat, and then centrifuged at 105,000 $\times$ g for 2 hr. The clear cytoplasmic supernatant fluid (300 ml) is carefully pipetted off taking care to exclude the cloudy layer at the top.

pH 5 Step

The cytoplasmic supernatant fluid (300 ml) is adjusted to pH 5.1 by slow addition of 0.2 N acetic acid with stirring. The solution is then stirred for an additional 30 min. The precipitate is collected by centrifuging for 10 min at $10,000 \times g$, washed with 0.05 M potassium acetate buffer, pH 5.2, and dissolved in 50 ml of 0.01 M Tris buffer, pH 8.5, to yield a final pH of 7.4.

Streptomycin Step

5.0 ml of a 10% streptomycin sulfate solution (neutralized to pH 7) are added slowly, with stirring, to the "pH 5 fraction" (50 ml). The stirring is continued for 20 min after the addition of streptomycin. The precipitate is removed by centrifugation for 10 min at $10,000 \times g$ and the supernatant fluid is saved. The precipitate is washed with 10 ml of neutral 1% streptomycin and the washings are added to the supernatant solution. Most of the endogenous soluble RNA is removed by streptomycin precipitation. The enzyme remains in the streptomycin supernatant fluid. This fraction may be stored frozen.

Ammonium Sulfate Fraction

The streptomycin supernatant fraction is brought to 70% saturation with saturated ammonium sulfate solution (adjusted to pH 7.6 with NH_4OH). The ammonium sulfate solution is added with rapid stirring over a 5-min interval; stirring is continued for 30 min, after which the suspension is centrifuged for 10 min at $10,000 \times g$, and the precipitate discarded. Solid ammonium sulfate is added to the supernatant fluid over a period of 30 min to attain 100% saturation. The suspension is stirred for 60 min, centrifuged at $10,000 \times g$ for 30 min, and the precipitate then dissolved in 6.0 ml of 0.05 M Tris, pH 7.4. The ammonium sulfate fraction is freed from salt by passing it through a polydextran column (4): a 2×20-cm Sephadex G-50 (medium) column is prepared and washed at 0 C with 200 ml of 0.01 M Tris buffer, pH 7.4, containing 0.005 M EDTA. A 4.0-ml portion of the enzyme fraction is pipetted onto the column and 2.0-ml fractions are collected with 0.01 M Tris, 7.4–0.005 M EDTA as eluent. Over 90% of the added protein is recovered from the column and no sulfate ions can be detected in the Sephadex-treated fraction. The enzyme solution may be stored frozen for several months.

Calcium Phosphate Gel Adsorption

This procedure is carried out in two steps. For each batch of enzyme the exact amounts of calcium phosphate gel needed in the two steps have to be determined first on a small scale. 0.5-ml portions of enzyme solutions (Sephadex-treated ammonium sulfate fraction) are titrated with increasing amounts of calcium phosphate gel; first to determine the maximal amounts of protein absorbable without loss of enzymatic activity and then to determine the amount needed to adsorb all the enzyme in the second step. In the preparation described in Table 1, in the first step, enough gel is added to adsorb 40% of the ammonium sulfate fraction protein. Calcium phosphate gel suspension (2.4 ml, 1.42 mg of dry weight per ml) is centrifuged and the supernatant fluid discarded. 10 ml of the Sephadex-treated ammonium sulfate fraction (1.5 mg of protein/ml) are mixed with the gel, using a closely fitting glass pestle, centrifuged for 15 min, and the precipitate discarded. In the second step, enough calcium phosphate gel is added to adsorb 90–100% of the enzyme activity. 7.2 ml of the calcium phosphate gel are centrifuged, the supernatant fluid discarded, and the enzyme supernatant liquid of the previous steps is then added. The gel is mixed with the enzyme solution, allowed to stand for 15 min, and then centrifuged. The supernatant fluid is discarded and the yellowish-pink gel precipitate is washed twice with 2.0 ml of 0.01 M potassium phosphate buffer, pH 7.4. The gel is mixed with 2.0 ml of 0.05 M potassium phosphate buffer, pH 7.4, centrifuged immediately, and the supernatant fluid then collected. The purified enzyme (calcium phosphate gel eluate) is stable when stored at -10 C and is not affected by repeated freezing and thawing.

COMMENTS

A summary of a typical enzyme purification is presented in Table 1. The over-all purification is between 350- and 550-fold.

The requirement of added tRNA for the activity of the enzyme varies during the purification procedures. tRNA is essential for the activity of the purified enzyme fractions. The initial $105,000 \times g$ supernatant fluid contains a considerable amount of tRNA, sometimes missing the AMP terminal unit, and therefore this extract shows activity even in the absence of added tRNA. In the purified enzyme fractions, which contain no detectable amounts of tRNA, the activity of the enzyme is directly dependent upon the addition of "incubated" or "pyrophosphorolyzed" tRNA. The requirement of the "pH 5 fraction" for tRNA addition is very low. This can be explained by the higher RNA-to-enzyme ratio found in the "pH 5 fraction." It was observed that almost all the tRNA of the $105,000 \times g$ supernatant fluid is precipitated in the pH 5 fraction, whereas only 30–40% of the enzyme activity are recovered in this fraction.

PROPERTIES OF ENZYME

Contamination with Other Enzymes

The "pH 5 fraction" catalyzes the activation of all the amino acids (5,6) as measured by the pyrophosphate exchange assay (7). In the purified enzyme preparation, no detectable amino acid-activating enzymes were found; only a slight exchange activity in the presence of threonine was detected (0.15 unit of enzyme will catalyze the exchange of 0.7 mμmole of PPi[32] per 10-min incubation).

Ribonuclease activity was not detected in calcium phosphate gel eluate fraction; 0.15 units of enzyme liberated less than 3.0 mμmoles of acid-soluble nucleotide per hour when incubated with yeast RNA. Also, the infectivity of TMV RNA was not reduced after incubating 1.5 mg of this RNA in the presence of 0.12 unit of enzyme for 3 hr at 37 C. The enzyme is free of ATP-ase, CTP-ase, UTP-ase, and pyrophosphatase (0.15 units of enzyme liberated less than 0.8 mμmole of inorganic phosphate from ATP-γ-P[32], CTP-γ-P[32], UTP-γ-P[32], and PPi[32] after 30-min incubation at 37 C).

Adenylate kinase activity is still present in calcium phosphate gel eluate fraction; 0.15 units of enzyme catalyzed the formation of 2.4 μmoles of ADP per hour from ATP and AMP when measured with a coupled pyruvate-phosphokinase-lactic dehydrogenase system (8).

Specificity

The purified rat liver enzyme incorporates AMP and CMP into pyrophosphorolyzed tRNA chains to form a terminal nucleotide sequence tRNA . . . pCpCpA. The reaction is reversible, the enzyme catalyzing the pyrophosphorolytic removal of the terminal three nucleotides of tRNA yielding the corresponding nucleoside triphosphates ATP and CTP, equation (1). The extent of AMP and CMP incorporation is dependent upon the degree of previous removal of the terminal nucleotides from tRNA. A twice pyrophosphorolyzed tRNA preparation can accept 2 CMP/1 AMP unit and the incorporation of AMP is dependent upon the presence of CTP in the reaction mixture. When using a mixture of all four nucleoside triphosphates, only AMP and CMP are incorporated into the terminal positions of the tRNA. The rat liver enzyme can also incorporate AMP or CMP into tRNA chains with one terminal cytidylic acid (RNA . . . pXpC), equations (2–4) (X is the fourth original nucleotide of the RNA chains). In the absence of added CTP, AMP residues can be attached

TABLE 1. *Purification of tRNA . . . of pCpCpA Pyrophosphorylase from Rat Liver*

Fraction	AMP Incorporating System				Ratio of Activity	
	Protein (mg/ml)	Specific Activity (units/mg of protein)	Total Units	tRNA Activation[a]	CMP/AMP	UMP/AMP
105,000 × g supernatant fluid	34	0.015	144	17	1.4	0.32
pH 5 precipitate	30	0.035	59	2	1.1	0.30
Streptomycin supernatant fluid	12.5	0.067	54	18	1.4	0.31
Ammonium sulfate	1.47	0.63	12	42	1.2	0.25
Calcium phosphate gel	0.43	6.3	11	87	1.0	0.25

[a] The ratio of activities of the enzyme assayed with and without addition of "incubated" tRNA.

to these chains to form RNA . . . pXpCpA, equation (2). On the other hand, when ATP and CTP are present in the reaction mixture RNA . . . pXpCpCpA is formed, equation (4) (9).

$$\text{RNA} \ldots \text{pXpC} + \text{ATP} \rightarrow \text{RNA} \ldots \text{pXpCpA} + \text{PP}_i \qquad (2)$$
$$\text{RNA} \ldots \text{pXpC} + \text{CTP} \rightarrow \text{RNA} \ldots \text{pXpCpC} + \text{PP}_i \qquad (3)$$
$$\text{RNA} \ldots \text{pXpC} + \text{CTP} + \text{ATP} \rightarrow$$
$$\rightarrow \text{RNA} \ldots \text{pXpCpCpA} + 2\,\text{PP}_i \quad (4)$$

It was observed that, unlike a similar tRNA . . . pCpCpA-pyrophos-phorylase from *E. coli* (10,11) the rat liver enzyme can also incorporate UMP into pyrophosphorolyzed tRNA when only UTP is present in the reaction mixture. In this case a limited incorporation of UMP was observed replacing one of the CMP terminal units in the pCpCpA sequence. A constant ratio of the rates of incorporation of AMP/CMP and AMP/UMP throughout the purification steps of the enzyme was observed, suggesting that a single enzyme may be responsible for the incorporation reaction (1). tRNA, which has lost four terminal nucleotides, becomes inactive as an AMP and CMP acceptor (9).

Specificity of RNA Requirement

The incorporation of AMP and CMP is limited only to tRNA preparations. Rat liver microsomal RNA, *E. coli* ribosomal RNA, *Bacillus cereus* RNA, TMV-RNA, synthetic poly A, poly C, poly AC, poly AGUC are unable to serve as acceptors for AMP or CMP. tRNA preparations from different sources [yeast, calf liver, chicken liver, *E. coli*, wheat germ (1,12)], were all found to be active AMP and CMP acceptors, their activity depending on previous removal of the terminal pCpCpA sequence.

Preparation of Pyrophosphorolyzed RNA

This RNA is a useful tool for the determination of the composition and sequence of nucleotides occurring next to the common terminal trinucleotide sequence pCpCpA of tRNA chains. The normally existing pCpCpA end groups are enzymatically removed to yield pyrophosphorolyzed RNA (RNA . . . pX). This terminal nucleotide sequence is replaced by $p^{32}Cp^{32}C$ and the labeled RNA is degraded with alkali, pancreatic ribonuclease or T_1 ribonuclease. The labeled fragments produced are then analyzed by column chromatography, paper electrophoresis, and paper chromatography (13,14,1).

Pyrophosphorolyzed RNA can be prepared by incubating the "pH 5 fraction" of rat liver homogenate in the presence of inorganic pyrophosphate and $MgCl_2$ as described above. However, some of the RNA is degraded during the incubation due to the presence of nucleases in the "pH 5 fraction." An alternative method is to use the purified, nuclease free, enzyme for the pyrophosphorolysis of the terminal trinucleotide sequence pCpCpA. This reaction mixture contains in 0.5 ml : 3 μmoles of inorganic pyrophosphate, 3 μmoles of $MgCl_2$, 20 μmoles of Tris buffer, pH 7.4, 5 μmoles of KF, 0.035 unit of enzyme, and 250 μg of tRNA. After 2 hr of incubation at 37 C, the RNA is extracted with phenol-water, precipitated by ethanol-potassium acetate and dialyzed against 0.2 M NaCl, followed by dialysis against water. The RNA is then incubated again in the presence of the enzyme and pyrophosphate and isolated as above.

REFERENCES

1. DANIEL, V., and U. Z. LITTAUER. 1963. J. Biol. Chem. *238:* 2102.
2. HECHT, L. I., P. C. ZAMECNIK, M. L. STEPHENSON, and J. F. SCOTT. 1958. J. Biol. Chem. *233:* 954.
3. LITTAUER, U. Z., and H. EISENBERG. 1959. Biochim. Biophys. Acta. *32:* 320.
4. PORAT, J., and P. FLODIN. 1959. Nature. *183:* 1657.
5. LITTAUER, U. Z. 1960. *In* R. J. C. Harris, Editor, Symposium on protein biosynthesis. Academic Press, New York. p. 143.
6. LITTAUER, U. Z., and V. DANIEL. 1961. International symposium on ribonucleic acids and polyphosphates, Strasbourg. C.N.R.S. Publ. p. 277.
7. HOAGLAND, M. B., E. B. KELLER, and P. C. ZAMECNIK. 1956. J. Biol. Chem. *218:* 345.
8. KORNBERG, A., and W. E. PRICER, JR. 1951. J. Biol. Chem. *193:* 481.
9. DANIEL, V., and U. Z. LITTAUER. 1965. J. Mol. Biol. *11:* 692.
10. PREISS, J., M. DIECKMANN, and P. BERG. 1961. J. Biol. Chem. *236:* 1748.
11. FURTH, J. J., J. HURWITZ, R. KRUG, and M. ALEXANDER. 1961. J. Biol. Chem. *236:* 3317.
12. GLITZ, D. G., and C. A. DEKKER. 1963. Biochemistry. *2:* 1185.
13. LAGERKWIST, U., and P. BERG. 1962. J. Mol. Biol. *5:* 139.
14. BERG, P., U. LAGERKWIST, and M. DIECKMANN. 1962. J. Mol. Biol. *5:* 159.

tRNA Methylases from

Escherichia coli (**1**)

JERARD HURWITZ AND MARVIN GOLD

ALBERT EINSTEIN COLLEGE OF MEDICINE

YESHIVA UNIVERSITY

BRONX, NEW YORK

ASSAY

tRNA + S-adenosylmethionine (C^{14}-methyl-labeled) $\longrightarrow$
C^{14}H$_3$-tRNA + S-adenosylhomocysteine

Reagents

The routine assay mixture (total volume 0.25 ml) contains

10 mμmoles of C^{14}-methyl-s-adenosylmethionine (1 to 2 $\times$ 10^7 cpm/
μmole). This material was obtained from Tracerlab, Inc., Waltham,
Massachusetts, and stored frozen in dilute sulfuric acid.
1 μmole of MgCl$_2$
2 μmoles of 2-mercaptoethanol
10 μmoles of triethanolamine buffer (either pH 8.0 or pH 8.8)
100–500 mμmoles of nucleotide residues as methyl-deficient *E. coli*
tRNA
Enzyme

Procedure

The methylation of tRNA was measured by the amount of radioactivity of C^{14}-methyl-S-adenosylmethionine converted into an acid-
insoluble form in the presence of a suitable RNA acceptor.

After incubation for 15 min at 38 C, 5 μmoles of sodium pyrophosphate, 0.05 ml of 0.5% bovine plasma albumin, and 0.2 ml of 7% $HClO_4$ are added, and the insoluble material is isolated by centrifugation. The pellet is suspended in 2% $HClO_4$, containing 2×10^{-3} M sodium pyrophosphate and centrifuged, and the washing procedure repeated. The washed pellets are dissolved with 1.5 ml of 0.2 M Na_4OH, decanted into metal planchets, dried, and counted in a windowless Geiger-Mueller counter. No correction for self-absorption is applied. One unit of enzyme is defined as that amount which transfers 1 mμmole of methyl group to tRNA in 1 hr.

ISOLATION PROCEDURE

Growth of Cells

Escherichia coli W is grown on the following medium: K_2HPO_4, 0.1%; KH_2PO_4, 0.3%; sodium citrate, 0.05%; $MgSO_4$, 0.0098%; glucose, 0.5%; and Difco yeast extract, 0.1%. Cultures are grown with vigorous aeration and harvested during late exponential growth. The cells are washed with a solution containing 0.5% NaCl and 0.5% KCl (300 ml/100 g of packed wet cells) and stored at -10 C.

Preparation of tRNA

All tRNA preparations from *E. coli* are prepared by the phenol procedure, after the bacteria has been disrupted by grinding with Alumina A-301 (Aluminum Company of America). The following procedure is routinely used: 10 g of *E. coli,* wet weight, are ground in the cold with a mortar and pestle with 20 g of alumina for approximately 10 min. The resulting paste is suspended in 30 ml of 0.01 M Tris buffer, pH 8.0, containing 0.01 M $MgCl_2$ and 150 μg of pancreatic deoxyribonuclease, and the suspension is centrifuged at 30,000 $\times$ g for 15 min. The supernatant solution is decanted and further centrifuged for 90 min at 78,000 $\times$ g in the No. 30 rotor of a Spinco preparative ultracentrifuge. The supernatant solution is decanted, incubated at 38 C for 30 min, and then stirred with an equal volume of 80% redistilled phenol for 60 min. The aqueous phase is removed and extracted three times with an equal volume of ether. The aqueous layer was made 2% with potassium acetate buffer, pH 5.5, and 2 volumes of 95% ethanol were added. After 30 min at 0 C, the flocculent precipitate is collected by centrifugation, dissolved in 5 ml of 0.05 M Tris buffer, pH 7.5, and dialyzed overnight against 4 liters of 0.02 M Tris buffer, pH 8.0. The tRNA is sometimes further purified by chromatography on DEAE-cellulose columns. In most cases, however, the latter step is omitted, since there is little change in the ability of tRNA to accept methyl groups after this chromatography.

E. coli strain K12-58-161-F⁻, methionine⁻, which synthesizes RNA in the absence of methionine (2), was obtained from Dr. W. K. Maas of the Department of Microbiology, New York University. The organism is grown on the following medium (all ingredients in g/liter): KH_2PO_4, 3; Na_2HPO_4, 6; NH_4Cl, 1; $MgSO_4 \cdot 7 H_2O$, 0.49; $FeSO_4 \cdot 7 H_2O$, 0.0005; $CaCl_2$, 0.055; L-methionine, 0.05; and glucose, 5. The methionine and glucose are autoclaved separately.

The medium is inoculated with 2 ml of an overnight broth culture, and cells are grown with vigorous aeration at 38 C for 10 to 13 hr. tRNA isolated from cells grown by the above procedure contains its full complement of methyl groups as indicated by the inactivity of the tRNA as a methyl group acceptor, as described below. Such tRNA preparations are referred to as normal tRNA. The same medium, containing only 0.003 g of methionine per liter, yields cells from which methyl-deficient tRNA is isolated. After 16–18 hr of incubation in the latter medium, the optical density (measured at 650 mμ with a 1-cm light path in the Beckman spectrophotometer) is approximately 0.45. Between 1 and 1.5 g of cells, wet weight, are obtained per liter.

Separation of Enzyme Fractions

All purification procedures are carried out at 0–10 C, and enzyme fractions at various stages are stored at 0 C and not frozen. All buffers employed, unless otherwise indicated, contain 5×10^{-3} M 2-mercaptoethanol and 10^{-3} M versene.

INITIAL PURIFICATION
Crude Extract. E. coli W (100 g) is ground with 200 g of alumina for 10 min with a mortar and pestle. The mixture is extracted with 300 ml of 0.01 M Tris buffer, pH 7.5, containing 0.01 M $MgCl_2$, and centrifuged for 30 min at $25,000 \times g$. The residue is re-extracted with 250 ml of the above buffer solution; after centrifugation, the two supernatant solutions are combined and further centrifuged at 78,000 $\times g$ for 90 min in the No. 30 rotor of the Spinco preparative ultracentrifuge. The supernatant solution (494 ml) is used in the subsequent purification procedure.

Protamine Fractionation. To the crude extract (490 ml), 245 ml of 0.5% protamine sulfate are added. After 15 min, the mixture is centrifuged for 30 min at $20,000 \times g$, yielding a clear supernatant solution, which contains most of the adenine-methylating activity (supernatant solution after protamine precipitation). The activity of this fraction is stable after storage for 2 months. The precipitate, which contains other methylating enzymes, is extracted with 245 ml of 0.3 M potassium succinate buffer, pH 6.0, and the suspension is centrifuged at 10,000 × g for 20 min. The resulting supernatant solution contains approximately 55% of the total activity of the crude extract.

Ammonium Sulfate I. Solid ammonium sulfate (48 g) is added to the succinate eluate (248 ml), and after centrifugation, the precipitate is discarded. An additional 23 g of ammonium sulfate is added to the supernatant solution, and the resulting precipitate is collected by centrifuging for 15 min at 20,000 × g. The precipitate is dissolved in 20 ml of 0.05 M triethanolamine buffer, pH 8.0, and this solution is dialyzed for 120 min against two changes of a solution (2.5 liters) containing 0.05 M triethanolamine buffer, pH 8.8.

Chromatography on Phosphocellulose. The dialyzed ammonium sulfate fraction is diluted threefold with 0.05 M triethanolamine buffer, pH 8.8, and poured onto a column of phosphocellulose (30 cm × 3 cm) previously washed with 0.05 M triethanolamine buffer, pH 8.8. Stepwise elution of protein was carried out with the following buffers: 150 ml of 0.05 M triethanolamine, pH 8.8; 150 ml of 0.05 M potassium phosphate, pH 8.4; and 150 ml of 0.5 M potassium phosphate, pH 6.5. Four discrete peaks of activity are obtained. Peak I (a mixture of two enzymes that methylate guanine residues of tRNA) contains 28 and 84%, respectively, of the initial activity and protein applied to the column; Peak II (uracil-methylating enzyme), 18 and 3%, respectively; and Peak III (cytosine-methylating activity), 13 and 2.4%; Peak IV (a third guanine-methylating enzyme) contains 33% and less than 1% of the initial activity and protein applied to the column.

Peaks I and II are relatively unstable at this stage, losing about 15 and 30%, respectively, of the activity in 48 hr. Peaks III and IV are stable and show no loss of enzyme activity after 2 months at 0 C.

PURIFICATION OF GUANINE-METHYLATING ENZYMES I
AND II FROM PEAK I

Acetone Fractionation. The pooled triethanolamine buffer eluate (81.5 ml) is made 0.05 M with respect to $MnCl_2$, and after 15 min the insoluble material is removed by centrifugation. The supernatant solution (79 ml) is adjusted to pH 5.0 with 4 ml of 2 M ammonium acetate buffer, pH 5.0, and treated with 27.6 ml of acetone that has been cooled to −20 C. The precipitate is discarded. To the supernatant solution (104 ml), 12 ml of acetone are added; after centrifugation, the precipitate is suspended in 6 ml of 0.05 M triethanolamine buffer, pH 8.8. The insoluble protein is removed by centrifugation and re-extracted with 4 ml of the same buffer. The two supernatant solutions are combined (acetone fraction).

Alumina Cγ Gel Treatment. The acetone fraction (10 ml) was diluted to 50 ml with 0.05 M triethanolamine buffer, pH 8.8, and 15 ml of alumina Cγ gel (17.5 mg/ml) are added. After 10 min, the suspension is centrifuged and the precipitate washed three times with 6 ml of 0.02 M potassium phosphate buffer, pH 6.5. The amounts of methylating activity removed with each successive washing are (in total units) 160, 84, and 24; these three eluates contain guanine-methylating enzyme I and are pooled. The alumina Cγ gel residue is then washed three additional times with 6 ml of 0.3 M potassium phosphate buffer, pH 6.5. The amounts of activity extracted from the gel with each successive washing are 104, 76, and 25 units. These pooled fractions contain guanine-methylating enzyme II.

Calcium Phosphate Adsorption of Guanine-Methylating Enzyme I and Ammonium Sulfate Precipitation. The pooled 0.02 M potassium phosphate eluate (17.4 ml) is diluted with 35 ml of H_2O, and 26 ml of calcium phosphate gel (12.7 mg/ml) are added. After 15 min, the gel is collected by centrifugation and washed successively with 35 and 17 ml of 0.1 M Tris buffer, pH 8.0. The washings are combined, and 31.4 g of solid ammonium sulfate are added. The precipitate obtained after centrifugation is dissolved in 2 ml of 0.01 M potassium phosphate buffer, pH 6.5. This enzyme fraction (I, 3c of Table 1) is used as the source of guanine-methylating enzyme I.

Calcium Phosphate Adsorption of Guanine-Methylating Enzyme II and Ammonium Sulfate Precipitation. The pooled 0.3 M potassium phosphate eluate (17.8 ml) is diluted fivefold with H_2O and treated with 58.4 ml of calcium phosphate gel (12.7 mg/ml). After 15 min, the gel is collected by centrifugation and washed twice with 20 ml of 0.2 M β,β-dimethylglutarate buffer, pH 7.5. The washings are combined, and 30.6 g of solid ammonium sulfate are added. The precipitate is dissolved in 3 ml of 0.01 M potassium phosphate buffer, pH 6.5 (I, 4c of Table 1, guanine-methylating enzyme II).

PURIFICATION OF URACIL-METHYLATING ENZYME

Alumina Cγ Gel Treatment and Ammonium Sulfate Precipitation. The pooled Peak II material obtained from the eluates of the phosphocellulose column (66 ml) is treated with 6.6 ml of alumina Cγ gel; after 10 min, the suspension is centrifuged and the gel is washed with 26 ml of 0.1 M potassium phosphate buffer, pH 6.5. This washing is discarded after centrifugation, and the enzyme activity is eluted from the gel with 6 ml of 0.5 M ammonium sulfate, pH 7.5. Additional activity (15%) is removed from the gel by a second ammonium sulfate elution. To the combined eluates, 6 g of solid ammonium sulfate are added; after centrifugation, the precipitate is dissolved in 1 ml of 0.05 M potassium phosphate buffer, pH 6.5 (uracil-methylating enzyme; II, 3 of Table 1).

PURIFICATION OF CYTOSINE-METHYLATING ENZYME

Alumina Cγ Gel Treatment. The fractions composing Peak III (87 ml) are concentrated by addition of 40 g of solid ammonium sulfate (75% saturation). The precipitate obtained after centrifugation is dissolved in 150 ml of H_2O, and 15 ml of an alumina Cγ gel (17.5 mg/ml) suspension are added. After 10 min, the suspension is centrifuged and washed twice with 20 ml of 0.2 M potassium phosphate buffer, pH 6.5. These washings are discarded, and the enzyme activity is eluted from the gel by washing twice with 15 ml of 0.5 M ammonium sulfate, pH 7.5 (alumina Cγ gel eluate).

Ammonium Sulfate Fractionation. The pooled alumina Cγ gel eluate is adjusted to 70% saturation with solid ammonium sulfate. The precipitate obtained after centrifugation is extracted successively with 3-ml quantities of 70, 60, 50, and 40% saturated solutions of ammonium sulfate. The fraction containing the highest specific activity, usually the 50% fraction, is retained. This enzyme fraction (III, 3 of Table 1) is used as the cytosine-methylating enzyme.

PURIFICATION OF GUANINE-METHYLATING ENZYME III

Ammonium Sulfate Concentration. The fractions that constitute Peak IV (142 ml) are pooled, adjusted to 75% saturation with solid ammonium sulfate, and centrifuged. The precipitate is dissolved in 10 ml of 0.02 M potassium phosphate buffer, pH 6.5 (ammonium sulfate I).

Ammonium Sulfate II. Ammonium sulfate Fraction I is dialyzed against two changes of 500 ml of 0.02 M triethanolamine buffer, pH 8.0, for a total of 2 hr. The dialyzed fraction (11.4 ml) is diluted to 34 ml with H_2O, and 11.4 ml of calcium phosphate gel (12.7 mg/ml) are added. The gel, after centrifugation, is washed once with 10 ml of 0.3 M ammonium sulfate, pH 8.5; the supernatant solution is then adjusted to 75% with solid ammonium sulfate, and the precipitate is dissolved with 1 ml of 0.02 M triethanolamine buffer, pH 8.0 (ammonium sulfate II, guanine-methylating enzyme III).

PURIFICATION OF ADENINE-METHYLATING FRACTION

Whereas crude extracts of *E. coli* catalyze the methylation of all the bases (measured after alkaline degradation and electrophoretic separation of the ribonucleotides), none of the purified enzyme preparations thus far described catalyze the formation of methylated adenine derivatives. The supernatant solution after protamine precipitation (see above), however, catalyze demonstrable methylation of both adenine and uracil. This fraction is used for the further purification of the adenine-methylating activity. At all steps in the purification procedure described below, the bases methylated in tRNA are characterized after degradation with alkali and electrophoresis.

Ammonium Sulfate Fraction I. To the supernatant solution (810 ml), after protamine precipitation, 133 g of ammonium sulfate are added and the precipitate is discarded. An additional 100 g of ammonium sulfate are added to the supernatant solution (860 ml), and the precipitate is again discarded. The enzymatic activity is then precipitated from the supernatant solution (890 ml) by the addition of 142 g of ammonium sulfate, and is dissolved in 40 ml of 0.05 M triethanolamine buffer, pH 8.8 (ammonium sulfate I).

Chromatography on DEAE-Cellulose. The ammonium sulfate fraction is dialyzed for $2\frac{1}{2}$ hr against three changes, 2 liters each, of 0.05 M triethanolamine buffer, pH 8.8. The ammonium sulfate concentration decreases to 0.23 M as measured with the Barnstead purity meter. The solution is diluted to 100 ml with 0.05 M triethanolamine buffer, pH 8.8, and passed through a column of DEAE-cellulose (22 cm × 3 cm). The column is washed successively with 150-ml volumes of 0.1 M triethanolamine buffer, pH 8.8, 0.1 M potassium phosphate buffer, pH 6.5, 0.2 M potassium phosphate buffer, pH 6.5, and 200 ml of 0.5 M potassium phosphate buffer, pH 6.5. Two peaks of methylation activity are detected; one is eluted with 0.1 M triethanolamine buffer, pH 8.8, and the second with 0.2 M potassium phosphate buffer. The first peak (DEAE-cellulose eluate) contains approximately 40% of the activity applied to the column. This activity catalyzes the methylation of adenine residues of S-RNA. The second peak contains 53% of the initial activity and catalyzes the methylation of uracil. This fraction is discarded.

Alumina Cγ Gel Treatment and Ammonium Sulfate Precipitation. The DEAE-cellulose eluate (100 ml) is combined with 34 ml of alumina Cγ gel suspension; after 10 min, the gel is collected by centrifugation and washed three times with 40 ml of 0.2 M β,β-dimethylglutarate buffer, pH 7.5. These washings are discarded, and the adenine-methyl-ating activity is eluted twice with 20-ml volumes of 0.3 M potassium phosphate buffer, pH 7.5. To the combined eluates (39 ml), 12.7 g of ammonium sulfate are added; after centrifugation, the precipitate is dissolved in 4 ml of 0.05 M triethanolamine buffer, pH 8.8 (ammonium sulfate II).

Chromatography on Phosphocellulose and Ammonium Sulfate Pre-cipitation. Ammonium sulfate Fraction II (3.9 ml) is dialyzed against two 500-ml volumes of 0.05 M triethanolamine buffer, pH 8.8, for a total period of 1½ hr, diluted to 20 ml with 0.05 M triethanolamine buffer, pH 8.8, and then added to a column of phosphocellulose (15 cm × 1 cm). The column is washed successively with 20 ml of 0.05 M tri-ethanolamine buffer, pH 8.8, 40 ml of 0.1 M potassium phosphate buffer, pH 7.5, and 40 ml of 0.2 M potassium phosphate buffer, pH 7.5. The methylating activity (84% of activity applied to the column) is eluted with the latter buffer. The pooled fraction (21 ml) is treated with 8.2 g of solid ammonium sulfate; after centrifugation, the precipitate is dissolved in 2 ml of 0.05 M triethanolamine buffer, pH 8.8 (ammo-nium sulfate III, adenine-methylating fraction).

A summary of these purification procedures is given in Table 1.

IDENTIFICATION OF BASES METHYLATED

During the purification of the above enzymes, each fraction is further characterized by identification of the methylated nucleotide formed by its action. For routine examination, RNA is degraded by alkali and the resulting ribonucleotides are separated by paper electro-phoresis. The methylated derivatives are characterized by chromatog-raphy with authentic markers, and in some cases, by their ultraviolet spectra.

Products Formed with Guanine-Methylating Enzymes I and II

The base formed in tRNA methylated by these enzyme preparations is 1-methylguanine. This is readily demonstrated by the isolation of C^{14}-methyl-labeled 1-methylguanine, which was characterized by its char-acteristic ultraviolet absorption spectra in acid and alkali.

Product Formed with Uracil-Methylating Enzyme

In all solvents, the methylation product formed in this reaction, after various types of degradation procedures, cochromatograph with authentic ribothymidylate, ribothymidine, and thymine.

TABLE 1. *Summary of Purification Procedures*

Enzyme Fractions	Total Units	Specific Activity[a] (mμmoles/hr/ mg of protein)
Crude extract	9250	2.8
Supernatant solution after protamine precipitation	3210	1.1
Succinate buffer extract of protamine precipitate	4900	3.7
Ammonium sulfate fraction	4230	3.9
I. Guanine-methylating enzymes I, II		
1. Pooled Peak I from phosphocellulose column	1088	1.6
2. Acetone fraction	732	9.6
3. Alumina Cγ eluate, guanine-methylating enzyme I		
a. 0.02 M phosphate eluate	268	65
b. Calcium phosphate gel eluate	156	310
c. Ammonium sulfate, 0 to 75%	140	318
4. Alumina Cγ eluate; guanine-methylating enzyme II		
a. 0.3 M phosphate eluate	211	34
b. Calcium phosphate gel eluate	149	228
c. Ammonium sulfate, 0–75%	96	208
II. Uracil-methylating enzyme		
1 Pooled Peak II from phosphocellulose column	632	67
2. Alumina Cγ gel eluate	536	337
3. Ammonium sulfate, 0 to 75%	428	305
III. Cytosine-methylating enzyme		
1. Pooled Peak III from phosphocellulose column	584	84
2. Alumina Cγ gel eluate	416	272
3. Ammonium sulfate, 50% extract	228	440
IV. Guanine-methylating enzyme III		
1. Pooled Peak IV from phosphocellulose column	976	373
2. Ammonium sulfate I	754	318
3. Ammonium sulfate II	407	924
V. Adenine-methylating fraction		
1. Supernatant solution after protamine precipitation[b]	1980	0.7
2. Ammonium sulfate I	1064	0.7
3. DEAE-cellulose fractionation	456	7.0
4. Ammonium sulfate II	364	30
5. Ammonium sulfate III	292	212

a Protein was measured by the procedure of Bücher (3).

b This supernatant solution, after protamine precipitation employed for the purification of the adenine-methylating fraction, is not the same solution described above.

Identification of Products Formed with the Cytosine-Methylating Enzyme

Degradation of the methylated RNA product formed after the action of the cytosine-methylating enzyme results in the isolation of a labeled derivative of cytosine. The characterization of the methylated cytosine derivative is limited by difficulties in degrading the mononucleotide (isolated after alkaline degradation) to the free base. This is also true of attempts to isolate the free base directly from tRNA. Degradation of either substance with concentrated formic acid or 35 or 70% $HClO_4$ leads to a mixture of materials. On occasion, the degradation with 70% $HClO_4$ yields a radioactive material, which migrates with the same R_f as 5-methylcytosine. Attempts to isolate the mononucleotide also fail, since none of the chromatographic procedures employed resolve the methylated CMP derivative from CMP. In all solvents, the radioactive mononucleotide migrates very closely to the CMP region, and no evidence of more than one radioactive compound is detected. When the $2'(3')$-CMP region obtained after electrophoresis at pH 3.5 in 0.05 M ammonium formate is eluted and converted to the nucleoside by the action of alkaline phosphatase, a positively charged radioactive material is obtained. This substance migrates toward the cathode at pH 3.5, as well as at pH 9.5, but again, this material is not separated from cytidine. Indirect evidence that the methylated cytosine derivative is 5-methyl cytosine is obtained by examining the product obtained after deamination, which yields a material with the properties of ribothymidylate. After nitrous acid treatment, approximately 70% of the radioactivity is detected in the UMP region where ribothymidylate is expected to migrate. Further degradation of this material with 35% $HClO_4$ yields a radioactive base, found to have the same R_f as authentic thymine in a number of different solvents.

Identification of Products Formed with the Adenine-Methylating Fraction

The availability of known methylated adenine derivatives permits the examination of the chromatographic behavior of the C^{14}-containing bases. After degradation of RNA (labeled with C^{14}-methyl groups in the presence of the adenine-methylating fraction) with 1 N HCl, the migration of the bases in four different solvents shows correspondence between C^{14} and ultraviolet absorption with 6-dimethylaminopurine, 6-methylaminopurine, and 2-methyladenine. The following compounds are excluded: 7-methyladenine, 9-methyladenine, 3-methyladenine, and 1-methyladenine.

Identification of the Product Formed with Guanine-Methylating Enzyme III

Degradation of tRNA (labeled by the action of guanine-methylating enzyme III) with 1 N HCl for 1 hr at 100 C liberates the radioactive compound as the free base. Electrophoresis of the acid-hydrolyzed material at pH 2 in phosphate buffer results in the detection of radioactivity, which migrates faster than guanine toward the cathode. No other labeled region is detected. This suggests that the product is a methylated purine, presumably a derivative of guanine. Paper chromatography of the acid-liberated material in a variety of solvents shows that this material cochromatographs with the same R_f as 7-methylguanine and could be distinguished from a variety of methylated purine derivatives.

The labeled base is further characterized by chromatography on Dowex 50-H$^+$ resin. The radioactivity applied to the column is eluted as a single peak with 3 N HCl and appears after guanine but before adenine; the labeled material is further separated from guanine by paper chromatography and possesses an ultraviolet spectra in acid and alkali characteristic of 7-methylguanine.

SPECIFICITY OF METHYLATING AGENT

To date, no agent other than S-adenosylmethionine has been found to act as a methylating agent with nucleic acid acceptors. Other methyl donors such as C^{14}-methyl B12, C^{14}-5-CH$_3$, folate-H$_4$, or C^{14}-formaldehyde plus tetrahydrofolic acid incubated with tRNA and purified enzymes or crude extract do not lead to detectable incorporation of C^{14} into an acid-insoluble form.

SPECIFICITY OF METHYLATING ACCEPTOR

The only naturally occurring RNA that acts as a methyl group acceptor in the reactions catalyzed by the above enzymes is tRNA. RNA formed *in vitro* in the DNA-dependent RNA polymerase system is also methylated to a very low extent (4). A variety of different RNA preparations including viral, ribosomal, and synthetic (formed with polynucleotide phosphorylase) are inactive as methyl group acceptors.

In general, reaction rates and yields of methylation with the purified enzyme fractions are measured with methyl-deficient tRNA. Whereas the initial rate of methylation is proportional to the amount of enzyme added, when large amounts of enzyme are added or when incubation is prolonged, finite amounts of methyl groups are incorporated. The extent of methylation is directly proportional to the amount of tRNA added. The following experiment suggests that the reaction comes to a halt because the sites that can be methylated are exhausted during the reaction. With each enzyme fraction, two identical reaction mixtures are used. After the reaction has ceased, more enzyme is added to one reaction mixture while additional methyl-deficient tRNA is added to the second. Only in the latter case is there further incorporation of labeled methyl groups. The extent of methylation of methyl-deficient tRNA catalyzed by the enzymes is the following (in percentage of nucleotide residues methylated): guanine I, 0.04; guanine II, 0.034; uracil, 0.50; cytosine, 0.05; adenine, 0.013; and guanine III, 0.19.

Evidence that indicates that the methylation reaction is species and strain specific (5–7) has also accumulated. In general, methylation of nucleic acids does not occur using enzymes obtained from the homologous species. When heterologous systems are employed, methylation may occur. For example, cell extracts prepared from *E. coli* do not catalyze detectable methylation of *E. coli* tRNA, but transfer methyl groups to tRNA isolated from *Micrococcus lysodeikticus, Clostridium pasteurianum,* etc. Cell extracts prepared from *M. lysodeikticus* catalyze methylation of tRNA from *E. coli* and *Cl. pasteurianum,* but are not active when measured with tRNA from *M. lysodeikticus.* These observations are in keeping with the idea that there are a limited number of sites available for methylation and that these sites (presumably nucleotide sequences) are species and strain specific.

Properties of the Purified Enzymes

EFFECT OF pH ON THE RATE OF REACTION. Optimal activities for the different methylating enzymes are found in the following pH ranges: guanine I, 8.0 to 8.5 in both Tris and triethanolamine buffers; guanine II and cytosine, triethanolamine buffer, pH 8.0 to 9.0; adenine and uracil, triethanolamine buffer, pH 8.5 to 9.0; and guanine III, dimethylglutarate buffer, pH 7.5 to 8.0.

REQUIREMENTS FOR METALS AND SULFHYDRYL AGENTS. All enzymes show some activity in the absence of Mg^{2+}; the methylation of cytosine is not affected by Mg^{2+}, whereas the uracil-methylating and the guanine-methylating activities I and II are increased approximately fourfold, and guanine-methylating enzyme III, twofold by the presence of Mg^{2+}. Methylation of adenine is stimulated only twofold by Mg^{2+}.

The enzyme preparations are routinely stored in the presence of 2-mercaptoethanol; in some cases, there is a marked decrease in methylation activity when this compound is omitted from the reaction mixtures, especially in the case of the uracil-methylating enzyme. The addition of p-hydroxymercuribenzoate decreases the activity of all the enzyme fractions tested.

REFERENCES

1. HURWITZ, J., M. GOLD, and M. ANDERS. 1964. J. Biol. Chem. 239: 3462, 3474.
2. BOREK, E., and A. RYAN. 1958. J. Bacteriol. 75: 72.
3. BÜCHER, T. 1947. Biochim. Biophys. Acta. 1: 292.
4. HURWITZ, J., A. EVANS, C. BABINET, and A. SKALKA. 1963. Cold Spring Harbor Sym. on Quant. Bio. Long Island Biological Association, Cold Spring Harbor, New York. 28: 59.
5. GOLD, M., J. HURWITZ, and M. ANDERS. 1963. Proc. Natl. Acad. Sci., U.S. 50: 164.
6. SVENSSON, E., H. G. BOMAN, K. G. ERICKSSON, and K. KJELLIN. 1963. J. Mol. Biol. 7: 254.
7. SRINIVASAN, P. R., and E. BOREK. 1963. Proc. Natl. Acad. Sci., U.S. 49: 529.

Preparation of Aminoacyl

Ribonucleic Acid Synthetases

from *Escherichia coli*

KARL H. MUENCH

DEPARTMENT OF MEDICINE

UNIVERSITY OF MIAMI

MIAMI, FLORIDA

PAUL BERG

DEPARTMENT OF BIOCHEMISTRY

STANFORD UNIVERSITY SCHOOL OF MEDICINE

STANFORD, CALIFORNIA

ASSAY

Principle

The rate of the forward reaction

$$AA^* + tRNA + ATP \rightleftharpoons AA^*\text{-}tRNA + AMP + PP\dagger$$

is measured by determination of the amount of labeled amino acid converted to an acid-insoluble form.

We wish to acknowledge the excellent technical assistance of Mrs. Sally Sonnichsen.

† The following abbreviations are employed: AA, amino acid; AA*, amino acid labeled with C^{14} or H^3; Ala, alanine; Arg, arginine; CySH, cysteine; Glu, glutamic acid; Glu-NH$_2$, glutamine; Leu, isoleucine; Ser, serine; Thr, threonine; Trp, tryptophan; ATP, adenosine triphosphate; AMP, adenosine monophosphate; PP, pyrophosphate; RNA, ribonucleic acid; tRNA, transfer ribonucleic acid; EDTA, ethylenediaminetetraäcetic acid; DEAE-, diethylaminoethyl-; A_{260}, absorbance at 260 mμ; A_{280}, absorbance at 280 mμ.

Reaction Mixture

For assay of all aminoacyl RNA synthetases except prolyl RNA synthetase the 0.5-ml reaction mixture contains

50 μmoles of Sodium cacodylate buffer, pH 6.9
0.5 μmole of ATP
5.0 μmoles of MgCl$_2$
5.0 μmoles of KCl
2.0 μmoles of reduced glutathione
100 μg of bovine serum albumin
50 or 100 mμmoles of C^{14}- or H^3-labeled L-amino acid† containing from
 3 to 8 $\times$ 10^3 cpm/mμmole
1–6 μmoles of *Escherichia coli* tRNA nucleotide‡
0.05–0.5 units of aminoacyl RNA synthetase

For prolyl RNA synthetase the 0.5-ml reaction mixture contains

50 μmoles of potassium phosphate buffer, pH 6.8
0.3 μmole of ATP
10 μmoles of MgCl$_2$
150 mμmoles of C^{14}-labeled L-proline containing 3.5 $\times$ 10^3 cpm/
 mμmole
tRNA and enzyme as above

Procedure

The reaction mixture is incubated for 10 min at 37 C. A blank containing no enzyme is incubated with each set of assay tubes. The reaction is terminated by rapid cooling to 0 C and addition of 3 ml of 2 N HCl. The tRNA precipitate is collected by aspiration onto a 2.4-cm Whatman glass fiber filter (GF/C) placed in a stainless steel holder§ designed to allow thorough washing and reproducible blanks. The precipitate is washed five times on the filter with 2 ml of 2 N HCl. The filter is then placed in a scintillation vial, dried under an infrared

---

† Presence of the D-isomer does not interfere with the reaction. A mixture containing 250 mμmoles of each of the other 19 amino acids, unlabeled, may be added. To 100 mμmoles of labeled L-asparagine and L-glutamine 500 mμmoles of unlabeled L-aspartic acid and L-glutamic acids are added, respectively. Cysteine is prepared by mixing cystine with a 1.5-fold molar excess of dithioerythritol in 0.1 M Tris-HCl Buffer, pH 8.0 (1).

‡ The preparation of the tRNA has been described (2). Ten absorbance units at 260 mμ, pH 12, is assumed to equal one μmole of tRNA nucleotide. The capacity of tRNA to accept different amino acids varies from 0.08 mμmole tryptophan per μmole tRNA to 1 mμmole leucine per μmole tRNA. Accordingly, tRNA is added in different amounts to the reaction mixtures for different amino acids.

§ Available from Peter Hoefer, 2609 California Street, San Francisco, California.

lamp, suspended in 5 ml of toluene containing 0.4% 2,5-diphenyl-oxazole (PPO) and 0.01% 1,4-bis-2-(4-methyl-5-phenyloxazolyl)-benzene (dimethyl POPOP), and counted in a scintillation counter.

Under these conditions the amount of labeled aminoacyl tRNA formed is directly proportional to the amount of enzyme added to the reaction mixture. Blank values are independent of the amount of enzyme used.

Certain preparations of labeled phenylalanine, tryptophan, and tyrosine may give a high blank value in the standard assay. The problem may be corrected by purification of these amino acids on Dowex-1 and Dowex-50 (3) prior to use. In addition, the assay for tryptophanyl RNA synthetase requires a modified procedure: The reaction is stopped by rapid cooling to 0 C and addition of 0.1 ml of cold 2 M potassium acetate buffer, pH 5, followed by 2 volumes of cold ethanol. The precipitate is collected by centrifugation at $10,000 \times g$ for 5 min, and dissolved in 1 ml of 0.1 M potassium acetate buffer, pH 5, then carried through the routine HCl precipitation and filter assay.

Definition of Units

One unit of enzyme is equivalent to the formation of 1 mμmole of aminoacyl tRNA in 10 min at 37 C. Specific activities of the enzymes are expressed as units per milligram of protein. Protein is determined by the method of Lowry (4) with crystalline bovine serum albumin as the standard.

ISOLATION PROCEDURE

Growth of Cells

E. coli strain B is grown at 37 C in a medium consisting of 10^{-3} M MgCl$_2$, 3×10^{-2} M (NH$_4$)$_2$SO$_4$, 10^{-5} M FeCl$_3$, 6×10^{-2} M K$_2$HPO$_4$, 4×10^{-2} M KH$_2$PO$_4$, and 0.8% glucose in distilled water. Growth is followed by turbidity measured at 420 mμ. The cells are cooled to 0 C in late exponential phase and harvested by continuous flow centrifugation. The doubling time is 45 min for cells grown either in flasks on rotary shakers or in an 80-liter chemostat vigorously aerated with pre-warmed, hydrated, filtered air. The yield is 2.5 g of packed wet cells per liter of medium. The cells are stored in sealed containers at -15 C.

Preparation of Extract

This and all subsequent steps are performed at 0–2 C. Twelve grams of the frozen cells are suspended in 0.01 M Tris-HCl buffer, pH 8.0,

0.01 M MgCl$_2$, and 10% glycerol,† thawed, then brought to 42 ml with the same buffer. The cell suspension is passed through a French pressure cell at a pressure of 8000 psi. The lysed cell suspension is centrifuged at 198,000 × g (50,000 rev/min in a Beckman no. 50 titanium rotor) for 2 hr, and the clear supernatant solution is withdrawn to a level even with the uppermost portion of the pellet.

Fractionation on DEAE-Cellulose

DEAE-Cellulose (BioRad Cellex D, 0.9 mq/gm) prepared by alkali wash (5) and stored in 0.01 M EDTA, 0.1 M potassium phosphate buffer, pH 6.5, is packed at 5 psi into a 24- × 2-cm column and equilibrated with an initial buffer consisting of 0.02 M potassium phosphate, pH 7.5, 0.02 M 2-mercaptoethanol, 0.001 M MgCl$_2$, and 10% glycerol.

The extract is applied, and the column is washed with 370 ml of the initial buffer at a rate of 80 ml/hr. Then the enzymes are eluted with a buffer containing 0.25 M potassium phosphate, pH 6.5, 0.02 M 2-mercaptoethanol, 0.001 M MgCl$_2$, and 10% glycerol. The absorbance at 280 mμ in the effluent is followed, and the peak resulting from the change of buffer, 25–50 ml, is concentrated fivefold by dialysis versus 60 volumes of buffer consisting of 0.001 M potassium phosphate, pH 6.8, 0.02 M 2-mercaptoethanol, 10% glycerol, and 15% polyethylene glycol, mol. wt. 6000.

Fractionation on Hydroxylapatite

Hydroxylapatite (6) is prepared as the "CPA" material described by Main et al. (7), and poured under 30-cm hydrostatic pressure to form a 14- × 0.90-cm column. The column is equilibrated with an initial buffer composed of 0.01 M potassium phosphate, pH 6.8, 0.02 M 2-mercaptoethanol, and 10% glycerol.

One-fifth of the concentrated DEAE-cellulose fraction is diluted fivefold with the initial buffer and applied to the column. The column is then washed with 110 ml of this buffer, pumped at a rate of 30 ml/hr.‡ A linear gradient of increasing phosphate concentration is used to elute the enzymes. The mixing chamber contains 250 ml of the initial buffer, and the reservoir 250 ml of 0.20 M potassium phosphate, pH 6.8, 0.02 M 2-mercaptoethanol, and 10% glycerol. The resulting resolution of aminoacyl RNA synthetases is illustrated in Fig. 1. A summary of the purification procedure appears in Table 1. Peak fractions from the hydroxylapatite column may be concentrated by dialysis

---

† Ten volumes glycerol per 100 volumes of final solution.
‡ The LKB Miniflow Micropump Type 4501 is suitable for this purpose.

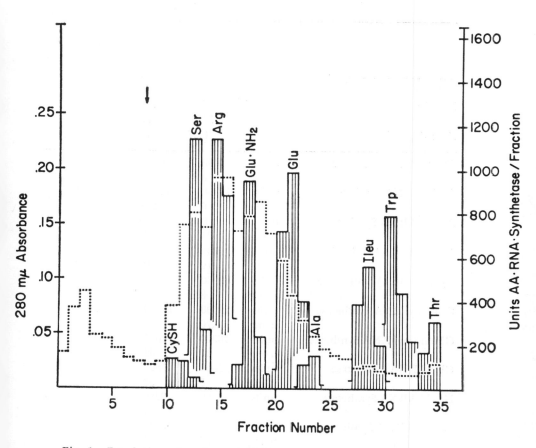

Fig. 1. Resolution of aminoacyl RNA synthetases on hydroxylapatite. The broken line represents absorbance at 280 mμ. The arrow indicates the start of the gradient. Each fraction was 15 ml. The shaded areas represent the aminoacyl RNA synthetase activities for the designated amino acids. The positions of enzyme peaks, including the activities not shown, are as follows: Fraction 11, prolyl and cysteinyl; fraction 13, seryl; fraction 14, asparaginyl; fraction 15, aspartyl, histidyl, and arginyl; fraction 16, glycyl; fraction 18, glutaminyl, valyl, and phenylalanyl; fraction 21, lysyl$_I$, tyrosyl, and methionyl; fraction 22, glutamyl and leucyl; fraction 24, alanyl and lysyl$_{II}$; fraction 28, lysyl$_{III}$; fraction 29, isoleucyl; fraction 31, tryptophanyl; and fraction 35, threonyl RNA synthetase.

TABLE 1. *Purification of 20 Aminoacyl RNA Synthetases*

		Extract	DEAE-Cellulose Fraction	Hydroxyl-apatite Peak[a]
Volume	ml	22	13	
Protein	mg/ml	17	14	
A_{260}		57	9.5	
$A_{280} : A_{260}$ ratio		0.67	1.6	
Alanyl RNA Synthetase	units	3400	5000[b]	1400
	u/mg	8.8	26	150
Arginyl RNA Synthetase	units	18000	18000	11000
	u/mg	46	93	300
Aspartyl RNA Synthetase	units	9500	12000[b]	4900
	u/mg	25	66	95
Asparaginyl RNA Synthetase	units	4700	3800	1300
	u/mg	12	19	26
Cysteinyl RNA Synthetase	units	3200	2300	1400
	u/mg	8.2	12	73
Glutamyl RNA Synthetase	units	29000	18000	9100
	u/mg	76	93	600
Glutaminyl RNA Synthetase	units	16000	12000	5000
	u/mg	41	62	370
Glycyl RNA Synthetase	units	2600	5800[b]	900
	u/mg	6.7	30	24
Histidyl RNA Synthetase	units	4500	2200	580
	u/mg	12	11	16
Isoleucyl RNA Synthetase	units	13000	10000	5000
	u/mg	34	51	1800
Leucyl RNA Synthetase	units	9500	5400	2900
	u/mg	25	28	230
Lysyl RNA Synthetase	units	11000	15000[b]	900, 1300, 1600[c]
	u/mg	28	76	34, 190, 370
Methionyl RNA Synthetase	units	11000	8800	2400
	u/mg	28	46	160
Phenylalanyl RNA Synthetase	units	11000	6200	5800
	u/mg	28	32	210
Prolyl RNA Synthetase	units	7900	6600	310
	u/mg	21	34	50
Seryl RNA Synthetase	units	8100	12000[b]	6000
	u/mg	21	62	420
Threonyl RNA Synthetase	units	2400	3700[b]	2500
	u/mg	6.2	19	620

Table 1   (Continued)

		Extract	DEAE-Cellulose Fraction	Hydroxyl-apatite Peak[a]
Volume	ml	22	13	
Protein	mg/ml	17	14	
A_{260}		57	9.5	
$A_{280} : A_{260}$ ratio		0.67	1.6	
Tryptophanyl RNA Synthetase	units	14000	17000[b]	6500
	u/mg	35	89	2400
Tyrosyl RNA Synthetase	units	20000	15000	8500
	u/mg	52	78	570
Valyl RNA Synthetase	units	34000	28000	15000
	u/mg	88	145	560

[a] The values for total units have been corrected by a factor of five, since only 20% of the DEAE-cellulose fraction was chromatographed on hydroxylapatite.

[b] In certain cases there is an apparent increase in total enzymatic activity at this step. The reason is unknown. Since assays were simultaneous for all purification steps for a given enzyme, an enzyme more stable in the DEAE-cellulose fraction than in the extract would give this result. The extract contains insufficient free amino acids, 25 μmoles per ml, to decrease significantly the value for total units in the extract by dilution of the labeled amino acid in the reaction mixture.

[c] Lysyl RNA synthetase gave three apparent peaks on hydroxylapatite. The values here correspond from left to right with the subscripts I, II, and III noted in the legend to Fig. 1. In a reaction mixture containing 100 mμmoles of L-lysine-C[14] the addition of 250 mμmoles of each of the other 19 L-amino acids, unlabeled, did not alter this result.

against 0.01 M potassium phosphate buffer, pH 6.8, 0.02 M 2-mercapto-ethanol, 10% glycerol, and 15–30% polyethylene glycol. Glycerol is added to give a final concentration of 50%, and the enzymes are stored at −15 C.

DISCUSSION

Assay Conditions

The procedure is designed to provide stabilized aminoacyl RNA synthetases free of tRNA and ribonuclease for studies of tRNA. The reaction mixtures are suitable for preparation of aminoacyl tRNA when enzyme is added in excess (8). For different aminoacyl RNA synthetases from *E. coli* (8–12) K_m values for amino acids, ATP, and Mg^{2+} vary by as much as two orders of magnitude, and in some cases high levels of ATP and Mg^{2+} are inhibitory. Therefore, no single reaction mixture is likely to yield optimal activity for all enzymes. Prolyl RNA synthetase is nearly undetectable in the reaction mixture suitable for the other 19 enzymes and, therefore, is assayed in a mixture derived from Norton's data (9).

Growth of Cells and Purification

At various times we have used cells grown commercially in complex media and harvested in exponential phase (13). Higher initial specific activities of the enzymes are achieved when the cells are harvested before growing to a limit (14).

We have also used sonication and mixing with 200-μ glass beads in a Waring Blendor to prepare cell lysates with comparable specific activities for certain of the enzymes. However, we have not employed those procedures in the presence of glycerol.

The DEAE-cellulose step is modified from the work of Bergmann (8). He found that a gradient of decreasing pH and linearly increasing phosphate concentration elutes the enzymes in the order tryptophanyl, isoleucyl, tyrosyl, methionyl, valyl, and leucyl RNA synthetase from a column of DEAE-cellulose (15). The DEAE-cellulose gradient followed by the hydroxylapatite gradient yields more highly purified aminoacyl RNA synthetases than are obtained when the one-step elution is employed for the DEAE-cellulose step.

Stabilization by Glycerol

The use of glycerol throughout the purification procedure was tried after the finding that certain purified aminoacyl RNA synthetases lost no activity when stored 1 year or longer at −15 C in 50% glycerol. Other enzymes have been purified in this fashion (16). When glycerol is not present during cell lysis, glycyl, prolyl, and threonyl RNA synthetases are nearly undetectable in the extract. Seryl RNA synthetase activity is increased at least 2½-fold in extracts containing 10% glycerol. Twelve other aminoacyl RNA synthetases examined are unaffected by the presence of glycerol. Contrary to reported data (17) we find that the presence of 5% glycerol in the reaction mixture has no effect on the extent of esterification of leucine and valine to tRNA.

Contamination by Ribonuclease and tRNA

An assay for ribonuclease is performed by preincubation of tRNA with excess enzyme in the reaction mixture containing all components except the amino acid. Upon addition of the labeled amino acid with or without additional ATP the tRNA is incubated for sufficient time to esterify all functional chains, any decrease of which is measured by the usual filter assay. By this criterion the extract contains a ribonuclease removed during the DEAE-cellulose procedure. During a 30-min prior incubation at 37 C in either reaction mixture 0.055 ml of DEAE-cellulose fraction does not detectably damage the leucine acceptor ability of one μmole of tRNA. When $MgCl_2$ is omitted from the buffers used in the DEAE-cellulose step, the ribonuclease is not removed by that procedure.

Only 10% of the absorbance units at 260 mμ present in the extract remains in the DEAE-cellulose fraction, which contains less than 0.07 μmole of RNA ribose/ml by the orcinol reaction (18).

REFERENCES

1. CLELAND, W. W. 1964. Biochem. 3: 480.
2. MUENCH, K., and P. BERG. In press.
3. HIRS, C. H. W., S. MOORE, and W. H. STEIN. 1954. J. Am. Chem. Soc. 76: 6063.
4. LOWRY, O., N. ROSEBROUGH, A. FARR, and R. RANDALL. 1951. J. Biol. Chem. 193: 265.
5. PETERSON, E. A., and H. A. SOBER. 1962. In S. P. Colowick and N. O. Kaplan, editors, Methods in enzymology. Academic Press: New York. Vol. V, p. 3.
6. LEVIN, O. 1962. In S. P. Colowick and N. O. Kaplan, editors, Methods in enzymology. Academic Press: New York. Vol. V, p. 27.
7. MAIN, R. K., M. J. WILKINS, and L. J. COLE. 1959. J. Am. Chem. Soc. 81: 6490.
8. BERGMANN, F. H., P. BERG, and M. DIECKMANN. 1961. J. Biol. Chem. 236: 1735.
9. NORTON, S. J. 1964. Arch. Biochem. Biophys. 106: 147.
10. FANGMAN, W. L., and F. C. NEIDHARDT. 1964. J. Biol. Chem. 239: 1839.
11. RAVEL, J., S. WANG, C. HEINEMEYER, and W. SHIVE. 1965. J. Biol. Chem. 240: 432.
12. LAZZARINI, R. A., and A. H. MEHLER. 1964. Biochem. 3: 1445.
13. NORRIS, A. T., and P. BERG. 1964. Proc. Nat. Acad. Sci. U.S. 52: 330.
14. SHORTMAN, K., and I. R. LEHMAN. 1964. J. Biol. Chem. 239: 2964.
15. BERGMANN, F. H., and S. B. ZIMMERMAN. Unpublished data.
16. JARABAK, J., J. A. ADAMS, H. G. WILLIAMS-ASHMAN, and P. TALALAY. 1962. J. Biol. Chem. 237: 345.
17. SARIN, P. S., and P. C. ZAMECNIK. 1965. Biochem. Biophys. Res. Comm. 19: 198.
18. ASHWELL, G. 1957. In S. P. Colowick and N. O. Kaplan, editors, Methods in enzymology. Academic Press: New York. Vol. III, p. 73.

Tyrosyl tRNA Synthetase

from *Escherichia coli* B

R. CALENDAR AND PAUL BERG
DEPARTMENT OF BIOCHEMISTRY
STANFORD UNIVERSITY SCHOOL OF MEDICINE
STANFORD, CALIFORNIA

ASSAY

i. $ATP + \text{L-tyrosine} + Enzyme \rightarrow Enzyme \ldots (\text{L-tyrosyl-AMP}) + PP_i$

$PP^{32} + Enzyme \ldots (\text{L-tyrosyl-AMP}) \rightleftharpoons ATP^{32} + \text{L-tyrosine} + Enzyme$

ii. $ATP + \text{L-tyrosine } (H^3) + tRNA \rightleftharpoons \text{L-tyrosyl } (H^3)\text{-tRNA} + AMP + PP_i$

Reagents

ASSAY I

a. The 1-ml reaction mixture contains

100 mM sodium cacodylate buffer, pH 7.0
5 mM magnesium chloride ($MgCl_2$)
2 mM adenosine triphosphate (ATP)
2 mM sodium pyrophosphate ($10^4 - 10^5$ cpm/μmole)†
10 mM 2-mercaptoethanol
10 mM potassium fluoride (KF)‡

† Pyrophosphate labeled with P^{32} was prepared according to Bergmann *et al.* (6).
‡ KF was added to inhibit pyrophosphatase and was used in the assay of Fractions I–III.

0.1 mg/ml of bovine plasma albumin

2 mM L-tyrosine

b. 0.4 M sodium pyrophosphate in 15% perchloric acid, 5 C

c. A suspension of acid-washed Norite A (150 mg/ml)

d. Enzyme diluent:

50 mM potassium phosphate, pH 6.5

10 mM 2-mercaptoethanol

0.1 mg/ml of bovine plasma albumin

e. Enzyme 0.01–0.1 unit

ASSAY II

a. The 0.4-ml reaction mixture contains

100 mM sodium cacodylate buffer, pH 7.0

5 mM $MgCl_2$

2 mM ATP

10 mM 2-mercaptoethanol

0.1 mg/ml of bovine plasma albumin

0.25 mM L-tyrosine (H^3) (5×10^6 cpm/μmole)

tRNA (1,2) about 40 OD $_{260}$† (an amount capable of accepting 1 mμmole L-tyrosine)

b. 2 M HCl, 5 C

c. Enzyme 0.0005–0.015 unit

Procedures

ASSAY I. This assay measures the incorporation of PP^{32} into ATP according to reaction i and is used to follow enzymatic activity during the purification procedure. Enzyme (0.01 to 0.1 unit) in diluent (d) is added to assay mixture (a) and incubated for 15 min at 37 C. The reaction is stopped by the addition of 0.7 ml of reagent (b) and ATP is adsorbed to charcoil by the addition of 0.1 ml of reagent (c). The charcoal suspensions are filtered through Whatman GF/C glass filters and the filters washed 5 times with 5-ml portions of cold distilled water. The filters are dried under a heat lamp and counted in an end-window counter. The values are corrected for a blank run without tryosine; no self-absorption correction was made. One unit of enzyme activity is defined as that amount incorporating 1 μmole of PP_i^{32} into ATP in 15 min, under the conditions described, and specific activity is defined

† Concentrations of tRNA have been expressed in two ways. The amount of specific tyrosine acceptor chains ($tRNA_{tyr}$) is given in molar quantities based on the amount of tyrosine, which can be esterified to tRNA with excess enzyme, ATP, and amino acid. Concentration of bulk tRNA has been expressed as $OD_{260m\mu}$ as measured at pH 12.

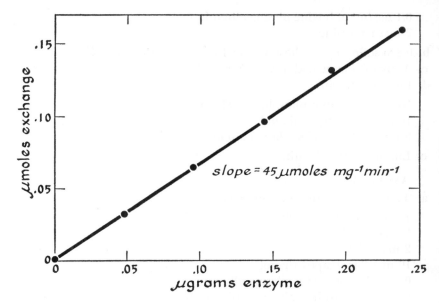

Fig. 1. Linearity with respect to enzyme using assay i. The conditions are given in the text. Fraction VII was the source of enzyme.

as enzyme units per milligram protein measured according to Lowry *et al.* (3). If less than 0.2 unit of enzyme is used in an assay, the exchange of PP^{32} with ATP is proportional to enzyme added (Fig. 1) and time for 20 min (Fig. 2).

ASSAY II.   This assay, measuring tyrosyl RNA formation by the conversion of L-tyrosine (H^3) to a form insoluble in cold acid, is used to measure the kinetics of reaction ii with purified enzyme (Fraction VII). After 10 min of incubation at 37 C, the reaction is stopped by the addition of 3 ml of cold 2 M HCl and the reaction mixture is filtered through a Whatman GF/C glass filter pad. The filter is washed 5 times with 3-ml portions of cold 2 M HCl, and with 3 ml of cold 95% ethanol; the filters are then dried under a heat lamp and counted in a Packard Tri-Carb Scintillation Counter using a toluene scintillation medium. A blank without enzyme is run with each set of samples, and its value is subtracted from that of each sample. With 2 mμmoles of $tRNA_{tyr}$† and less than 0.015 unit (0.02 μg) of purified enzyme (Fraction VII), tyrosyl RNA synthesis is proportional to the amount of en-

---

† tRNA purified by Dr. Karl Muench (2) was used to avoid adding a very large amount of the crude tRNA preparation. Aminoacyl sRNA formation was less than 10% of the total capacity measured for the tRNA added, and thus the rate of the back reaction could be neglected.

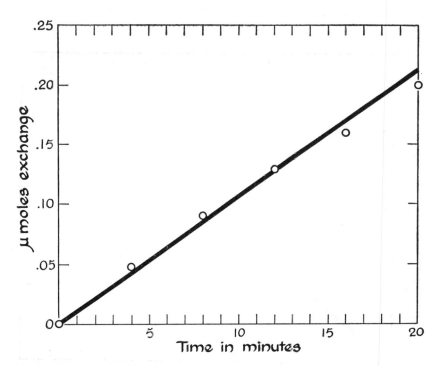

Fig. 2. Linearity with respect to time using assay i. The conditions are given in the text. 0.19 μg of Fraction VII enzyme was used.

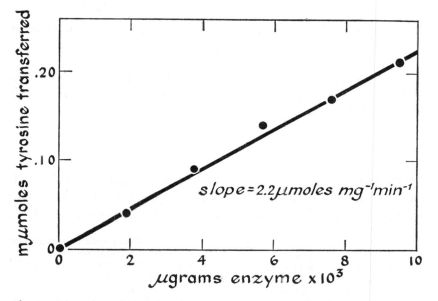

Fig. 3. Linearity with respect to enzyme using assay ii. The conditions are given in the text. Fraction VII was the source of enzyme.

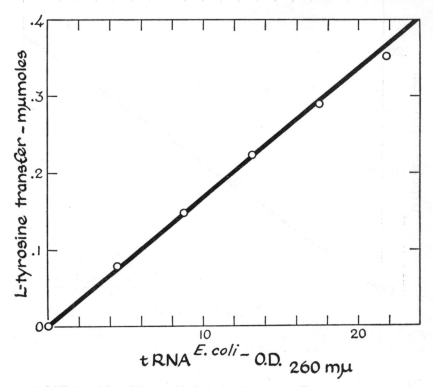

Fig. 4. Linearity with respect to tRNA using modified assay ii. 33 μg of Fraction VI enzyme was used. tRNA was limiting.

zyme added (Fig. 3). With limiting quantities of tRNA$_{tyr}$ (0.1–0.4 mμ-mole) and excess enzyme (3 units), the extent of tyrosyl RNA synthesis is proportional to tRNA (Fig. 4).

PREPARATION OF CELLS

Escherichia coli B/T1† was grown at 37 C in continuous culture (4) with forced aeration in a 120-liter biogen apparatus (American Sterilizer Corporation) in M56 medium as described by Cohn (5) with 1%

† From wild-type *E. coli* B, obtained from Dr. A. D. Kaiser, a spontaneous mutant was selected by plating on an excess of T1 phage. The colonial morphology and microscopic appearance of the mutant was indistinguishable from that of the wild type, and the mutant was sensitive to T7 bacteriophage. This T1-resistant strain is used for growing large cultures in our laboratory in order to avoid lysis by T1 phage infection. The purification given can be used on *E. coli* B cells, and the enzyme from *E. coli* B is immunologically indistinguishable from the enzyme of the T1-resistant strain.

glucose as carbon source. Cells were removed from the biogen, quick-cooled to 5 C by passage through a cooling coil immersed in a −15 C ethylene glycol bath, centrifuged in a Spinco model 170 continuous-flow centrifuge at 29,000 × g, and frozen in thin sheets at −20 C. Cells stored in a closed container at −20 C were satisfactory for at least 6 months.

ENZYME PURIFICATION PROCEDURE

All operations were carried out at 5 C and all centrifugations were carried out at 5 C in the GSA head of a Sorvall centrifuge at 8000 rev/min.

I. Preparation of Extract

Five hundred grams of cells, 500 ml of 25 mM K_2HPO_4, and 1 kg of glass beads† were blended for 10 min at low speed in a stainless steel Waring Blendor maintained at 5 C by circulating −15 C ethylene glycol through a cooling jacket. After 10 min, 1 liter of 25 mM K_2HPO_4 was added, and blending was continued for 3 min. The supernatant fluid was decanted and the beads were washed twice with 500-ml portions of 25 mM K_2HPO_4. The blendorate and the two washes were pooled and centrifuged for 40 min.

II. Autolysis

The volume of the blendorate was adjusted to 4.75 liters (about 10 mg of protein/ml) and the phosphate concentration was adjusted to 100 mM by addition of 80 g of solid K_2HPO_4. The extract was then incubated at 37 C for 2 hr. During this incubation the acid-soluble OD_{260} rose from 15 to 70% of the total OD_{260} with little loss of enzyme activity. The material was cooled to 5 C in an ethylene glycol bath and centrifuged; the precipitate was discarded.

III. Ammonium Sulfate Fractionation

Thirty-four g of solid ammonium sulfate was added for every 100 ml of autolysate supernatant fluid. After stirring for 5 min at 5 C, the suspension was centrifuged for 40 min at top speed in the Sorvall centrifuge. An additional 12.9 g of ammonium sulfate per original 100 ml of autolysate supernatant fluid was added to the centrifuged supernatant

† Superbrite glass beads, 200 μ average diameter, obtained from Minnesota Mining and Manufacturing Company, were washed before use with 1 N HCl and then with water.

liquid. After stirring for 5 min at 5 C, the suspension was centrifuged as above. The precipitate was dissolved in about 250 ml of 10 mM potassium succinate buffer, pH 6.0, containing 3 mM 2-mercaptoethanol, and the solution was dialyzed overnight against two successive 30-liter portions of the same buffer. A small amount of precipitate that appeared during dialysis was removed by centrifugation.

From this point all solutions contained 3 mM 2-mercaptoethanol.

IV. Alumina Cγ Gel Fractionation

Alumina Cγ gel [prepared according to Willstatter (7)]† was added to the dialyzed ammonium sulfate fraction (58 mg of dry weight gel/mg of portein). The suspension was centrifuged immediately and the gel was washed twice with 375-ml samples of 20 mM potassium phosphate buffer, pH 7.5, and then eluted twice with 375-ml portions of 110 mM potassium phosphate buffer, pH 7.5.

V. DEAE Fractionation

The gel eluate was diluted threefold with 3 mM 2-mercaptoethanol and adsorbed to a 2- × 20-cm DEAE-cellulose‡ column previously equilibrated with 50 mM potassium phosphate, pH 6.5. A constant gradient was run from 50 to 300 mM potassium phosphate, pH 6.5, the total volume of the eluant being 1 liter. Twenty-ml fractions were collected and the tubes containing enzyme purified twofold or greater were pooled.

VI. Hydroxylapatite Fractionation

A 1.5- × 25-cm column of hydroxylapatite (Clarkson Chemical Corporation, Williamsport, Pennsylvania) was poured and washed with 1 liter of 50mM potassium phosphate, pH 6.5. The pooled DEAE column fractions were diluted threefold with 3 mM 2-mercaptoethanol and adsorbed to the column. The column was washed with 200 ml of 90 mM potassium phosphate, pH 6.5, and a constant gradient from 90 to 250 mM in potassium phosphate, pH 6.5, was applied, the total volume of the eluant being 400 ml. A flow rate of about 1 ml/min was maintained by an applied pressure of 2 psi. Seven-ml fractions were collected and the tubes containing greater than twofold purified were pooled.

---

† Commercially obtained gels also give good fractionation, but the buffer concentrations used for washing and elution vary somewhat from those given here.

‡ With DEAE purchased from Brown Paper Company, Berlin, New Hampshire (0.9 meq/g) the enzyme was eluted at 120 mM phosphate, and with DEAE purchased from BioRad Laboratories, Richmond, California (0.8 meq/g) elution occurred at 180 mM.

VII. Second DEAE Fractionation

Fraction VI was diluted threefold with 3 mM 2-mercaptoethanol and passed over a 1- × 30-cm DEAE-cellulose column. A constant gradient from 50 to 300 mM in potassium phosphate, pH 8.0, was run with 250 ml in the reservoir and 250 ml in the mixer. Ten-ml fractions were collected and analyzed for protein and enzyme content. Analysis of a typical column is shown in Fig. 5. The enzyme peak (tubes 6–8) was

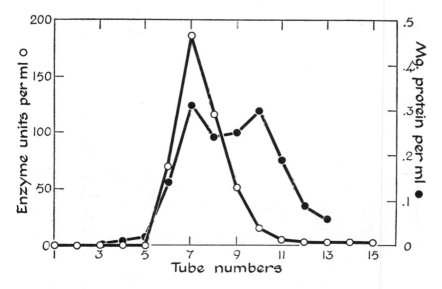

Fig. 5. Purification Step VII (DEAE column fractionation). The gradient was 50–250 mM in potassium phosphate, pH 8.0, and elution of the enzyme peak was at 120 mM.

pooled and dialyzed under pressure to a volume of 1 ml against 20 mM potassium phosphate, pH 6.5. When pressure dialysis was carried out against a buffer containing 3 mM 2-mercaptoethanol, the enzyme was stable at 0 C for several months. When mercaptoethanol was replaced with glutathione (3mM) by dialysis, the enzyme could be frozen indefinitely in a liquid nitrogen refrigerator. Upon thawing, addition of 2-mercaptoethanol was necessary to restore full activity.

VIII. Preparative Electrophoresis

Fraction VII from one preparation was subjected to preparative electrophoresis on acrylamide gel as described by Jovin *et al.* (12). The yield of enzyme units was 75%, and there was no significant rise in

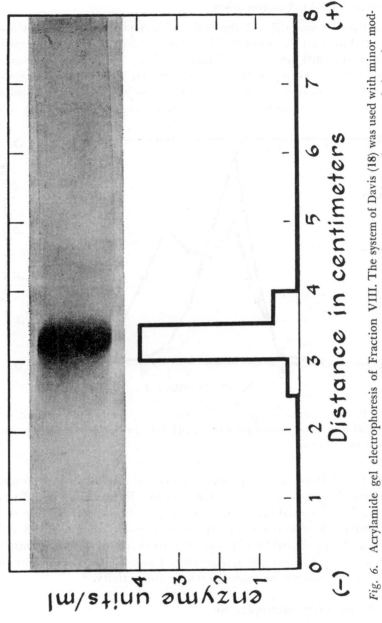

Fig. 6. Acrylamide gel electrophoresis of Fraction VIII. The system of Davis (18) was used with minor modifications. 20 µg (0.08 ml) of the electrophoretically purified enzyme were layered on top of the gel.

specific activity. However, several minor impurities visible on analytical electrophoresis were removed. Analytical acrylamide electrophoresis of Fraction VIII is illustrated in Fig. 6.

A resume of a typical preparation is shown in Table 1.

TABLE 1. *Purification of* E. coli L-*tyrosyl tRNA Synthetase*

Fraction	Vol- ume (ml)	Enzyme (units/ ml)	Protein (mg/ ml)	Specific Activity (units/mg)	Total Units	Yield (%)
I. Crude extract	2240	18	20	0.9	40,500	100
II. Autolysis	4525	8	8.8	0.9	36,000	90
III. 55–75% ammo- nium sulfate	350	41	18	2.3	14,300	39
IV. C$_\gamma$gel eluate	750	12	1.6	7.5	9,000	23
V. DEAE, pH 6.5	140	43	0.6	72	6,060	15
VI. Hydroxylapatite	135	23	0.15	153	3,120	8
VII. DEAE, pH 8.0	42	52	0.076	680	2,180	5

PROPERTIES OF THE ENZYME

Purity

The chromatogram of the second DEAE column indicates that Fraction VII might be contaminated with protein eluting subsequent to the enzyme. Nevertheless, no stimulation of ATP–pyrophosphate exchange was obtained with Fraction VII upon addition of any natural L-amino acid other than L-tyrosine. When subjected to starch gel electrophoresis at pH 8.0 in 0.02 M potassium phosphate buffer, this preparation gave one major protein band, accounting for approximately 75% of the protein, and this band contained the enzymatic activity. When Fraction VII was sedimented in a sucrose gradient according to the method of Martin and Ames (8), a single peak of protein was observed, which corresponded well with the enzyme activity (see Fig. 7).

Specificity

AMINO ACID. Numerous tyrosine analogs were tested for activity in the ATP–PP^{32} exchange reaction. Several gave varying levels of exchange and were examined further to determine whether the activity was due to the analog per se or to contaminating tyrosine. Each analog was chromatographed on Whatman 3-mm filter paper in

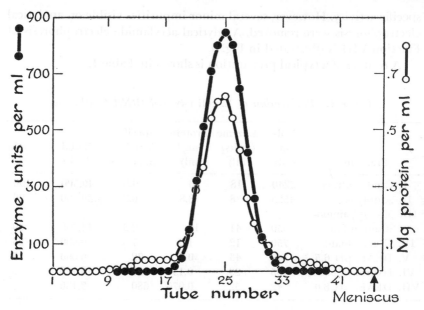

Fig. 7. Zone sedimentation of Fraction VII. 1 mg (0.13 ml) of this material was layered on top of 4.8 ml of a 5–20% sucrose gradient in 10 mM potassium phosphate buffer, pH 6.5, 100 mM KCl, 10 mM 2-mercaptoethanol. The gradient was centrifuged 16 hr at 3.90×10^4 rev/min at 2.5 C in a Spinco model L centrifuge. Two-drop fractions were collected. Protein and enzyme recovery were 66 and 87%, respectively.

one of several chromatographic systems. One μmole of the analog was spread on the origin, and two markers, tyrosine and analog, were spotted separately. After chromatography, the markers were sprayed with 0.4% ninhydrin in *n*-butanol to locate the L-tyrosine and analog. The location of the material active in assay i was determined using the eluates of successive 1-cm strips of the chromatogram. Of all the analogs tested, only 3-fluoro-L-tyrosine, DL-5-hydroxy-2-pyridine-alanine, 3,4-dihydroxyl-L-phenylalanine, and D-tyrosine gave significant activation of the exchange reaction (Table 2). For the others, any activity initially observed could be attributed to contamination with L-tyrosine. The activity measured with D-tyrosine as substrate was sensitive to D-amino acid oxidase,† but not to L-amino acid oxidase.‡ Under the same conditions, L-amino acid oxidase completely destroyed the activity of added L-tyrosine.

† Electrophoretically purified from hog kidney by Worthington Biochemical Corporation, Freehold, New Jersey.
‡ Crude *Crotalus adamanteus* venom.

TABLE 2.   *The Ability of Tyrosine and Tyrosine Analogs to
Support or Inhibit ATP–PP³² Exchange*

Amino Acid	Activator	Inhibitor
L-Tyrosine	$+^a$	$—^b$
D-Tyrosine	+	
2-Hydroxy-L-phenylalanine	−	−
3-Hydroxy-L-phenylalanine	−	−
3-Fluoro-L-tyrosine	+	
3-Chloro-L-tyrosine	−	
3-Iodo-L-tyrosine	−	
3-Amino-L-tyrosine	−	−
3-Nitro-L-tyrosine	−	
3,4-Dihydroxy-L-phenylalanine	+	
4-Amino-DL-phenylalanine	−	−
4-Fluoro-L-phenylalanine	−	−
4-Chloro-DL-phenylalanine	−	
L-Tyrosine-*O*-sulfate	−	−
α-Methyl-DL-tyrosine	−	−
N-Acetyl-L-tyrosine	−	−
N-Glycyl-L-tyrosine	−	−
β(*p*-hydroxyphenyl) propionate	−	−
β(*p*-hydroxyphenyl)-DL-lactate	−	−
β(*p*-hydroxyphenyl) pyruvate	−	−
L-Tyrosinol	−	+
L-Tyrosine amide	−	+
L-Tyrosine methyl ester	−	+
Tyramine	−	+
5-Hydroxy-2-pyridine-DL-alanine	+	

^{a} + denotes that the analog is activated or inhibits activation of tyrosine.
^{b} − indicates that the analog is not activated or does not inhibit activation of tyrosine.

Competitive inhibition of the exchange reaction was tested only for those analogs containing no tyrosine contaminant. Tyramine, L-tyrosinol, L-tyrosine ethyl ester, L-tyrosine methyl ester, and L-tyrosine amide inhibited the exchange reaction in a competitive manner (Table 2).

Even though a given amino acid is activated to an aminoacyl adenylate, it is not necessarily transferred to tRNA (6,9,10). Transfer of activated amino acid to tRNA with Fraction VII has been shown only for L-tyrosine (H^3) and for DL-3-fluorotyrosine (H^3). Further study on the other L-tyrosine analogs activated is in progress.

NUCLEOTIDE. ATP could not be replaced in the exchange reaction by ADP, AMP, dATP, GTP, CTP, or UTP. When used at 2×10^{-3} M, only dATP inhibited the exchange reaction caused by 4×10^{-4} M ATP. The nature of the inhibition by dATP has not been analyzed in detail.

Kinetics

The rate of transfer to tRNA was measured with $tRNA_{tyr}$ purified by Dr. Karl Muench†(2). The rate of transfer of tyrosine to tRNA was only 5% that of the ATP–PP^{32} exchange reaction (see Figs. 1 and 3). $tRNA_{tyr}$ (1 mμmole) did not significantly alter the rate of the exchange reaction (assay i).

The constants K_m, K_i, and V_{max} were obtained for several substrates and inhibitors according to Lineweaver and Burk (11) and are listed in Table 3.

Due to technical difficulties in running large assay mixtures, we have not been successful in measuring significant concentration dependence of reaction ii upon $tRNA_{tyr}$.

Values for Mg^{2+} are not included, since the concentration dependence for Mg^{2+} does not obey typical Michaelis–Menten kinetics. The maximum stimulation of reaction i was obtained with 5mM $MgCl_2$ at 2 mM ATP concentration.

pH Optimum

Fraction VII showed a broad pH optimum between 6 and 9 using the ATP–PP^{32}_i exchange assay.

Amino Acid Composition

Fraction VIII was used to determine amino acid composition. Hydrolyses were performed *in vacuo* in 6 N HCl at 110 C for 22 hr. Performic acid oxidation according to Moore (13) preceded one hydrolysis; in the others a crystal of phenol was added to protect tyrosine residues from air oxidation. Amino acid composition was determined on the Moore–Stein amino acid analyzer (14).

Mole fractions of the various amino acids are listed in Table 4. No value was determined for tryptophan. From these data and the known specific volumes of the amino acids, a partial specific volume of 0.730 cm^3/g was estimated for this enzyme.

TABLE 3. *Kinetic Constants for Substrates and Inhibitors in the Tyrosine-Dependent ATP–PP[32] Exchange Reaction and in Tyrosyl RNA Synthesis*

Substrate	K_m (M)	V_{max} $\left(\frac{\mu moles}{mg\,min}\right)$	K_I (M)
A. ATP–PP[32] Exchange Reaction:			
L-Tyrosine	6.1×10^{-6}	56	
D-Tyrosine	1.4×10^{-4}	11	
3-Fluoro-L-tyrosine	3.9×10^{-5}	29	
3-Fluoro-DL-tyrosine	1.3×10^{-4}	38	
3,4-Dihydroxy-DL-phenylalanine	1.4×10^{-3}	25[a]	
3,4-Dihydroxy-DL-phenylalanine	2.1×10^{-3}	20[a]	
5-Hydroxy-2-pyridine-DL-alanine	1.9×10^{-4}	21	
ATP	2.5×10^{-4}	70	
PP$_i$	3.2×10^{-5}	62	
L-Tyrosinol		56	4.1×10^{-6}
L-Tyrosine methyl ester		56	1.7×10^{-5}
L-Tyrosine amide		56	8.1×10^{-6}
Tyramine		56	6.0×10^{-6}
B. Tyrosyl RNA Formation:			
L-Tyrosine	2.7×10^{-5}	2.6	
3-Fluoro-DL-tyrosine	4.8×10^{-4}	2.2	
ATP	4.0×10^{-4}	2.3	
tRNA$_{tyr}$	$\leqq 2.0 \times 10^{-7}$	2.3	

[a] Extrapolated value, ignoring substrate inhibition.

Molecular Size

Sedimentation velocity experiments were carried out on Fraction VII in the Beckman-Spinco model E analytical ultracentrifuge using a black, anodized aluminum rotor and a 12-cm, 2.5 C Epon double sector cell at a speed of 50,740 rev/min. The buffer used was 20 mM potassium phosphate, pH 6.5, 100 mM KCl, 3 mM 2-mercaptoethanol and the column height was 3 mm. Varying the protein concentration from 10 to 2 mg/ml did not change the sedimentation coefficient, $s_{20,\,w}$, more than 2%. Temperatures from 5 to 23 C did not affect the extrapolated value of $s_{20,\,w}$. The average value obtained on many runs with many enzyme preparations was $s_{20,\,w} = 5.1$ Svedbergs.

TABLE 4. *Amino Acid Composition*

Amino Acid	Mole Fraction	Approximate Residues per Molecule of Enzyme
Aspartic acid	0.103	92
Threonine	0.046	41
Serine	0.043	39
Glutamic acid	0.126	113
Proline	0.042	38
Glycine	0.090	81
Alanine	0.088	79
Cysteic acid	0.016	14
Valine	0.058	52
Methionine	0.020	18
Isoleucine	0.058	52
Leucine	0.095	85
Tyrosine	0.030	27
Phenylalanine	0.047	42
Lysine	0.070	63
Histidine	0.015	13
Arginine	0.051	46
Tryptophan	—	—

Sedimentation equilibrium (15) analyses of two preparations were done in the above buffer (column height 1 mm) at initial protein concentrations of 3.7 and 5.0 mg/ml. The temperature was 6.2 C and the rotor speeds were 19,160 and 17,250 rev/min, respectively. M_z for the two preparations was determined as 95,000 and 98,000, respectively, based on a partial specific volume of 0.730 cm³/g.

The diffusion coefficient, $D_{20, w}$, was determined by boundary spreading in a synthetic boundary cell; its value was 4.7×10^{-7} cm²/sec on a low speed run (rotor speed = 8225 rev/min). The same buffer as above was used and the temperature was 25 C. A molecular weight of 97,000 was calculated from the Svedberg equation (16) using the values of S, D, and $\overline{v}$ determined above.

Immunology

The gamma globulin fraction isolated (17) from the sera of rabbits immunized with Fraction VII quantitatively neutralized the activity of

Fraction VII (assay i) after antibody and enzyme were reacted for 1 hr at 23 C and then overnight at 5 C. Centrifugation was not necessary for neutralization, and no release of enzyme activity occurred in the region of antibody excess.

This gamma globulin, which neutralized tyrosyl tRNA synthetase purified from *E. coli* B, did not neutralize isoleucyl tRNA synthetase purified from *E. coli* B (19), nor did it neutralize tyrosyl tRNA synthetase purified from *B. subtilis* (20).

The tyrosine-dependent ATP–PP^{32} exchange activity of crude extracts of *E. coli* B was totally neutralized by this immune gamma globulin. The amount of gamma globulin necessary to neutralize one unit of enzyme was approximately the same for the crude extract as for the purified material. Thus it appears that

1. Immunologically reacting but enzymatically inactive material in Fraction I cannot exceed that in Fraction VII.
2. The enzyme is not greatly inactivated or modified by the purification procedure.
3. There is no second, immunologically distinct, enzyme in crude extract that carries out reaction i.

REFERENCES

1. ZUBAY, G. 1962. J. Mol. Biol. *4:* 347.
2. MUENCH, K., and P. BERG, manuscript in preparation.
3. LOWRY, O., N. ROSEBOROUGH, A. FARR, and R. RANDALL. 1951. J. Biol. Chem. *193:* 265.
4. NOVICK, A. 1955. Ann. Rev. Microbiol. *9:* 97.
5. WIESMEYER, H., and M. COHN. 1960. Biochim. Biophys. Acta *39:* 417.
6. BERGMANN, F., P. BERG, and M. DIECKMANN. 1961. J. Biol. Chem. *236:* 1735.
7. WILLSTÄTTER, R., and H. KRAUT. 1923. Ber. Chem. Ges. *56:* 1117.
8. MARTIN, R., and B. AMES. 1961. J. Biol. Chem. *236:* 1372.
9. EZEKIEL, D. 1965. Biochim. Biophys. Acta *95:* 54.
10. STERN, R., and A. MEHLER. 1965. Fed. Proc. *24:* 217.
11. LINEWEAVER, H., and D. BURK. 1934. J. Am. Chem. Soc. *56:* 658.
12. JOVIN, T., A. CHRAMBACH, and M. NAUGHTON. 1964. Anal. Biochem. *9:* 351.
13. MOORE, S. 1963. J. Biol. Chem. *238:* 235.
14. SPACKMAN, D., W. STEIN, and S. MOORE. 1958. Anal. Chem. *30:* 1190.
15. VAN HOLDE, K., and R. L. BALDWIN. J. Phys. Chem. *62:* 734.
16. SVEDBERG, T., and K. PEDERSEN. 1940. The ultracentrifuge. Oxford University Press, New York.
17. SOBER, H. F., F. GUTTER, M. WYCKOFF, and E. A. PETERSON. 1956. J. Am. Chem. Soc. *78:* 756.
18. DAVIS, B. J. 1964. Ann. N. Y. Acad. Sci. *121:* 404.
19. BALDWIN, A. N., and P. BERG. 1965. This volume, page 400.
20. CALENDAR, R., and P. BERG, manuscript in preparation.

Isoleucyl RNA Synthetase

from *Escherichia coli*

ANNE NORRIS BALDWIN AND PAUL BERG
DEPARTMENT OF BIOCHEMISTRY
STANFORD UNIVERSITY SCHOOL OF MEDICINE
STANFORD, CALIFORNIA

ASSAY

$$\text{i. Ileu + ATP + Enzyme} \overset{Mg^{2+}}{\rightleftarrows} \text{Enzyme} \ldots \text{Ileu-AMP} + PP_i$$

$$\text{ii. Enzyme} \ldots \text{Ileu-AMP} + tRNA_{ileu} \rightleftarrows \text{Ileu tRNA} + AMP + \text{Enzyme}$$

$$\text{iii. Ileu + ATP} + tRNA_{ileu} \overset{Mg^{2+}}{\rightleftarrows} \text{Ileu tRNA} + PP_i + AMP$$

Reagents

1. The reaction mixture (total volume 1.0 ml) contains

    100 mM Tris-CHl, pH 8.0
    5 mM magnesium chloride ($MgCl_2$)
    10 mM potassium fluoride (KF)
    10 mM 2-mercaptoethanol
    2 mM ATP
    2 mM L-isoleucine
    2 mM sodium pyrophosphate (10^4–10^5 cpm/μmole)†

    † Pyrophosphate labeled with P^{32} was prepared according to Bergmann *et al.* (7).

2. Perchloric acid (14%) and a suspension of acid-washed Norit A (15% by weight)

Procedure

The aminoacyl tRNA synthetases may be assayed by (a) the amino acid-dependent ATP-PP$_i^{32}$ exchange reaction (1); (b) the rate of formation of aminoacyl-C^{14} tRNA (2); or (c) the formation of aminoacyl-C^{14} hydroxamate where hydroxylamine replaced tRNA as acceptor (3).

For the preparation described here, we have used assay (a) to follow the purification. The reaction mixtures are incubated in 2-ml glass centrifuge tubes that fit the International Centrifuge rotor no. 859. After 15 min at 37 C, the reaction is stopped by the addition of 0.25 ml of 14% perchloric acid and 0.25 ml of 15% acid-washed Norit. The tubes are shaken briefly, chilled at 0 C for 5 min, and then centrifuged for 2 min at 2000 × g. The Norit is washed three times with 3-ml portions of cold water and collected each time by centrifugation. Finally, the Norit is suspended in 2.0 ml of a solution containing 8 ml of ammonia in 400 ml of 50% ethanol. The suspension is mixed well and a 0.5-ml portion is dried in a planchet and counted in a Nuclear Chicago end-window counter. The assay is linear with enzyme in the range 0–0.4 unit, where one unit of activity is defined as the incorporation of 1 μmole of PP$_i^{32}$ into ATP in 15 min at 37 C.

ISOLATION PROCEDURE

I. Cells

Escherichia coli B was purchased from Grain Processing Company, Muscatine, Iowa. These commercially grown cells gave extracts of approximately the same total activity (45,000 units/lb of cells) and specific activity (2.0 units/mg of protein) as cells grown in the laboratory on glucose–salts medium (4). The commercially grown cells were therefore used for all studies on this enzyme.

II. Crude Extract

A block of frozen cells (1 lb) is broken into small pieces and softened at 4 C in 300 ml of 0.01 M potassium phosphate buffer, pH 7.0, containing 0.01 M 2-mercaptoethanol. The suspension is homogenized by blending at low speed for a few seconds in a 4-liter Waring Blendor jacketed and cooled with antifreeze. After addition of 1370 g of acid-washed glass beads ("Superbrite," 200 μ average diameter, obtained from Minnesota Mining and Manufacturing Company), the blending is continued at 90 v, interrupting the process whenever the temperature exceeds 10 C. After a total of 25 min of blending, the extract is diluted with 800 ml of the same buffer, and blended briefly at low speed. The beads are allowed to settle and the supernatant liquid is decanted. The debris and the beads are mixed with 250 ml of buffer, and after the beads settle the supernatant fluid is decanted. The beads are washed once more and the combined supernatant liquids are centrifuged (Servall, GSA rotor) for 30 min at 12,000 × g to remove cell debris. The resulting extract (1500 ml) contains about 15 mg of protein per ml and has a specific activity of 2.0 for the isoleucyl RNA synthetase.

III. Autolysis

The crude extract is incubated at 37 C in order to degrade nucleic acids. The high concentration of phosphate buffer in the extract dissociates ribosomes, thereby promoting the autodigestion of the bulk of the nucleic acid in the extract. The autolysis is followed by removing 1-ml portions and determining the extend of increase in the 260 mμ absorbance of the cold acid-soluble (3.5% perchloric acid) fraction. When 90% of the 260 mμ absorbance is acid soluble, the autolysate is chilled to 0 C and the heavy precipitate is removed by centrifugation for 10 min at 12,000 × g. The time required for complete autolysis varies widely from one batch of cells to another. Two–six hours is a normal incubation period, and does not result in appreciable loss of enzyme activity (90–100% recovery). The specific activity of the isoleucyl tRNA synthetase after the autolysis is 4.0–6.0, depending on the amount of protein precipitated during the autolysis period.

IV. Ammonium Sulfate Fractionation

Additional mercaptoethanol (final concentration 0.01 M) and EDTA 0.001 M) are added to the autolysate (1320 ml). Then 368 g of solid ammonium sulfate are added and, after vigorous stirring for 10 min at 4 C, the mixture is centrifuged for 20 min at 12,000 × g (Servall, GSA rotor). The precipitate is discarded and 203 g of solid ammonium sulfate are added to the supernatant fluid. After stirring for 10 min, the precipitate is collected by centrifugation (20 min, 12,000 × g) and the supernatant liquid is discarded. The precipitate is immediately dissolved in 75 ml of 0.02 M sodium succinate buffer, pH 6.0, containing 0.01 M 2-mercaptoethanol, and dialyzed overnight against 6 liters of the same buffer. The small amount of precipitate after dialysis against succinate at pH 6.0 is removed by centrifugation for 10 min at 10,000 × g. Total protein at this stage is about 3–4 g, with a specific activity of 9–12.

The entire procedures from the first addition of ammonium sulfate until the beginning of the dialysis is completed in 90 min, since the enzyme was found to be unstable in the presence of ammonium sulfate.

The dialysis against succinate at pH 6.0 is necessary in order to adsorb the enzyme onto alumina C_γ gel at the next fractionation step. The enzyme is stable for 24 hr at 4 C in this buffer, but should not be stored for long periods of time at this pH. The enzyme may be stored at 0 C at this stage if instead it is dialyzed against 0.02 M potassium phosphate buffer, pH 7.5, containing 0.01 M 2-mercaptoethanol. In this buffer, 60% of the activity is recovered after 6 months at 0 C.

V. Adsorption and Elution from Alumina C_γ Gel

A suspension of alumina C_γ gel (15–20 mg dry weight/ml) is added to the protein solution (3–4 g in 400 ml) to give a gel/protein ratio of 0.75. The suspension is stirred for 10 min and then centrifuged at low speed (4000 × g, Serval GSA rotor) for 5 min. The gel is then washed successively with 200 ml of each of the phosphate buffers, shown in Table 1. In each case, the gel is suspended evenly and stirred vigorously for 10 min at 4 C, then collected by centrifugation.

TABLE I.   *Alumina C_γ Gel Fractionation*

Buffer	pH	[PO$_4$] (M)	Protein (mg)	Total Units	Specific Activity
I	6.5	0.05	900	1650	1.8
II	7.0	0.05	700	4000	5.7
III	7.5	0.02	100	1630	16.0
IV	7.5	0.10	224	4380	19.6
V	7.5	0.20	350	7115	20.3
VI	7.5	0.50	226	4560	20.2

After being assayed for enzyme activity and protein, Fractions IV, V, and sometimes VI are pooled and dialyzed overnight against 6 liters of 0.02 M potassium phosphate buffer, pH 7.5, containing 0.01 M 2-mercaptoethanol. The recovery of enzyme activity in this step is 50–60%, the rest of the activity being discarded with the earlier gel fractions. The specific activity of the pooled fractions is 20 and total protein 1 g.

VI. DEAE-Cellulose Chromatography

DEAE-cellulose (500 g), obtained from Brown Company, Keene, New Hampshire, is washed on a suction funnel with 2 liters of 0.5 M HCl, then 2 liters of 0.5 M NaOH, several liters of distilled water, and finally with 0.5 M potassium phosphate until the pH of the supernatant solution is 7.5. The DEAE is stored at 4 C in 0.5 M potassium phosphate buffer, pH 7.5, until use. The column is packed to a volume of 375 ml (3.5 cm × 45 cm) under slight pressure, and then washed with 2 liters of 0.02 M potassium phosphate buffer, pH 7.5, containing 0.01 M 2-mercaptoethanol.

The protein (1 g in 600 ml) is adsorbed to the column, which is then washed with 1 liter of the same buffer. The protein is eluted with a linear gradient of phosphate buffer. The mixing chamber contains 2 liters of 0.02 M potassium phosphate, pH 7.5, and the reservoir contains 2 liters of 0.10 M potassium phosphate, pH 7.5, both buffers containing 0.01 M 2-mercaptoethanol. The column is run at a flow rate of 120 ml/hr. Forty-ml fractions are collected and every fourth fraction is assayed for enzyme activity. The elution of protein may be followed conveniently by the 280 mμ absorbance.

Fractions containing enzyme activity are pooled and concentrated by dialysis against polyethylene glycol (Carbowax 6000, Union Carbide), 30% by weight in 0.02 M potassium phosphate, pH 7.5, plus 0.01 M 2-mercaptoethanol. When the dialysis sack is nearly flat, it is rinsed well on the outside with water, then opened and the inside rinsed three times with small portions of buffer. Total protein at this stage is 200 mg, and the specific activity of the enzyme is about 100.

VII. Hydroxylapatite Chromatography

Hydroxylapatite (Hypatite C, Clarkson Chemical Company) is packed to a volume of 90 ml in a column 2.4 cm × 20 cm. The enzyme is adsorbed to the column in 0.02 M potassium phosphate buffer, pH 7.5, plus 0.01 M 2-mercaptoethanol, and the column is then washed with 100 ml of 0.05 M potassium phosphate, pH 7.5, 0.01 M 2-mercaptoethanol. A linear gradient produced with 400 ml of 0.05 M potassium phosphate, pH 7.5, to 400 ml of 0.30 M potassium phosphate, pH 7.5 (both containing 0.01 M 2-mercaptoethanol), is employed. The elution of protein and of ultraviolet-absorbing impurities from the Carbowax is followed by the absorbance at 280 mμ. Fifteen-ml fractions are collected at a flow rate of 10–20 ml/hr. The isoleucyl RNA synthetase is eluted between 0.20 and 0.25 M phosphate and is the last protein peak to be eluted.

The pooled enzyme fractions are concentrated by vacuum dialysis against 0.02 M potassium phosphate, pH 7.5, containing 0.01 M 2-mercaptoethanol until the last buffer change, when mercaptoethanol is replaced by 0.001 M glutathione.

A piece of thick-walled dialysis tubing (0.5 cm × 20 cm) is knotted twice at one end. The open end is slipped through a hole in a rubber stopper. The tubing is held against the stopper by a small funnel, the tip of which is inserted into the mouth of the dialysis tubing and then pressed into the hole in the stopper. The stopper is fitted into the mouth of a vacuum flask, filled with the desired buffer, and connected to a water aspirator. Each dialysis sack is tested under vacuum before enzyme is introduced. The enzyme is then added through the funnel. Addition is repeated periodically as the volume within the sack decreases.

The concentrated enzyme (20 mg in 2 ml) is stored frozen, and is stable indefinitely.

VIII. General Remarks About the Purification Procedure

The purification procedure, starting with 1 lb wet weight of cells, is summarized in Table 2. The over-all yield of enzyme has been about 20% and the purification achieved is approximately 325-fold.

TABLE 2.   *Purification of Isoleucyl-RNA Synthetase from* E. coli

Fraction	Total Protein (mg)	Total Units	Yield (%)	Specific Activity (units/mg of protein)
I. Crude extract	21,400	47,200		2.2
II. Autolysate	7,200	46,800	99	6.5
III. Ammonium sulfate	3,290	40,000	85	12.1
IV. Alumina C_γ gel	1,120	22,400	47	20
V. DEAE	246	20,100	42	92
VI. Hydroxylapatite	19	12,400	26	650

The procedure has been described on a scale (1 lb of cells), which may be carried out easily with standard apparatus in a 7–8 day period. However, the procedure has also been carried out on approximately 35 times this scale by using pilot-plant facilities. The yield and specific activity of the final enzyme preparation from such a large preparation was approximately the same as that described here. The large-scale preparation was rechromatographed on hydroxylapatite. The elution pattern obtained is shown in Fig. 1. Acrylamide gel electrophoresis pat-

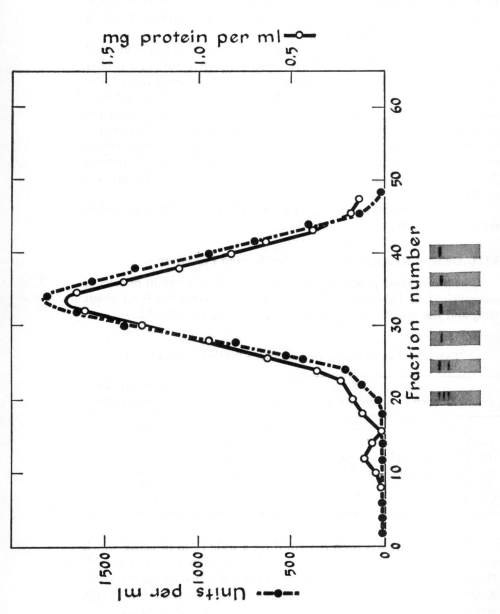

Fig. 1. Chromatography of purified isoleucyl-RNA synthetase on hydroxylapatite. Acrylamide gel electro-phoresis patterns are shown below the corresponding fractions from the column.

terns of various fractions across the enzyme peak are shown below the elution pattern. Fractions containing no detectable impurity by acrylamide gel electrophoresis were pooled and used in the physical characterization of this enzyme.

PROPERTIES OF PURIFIED ENZYME

Physical Properties

The purified enzyme appears homogeneous by acrylamide gel electrophoresis. It shows a single boundary by velocity sedimentation, with an $s_{20,w}$ of 5.8 S. The z average molecular weight determined by equilibrium sedimentation (5) was $112,000 \pm 5\%$.

The sedimentation coefficient of the enzyme activity and protein in a sucrose gradient was 5.4 S compared to galactokinase (6).

Specificity and Mechanism

The isoleucyl RNA synthetase from *E. coli* activates only isoleucine if one defines activation by the formation of aminoacyl-C^{14}-tRNA. However, Bergmann *et al.* (7) observed that the partially purified enzyme would carry out the ATP-PP$_i^{32}$ exchange reaction in the presence of either isoleucine or valine.

The homogeneous preparation described here retains its ability to activate valine to the level of the aminoacyl adenylate. By using this purified enzyme, it has been shown that the enzymatically synthesized isoleucyl adenylate or valyl adenylate forms a complex with the enzyme sufficiently stable to be isolated by Sephadex gel filtration (8). Isoleucine-C^{14} and ATP-H^3 react to give enzyme . . . ileu-C^{14}-AMP-H^3 with an enzyme:C^{14}:H^3 ratio of 1:0.95:0.94. When isoleucine is replaced by valine-C^{14}, the ratio observed was 1:0.64:0.65 (8).

Even at substrate levels of enzyme, no transfer of valine-C^{14} to tRNA is observed. Whereas the isolated enzyme . . . ileu-AMP complex transacylates the isoleucine to isoleucine-specific tRNA, no transfer of valine-C^{14} from enzyme$_{ileu}$ . . . val-AMP can be demonstrated.

The lack of val-C^{14}-RNA$_{ileu}$ formation is not due, however, to a lack of binding of isoleucine-specific tRNA chains to the enzyme$_{ileu}$ . . . val-AMP complex. When tRNA is added to this complex, a hydrolysis of the valyl adenylate is observed with subsequent breakdown of the complex. The hydrolytic activity is completely dependent on the presence of intact, isoleucine-specific tRNA. Any modification of the RNA molecule that destroys its ability to accept isoleucine also destroys its capacity to induce the hydrolysis of enzyme$_{ileu}$ . . . val-AMP. It has not been established whether valine is actually transferred to the tRNA$_{ileu}$ and then rapidly hydrolyzed, or whether some transition state necessary for the formation of aminoacyl-tRNA decomposes in a different manner if isoleucine is replaced by valine.

REFERENCES

1. BERG, P. 1956. J. Biol. Chem. *222:* 1025.
2. MUENCH, K., and P. BERG. This volume, page 375.
3. LOFTFIELD, R. B., and E. A. EIGNER. 1963. Biochim. Biophys. Acta. *72:* 372.
4. WIESMEYER, H., and M. COHN. 1960. Biochim. Biophys. Acta. *39:* 417.
5. VAN HOLDE, K., and R. L. BALDWIN. 1958. J. Phys. Chem. *62:* 734.
6. WILSON, D. B., and D. S. HOGNESS. 1964. J. Biol. Chem. *239:* 2469.
7. BERGMANN, F. H., P. BERG, and M. DIECKMANN. 1961. J. Biol. Chem. *236:* 1735.
8. NORRIS, A. T., and P. BERG. 1964. Proc. Nat. Acad. Sci., U.S. *52:* 330.

Glutamyl- and Glutaminyl-sRNA† Synthetases from *Escherichia coli* (1)

ROBERT A. LAZZARINI

NATIONAL INSTITUTES OF HEALTH

BETHESDA, MARYLAND

ALAN H. MEHLER

MARQUETTE UNIVERSITY SCHOOL OF MEDICINE

MILWAUKEE, WISCONSIN

ASSAY

C^{14}-Amino acid + ATP + sRNA $\longrightarrow$
$$C^{14}\text{-Amino acyl-sRNA} + AMP + PP$$

Reagents

The reaction mixture contains in 0.2 ml

1. 25 μmoles of potassium cacodylate, pH 7.0
   0.2 μmole of ATP
   1.0 μmole of $MgCl_2$
   0.25 μmole of mercaptoethanol
   0.5 mg of sRNA
   0.01 μmole of C^{14}-amino acid (about 10^5 cpm)
   Enzyme

† sRNA is equivalent to tRNA.

409

2. 10% trichloracetic acid
   5% trichloracetic acid
   1.5 N NH_4OH
   Scintillator solution (2)

Procedure

This assay measures the conversion of radioactive amino acid to a form precipitated by acid.

The reaction is started by the addition of enzyme and the mixture is incubated at 37 C for 10 min. The reaction is stopped by the addition of 1 ml of 10% trichloracetic acid and the resulting suspension is chilled in an ice bath for 10 min. The precipitate is collected on a Millipore filter and is washed with 50 ml of 5% trichloracetic acid. The filter disk is transferred to a counting vial, neutralized with 1 ml of 1.5 N NH_4OH, and dissolved in 10 ml of scintillator fluid. The radioactivity is determined in a scintillation counter. Blank reactions without enzyme are run and the values obtained are subtracted from those obtained with the complete system. One unit of synthetase activity is the amount of enzyme that esterifies 1 millimicromole of amino acid with RNA in 10 min under these conditions. Specific activity is defined as units per mg of protein. Under the conditions described, the reaction is proportional to enzyme concentration and to time of incubation until most of the glutamic acid or glutamine has been esterified.

ISOLATION PROCEDURE

E. coli

E. coli strain (BM) is grown aerobically until late log phase in a medium containing 1.1% K_2HPO_4, 0.85% KH_2PO_4, 0.6% Difco yeast extract, and 1% glucose. The cells are harvested by centrifugation at a low temperature, washed once with cold ½% NaCl, and frozen until used.

Crude Extract

A crude extract of *E. coli* B is prepared by blending, at ⅔ line voltage in a Waring Blendor, 50 g of frozen *E. coli* cells, 100 ml of 0.025 M Tris, pH 8.0, and 150 g of Superbrite glass beads. The mixture is blended until the temperature rises to 8 C. It is then cooled in an acetone-water-Dry Ice slurry until ice forms in the extract. The blending-cooling cycle is repeated until the extract has been blended for a total of 15 min. Seventy-five ml of 0.025 M Tris, pH 8.0, is then added and the diluted suspension is blended for an additional 2 min. The sediment is allowed to settle and the supernatant fluid is decanted. The sediment is further extracted with 150-ml portions of Tris buffer and the combined extracts are clarified by centrifugation for 90 min at $11,000 \times g$.

Protamine Precipitation

A warm (40 C) protamine sulfate solution (10 mg/ml) is added slowly to the rapidly stirred crude extracts until 10 mg of protamine has been added for every 100 mg of bacterial protein. The precipitate is allowed to coagulate for 15 min at ice-bath temperature and is then removed by centrifugation.

First DEAE Chromatography

The slightly turbid supernatant fluid is adjusted to pH 7.0 with 1 M KH_2PO_4 and applied to a DEAE-cellulose column (3 cm $\times$ 30 cm) previously equilibrated with 0.02 M potassium phosphate, pH 7.0, containing 3×10^{-3} M mercaptoethanol. The column is washed with 0.02 M potassium phosphate, pH 7.0, containing 10^{-3} M mercaptoethanol, until the E_{280} of the effluent falls below 0.1. The activities are then eluted with a linear gradient formed between 750 ml of 0.02 M potassium phosphate, pH 7.0, and 750 ml of 0.33 M potassium phosphate, pH 7.0, both containing 3×10^{-3} M mercaptoethanol. Fractions 29 through 41, inclusive, are combined and saved as glutaminyl-RNA synthetase.

Hydroxylapatite Chromatography

Fractions 62–74, inclusive, are combined, desalted by passage through a column of Sephadex G-25 equilibrated with 0.01 M potassium phosphate (pH 6.7), and adsorbed on a hydroxylapatite column (70-ml vol). The column is eluted sequentially with 150-ml portions of 0.02 M, 0.05 M, and 0.08 M potassium phosphate, pH 6.7. The glutamyl-RNA synthetase is then eluted with 300 ml of 0.1 M and 150 ml of 0.15 M potassium phosphate, pH 6.7.

Second DEAE Chromatography

After dialysis against 10 liters of 0.005 M potassium phosphate, pH 7.0, the combined eluates are concentrated and further purified by adsorption on a small DEAE-cellulose column (1 cm $\times$ 5 cm). The column is first developed with 50-ml portions of 0.02 M, 0.07 M, and

0.1 M phosphate, pH 7.0. The activity is then eluted with 50 ml of 0.13 M and 25 ml of 0.17 M phosphate, pH 7.0.

A summary of the purification is given in Table 1. The glutaminyl-sRNA synthetase activity of the crude extract has a specific activity of 3.2 and the partially purified enzyme (fractions 29–41 of the first DEAE chromatography) has a specific activity of 36.1 u/mg and contains less than 0.03 u/mg of glutamyl-sRNA synthetase.

TABLE 1. *Summary of Purification of Glutamyl-RNA Synthetase*

Fraction	Volume (ml)	Activity (units)	Protein (mg)	Specific Activity (units/mg)	Recovery (%)
Crude extract	230	83,000	9,300	8.9	
Protamine supernatant	285	74,000	2,480	29.9	89
Combined DEAE fractions	175	45,400	193	235	54
Hydroxylapatite eluate	470	30,200	52	586	37
2nd DEAE eluate	75	26,200	16	1640	32

PROPERTIES OF THE ENZYME

Specificity

Glutamyl- and glutaminyl-sRNA synthetases are specific for their respective amino acids; that is, neither activates the amino acid activated by the other. The sRNA species that accept the two amino acids are also specific; charging with glutamate does not interfere with subsequent esterification of glutamine and vice versa. The amino acids esterified to sRNA by the two enzymes can be identified as glutamic acid and glutamine, respectively.

Exchange Reactions

Neither enzyme catalyzes an ATP-pyrophosphate exchange under the conditions ordinarily used for such reactions. The glutamate enzyme catalyzes this exchange at measurable rates in the presence of very high concentrations of glutamate (K_m 0.4 M). Both enzymes catalyze the pyrophosphate exchange in the presence of sRNA and the appropriate amino acid (3). The rates of the exchange reactions are similar to the rates of the corresponding overall reactions,† and it is not yet known whether the enzymes catalyze simple exchange reactions in the presence of sRNA or whether the exchange of pyrophosphate is a measure of reversal of the esterification reaction.

Kinetic Properties

The activity of glutamyl-sRNA synthetase maximal is between pH values of 6.7 to 7.2. The K_m values for the two enzymes are given in Table 2. AMP is an effective inhibitor of the glutamate enzyme; other related nucleotides have no effect.

TABLE 2. K_m Values of Glutamyl- and Glutaminyl-sRNA
Synthetase (3)

| | K_m values | |
| | Glutamyl-RNA | Glutaminyl-RNA |
Substrate	Synthetase	Synthetase
L-Glutamate	1.2×10^{-4} M	
L-Glutamine		1.8×10^{-4} M
ATP	4.2×10^{-4} M	4.4×10^{-4} M
Mg^{2+}	1.2×10^{-2} M	3.3×10^{-3} M
sRNA	0.6 mg/ml	1.0 mg/ml

Other Properties

The glutamine enzyme is inactivated at an appreciable rate at 45 C, whereas the glutamate enzyme is relatively stable at 55 C; both are inactivated rapidly at 65 C. The molecular weight of the glutamate enzyme estimated from the sucrose gradient sedimentation method of Martin and Ames (4) is about 50,000.

REFERENCES

1. LAZZARINI, R. A., and A. H. MEHLER. 1964. Biochemistry. 3: 1445.
2. BRAY, G. 1960. Anal. Biochem. 1: 279.
3. RAVEL, J. M., S.-F. WANG, C. HEINEMEYER, and W. SHIVE. 1965. J. Biol. Chem. 240: 432.
4. MARTIN, R. G., and B. M. AMES. 1961. J. Biol. Chem. 236: 1372.

† R. A. Lazzarini and A. H. Mehler, unpublished experiments. The purest glutamyl-sRNA synthetase preparations contain an active inorganic pyrophosphatase that interferes with measurements of the pyrophosphate exchange reaction, even in the presence of sRNA.

Lysine-sRNA† Synthetase from

Escherichia coli (**1**)

ALAN H. MEHLER
MARQUETTE UNIVERSITY SCHOOL OF MEDICINE
MILWAUKEE, WISCONSIN

ROBERT STERN
WEIZMANN INSTITUTE OF SCIENCE
REHOVOTH, ISRAEL

ASSAY

i. C^{14}-lysine + ATP + sRNA $\rightarrow$ C^{14}-lysyl-sRNA + AMP + PP

ii. ATP + PP^{32} $\xrightarrow{\text{lysine}}$ ATP^{32} + PP

Assay i Reagents

The reaction mixture (0.2 ml) contains

a. 25 μmoles of Tris buffer, pH 8.0
  1 μmole of $MgCl_2$
  0.2 μmoles of ATP
  0.5 mg of sRNA
  10 mμ moles of C^{14}-lysine (approximately 50,000 cpm)
  Enzyme
b. 10% Trichloracetic acid
  1% Trichloracetic acid

† sRNA is equivalent to tRNA.

1.5 N NH_4OH

Scintillator solution (2)

Procedure

This assay measures the conversion of radioactive amino acid to a form precipitated by acid.

The reaction is started by the addition of enzyme and the mixture is incubated at 37 C for 10 min. The reaction is stopped by the addition of 1 ml of 10% trichloracetic acid and the resulting suspension is chilled in an ice bath for 10 min. The precipitate is collected on a Millipore filter and is washed three times with 20 ml of 1% trichloracetic acid. The filter disk is transferred to a counting vial, neutralized with 1 ml of 1.5 N NH_4OH, and dissolved in 10 ml of scintillator fluid. The radioactivity is determined in a scintillation counter. Blank reactions without enzyme are run and the values obtained are subtracted from those obtained with the complete system. One unit of synthetase activity is the amount of enzyme that esterifies 1 millimicromole of lysine wih RNA in 10 min under these conditions. Specific activity is defined as units per mg of protein. Under the conditions described, the reaction is proportional to enzyme concentration and to time of incubation until most of the lysine has been esterified.

Assay ii Reagents

The reaction mixture (1.0 ml) contains

a. 100 μmoles of Tris buffer, pH 8.0
    8 μmoles of $MgCl_2$
    2 μmoles of ATP_{32}
    2 μmoles $Na_4P_2O_7$, 10^4 cpm/μmole
    2 μmoles of lysine
    Enzyme
b. 7% $HClO_4$ containing 0.2 M $Na_4P_2O_7$
    A suspension of acid-washed Norit in H_2O, 30 mg/ml

Procedure

This assay measures the incorporation of P^{32} of inorganic pyrophosphate into ATP, which is adsorbed on activated charcoal and counted.

The reaction is initiated by addition of enzyme and the mixture is incubated at 37 C. After 15-min incubation, 0.5 ml of the perchloric acid-pyrophosphate mixture is added to stop the reaction and 1 ml of the suspension of Norit is added. The suspension is filtered on a 25 mm

Millipore filter and the residue is washed with three 20-ml portions of distilled water. The filters are glued to planchets with the charcoal surface down, dried, and counted. A blank reaction without lysine is run and its value is subtracted from that of each sample. One unit of exchange activity is defined as the amount of enzyme that incorporates 1 micromole of pyrophosphate into ATP in 15 min under the conditions described. Under these conditions, the exchange reaction is proportional to the amount of enzyme and to the time of incubation until approximately 10% of the pyrophosphate has been exchanged.

ISOLATION PROCEDURE

E. coli

E. coli strain B(M) is grown aerobically until late log phase in a medium containing 1.1% K_2HPO_4, 0.85% KH_2PO_4, 0.6% Difco yeast extract, and 1% glucose. The cells are harvested by centrifugation at a low temperature, washed once with cold 1/2% NaCl, and frozen until used.

All subsequent operations are carried out at 5 C unless otherwise specified

Crude Extract

Partially thawed *E. coli* cell paste, 450 g wet weight, is blended in a 3-liter stainless steel Waring Blendor run at 90 v together with 900 ml of 0.025 M Tris buffer, pH 8.0, and 700 g of Superbrite glass beads. The mixture is blended until the temperature rises to 8 C. It is then cooled in an ethanol-water-Dry Ice slurry. The blending-cooling cycle is repeated until the extract has been blended for a total of 15 min, usually three cycles of 5 min each. 900 ml of 0.025 M Tris buffer, pH 8.0, are then added and the diluted suspension is blended for an additional 2 min. The beads are washed with two 450-ml portions of buffer and the combined extracts are centrifuged for 90 min at 11,000 × g in a refrigerated Servall Centrifuge and the precipitate discarded. The procedure is repeated with another 450-g portion of frozen cell paste, so that the extract from 900 g of cells is carried through the remainder of the purification procedure. The total volume of extract is about 6.2 liters.

Streptomycin Supernatant Fluid

Thirty percent of the crude extract volume of a 6% aqueous solution of streptomycin sulfate prepared at room temperature is added over a 10-min period with constant stirring. The precipitate is allowed to coagulate and settle overnight. 7.6 l of clear yellow supernatant fluid are siphoned from the sediment.

Absorption and Elution from Calcium Phosphate Gel

The calcium phosphate gel (3), adjusted to 20 mg per ml dry weight, is slowly added with stirring to the streptomycin supernatant fluid. Small pilot runs are made to determine optimal amounts. Eight percent by volume of the streptomycin supernatant fluid is the amount of calcium phosphate usually added. The slurry is stirred for 10 min and the gel is separated by centrifugation. All sedimentations at this step are performed in a refrigerated centrifuge for 10 min at 1200 × g. The supernatant fluid, containing 95% of the protein, can be stored for preparations of other enzymes. The pellets are resuspended in 500 ml of 0.02 M potassium phosphate buffer, pH 6.5, incubated 10 min at 0 C and the suspension again centrifuged. The supernatant fluid is discarded and the pellets are suspended in 500 ml of distilled water at 0 C, incubated 10 min at 0 C, and centrifuged. The supernatant fluid is discarded and the pellet is suspended in 0.05 M potassium phosphate buffer, pH 7.5, incubated for 10 min at 0 C, and centrifuged. The pellet is discarded.

DEAE-Cellulose Chromatography

The clear calcium phosphate eluate is applied directly to a DEAE-cellulose column (3.3 cm × 42 cm) previously equilibrated with 0.05 M potassium phosphate buffer, pH 7.5. The column is washed with 0.10 M potassium phosphate buffer, pH 7.0, until the E_{280} of effluent falls below 0.02. The enzyme is eluted with a linear gradient formed between 1.0 liter of 0.10 M potassium phosphate buffer, pH 7.0, and 1.0 liter of 0.40 M KPO_4 buffer, pH 6.5. 200 fractions of 10 ml each are collected. The active fractions (approximately numbers 130 through 135) are combined and dialyzed against three changes of 0.02 M potassium phosphate, pH 7.0.

Hydroxylapatite Elution

The dialyzed DEAE-cellulose eluate is adsorbed on a hydroxylapatite (4) column (3.3 cm × 30 cm) and the column is sequentially developed with 300-ml portions of 0.2 M, 0.05 M, 0.08 M, 0.11 M, 0.15 M potassium phosphate buffer, pH 7.0. The activity is eluted with 0.15 M buffer. The solution is then concentrated by pressure dialysis against 0.05 M Tris buffer, pH 8.0, to approximately 5 ml, and then dialyzed against fresh 0.05 M Tris buffer, pH 8.0. The purification scheme is summarized in Table 1 together with yield and the specific activity at each step.

TABLE 1. *Purification of Lysyl-RNA Synthetase*

Fraction	Volume (ml)	Protein (mg)	Activity[a] (units)	Specific Activity (units/mg)	Recovery (%)
Crude extract	6,200	99,000	36,000	0.36	100
Streptomycin supernatant fluid	7,600	16,700	37,000	2.2	100
Ca$_3$(PO$_4$)$_2$ gel eluate	600	732	33,000	45.	92
Combined DEAE fractions	550	150	22,000	146.	61
Hydroxylapatite eluate	318	40	12,600	312.	35

[a] Activity was determined by the ATP-pyrophosphate exchange assay.

PROPERTIES OF THE ENZYME

Homogeneity

The final preparation appears to be essentially homogeneous. Only a single, sharp, symmetrical peak of constant specific activity was found after electrophoresis at pH 8, chromatography on DEAE-cellulose, or chromatography on IRC50 (X)E64. No N-terminal amino acids were detected after reaction with DNFB. Ultra-centrifugation shows evidence of some aggregation.

Specificity

Only lysine of the amino acids usually found in proteins is a substrate for this enzyme. Orhithine is a competitive inhibitor. Hydroxylysine and thiosine (S-(β-aminoethyl)-L-cysteine) are substrates in the pyrophosphate exchange reaction and thiosine is a substrate in the esterification reaction.

Kinetic Properties

The pH optimum of the esterification reaction is at pH 8.0, with steep decreases on both sides. The pyrophosphate exchange also has an optimum at pH 8, but with little change in activity between pH 7 and 9, and activity can be measured between pH 4.8 and 10. The K_m values in the esterification reaction are 1.6×10^{-6} M for lysine and

1.3×10^{-3} M for thiosine; in the pyrophosphate exchange reaction K_m values are lysine, 5.7×10^{-7} M; thiosine 1.4×10^{-6} M; and δ-hydroxy-lysine, 3.0×10^{-4} M.

Stability of the Enzyme

Concentrated enzyme preparations are stable for several days at room temperature, at -15 C for 6 months, and can be frozen and thawed without loss of activity. Enzyme solutions more dilute than 0.1 mg/ml are unstable at 0 C and at -15 C. Bovine serum albumin added to dilute enzyme preparations prevents this loss of activity. High salt concentrations and glutathione, but not mercaptoethanol, par-tially protect the dilute enzyme. Enzymatic activity is destroyed on freezing in the presence of mercaptoethanol. Mercaptoethanol in the standard reaction mixture also inhibits ATP-PP^{32} activity.

Other Properties

Two sulfhydryl groups react readily with p-mercuribenzoate and other sulfhydryl reagents. A third -SH group can be detected with enzyme denatured by urea. None of these appears to be essential for enzyme activity; the enzyme is fully active in the presence of p-mercuri-benzoate in concentrations that inhibit all of the other amino acyl-sRNA synthetases of E. coli (5).

REFERENCES

1. STERN, R., and A. H. MEHLER, 1965. Biochem. Z. *342*: 400.
2. BRAY, G. 1960. Anal. Biochem. *1*: 279.
3. KEILIN, D., and E. F. HARTREE. 1938. Proc. Roy. Soc. (London). *B124*: 397.
4. LEVIN, O. 1962. Meth. Enzymol. *5*: 27.
5. STERN, R., M. DELUCA, A. H. MEHLER, and W.D. MCELROY. Biochemistry. Sub-mitted for publication.

Prolyl-sRNA† Synthetase of

Escherichia coli (1)

ALAN H. MEHLER
MARQUETTE UNIVERSITY SCHOOL OF MEDICINE
MILWAUKEE, WISCONSIN

CELIA JESENSKY
NATIONAL INSTITUTES OF HEALTH
BETHESDA, MARYLAND

ASSAY

$$C^{14}\text{-proline} + ATP + sRNA \longrightarrow C^{14}\text{-prolyl-sRNA} + AMP + PP$$

Reagents

The reaction mixture contains in 0.2 ml

1. 25 μmoles of Tris buffer, pH 7.0
   0.2 μmole of ATP
   1.0 μmole of MgCl$_2$
   0.2 μmole of mercaptoethanol
   0.5 mg of sRNA
   0.2 mg of bovine serum albumin
   0.01 μmole of C^{14}-L-proline (about 10^5 cpm)
   Enzyme
2. 10% trichloracetic acid
   5% trichloracetic acid

† sRNA is equivalent to tRNA.

420

1.5 N NH$_4$OH
Scintillator solution (2)

Procedure

This assay measures the conversion of radioactive proline to a form precipitated by acid.

The reaction is started by the addition of enzyme and the mixture is incubated at 37 C for 10 min. The reaction is stopped by the addition of 1 ml of 10% trichloracetic acid and the resulting suspension is chilled in an ice bath for 10 min. The precipitate is collected on a Millipore filter and is washed with 50 ml of 5% trichloracetic acid. The filter disk is transferred to a counting vial, neutralized with 1 ml of 1.5 N NH$_4$OH, and dissolved in 10 ml of scintillator fluid. The radioactivity is determined in a scintillation counter. Blank reactions without enzyme are run and the values obtained are subtracted from those obtained with the complete system. One unit of synthetase activity is the amount of enzyme that esterifies 1 millimicromole of proline with RNA in 10 min under these conditions. Specific activity is defined as units per mg of protein. Under the conditions described, the reaction is proportional to enzyme concentration and to time of incubation until most of the proline has been esterified.

ISOLATION PROCEDURE

E. coli

E. coli strain B(M) is grown aerobically until late log phase in a medium containing 1.1% K$_2$HPO$_4$, 0.85% KH$_2$PO$_4$, 0.6% Difco yeast extract, and 1% glucose. The cells are harvested by centrifugation at a low temperature, washed once with cold ½% NaCl, and frozen until used.

Crude Extract

All of the following steps are carried out in the cold. Twenty-five grams of frozen E. coli cells are ground in a Waring Blendor with 50 ml. of 0.025 M Tris, pH 8, and 75 g of Superbrite glass beads (Minnesota Mining & Manufacturing Type 100–5005). Approximately 5 min is enough time to break up the cells. The material is poured into centrifuge tubes and the blendor rinsed twice with 25-ml portions of the Tris buffer. Unbroken cells and debris are removed by centrifugation at 30,000 × g for 1½ hr.

Streptomycin Supernatant Fluid

To the crude extract, one-fifth the volume of 6% streptomycin sulfate is added slowly with stirring. The suspension is stirred for 30 min, then centrifuged for 15 min at 30,000 × g. The precipitate is discarded.

Ammonium Sulfate Fractionation

The streptomycin supernatant fluid is stirred with enough solid ammonium sulfate (Merck, Reagent Grade) to give a 35% saturated solution at 0 C. Precipitation is allowed to occur for 30 min with stirring, then the solution is centrifuged at 30,000 × g for 15 min. The small precipitate, which contains no prolyl RNA synthetase activity, is discarded. To the supernatant fluid enough ammonium sulfate is added to bring the solution to 55% saturation. Again aggregation is allowed to occur for 30 min, then the solution is centrifuged at 30,000 × g for 15 min. The supernatant fluid is discarded and the precipitate is dissolved in 0.02 M potassium phosphate buffer, pH 7.5, and dialyzed overnight against 100 volumes of the same solution.

Diethylaminoethyl Cellulose Chromatography

The ammonium sulfate fraction is put on a column of DEAE-cellulose (1 cm × 30 cm) adjusted to pH 7.5 and then washed with 0.02 M potassium phosphate until at 280 and 260 absorbance is essentially nil. Elution is performed with a linear gradient of potassium phosphate from 0.02 M, pH 7.5, to 0.25 M, pH 6.5. Nine-ml fractions are collected in each of approximately 50 tubes. The activity is obtained in two partially separated peaks in fractions 30–45. No differences have been found between the two fractions.

Although the enzyme is relatively crude at this stage, further attempts at purification have not been successful because of large losses. The purification is summarized in Table 1.

PROPERTIES OF THE ENZYME

Exchange Reaction

Prolyl-sRNA synthetase catalyzes an exchange of inorganic pyrophosphate with the labile phosphates of ATP in the presence of L-proline. The analogues 4-hydroxyproline and azetidine-2-carboxylic acid also support the exchange reaction. Pipecolic acid is inert in this system. The Km values for amino acids in the exchange reaction are 10^{-4} M, 5.5×10^{-3} M, and 7.1×10^{-3} M, for proline, hydroxyproline, and azetidine-2-carboxylic acid, respectively. NaF, which is often added to similar reaction mixtures, is inhibitory.

Esterification of sRNA

The esterification reaction appears to be completely specific for L-proline; the analogues that react in the pyrophosphate exchange not only are not combined with sRNA, but they do not inhibit the esterification of proline. The pH optimum of this reaction is from pH 6.9 to 7.5. Cacodylate and phosphate buffer are inhibitory, as is mercaptoethanol in high concentrations. The K_m for proline is 5×10^{-4} M and for ATP 6.9×10^{-5} M.

Stability of the Enzyme

Crude preparations of prolyl-sRNA synthetase are relatively stable under various conditions of storage at low temperature. After purification on DEAE-cellulose the enzyme loses activity on storage in the cold. On warming, the activity is rapidly restored (e.g., 2 min at 37 C). The inactivation and activation processes are fully reversible. The physical basis for this phenomenon has not been determined; no clear effect of temperature was found on the rate of sedimentation in a sucrose gradient (3); molecular weights were estimated to be 85,000–103,000, using aldolase and methemoglobin as reference compounds.

TABLE 1. *Purification of prolyl RNA synthetase from* Escherichia coli

Enzyme Fraction	Protein (mg/ml)	Volume (ml)	Specific Activity	Total Yield (%)
Crude extract	9.7	151	0.0047	100
Streptomycin supernatant fluid	3.6	175	0.0066	61
35–55% Ammonium sulfate (after dialysis)	16.5	11	0.023	61
DEAE-Cellulose (Peak I)	0.46	48	0.073[a]	24[a]
DEAE-Cellulose (Peak II)	0.30	48	0.076[a]	17[a]

[a] Assayed as collected. These fractions are more active when preincubated at 37 C.

REFERENCES

1. JESENSKY, C. 1965. Masters Thesis, Georgetown University.
2. BRAY, G. 1960. Anal. Biochem. *1:* 279.
3. MARTIN, R. G., and B. N. AMES. 1961. J. Biol. Chem. *236:* 1372.

Seryl, Phenylalanyl, Arginyl, and Leucyl sRNA† Synthetases from Baker's Yeast (1)

MAYNARD H. MAKMAN

ALBERT EINSTEIN COLLEGE OF MEDICINE

YESHIVA UNIVERSITY

BRONX, NEW YORK

ASSAY

$$\text{ATP} + \text{C}^{14}\text{-amino acid} + \text{sRNA} \rightleftharpoons$$
$$\text{C}^{14}\text{-aminoacyl sRNA} + \text{PP}_i + \text{AMP}$$

Reagents

1. The reaction mixture (total volume 0.19 ml) for measurement of aminoacyl sRNA synthetase activity contains

   0.02 M potassium phosphate buffer, pH 7.5
   0.005 M ATP (sodium salt, neutralized)
   0.013 M $MgCl_2$
   0.004 M reduced glutathione
   0.2 mg/ml of bovine serum albumin (twice crystallized)
   0.025 μmole/ml of C^{14}-amino acid (specific activity, 20 $\mu c/\mu$mole)
   40 absorbancy units (260mμ)/ml of yeast sRNA [sRNA is prepared according to the procedure of Apgar et al. (2)]
   Enzyme

2. A solution containing 0.05 M potassium phosphate buffer (pH 7.5) and 2.5 mg/ml of gelatin (enzyme diluent)

   † sRNA is equivalent to tRNA.

424

Procedure

The enzymatic reaction utilized for this assay is the sum of the two partial reactions, the first involving formation of inorganic pyrophosphate and aminoacyl adenylate (enzyme bound) from amino acid and ATP, and the second involving transfer of the aminoacyl moiety from AMP to the terminal adenosine of sRNA. The assay measures formation of C^{14}-aminoacyl sRNA from C^{14}-amino acid.

For dilution of enzymes to be assayed, a gelatin-phosphate buffer solution (reagent 2) is used (purified seryl sRNA synthetase is not stable when diluted in buffer alone). A blank without enzyme is run with each set of assays. Assay tubes are incubated for 30 min at 37 C. For termination of the reaction, 0.025 ml of 0.02 M C^{12}-amino acid is added to each tube, the tube is shaken, and an 0.1-ml portion delivered to a filter paper disk (Whatman No. 3 MM chromatography paper, 2.3-cm diameter, previously numbered and mounted on a straight pin) (3). The disk is exposed to a stream of war air for 10–15 sec and then immersed in an ice-cold solution of 10% trichloracetic acid (TCA) (3). The entire operation for termination of incubation and TCA precipitation of a single sample requires about 30 sec. The disks are allowed to remain for at least 20 min in a single beaker containing 10 ml of cold 10% TCA per disk with occasional agitation. After the TCA wash the paper disks are washed successively in 3% perchloric acid (4 times), ethanol (4 times), and ether (2 times) (approximately 3 ml/disk/wash), and then dried. Each disk is placed in a standard 20-ml glass counting vial, 5 ml of scintillation mixture [0.4% 2,5-diphenyl oxazole, 0.01% 1,4-bis-2 (5 phenyl oxazolyl)-benzene in toluene] added, and the samples counted with a liquid scintillation spectrometer. The value for the blank without enzyme is subtracted from each sample value. Under these conditions the formation of aminoacyl sRNA is directly proportional to enzyme concentration up to about 0.3 mμmoles aminoacyl sRNA/ml. A unit of enzyme catalyzes the formation of 1 μmole C^{14}-aminoacyl sRNA during the 30-min assay incubation.

PURIFICATION PROCEDURE

The fractionation procedure was developed primarily for isolation of the seryl sRNA synthetase. However, this procedure also yields a highly purified phenylalanyl sRNA synthetase and partially purified preparations of arginyl sRNA synthetase and leucyl sRNA synthetase. For enzyme purification all operations are carried out in the cold room unless otherwise indicated, and all centrifugations are carried out in refrigerated centrifuges.

Step 1. Initial Extraction and Centrifugation

Glass beads (No. 150, 75 μ, Minnesota Mining and Manufacturing Co.) are treated with nitric acid (70% nitric acid diluted 1:1 with water) in a steam bath for 60 min, washed with distilled water, dried, and precooled in the cold room prior to use. For routine preparation, 400 g of fresh pressed baker's yeast (Fleishman's) are homogenized in four Waring Blendors and cooled with ice, as follows: Each 100 g portion of yeast is homogenized at the speed obtained by connection to a powerstat set at 90 v, with 300 g of glass beads, 160 mg of reduced glutathione, 0.4 ml of n-octyl alcohol, and 100 ml of buffer containing 0.016 M K_2HPO_4, 0.004 M KH_2PO_4, and 0.002 M $MgSO_4$(4). To keep the temperature below 15 C during the procedure, homogenization is carried out for five intervals of 3 min each, separated by periods of additional cooling on ice; the whole procedure usually requires 45 min.

After homogenization, an additional 200-ml buffer is added, and the suspension is mixed, allowed to settle, and decanted. The glass beads are washed twice with 100 ml of buffer each time. The extracts and washing decanted from the four Waring Blendors are combined and centrifuged for 30 min at 9000 $\times$ g. The supernatant fluid is then poured off and centrifuged for 60 min at 78,000 $\times$ g in a Spinco Model L ultracentrifuge. About 1700 ml of supernatant fluid containing 30 g of protein is recovered. This supernatant fraction contains aminoacyl sRNA synthetase activity for all amino acids, which have been examined (alanine, arginine, aspartate, glutamate, glycine, histidine, isoleucine, leucine, lysine, methionine, phenylalanine, proline, serine, threonine, tryptophan, tyrosine, and valine).

Step 2. Ammonium Sulfate Fractionation and Dialysis

Solid ammonium sulfate in the amount of 351 g/liter is added slowly with stirring to the Step 1 supernatant fraction. After standing for 20 min, with stirring the mixture is centrifuged in a refrigerated Lourdes centrifuge. The clear (decanted) supernatant fluid is then retained, and to it is added 81 g of solid $(NH_4)_2SO_4$/liter. This mixture, after stirring for 20 minutes, is centrifuged and the supernatant fluid is discarded. The precipitate [55–67% saturation $(NH_4)_2SO_4$ fraction] is resuspended in a small volume of buffer (0.016 M K_2HPO_4, 0.004 M KH_2PO_4, 0.001 M EDTA, 0.0002 M reduced glutathione) and dialyzed against the same buffer overnight or until free of ammonium sulfate. The protein concentration after dialysis is 80–100 mg/ml. If desired, the dialyzed fraction can be stored at −80 C for several weeks without appreciable loss of seryl S-RNA synthetase activity.

Step 3. XE-64 Column Fractionation

Prior to use the XE-64 (Amberlite) resin, 100–400 mesh (Rohm and Haas Co.), is washed by suspension and (following settling) decantation of the supernatant fluid several times in water. This is followed by successive washings in 1 N NaOH, water, 1 N HCl, and water, and this cycle is repeated three times. The resin is then resuspended in 0.14 M potassium phosphate buffer and with suitable pH adjustments equilibrated with this buffer over a period of several days at pH 6.8 and 2–4 C.

To each ml of the dialyzed Step 2 fraction 0.075 ml of 1 M K_2HPO_4 and 0.065 ml of 1 M KH_2PO_4 is added. A total of 45 to 50 ml of this solution containing about 4 g of protein is passed through a 6.6- (diameter) × 67-cm column of XE-64 resin pre-equilibrated with 0.14 M potassium phosphate buffer (pH 6.8) and 0.001 M EDTA, and elution is carried out with the same buffer. The flow rate is 160 ml/hr and fractions of approximately 21 ml are collected. Under these conditions most of the protein put on the column is not retarded (about 90% of the protein recovered in fractions 45–65). An early peak of seryl sRNA synthetase activity (1) (approximately fractions 52–64) is not retained for further purification. The major peak of serine activity, a broad peak that also contains the arginine and phenylalanine activities, is eluted at approximately fractions 70–140. About 1300 ml of peak fraction eluate are pooled. The optical density at 280 mμ of these fractions ranges from 0.150 to 0.050 and the pooled fractions contain in total about 3% of the protein put on the column. Leucyl sRNA synthetase is eluted at approximately fractions 160–200 and these later fractions are pooled separately from the serine peak fractions.

The XE-64 column can be used repeatedly provided it is washed just before and after each use with the phosphate buffer. Also, the top cm of resin in the column should be replaced with fresh resin after every run.

The pooled serine peak fractions (also containing arginine and phenylalanine enzymes) are concentrated by the addition of 561 g of solid ammonium sulfate/liter and centrifugation at 56,000 × g for 30 min. The precipitate is transferred to a single tube by resuspension in a small portion of the supernatant fluid and recentrifugation. Finally, the precipitate is dissolved in 3 ml of buffer containing 0.02 M K_2HPO_4, 0.01 M KH_2PO_4, 0.001 M reduced glutathione, and 0.0001 M EDTA. Insoluble residue is removed by centrifugation. In order to remove ammonium sulfate the slightly hazy supernatant solution is passed through a Sephadex G-25 (coarse) column equilibrated with potassium phosphate buffer (pH 7.5), 0.001 M reduced glutathione, and 0.0001 M EDTA. The extract can be stored at this stage at −80 C for 14 days, or, prior to the Sephadex step, as a suspension with $(NH_4)_2SO_4$ at 80% saturation, in the cold room for 10 hr with only slight losses of seryl sRNA synthetase activity.

In an analogous manner the pooled XE-64 column peak fractions for leucine are concentrated by ammonium sulfate precipitation, desalted with Sephadex, and stored at −80 C. The leucine enzyme as eluted from the XE-64 column is quite labile and the fractions must be assayed, pooled, and concentrated with a minimum of delay.

Step 4. DEAE-Cellulose Column Fractionation

Prior to use DEAE-cellulose is washed with H_2O, 0.1 N NaOH, H_2O, and finally 0.03 M potassium phosphate buffer, pH 7.2. The Step 3 fraction containing the serine, arginine, and phenylalanine enzymes, after Sephadex filtration, is diluted with 0.6 volumes of distilled water and immediately placed on a 1.2- × 21-cm column of DEAE-cellulose in 0.03 M potassium buffer, pH 7.2. The column is washed with 30 ml of the phosphate buffer and then eluted with 600 ml of a linear gradient of 0.02 M NaCl plus 0.03 M phosphate buffer to 0.15 M NaCl plus 0.03 M phosphate buffer. Fractions of 10 ml each are collected in tubes, each of which contains 5.5 g of solid $(NH_4)_2SO_4$, 1 mg of reduced glutathione, and 0.005 ml of 0.2 M EDTA. The contents of the tubes are mixed in order to dissolve the $(NH_4)_2SO_4$ within 30 min after each fraction is collected.

Separate peaks are obtained for the arginyl, seryl, and phenylalanyl sRNA synthetases. The arginine enzyme is not retained on the column and is recovered in the earliest fractions (approximately 4–8 are pooled). The serine enzyme is eluted at NaCl concentration of about 0.065–0.090 M (a total of 8 or 9 fractions are pooled). The phenylalanine enzyme is eluted at NaCl concentrations of approximately 0.10–0.13 M (about 10 fractions are pooled).

Step 5. Final Ammonium Sulfate Fractionation

The fractions from each DEAE-cellulose enzyme activity peak are pooled separately and the precipitates (containing the enzymes) are collected by centrifugation at 56,000 × g for 20 min. Successive extractions of the precipitates with ammonium sulfate solutions are then carried out. For this step, $(NH_4)_2SO_4$ is first recrystallized in the presence of EDTA (5) and the solutions used for extraction contain 0.0005

M EDTA. The precipitates containing the serine and phenylalanine enzymes are each suspended in 1 ml and the arginine enzyme precipitate in 2 ml of 65% saturated (430 g/liter) ammonium sulfate solution. The suspensions are centrifuged at 41,000 × g for 15 min. The precipitates are extracted in similar manner successively with 55% (251 g/liter) and with 45% (277 g/liter) saturated ammonium sulfate solutions. The 55% extract in each case contains most of the enzymatic activity (about 75–80% of the total activity recovered in each set of extracts). The ammonium sulfate extracts are stored at 2–4 C.

Step 6. Crystallization of Seryl sRNA Synthetase

During the first few days of storage (at 3 C) of the final Step 5 serine enzyme (55% saturated ammonium sulfate extract), a small amorphous precipitate generally forms and is discarded. The enzyme solution is then kept in a small loosely covered test tube, and small needle-shaped crystals develop slowly over a period of several weeks. Crystal formation may be facilitated by occasionally bringing the enzyme solution to room temperature and immediately recooling in the refrigerator, or by addition of extremely small amounts of ammonium sulfate. Significant crystal formation usually occurs at a final ammonium sulfate concentration of about 57–58% saturation. At this point the test tube is tightly stoppered in order to avoid further increase in ammonium sulfate concentration and concomitant conversion of crystalline to amorphous precipitate.

Step 7. Further Purification of Arginyl sRNA Synthetase

Additional purification of the Step 5 arginyl sRNA synthetase preparation (55% saturation ammonium sulfate extract) may be obtained by fractional precipitation with the addition of small amounts of a saturated ammonium sulfate solution (Table 2, last line).

Comments

A summary of the recovery of protein and enzymatic activity at each step in the purification of seryl sRNA synthetase is shown in Table 1. Table 2 summarizes the over-all purification achieved for the serine, phenylalanine, and arginine enzymes. The specific activity of the final leucyl sRNA synthetase preparation (Step 3 concentrated column fraction) is approximately 0.6 units/mg.

A different fractionation procedure, which yields partially purified preparations of the phenylalanyl and leucyl sRNA synthetases from yeast, has been reported by Lagerkwist and Waldenstrom (6).

TABLE 1.   *Purification of Seryl sRNA Synthetase[a,b]*

Fraction	Volume (ml)	Total Units	Specific Activity (units/mg of protein)	Recovery (%)
Step 1. Supernatant (78,000 × g)[c]	1700	38.9	0.0013	100
Step 2. (NH₄)₂SO₄ fraction[c]	42	27.3	0.0070	70
Step 3. XE-64 column fraction	1200	15.3	0.102	40
Step 4. DEAE-cellulose eluate	80	4.4	1.10	11
Step 5. (NH₄)₂SO₄ extract (55%)	1	1.9	2.53	5

[a] Reproduced from Biochemistry. 1965. *4:* 1434. With the permission of the American Chemical Society, publisher and copyright owner.
[b] Starting material was 400 g of pressed baker's yeast.
[c] Dialyzed prior to assay.

TABLE 2.   *Summary of Purification of Enzymes[a]*

Aminoacyl sRNA Synthetase	Specific Activity (units/mg protein)		Purification
	Step 1[b]	Step 5	
Seryl	0.0013	2.53[c]	1946
Phenylalanyl	0.0340	6.13[c]	180
Arginyl	0.0078	0.89[c]	116
		2.49[d]	427

[a] Reproduced from Biochemistry. 1965. *4:* 1434. With the permission of the American Chemical Society, publisher and copyright owner.
[b] Dialyzed prior to assay.
[c] 55% saturated ammonium sulfate extracts.
[d] Extract obtained by further ammonium sulfate fractionation of the 55% extract.

PROPERTIES OF ENZYMES

Purity; Contamination with Other Enzymes; Nucleic Acid Content

The seryl sRNA synthetase preparation (Step 5, 55% saturated ammonium sulfate extract) has been found to be homogeneous and the phenylalanyl sRNA synthetase preparation at least 90% homogeneous as determined by equilibrium ultracentrifugation using the method of Yphantis (7). The seryl, phenylalanyl, and arginyl sRNA synthetases (Step 5, 55% saturated ammonium sulfate extracts) are each free of other aminoacyl sRNA synthetase activities, sRNA-CCA pyrophosphorylase activity and nuclease activity.

The ratio of absorbancy at 280 mμ to that at 260 mμ for purified seryl sRNA synthetase is 1.48. This value, taking into consideration the estimated tyrosine and tryptophan content of the enzyme (1), indicates the presence of about one nucleotide per mole of enzyme (however, the nucleotide has not yet been identified directly).

Molecular Weight and Sedimentation Constants

Seryl sRNA synthetase has a molecular weight of 89,000 as determined by equilibrium ultracentrifugation ($\overline{V} = 0.72$ assumed) (7) and an $S_{20,w}$ value of 6.7 as determined by sucrose density gradient centrifugation (8). By the same technique (7,8) phenylalanyl sRNA synthetase was found to have a molecular weight of 180,000 and an $S_{20,w}$ value of 8.2.

Stability

In the presence of small amounts of EDTA ($1–5 \times 10^{-4}$ M) purified seryl sRNA synthetase is stable for at least 8 months when stored at 2–4 C in ammonium sulfate solution (with the enzyme in solution or partly in the form of a crystalline precipitate). In the absence of EDTA a variable loss in activity may occur over a period of several weeks. A marked protective effect of EDTA is evident during incubation of the serine enzyme at 37 C (incubation carried out in a solution containing 2.5 mg/ml of gelatin and 0.05 M potassium phosphate buffer, pH 7.5) (1). At 45 C or 47 C the serine enzyme rapidly looses activity both with and without EDTA present (about 90% of the activity is lost in 15 min at 45 C). Arginyl sRNA synthetase exhibits greater thermal stability (about 7% of activity is lost in 15 min at 45 C) than the serine enzyme. No effect of EDTA on the stability of the arginine enzyme has been noted at any temperature studied.

The heat stability of the serine enzyme at 45 or 47 C is markedly increased in the presence of magnesium ions and Mg^{2+} plus ATP has an even greater effect on stability, whereas ATP alone is without effect (9). Since Mg^{2+} is required for the protective effect of ATP and the purified enzyme already contains bound nucleotide (see above), it is possible that the effect of Mg^{2+} alone is really due to Mg^{2+} plus bound nucleotide. Yeast serine sRNA was found to have no effect on thermal stability, either when present alone or when Mg^{2+} is also present.

Measurement of Total Acceptor Capacity of sRNA

The reaction mixture used for measurement of total acceptor capacity of sRNA generally is the same as that used for enzyme assay, except for the presence of less sRNA (0.25–1.5 mμmole/ml in terms of acceptor capacity for the C^{14}-amino acid present) and excess enzyme. The conditions for maximal formation of seryl sRNA with *E. coli* sRNA as substrate for the yeast enzyme are more stringent than with yeast or liver sRNA as substrate: For maximal seryl sRNA formation with the *E. coli* substrate the incubation is carried out at pH 7.9–8.1 (glycine buffer) and a higher serine concentration (0.06 μmole/ml or greater) is necessary, as well as more enzyme and/or longer incubation time (9).

Kinetic Studies

The K_m values for ATP in the formation of seryl, arginyl, and phenylalanyl sRNA are all in the range 0.0005–0.001 M. The optimal ratio of Mg/ATP for seryl sRNA synthetase is in the range 1.5 to 2.5 and rates are very much decreased with ratios below 1. The K_m for serine in the formation of seryl sRNA synthetase is about 1×10^{-5} M. The pH optimum for seryl sRNA formation is approximately pH 7.8 (measured using the standard assay system).

The turnover number for the phenylalanyl sRNA synthetase is approximately 100 moles of (yeast) phenylalanyl sRNA/min/mole of enzyme (measured using the standard enzyme assay system).

Detailed kinetic studies for the purified serine enzyme have been carried out using purified preparations of serine sRNA as substrate (9). Incubations were carried out with either Tris buffer (0.05 M, pH 7.5) phosphate buffer (0.05 M, pH 7.5), or Tris buffer (0.05 M) plus phosphate buffer (0.02 M), and also 0.065 μmole/ml of C^{14}-serine, a series of different concentrations of sRNA, and other assay components as indicated for enzyme assay. The K_m value of the seryl sRNA synthetase for purified yeast serine sRNA (11) is about 2.4×10^{-7} M; the turnover number is 50 moles of seryl sRNA/min/mole of enzyme (incubations in Tris buffer). When kinetic studies are carried out with serine sRNA from *E. coli* (12) the K_m is 2.6×10^{-6} M and the turnover number is 12 moles of seryl sRNA/min/mole of enzyme. Thus, both K_m and V_{max} are altered when *E. coli* serine sRNA is used in place of the yeast sRNA substrate.

The presence of 0.02 M phosphate in the incubation mixture has very little effect on reaction rates with yeast serine sRNA as substrate (V_{max} is practically unaffected and K_m is increased about 20%), but exerts a large effect on the reaction with *E. coli* serine sRNA as substrate: With the latter substrate 0.02 M phosphate produces about a tenfold increase in K_m for the sRNA and about a threefold decrease in maximal velocity. The reason for this differential effect of phosphate is not known.

The kinetics of seryl sRNA formation have been studied using purified yeast serine sRNA, which has been treated with *E. coli* phosphomonoesterase in order to remove the 5'-phosphate from the terminal guanosine moiety of sRNA. Reaction rates were not altered by the removal of this phosphate indicating that this terminal phosphate is not important in the interaction of serine sRNA with the seryl adenylate-enzyme complex (9).

Kinetic studies have also been carried out with yeast serine sRNA, which had been resolved into two species, one species terminating in -CCA and the other terminating in -CC (lacking the terminal adenosine and thus unable to accept serine) (10). The presence of -CC terminal serine sRNA did not alter the kinetics of the reaction involving the -CCA terminal species [both K_m for -CCA terminal sRNA and V_{max} were unaffected (9)]. Thus, the -CC species does not appear to have significant affinity for the enzyme complex at the site of seryl sRNA formation.

The presence of very high amounts of sRNA may inhibit the rate of seryl sRNA formation (9). The reason for the inhibition has not yet been determined.

REFERENCES

1. MAKMAN, M. H., and G. L. CANTONI. 1965. Biochemistry. *4:* 1434.
2. APGAR, J., R. HOLLEY, and S. H. MERRILL. 1962. J. Biol. Chem. *237:* 796.
3. MANS, R. J., and G. D. NOVELLI. 1961. Arch. Biochem. Biophys. *94:* 48.
4. MONIER, R., M. L. STEPHENSON, and P. C. ZAMECNIK. 1960. Biochim. Biophys. Acta. *43:* 1.
5. SUTHERLAND, E. W., and W. D. WOSILAIT. 1956. J. Biol. Chem. *218:* 459.
6. LAGERKWIST, U., and J. WALDENSTROM. 1964. J. Mol. Biol. *8:* 28.
7. YPHANTIS, D. A. 1964. Biochemistry. *3:* 297.
8. MARTIN, R. G., and B. N. AMES. 1961. J. Biol. Chem. *236:* 1372.
9. MAKMAN, M. H., and G. L. CANTONI. To be published.
10. RICHARDS, H. H., M. H. MAKMAN, P. LEBOWITZ, P. L. IPATA, and G. L. CANTONI. In press.
11. CANTONI, G. L., H. ISHIKURA, H. H. RICHARDS, and K. TANAKA. 1963. Cold Spring Harbor Symp. Quant. Biol. *28:* 123.
12. NATHENSON, S. G., and G. L. CANTONI. In press.

II.

ISOLATION, PREPARATION,

AND CHARACTERIZATION

OF NATURAL AND SYNTHETIC

NUCLEIC ACIDS

II.

The Isolation and Properties

of the Two High Molecular

Weight Fractions of

Escherichia coli

Ribosomal RNA

ELLIS T. BOLTON
DEPARTMENT OF TERRESTRIAL MAGNETISM
CARNEGIE INSTITUTION OF WASHINGTON
WASHINGTON, D.C.

Ribosomal RNA may be isolated from extracts of bacterial cells or from ribosomes that have been purified by ultracentrifugation. The procedures set forth here are applicable to many microorganisms (1) although they will be described with special reference to *Escherichia coli*. The details of the procedures can be varied according to the purposes for which the RNA is required.

GROWTH OF BACTERIA

The amount of ribosomal RNA per bacterial cell varies with the conditions under which the organisms are cultured (2). When *E. coli* is grown in a medium rich in organic constituents, such as broth or

437

casein hydrolysate, the ribosome content tends to be high, whereas cells grown in a glucose salts medium low in magnesium content contain few ribosomes (3). *De novo* ribosomal synthesis is inhibited strongly by submitting the culture to a "step down" condition (4), usually one in which a less readily available source of carbon is substituted for glucose and/or broth. In addition, the state of aggregation of the ribosomes in the cell also depends upon conditions of growth and upon the time during the life cycle of the culture at which the cells are harvested (5). Thus, culture conditions determine both total yield and relative amounts of ribosomal RNA.

A frequently used culture medium is the "C" medium described by Roberts *et al.* (6). When supplemented with 1 g/liter of glucose and heavily aerated at 37 C it will provide, after overnight culture, 1 g (wet weight) of bacteria, which contains approximately 30 mg of ribosomal RNA. During the exponential phase of growth the mass of bacteria doubles every 50 min.

C MEDIUM

NH_4Cl	2 g
Na_2HPO_4	6 g
KH_2PO_4	3 g
NaCl	3 g
Mg (as $MgCl_2$)	10 mg
S (as Na_2SO_4)	26 mg

Energy source (usually glucose) dissolved in 100 ml H_2O.
Total volume   1000 ml

The salt solution and energy source are generally autoclaved separately and mixed at the time of inoculation. Aeration may be accomplished either by shaking the culture or by pumping air through a fritted glass gas dispersion tube.

DISRUPTION OF BACTERIA

The bacteria are usually harvested from the culture by means of centrifugation, although small amounts can rapidly be collected on membrane filters. They are washed three times by centrifugation or filtration with 10^{-2} M Tris (tris-hydroxymethylaminomethane) chloride buffer, pH 7.4, which contains 10^{-2}M $MgCl_2$ (TCM). The cells are suspended in TCM and forced through the orifice of a French pressure cell (7) at 10–15,000 psi. Breakage is essentially complete over a wide range (tenths of milligrams to tenths of a gram wet weight of cells per ml) of concentrations.

Buffer Solutions

The Mg content is important since 10^{-2}M preserves large (70–100 S) ribosomes, higher concentrations cause aggregation of the particles, 10^{-4}M dissociates the large ribosomes into their 50 and 30 S components, and lack of Mg disrupts the particles and releases a latent ribonuclease, which degrades the RNA.

Temperature

E. coli can be washed and broken at 4 C or at room temperature. For ribosome preparation it is preferable to work at the lower temperature. Ribosomal RNA can be prepared from the pressure cell extract by squirting the cellular juice into an equal volume of preservative-free liquefied phenol (85%), which contains 0.5% sodium dodecyl sulfate (SDS) and is held at 4 C, room temperature 37 C, or 60 C. Such RNA preparations may be contaminated with "messenger" RNA as revealed by pulse-labeling experiments (8).

Pressure

E. coli cells can be disrupted, although less efficiently, at pressures as low as 2000 psi. The higher pressures also provide solutions relatively low in viscosity since DNA is efficiently shear degraded.

PREPARATION OF RIBOSOMES

The pressure-cell extract contains a few unbroken cells, fragmented cell walls and membranes, ribosomes, and lower molecular weight components including shear-degraded DNA. The ribosomes may be collected by differential centrifugation in the no. 40 angle rotor of the Spinco Model L centrifuge according to the following procedure.

1. Centrifuge the extract at 20,000 rev/min for 10 min. Discard the pellet that contains cells, walls, and most of the membranes.

2. Centrifuge the supernatant fluid at 40,000 rev/min for 45 min. The supernatant fluid of this centrifugation is discarded and the pellet that contains ribosomes and fragments of membranes is resuspended in TCM.

3. Centrifuge the suspension at 20,000 rev/min for 5 min and discard the pellet that contains mostly lipid-rich membrane material.

4. Centrifuge the supernatant fluid from 3 at 40,000 rev/min for 45 min and discard the supernatant fluid. The pellet contains essen-

tially all of the large ribosomes and most of the 50 and 30 S particles that are normal components of the extract. Total ribosomal RNA may be extracted from this sediment and the 18 and 28 S RNA components can be separated by zonal centrifugation.

Separation of 30 and 50 S Ribosomes

The 70 S (and any larger) ribosomes in the pellet from 4 (above) may be dissociated into 30 and 50 S particles by suspending them in TCM adjusted to contain 10^{-4}M Mg. The 30 and 50 S particles can be separated by zonal centrifugation in a sucrose density gradient. Alternatively, pure 30 S particles can be prepared by differential centrifugation in a sucrose density gradient or in the no. 40 angle rotor of the Spinco centrifuge.

Dissociation of Large Ribosomes

1. Suspend the pellet from 4 (above) in TCM (10^{-4}M Mg) and centrifuge at 40,000 rev/min for 4 hr in the no. 40 rotor.

2. Discard the supernatant fluid. Again disperse the pellet in low Mg TCM so that the solution contains about 5 mg/ml of ribosomes (optical density at 260 mμ 40–50) if zonal centrifugation is to be employed, or as much as 20 mg/ml if a pure sample of 30 S particles is to be prepared by differential centrifugation.

Zonal Centrifugation

The procedure developed by Britten and Roberts (9) has proved highly successful for separating ribosomes. All manipulations are carried out at 4 C.

1. Prepare three linear sucrose density gradients of 4.6-ml volume in the plastic tubes of the Spinco SW39 rotor. These gradients should run from 20 to 5% sucrose in TCM (10^{-4}M Mg) and are readily made with the simple device described in (9) or with one of the designs suggested by Bock and Ling (10).

2. With the same device, layer over the initial gradient 0.4 ml of a solution containing the ribosomes and sucrose, in which the sucrose concentration runs from 4% to zero and the sample concentration from zero to the original value.

3. Centrifuge in the SW39 rotor at 37,000 rev/min for 2 hr. The 30 S particles are located about half-way along the gradient and the 50 S ribosomes about three-quarters of the way. Any contaminating larger particles are packed at the bottom of the tube and low molecular weight components remain near the meniscus.

4. Collect 15-drop samples in a series of tubes after inserting a no. 26 hypodermic needle through the bottom of the plastic tube and extending it 1–2 mm into the gradient. The needle should be ground to a V-shaped point and contain a piece of piano wire, which serves as a valve preventing the introduction of air bubbles into the gradient and any pelleted material into the needle. Withdrawal of the piano wire initiates the flow of liquid. Most of the 50 or 30 S particles occur in three tubes. The region between these tubes contains varying proportions of both kinds of particles in small amounts. The location of the particles in the array of tubes is most readily determined by ultraviolet-absorption measurements at 260 mμ.

Differential Centrifugation

1. By using a linear gradient device deliver into the plastic centrifuge tube of the SW39 rotor a mixture containing 2.4 ml of sucrose solution and 2.4 ml of a suspension of 30 and 50 S ribosomes. The ribosomes should grade from zero concentration at the bottom of the tube to the original concentration at the top. The sucrose solution should grade from 20% at the bottom to 0% at the top.

2. Centrifuge at 37,000 rev/min for 2 hr and collect samples by the drip method. The 50 S ribosomes, together with some 30 S particles, lie in the lower quarter of the tube. The 30 S ribosomes, completely free of 50 S particles, occupy the middle quarter of the tube.

3. Pool the fractions that contain the 50 S ribosomes, dilute with TCM (10^{-4}M Mg), and centrifuge at 40,000 rev/min for 90 min in the no. 40 angle rotor. Repeat this centrifugation twice, suspending the pellet in low Mg TCM each time and discarding the supernatant fluid. The final pellet contains 50 S ribosomes essentially free of 30 S particles.

EXTRACTION OF RNA

RNA can be extracted from crude extracts, mixtures of ribosomes or purified particles by means of the phenol procedure.

1. Equilibrate liquefied (ca. 85%) preservative-free phenol with 0.02 M phosphate buffer, pH 7.0, 0.5% SDS, by shaking it several times and discarding the aqueous layer each cycle.

2. Add an equal volume of the phenol solution to a preparation containing ribosomes, shake the mixture vigorously, and separate the phases of the resulting emulsion by centrifugation.

3. Remove the aqueous (upper) layer without including the denatured protein in the interface.

4. Repeat the shaking procedure twice.

5. Shake the aqueous solution five times with an equal volume of ether discarding the ether each cycle.

6. Bubble nitrogen through the solution until it is free of ether.

7. If it is necessary to concentrate the RNA, adjust the solution to contain 0.1M NaCl, add two volumes of 95% ethanol and centrifuge.

8. Dissolve the precipitated RNA in an appropriate buffer.

Separation of 18 and 28 S RNAs

The high molecular weight ribosomal RNAs may be separated from one another by means of zonal centrifugation in a sucrose density gradient as described above for ribosome separation. The preparation should be centrifuged, however, at 37,000 rev/min for 4 hr.

Properties of the High Molecular Weight Ribosomal RNAs

PHYSICAL.   The sedimentation coefficients of the RNAs have been measured in several laboratories (11–13). $s^0_{20, w}$ values reported for the smaller RNA range from 16 to 19 and for the larger from 23 to 28. Measurements for which care was exercised to eliminate nuclease activity tend toward the higher values. The molecular weights are correspondingly 0.55×10^6 and 1.1×10^6. X-ray studies suggest regular patterns in the secondary structure of these nucleic acids, which probably result from double helical regions 50–150 Å long alternating with nonhelical regions (14,15). At neutral pH and moderate ionic strength

TABLE 1.   *Compositions of RNA fractions of* Escherichia coli *ML 30* (DNA composition: adenylic acid = thymidylic acid, 24 mole %; guanylic acid = cytidylic acid, 26 mole %)

Nucleotide	Total RNA	70 S	50 S	30 S	sRNA
Cytidylic acid	22.1	21.9	*21.5*	22.7	29.5
Adenylic acid	25.2	25.1	25.4	24.8	19.7
Guanylic acid	32.5	32.6	*33.5*	*31.0*	33.8
Uridylic acid	20.2	20.4	*19.6*	*21.5*	17.0
$\dfrac{\text{Purine}}{\text{Pyrimidine}}$	1.37	1.36	1.44	1.26	1.17
$\dfrac{\text{Guanylic acid} + \text{cytidylic acid}}{\text{Adenylic acid} + \text{uridylic acid}}$	1.20	1.20	1.22	1.16	1.71

Note: The italic values in the 30 and 50 S base-composition analyses are those that are different in the two subunits from the bacterial species. All nucleotide base-composition analyses are accurate to ± 1.5%.

(0.15) heated ribosomal RNA solutions exhibit approximately 40% hyperchromicity as indicated by ultraviolet ($\lambda = 260 \text{ m}\mu$) absorption measurements. The "melting curve" is very broad and extends from room temperature to about 75 C.

CHEMICAL. The nucleotide compositions of RNA fractions of *Escherichia coli* ML30 have been carefully determined by Midgley (16). (See Table 1.) It is evident that the nucleic acids extracted from the 30 and 50 S particles differ slightly in over-all composition. In addition, by means of elegant experiments in which 13 and 28 S ribosomal RNAs were hybridized to DNA, Yankofsky and Spiegelman (17) showed that the nucleotide sequences in the two classes were distinct.

REFERENCES

1. MIDGLEY, J. E. M. 1962. Biochim. Biophys. Acta. *61:* 513.
2. ROBERTS, R. B., R. J. BRITTEN, and B. J. MCCARTHY. 1963. *In* J. H. Taylor, editor, Molecular genetics. Academic Press: New York. P. 292.
3. MCCARTHY, B. J. 1962. Biochim. Biophys. Acta. *55:* 880.
4. HAYASHI, M., and S. SPIEGELMAN. 1961. Proc. Nat. Acad. Sci. U.S. *47:* 1564.
5. MCCARTHY, B. J. 1960. Biochim. Biophys. Acta. *39:* 563.
6. ROBERTS, R. B., P. H. ABELSON, D. B. COWIE, E. T. BOLTON, and R. J. BRITTEN. 1955. Studies of biosynthesis in *Escherichia coli.* Carnegie Institution of Washington: Washington, D.C. Publication 607, p. 5.
7. FRENCH, C. S., and H. W. MILNER. 1955. In N. Kaplan and S. Colowick, editors, Methods in enzymology. Academic Press: New York. Vol. I, p. 65.
8. MIDGLEY, J. E. M., and B. J. MCCARTHY. 1962. Biochim. Biophys. Acta. *61:* 696.
9. BRITTEN, R. J., and R. B. ROBERTS. 1960. Science. *131:* 32.
10. BOCK, R. M., and N. S. LING. 1954. Anal. Chem. *26:* 1543.
11. ARONSON, A. I., and B. J. MCCARTHY. 1961. Biophys. J. *1:* 215.
12. KURLAND, C. G. 1960. J. Mol. Biol. 2: 83.
13. BOEDTKER, H., W. MOLLER, and E. KLEMPERER. 1962. Nature. *194:* 444.
14. LANGRIDGE, R. 1963. Science. *140:* 1000.
15. TIMASHEFF, S. N., J. WITS, and V. LUZATTI. 1961. Biophys. J. *1:* 525.
16. MIDGLEY, J. E. M. 1962. Carnegie Institution of Washington Year Book 67 (1961–1962). Washington, D.C. P. 255.
17. YANKOFSKY, S. A., and S. SPIEGELMAN. 1962. Proc. Nat. Acad. Sci. U.S. *48:* 1466.

The Isolation of

Ribosomal RNA

from Mammals

J. BARLOW AND A. P. MATHIAS
DEPARTMENT OF BIOCHEMISTRY
UNIVERSITY COLLEGE LONDON
LONDON, ENGLAND

Three major forms of RNA have been described in nucleated and nonnucleated cells—ribosomal RNA (rRNA), soluble or transfer RNA (tRNA), and messenger RNA (mRNA). Of these rRNA is present in by far the largest amount, usually comprising 80–90% of the cellular RNA. It consists of two species, one with a molecular weight in the range $1.1–1.5 \times 10^6$ (sedimentation coefficient about 28 S) and the other approximately 0.5×10^6 (18 S). Most of the remaining RNA of the cell is soluble RNA, sharply distinguished from rRNA in that it occurs uncombined with protein, has a much lower molecular weight (approximately 2.5×10^4), and contains high proportions of uncommon nucleotides. Messenger RNA, normally less than 2% of the cellular RNA, ranges in molecular weight from a hundred thousand to many millions and most of it occurs in complexes with ribosomes known as polyribosomes, or polysomes. Unlike tRNA and mRNA, there is at present no biological assay for rRNA. It may be characterized by determination of its molecular weight and base composition.

Methods for isolation of rRNA can be broadly subdivided into those that involve a preliminary separation of the ribosomes, and those in which total RNA is extracted from whole cells. One of the problems

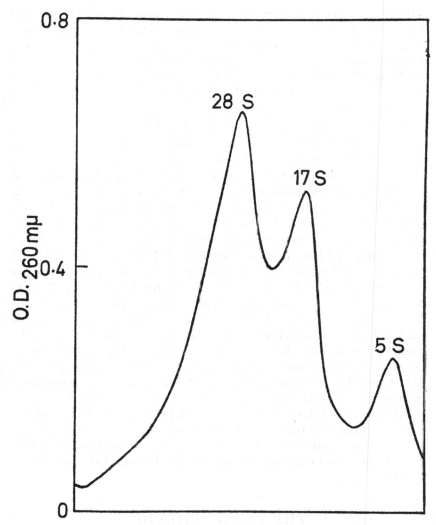

Fig. 1. Analysis of RNA extracted from reticulocytes with phenol on a 5–20% (w/v) gradient of sucrose in 0.005 M phosphate buffer, pH 7.0, using SW39 L rotor. Centrifugation was 3 hr at 37,500 rev/min and 5 C. Sedimentation is from right to left.

encountered with the latter approach is the separation of the RNA from other high molecular weight contaminants. Unless precautions are taken, DNA is usually liberated with RNA and has to be removed with specific enzymes. Tissues rich in polysaccharide (e.g., liver), yield preparations of rRNA heavily contaminated with these substances.

Lipids may also complicate the extraction procedures. An essential feature of all methods for the purification of rRNA is that they must bring about separation of rRNA from protein. The phenol method is probably more drastic in its denaturing action on protein than other methods. The separation of rRNA from tRNA is usually accomplished by taking advantage of the solubility of the latter in solutions of high salt concentration from which rRNA is precipitated.

Three procedures for the isolation of rRNA will be described. In every case, the quality of the product should be checked either in an analytical ultracentrifuge or by sucrose density gradient analysis. A satisfactory separation of the two ribosomal species of RNA is obtained in the Spinco swinging-bucket type SW39L Rotor if a solution (0.1 ml) containing approximately 200 μg RNA is layered over a 5–20% (w/v) gradient of sucrose in 0.01 M sodium acetate, pH 5, and centrifuged at 4 C for 4–5 hr at 35,000 rev/min. Alternatively, the sucrose solutions may be prepared from phosphate or Tris–HCl buffers in the 7–7.5 pH range. A typical gradient is shown in Fig. 1. The rRNA yields sharper peaks and the separation of the 28 and 18 S RNA is better if divalent cations are removed. This can be achieved by dialysis of the RNA at 2–4 C against 0.05 M EDTA (disodium salt, pH 7.0) or by treatment of the RNA solution with Chelex 100 resin Na form (Analytical Grade, Bio-Rad Laboratories, Richmond, California). EDTA may also be incorporated in the sucrose gradient, which should be prepared in 0.025 M EDTA and Tris–HCl buffer, pH 7.2. The position of the components in the gradients at the end of the centrifugation is determined either by piercing a hole in the base of the Lusteroid tube and collection of the contents in fractions that, after dilution with buffer, are read at 260 mμ, or by passing the contents of the tube through a flow cell in a recording spectrophotometer (e.g., 1), after which it can be collected in a fraction cutter.

THE USE OF PHENOL

One of the earliest reports on the use of phenol in the preparation of RNA dealt with the extraction of RNA from a whole tissue—liver— and gave a product free of DNA and polysaccharide (2). Phenol may also be used for the preparation of RNA from isolated ribosomes. Examples of both techniques are given.

Isolation of Ribosomal RNA from Brain Tissue

The method was devised by R. H. Kimberlin and is based on the procedures of Kirby (3,4).

Reagents

0.5% (w/v) Napthalene-1,5-disulfonic acid, sodium salt, pH 6.8
Phenol reagent, which contains freshly redistilled phenol–m-cresol–8-
  hydroxyquinoline–water (500:70:0.5:55 parts by weight)
Tri-isopropyl napthalene sulfonate (Na salt)
Sodium benzoate

Procedure

Mice are killed and the brains are rapidly removed and chilled on solid CO_2. The tissue is homogenized with the napthalene-disulfonate solution in a Potter-Elvehjem homogenizer to give a 10% homogenate. An equal volume of the phenol reagent is added, and the mixture heated at 65 C for 10 min with vigorous mixing using a mechanical shaker. The mixture is rapidly cooled to 4 C and centrifuged in the Spinco 30 rotor at 20,000 rev/min (35,000 × g) for 20 min. The aqueous layer is separated and sodium tri-isopropyl napthalene sulfonate added to give a final concentration of 5% (w/v). It is shaken with a half-volume of the phenol reagent at 4 C for 15 min, and centrifuged as above for 10 min. The aqueous layer is separated and sodium benzoate, NaCl, and m-cresol are added to give final concentrations of 20, 3, and 9% (w/v), respectively. After 1 hr at 0 C, the precipitated RNA is recovered by centrifugation at 10,000 × g for 10 min. The precipitate is washed once with an aqueous solution of sodium benzoate, NaCl, and m-cresol at the concentrations given above, twice with 75% (v/v) aqueous ethanol, twice with absolute ethanol, finally with ether, and then dried. The product is essentially free of tRNA, DNA, and protein. This method yields up to 70% of the ribosomal RNA of the tissue.

Comments

The comparatively high centrifugal forces used in the first two centrifugations are necessitated by the presence of large amounts of lipid in brain. This gives rise to a bulky interfacial layer, which must be compressed by centrifugation. The addition of 8-hydroxyquinoline to the phenol reagent minimizes oxidation of phenol and may be valuable in removing metal ions involved in binding ribosomal RNA to protein.

The product is virtually free of tRNA, which remains in solution in the presence of sodium benzoate and m-cresol.

The mRNA remains largely in the insoluble material at the interface (5). However, some is found in the aqueous phase. Extraction of polyribosomes with phenol seems to leave the bulk of mRNA in the aqueous phase.

Isolation of RNA from Rat Liver Microsomes

Reagents

SDS solution, which contains 10% (w/v) sodium dodecyl sulfate and
0.5% (w/v) napthalene-1,5-disulfonic acid, sodium salt adjusted to
pH 7.6
The SDS should be recrystallized from ethanol (6)
Phenol reagent: 90% aqueous redistilled phenol containing 0.1%
8-hydroxyquinoline

Procedure

Sufficient SDS solution is added to a suspension of microsomes (or
ribosomes) in 0.05 M Tris–HCl buffer, pH 7.6 (with or without 5×10^{-3}-
M Mg Cl$_2$) to give a final concentration of 1%. The suspension is extracted with an equal volume of phenol reagent for 15 min at 5 C with
vigorous mechanical shaking. After centrifugation for 10 min at
3000 $\times$ g at 5 C, the aqueous phase is separated and re-extracted twice
with a half-volume of phenol reagent. The aqueous phase is made 2%
with respect to sodium acetate and 70% with respect to ethanol. The
RNA precipitates during storage for 2–18 hr in a deep freeze, and is
collected by centrifugation. The precipitate is washed repeatedly with
70% ethanol, dissolved in 0.01 M sodium acetate buffer, pH 5.2, containing 0.1 M sodium chloride, and reprecipitated with ethanol.

Yields vary from 25–50% total rRNA.

Comments

The use of buffers containing K$^+$ ions should be avoided when
dodecyl sulfate is present because of the low solubility of its K$^+$ salt.

If the microsome fraction is contaminated with nuclei, the SDS
concentration should be lowered to 0.1% to avoid DNA extraction (7).
Alternatively, the SDS concentration may be kept at 1%. If there is
appreciable DNA present, the interphase layer is viscous and in the
first two extractions it should be removed and re-extracted with the
aqueous layer.

This technique also gives a satisfactory extraction of nuclear RNA
from isolated nuclei, but the product is heavily contaminated by DNA
(8). This may be removed by dissolving the nucleic acids in ice cold
0.01 M Tris-HCl, pH 7.5, containing 0.001 M MgCl$_2$ and incubating at
0 C with pancreatic deoxyribonuclease I (5 μg/ml of a preparation free
of ribonuclease, Worthington Biochemical Corporation) for 10 min.
The incubation mixture is extracted with an equal volume of phenol.

The RNA is precipitated as above from the aqueous phase, redissolved in 2 M potassium acetate, made 25% with respect to ethanol, and kept overnight in a deep freeze. This procedure must be repeated at least three times for complete removal of oligodeoxyribonucleotides. In our experience, SDS is best omitted when extracting RNA from isolated nuclei.

General Comments on Phenol Extraction

It should be emphasized that each tissue presents peculiar problems. A method using phenol that is satisfactory with one, may be unsuccessful with another. Among the conditions that may be varied are the temperature at which phenol extractions are carried out, the duration of the extraction, the presence or otherwise of chelating agents, and the pH of the aqueous phase.

Although phenol undoubtedly denatures many proteins, it is important to realize that it does not completely inactivate nucleases (9,10) and RNA prepared by various phenol methods is liable to be contaminated with these enzymes.

The simplest method of eliminating the nucleases is by treatment of aqueous solutions of RNA or ribosomes or crude homogenates with bentonite, which is a hydrated aluminum silicate possessing cation exchange properties. This seems to act by absorption of the nucleases, most of which are basic proteins. The bentonite is prepared (11,12) by suspending the crude powder in distilled water to a concentration of 50 mg/ml and recovering the fraction that sediments between 6000 × g for 10 min and 20,000 × g for 15 min. The precipitate is resuspended in 0.1 M sodium EDTA, pH 7.5, at a concentration of 10 mg/ml and stirred at room temperature for 24 hr. The suspension is centrifuged at 20,000 × g for 15 min. The sediment is resuspended in water and the EDTA removed either by repeated washing or dialysis against large volumes of distilled water.

Bentonite can be used at all stages of RNA preparation using phenol. During the initial phenol extraction it may be added at a concentration of 5–10 mg/ml. It is also helpful in many instances to add bentonite whenever RNA is redissolved. Although the nucleases absorb readily on bentonite, it is probable that the enzymes are still active when bound to this solid support. If the solution is to be kept for any time, the bentonite should be removed by centrifugation and fresh bentonite added.

One disadvantage of the phenol method is that polysaccharides, such as glycogen, remain in the aqueous phase. Although they may be removed by extraction with 2-methoxyethanol (2), degradation of RNA may occur during this procedure.† In the case of rat liver the problem may be avoided by starvation of the animals for 24–48 hr before killing them.

THE USE OF GUANIDINIUM CHLORIDE

The following procedure is based on the method of Cox and Arnstein (13).

Reagents

5 M guanidinium chloride containing 0.03 M EDTA is prepared by dissolving appropriate amounts of guanidinium carbonate (AnalaR grade) and EDTA in water, adjusting the pH to 4.5 with conc. HCl and bringing to the correct volume.

Procedure

Ribosomes are obtained by differential centrifugation [e.g., of a lysate of rabbit reticulocytes (14)] or by adjusting to pH 6, a postmitochondrial supernatant fluid fraction (15). They are suspended (approx. 10 mg/ml) in 0.05 M Tris, adjusted to pH 7.6 with HCl and containing 0.025 M KCl and 0.005 M $MgCl_2$, cooled to 0 C, and mixed with 5 volumes of previously cooled guanidinium chloride reagent. After 30 min, the precipitate is collected by centrifugation at 3000 × g for 5 min and washed with 6 M guanidinium chloride and then ethanol. Under these conditions the recovery of RNA is about 85%. It is influenced by the temperature, pH, and the Mg^{2+} concentration. The pelleted RNA does not readily redissolve either in water or salt solutions and may require repeated extraction. The first extraction, in which little RNA normally dissolves, may serve to remove most of the guanidinium chloride in the precipitate. The RNA may be converted to the K+ salt by passage through a column of Amberlite IRC-50 (chromatographic grade) in K+ form. This procedure also removes some of the contaminating nucleases.

Comments

It is a common experience that RNA precipitated by organic solvents or salts does not readily redissolve, unless care has been taken to remove the remaining precipitating agent. A full account of the method is soon to be published (20).

† Recently, Kirby has shown that DNA, sRNA, and glycogen may be removed from precipitated RNA by extraction with 3 M-sodium acetate (19).

THE USE OF LITHIUM CHLORIDE

Reagents

4 M Lithium chloride
2 M Lithium chloride
Tris buffer, which contains
0.05 M KCl
0.001 M Tris } adjusted to pH 7.4 at 4 C with HCl

Procedure

All operations should be carried out between 0 and 4 C. An equal volume of 4 M LiCl is added to the postmitochondrial (cytoplasmic) supernatant fluid and the solution left for the RNA to precipitate. The time required for precipitation of the ribosomal RNA will depend on the initial RNA concentration (Fig. 2).

If the RNP concentration is greater than 20 mg/ml, the RNA and protein do not dissociate before the RNA precipitates. The RNA is isolated by centrifugation at 3000 × g for 2 min and washed twice with 2 M LiCl. The precipitate may then be redissolved by gentle homogenization in a suitable buffer, preferably free of divalent cations. The RNA prepared by this method contains less than 1% protein and is virtually free of tRNA, which remains in solution in 2 M LiCl. Some at least of the mRNA appears to be precipitated with rRNA.

The isolation of RNA from washed ribosomes (16) occurs under the same conditions as required for the cytoplasm. Ribosomes are suspended in TKM buffer at a concentration of 2–20 mg/ml. An equal volume of 4 M LiCl is added and the recovery of rRNA is virtually quantitative. This method is satisfactory with the ribosomes from many tissues, but with those from *E. coli* it is necessary to use a final concentration of 3 M LiCl and to have 4 M urea present (17). SDS can not be used to assist the dissociation of the ribosomes because it causes some protein to precipitate.

THE SEPARATION OF 28 AND 18 S rRNA

The simplest method for isolating the two forms of RNA is separation by centrifugation in a sucrose density gradient column. The details of this procedure using the SW39L rotor have been described in an earlier section. With the Spinco SW25-1 rotor it is possible to centrifuge 0.2–1.0 ml of a solution containing 200–1000 μg of RNA layered over

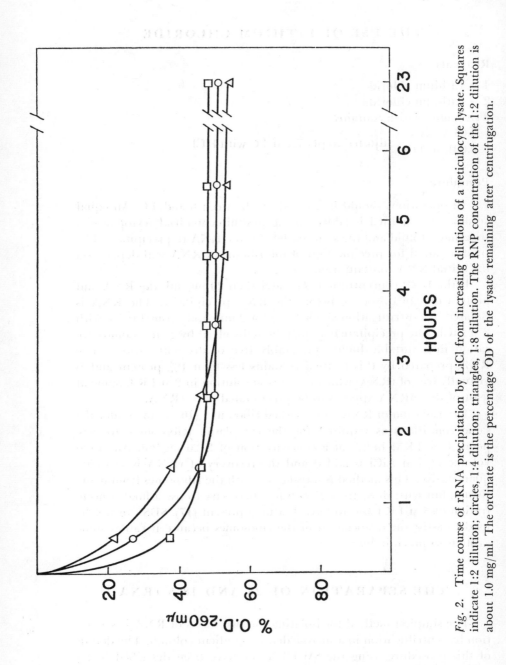

Fig. 2. Time course of rRNA precipitation by LiCl from increasing dilutions of a reticulocyte lysate. Squares indicate 1:2 dilution; circles, 1:4 dilution; triangles, 1:8 dilution. The RNP concentration of the 1:2 dilution is about 1.0 mg/ml. The ordinate is the percentage OD of the lysate remaining after centrifugation.

a 27 ml of 5–20% sucrose gradient (w/v) in sodium acetate solution (0.01 M, pH 5) or Tris or phosphate buffers. Separation of the two rRNA components requires 14–16 hr at 24,000 rev/min at 4 C. When the RNA is to be recovered it is advisable to pretreat the sucrose solutions with bentonite (3–5 mg/ml) before preparing the gradients. The RNA is recovered by bulking the appropriate fractions, adding 2 volumes of absolute ethanol containing 2% potassium acetate (w/v), and keeping at −10 C overnight. The precipitated RNA is collected by centrifugation and washed with 95% ethanol and dried over KOH or phosphorous pentoxide. Alternatively, the sucrose may be removed and the RNA concentrated by vacuum dialysis at 4 C against the required buffer. Another method for removing sucrose is passage through a column of Sephadex G-25 or G-50 equilibrated with the required buffer.

Two methods are available to recover RNA from gradient fractions for the determination of radioactivity. In the first, carrier protein (bovine serum albumin) or RNA (ca. 500 μg/ml) is added to the fraction followed by an equal volume of 10% TCA. The precipitate is collected on Millipore filters (0.45 μ pore size), washed with 5% TCA, and dried. In the second (10), the RNA is quantitatively extracted by shaking 1.8 ml of the sucrose solution with 1 ml of a mixture of n-butanol, 2,2′-diethyldihexylamine, and glacial acetic acid (100, 11.7, 2 v/v). The RNA is quantitatively transferred to the organic phase, which may be added directly to toluene-based scintillation fluids.

Another method that should offer a way of separating 28 and 18 S mammalian rRNA is chromatography on columns of methylated serum albumin supported on kieselguhr. This technique is satisfactory with bacterial rRNA (18). However, for some reason that remains obscure, we have not been successful in obtaining good resolution of rRNA from mammalian tissues on these columns. A large scale separation of the two rRNA species is now possible using the zonal ultracentrifuge (21). Up to 80 mg of RNA can be completely resolved in 6 hr. The RNA is recovered, even from fractions where the concentration is extremely low, by adding sodium acetate to a concentration of 10% (w/v). Redistilled acetone is then added, with mixing, until a slight turbidity is observed. After centrifugation to separate the two phases, the precipitated RNA is obtained (21).

REFERENCES

1. EDWARDS, J. G., and A. P. MATHIAS. 1963. Nature. *199:* 603.
2. KIRBY, K. S. 1956. Biochem. J. *64:* 405.
3. KIRBY, K. S. 1962. Biochim. Biophys. Acta. *55:* 545.

4. KIRBY, K. S. 1964. Biochem. J. *93:* 5C.
5. KIDSON, C., and K. S. KIRBY. 1964. J. Mol. Biol. *10:* 187.
6. CRESTFIELD, A. M., K. C. SMITH, and F. W. ALLEN. 1955. J. Biol. Chem. *216:* 185.
7. DINGMAN, W., and M. B. SPORN. 1962. Biochim. Biophys. Acta. *61:* 164.
8. DI GIROLAMO, A., E. C. HENSHAW, and A. H. HIATT. 1964. J. Mol. Biol. *8:* 479.
9. LITTAUER, U. Z., and M. SELA. 1962. Biochim. Biophys. Acta. *61:* 609.
10. KIDSON, C., K. S. KIRBY, and R. K. RALPH. 1963. J. Mol. Biol. *7:* 213.
11. BROWNHILL, T. J., A. S. JONES, and M. STACEY. 1959. Biochem. J. *73:* 434.
12. KELLER, P. J., E. COHEN, and R. D. WADE. 1964. J. Biol. Chem. *239:* 3292.
13. COX, R. A., and H. R. V. ARNSTEIN. 1965. Biochem. J. *89:* 574.
14. MATHIAS, A. P., R. WILLIAMSON, H. E. HUXLEY, and S. PAGE. 1964. J. Mol. Biol. *9:* 154.
15. COX, R. A., and H. R. V. ARNSTEIN. 1964. Biochem. J. *93:* 33C.
16. BARLOW, J. J., A. P. MATHIAS, R. WILLIAMSON, and D. B. GAMMACK. 1963. Biochem. Biophys. Res. Comm. *13:* 61.
17. SPITNIK-ELSON, P. 1965. Biochem. Biophys. Res. Comm. *18:* 557.
18. ISHIHAMA, A., M. MIZUNO, M. TAKAI, E. OTAKA, and S. OSAWA. 1962. J. Mol. Biol. *5:* 251.
19. KIRBY, K. S. 1965. Biochem. J. *96:* 268.
20. COX, R. A. *In* L. Grossman and K. Moldave, editors, Methods in enzymology: nucleic acids. Academic Press: New York. Vol. 1, in press.
21. KIRBY, K. S., J. R. B. HASTINGS, J. H. PARISH, and E. S. KLUCIS. 1965. Biochem. J. *97:* 25P.

2. tRNA

Isolation of Transfer RNA

GEOFFREY ZUBAY
DEPARTMENT OF ZOOLOGY
COLUMBIA UNIVERSITY
NEW YORK, NEW YORK

Escherichia coli is an ideal source for tRNA (transfer RNA) because it contains a relatively large amount of tRNA, about 2 g of tRNA/kg of *E. coli* paste; the tRNA is of high quality; the acceptor ability for various amino acids compares favorably with tRNA obtained from other sources; with the proper equipment, large quantities of *E. coli* of reproducible character can be grown with relative ease.

ISOLATION PROCEDURE

E. coli are grown according to the method of Littauer and Kornberg (1) and may be stored before use in the frozen state (−20 C or lower, at least a year at −120 C) after collection in the Sharples ultracentrifuge. If frozen, the thin cakes of frozen bacteria are allowed to soften for 3 hr at 5 C. It is preferable, however, to use the bacteria without freezing, since they are then easier to handle. All operations are carried out at 5 C and all centrifugations are carried out for 5 min at $5000 \times g$, except where otherwise specified. The essential steps in the preparation of the tRNA include a phenol-shaking step after Kirby (2), which removes most of the non-nucleic acid material; a 1 M NaCl extraction step, which separates the tRNA from most of the high molecular weight RNA and some protein; and an isopropanol fractionation step, which has been found to separate the tRNA from DNA and more high molecular weight RNA.

Special Reagents

PEP, 2 Phosphoenolpyruvic Acid, Trisodium salt A grade, Cal. Biochem.

PEP Kinase, A grade, Cal. Biochem.

Deoxyribonuclease, pancreatic deoxyribonuclease, Worthington Biochemical Corp.

ATP, Disodium salt, Cal. Biochem.

C^{14}-L-leucine, New England Nuclear Corp. Amino acid diluted with nonradioactive leucine to desired specific activity, 2–10 mc/mM.

Phenol, Mallinckrodt reagent grade liquified phenol without preservative is distilled, taking the distillate between 178 and 181 C. This is collected in a round bottom flask and stored at −20 C in a stoppered vessel. Just prior to use the phenol is melted at ∼65 C and adjusted to contain 12% by volume of water; the resulting solution is chilled to 5 C.

The preparation described here is for 2 kg of bacterial paste. (The procedure can, however, be conveniently adapted to amounts as small as 50 g.) The bacterial paste is suspended in 4 liters of 0.01 M magnesium acetate +0.001 M Tris buffer, pH 7.4, and when it has been dispersed by stirring, the suspension is equally distributed among eight 2-liter bottles. About 430 ml of 88% redistilled phenol are added to each bottle, and the mixture is vigorously agitated on a shaker for a period of not less than 1 hr. The mixture is then centrifuged at 18,000 × g for 30 min. The top layer, which contains the nucleic acid and may be turbid, is carefully decanted. The nucleic acid is precipitated from this top layer by the addition of 0.1 volumes of 20% potassium acetate and 2 volumes of absolute alcohol. This preparation may be stored as long as 36 hr at 5 C without damaging. The precipitate is then collected by centrifugation. The supernatant fluid is discarded, and 2 liters of 1 M NaCl are added to the precipitate. Vigorous stirring for 1 hr disperses the precipitate, and the suspension is then centrifuged for 30 min at 15,000 × g. The supernatant fluid is collected and the sediment is re-extracted with 1 liter of 1 M NaCl, recentrifuged, and this supernatant liquid is collected and the sediment discarded. The supernatant liquids from the two NaCl extractions are combined and the RNA precipitated by the addition of 2 volumes of ethanol. The precipitate is collected by centrifugation and the supernatant fluid is discarded. The ethanol precipitation step is repeated.

The above isolation procedure necessitates the incubation of the

RNA at an elevated pH to remove amino acids from the terminal adenosine groups of the tRNAs. This is accomplished by suspending the precipitate in 200 ml of 0.2 M glycine buffer, pH 10.3, and incubating for 3 hr at 36 C. [Sarin and Zamecnik (3) have indicated that the use of this high pH may partially degrade and/or denature the tRNA. They found that exposure to 1.8 M Tris-HCl, pH 8, at 37 C, for 90 min was at least 98% effective in removing amino acid from the tRNAs studied. When complete removal of amino acid is not required this procedure is probably the better one to follow.] This suspension is then made 0.4 M in NaCl by addition of 4 M NaCl and the RNA is precipitated by the addition of 2 volumes of ethanol. The precipitate is collected by centrifugation and the supernatant fluid is discarded. The precipitate is dissolved in 1.4 liters of 0.3 M sodium acetate, pH 7. To this is added 0.54 volumes of isopropyl alcohol. The addition is made slowly and with efficient stirring. The temperature is adjusted to 20 C, and the suspension is centrifuged for 5 min at 8000 $\times$ g. The supernatant liquid is collected and stored. The precipitate is redissolved in 0.7 liters of 0.3 M sodium acetate, pH 7. To this is added 0.54 volumes of isopropyl alcohol with the same precautions as described above. This suspension is again centrifuged as above and 745 ml of isopropyl alcohol is added to the combined supernatant fluids from the two centrifugations. The resulting precipitate, which contains the tRNA, is collected by centrifugation at 5 C. It is then dissolved in about 150 ml of H_2O, and dialyzed against distilled water overnight at 5 C. This dialyzed tRNA solution is usually stored in the frozen state, although it may be lyophilized before storing in the freezer. The yield of tRNA from 2 kg of *E. coli* is 3–5 g.

Method of Assaying tRNA

tRNA has several physical and chemical properties that distinguish it from other forms of nucleic acid and that may be used to estimate the quality of a preparation. The above procedure for the isolation of tRNA should result in a minimum of physical and chemical change. The final purified product, which is about 90% tRNA (the remainder is mostly high molecular weight RNA) has a λ_{max} of 258 mμ in 0.1 M NaCl and an $E_{1\%}^{258\,m\mu}$ of 201 $\pm$ 5 as determined by optical density and dry weight measurements. It contains 9.4 $\pm$ 1.0% phosphorus. The protein content, determined by the Lowry estimation (4), is less than 1%. Other physicochemical properties have been described elsewhere (5,6).

It has been demonstrated that tRNA is involved in two important biochemical reactions in protein synthesis (7). In the first of these reactions an amino acid becomes attached to a specific tRNA molecule. In the second reaction the amino acid–tRNA complex migrates to the ribosome where the amino acid is transferred to a polypeptide chain. The first reaction can be used as a most convenient method of quantitative biochemical assay of the quality of a tRNA preparation.

tRNA is usually assayed by determining its ability to combine with a single amino acid. The mixed incorporation of all twenty amino acids is not measured because (a) pure radioactive amino acid mixtures are very expensive and (b) the activity of some of the transfer enzymes, which are essential for the coupling reaction, is uncertain. Leucine, however, is a most convenient amino acid to use for general assay purposes because it makes up a relatively large amount of amino-acyl–tRNA and because the leucine transfer enzyme is relatively stable and easy to obtain in saturating amounts.

Preparation of Enzyme Extract Used in Coupling of Amino Acid to the tRNA

All operations are carried out at 1–5 C. 30 g of *E. coli* paste, fresh or frozen, is mixed with an equal volume of alumina powder and ground in a mortar for 10–15 min. To this mixture 60 ml of 0.01 M magnesium acetate + 0.001 M Tris buffer, pH 7.4, is added, to the resulting suspension 4 μg/ml of deoxyribonuclease is added. The alumina and bacterial membranes are removed by centrifugation at 17,000 $\times$ g for 15 min. The supernatant fluid is centrifuged further at 78,000 $\times$ g for 150 min. The top two-thirds of the resulting supernatant liquid are carefully decanted and dialyzed for 8 hr against 0.02 M potassium phosphate buffer, pH 7.7 + 5 mM β-mercaptoethanol. This dialyzed enzyme extract is adequate for most purposes. The main object of the subsequent steps is to separate the enzyme from the nucleic acid. 15 ml of the enzyme extract is applied to a 1.2- $\times$ 30-cm Selectacel DEAE column previously washed and equilibrated with the phosphate buffer, pH 7.7 + 5 mM β-mercaptoethanol. The column is then rinsed with about 70 ml of the phosphate buffer and the enzyme is subsequently eluted from the column with a solution of 0.25 M NaCl + 0.02 M potassium phosphate buffer, pH 7.7 + 5 mM β-mercaptoethanol. Fractions are collected in 5-ml portions. The tube with the highest optical density at 280 mμ is then used in the coupling reaction of amino acid to the tRNA. Several other methods of enzyme isolation and partial purification have been reported (8,9).

Coupling Reaction

The tRNA is assayed by its ability to combine with leucine. The leucine content is determined by using a predetermined amount of tRNA in the assay and by using radioactive leucine of known specific activity. The specific activity of the leucine is determined from the molarity of a concentrated stock solution and the counts/minute of equal samples registered on the Geiger counter under conditions identical to those used in the tRNA assay.

The standard incubation mixture for assay of the tRNA has a total volume of 1 ml containing 1 mg of tRNA test sample; 10 μmoles of Tris-HCl buffer, pH 7.0; 5.5 μmoles of $MgCl_2$; 8.0 μmoles of ATP, pH 7.0; 5.0 μmoles of PEP; 30 μg of pyruvate kinase, which is obtained as a suspension in ammonum sulfate, is diluted just before use; 0.03 μmoles of the appropriate C^{14}-L-leucine 2–10 mc/mM; and 0.05 ml of enzyme extract, all at pH 7.0. All ingredients are mixed except the enzyme extract: This is added after temperature equilibration at 37 C and the time of incubation is precisely timed from the point of addition of enzyme. After 10 min the reaction is stopped by the addition of 1 ml of 0 C 10% TCA (trichloroacetic acid). (Under the above conditions the reaction should reach completion in about 2 min; if considerably longer times are needed to achieve maximum coupling, the PEP kinase should be protected by the addition of 0.01 M β-mercaptoethanol.) The resulting precipitate is successively centrifuged and washed three times by suspending in 3 ml of 5% TCA at 0 C and centrifuging. The washed precipitate is finally suspended in 3 ml of 5% TCA and heated at 90 C for 15 min, followed by cooling to room temperature. The TCA is extracted by shaking three times with three equal volumes of ether. The aqueous phase is centrifuged to remove solid particles and 0.2-ml portions of the supernatant fluid are plated for counting. Zero time controls and controls made by incubating the system in the absence of added tRNA contain a negligible amount of radioactivity.

It is convenient to express the specific activity of the product in units of nucleotides/leucine. In this calculation we use an average molecular weight per nucleotide of 343. The other measured quantities are the weight of tRNA and the specific activity of the radioactive leucine. A sample calculation is given.

Counts for 0.2-ml portion = 1800 cpm
Total volume = 3.0 ml
Total tRNA added = 1 mg
Specific activity of leucine = 10^7 cpm/μM

$$\frac{\text{nucleotides}}{\text{leucine}} = \frac{1}{\dfrac{3.0}{0.2} \times \dfrac{1800}{10^7} \Big/ \dfrac{10^{-3}}{343} \times 10^6} = 1080$$

REFERENCES

1. LITTAUER, U. Z., and A. KORNBERG. 1957. J. Biol. Chem. 266: 1077.
2. KIRBY, K. S. 1954. Biochem. J. 58: 390.

3. SARIN, P. C., and P. C. ZAMECNIK. 1964. Biochim. Biophys. Acta. *91:* 653.
4. LOWRY, O. H., N. J. ROSEBROUGH, A. L. FARR, and R. J. RANDALL. 1951. J. Biol. Chem. *193:* 265.
5. ZUBAY, G. 1962. J. Mol. Biol. *4:* 347.
6. TISSIÈRES, A. 1959. J. Mol. Biol. *1:* 365.
7. SCHWEET, R., and J. BISHOP. 1963. *In* J. H. Taylor, editor, Molecular genetics. Academic Press, New York. Part 1, p. 353.
8. MUENCH, K. H., and P. BERG. This volume, p. 375.
9. MCCORQUODALL, D. J. 1964. Biochim. Biophys. Acta. *91:* 541.

Methyl-Poor sRNA†

from *Escherichia coli*

ERWIN FLEISSNER

THE ROCKEFELLER UNIVERSITY

NEW YORK, NEW YORK

ERNEST BOREK

COLLEGE OF PHYSICIANS AND SURGEONS

COLUMBIA UNIVERSITY

NEW YORK, NEW YORK

Relaxed Control of RNA Synthesis

The accumulation of RNA by *Escherichia coli* in the absence of a required amino acid was first observed in the strain K-12 W-6 auxotrophic for methionine (1). Subsequent genetic analysis revealed that this property is not a consequence of the mutation to methionine dependence, for if other amino acid requirements are introduced into the same strain by genetic techniques, the absence of these amino acids from the culture medium will also result in RNA accumulation (2). The genetic locus responsible for the RNA accumulation has been mapped and designated RC^{Rel} (i.e., RNA synthesis under relaxed control); the wild type is designated RC^{Str} (i.e., RNA synthesis under stringent control) (2).‡

Methyl-Poor RNA

It has been demonstrated that the methylated bases that are normally present in both soluble and ribosomal RNA of *E. coli* (and in

† sRNA is equivalent to tRNA.

‡ A number of new RC^{Rel} isolates have been obtained recently by Maaløe (13).

461

soluble and ribosomal RNA of all species examined in this regard) have methyl groups derived from the methyl group of methionine (3). This fact carries the implication that if the original RC[Rel] strain K-12 W-6 is starved for methionine, first of all it will accumulate RNA and secondly this RNA will lack the normal methylated bases. This inference can be experimentally verified (4), as explained below.

PROCEDURE FOR METHIONINE DEPRIVATION

Logarithmic Growth

Cultures of *E. coli* K-12 W-6 are maintained on slants of nutrient agar kept in the refrigerator and transferred at intervals of 3 months. Liquid inocula are prepared by growing a loopful of bacteria in a salts and glucose medium (minimal medium) (5).

The minimal medium is supplemented with biotin (12 γ per L) and DL-methionine (0.003%). If it is desired to keep the loop culture in the refrigerator for several days it is convenient to use minimal medium with only 0.03% glucose. The culture will run out of glucose at a population of about 2×10^8 cells/ml and is then more stable when stored. A similar technique works well in growing large shaker-flask cultures in the laboratory. Minimal medium with only 0.03% glucose plus methionine and biotin as above is inoculated with 1/200 volume of the loop culture and aerated at 37 C overnight. In the morning sterile glucose is added to 0.3% and growth will resume within half an hour. Under ordinary conditions the culture will now be in logarithmic growth phase for about two generations.

Methionine Starvation

A logarithmically growing culture is prepared as described in the preceding section. About one generation of growth is permitted after the addition of the full amount of glucose. The cells, at about $5 \times 10^8/$ ml, are harvested by centrifugation in the cold and washed twice with cold, sterile minimal medium. The final cell pellets are resuspended in minimal medium prewarmed to 37 C and transferred to a shaker flask, the cells being still at the original population level. The culture is incubated with vigorous aeration for 3 hr. (Note: if an isotope is added during this period to label the unmethylated RNA, it is advisable to wait until the methionine starvation has proceeded for 15 min so as to allow the cells to use up intracellular pools of methionine.) The starved cells are harvested by centrifugation and washed with cold isotonic saline. The cells are stored frozen as a pellet.

Assay for RNA Accumulation

To test the culture for RNA accumulation during methionine starvation 5-ml portions are centrifuged at the beginning and end of the starvation period. The cell pellets are washed with 5 ml of cold 5% trichloroacetic acid (TCA) and the RNA is extracted with 5 ml of hot 5% TCA (90 C for 15 min). RNA is now determined by the orcinol method (6). The orcinol determination should indicate a 60–100% increase in RNA during the starvation. This is also the RNA accumulation per cell, since the cell population remains constant during the starvation.

EXTRACTION OF THE sRNA

Phenol Extraction of Whole Cells (7)

The procedure will be described for 10 g (wet weight) of cells, the yield from 20 liters of culture under the conditions described above. The cell cake is homogenized for 1 min in a small blender with 15 ml of buffer containing 0.01 M Tris-HCl, pH 7.4, and 0.01 M MgCl$_2$. The creamy cell suspension is transferred to a beaker and 15 ml of water-saturated, redistilled phenol is added with vigorous mechanical stirring. The stirring is continued for 5 min. These steps may all be carried out at room temperature. The extract is centrifuged in the cold at 15,000 × g for 1 hr. The aqueous layer is pipetted off and the RNA precipitated with 0.1 volume of 20% potassium acetate, pH 5, and 2.2 volumes of cold ethanol. The precipitation is allowed to proceed for several hours or overnight at −20 C, and the precipitate is then collected by centrifugation. The pellet will contain considerable DNA as well as contaminating protein and will be difficult to put into suspension. By homogenization or prolonged stirring the pellet is evenly suspended in 5 ml of 1 M NaCl containing 0.02 M Tris, pH 7.8. The suspension is stirred in the cold for 2 hr and is then centrifuged for 20 min at 20,000 × g. The RNA is precipitated from the supernatant fluid by addition of 2 volumes of ethanol and storage at −20 C.

Deoxyribonuclease, Stripping, and DEAE Treatment

The RNA precipitate is collected and dissolved in 4 ml of 0.1 M Tris, pH 9.2. After incubation at 37 C for 45 min to remove attached amino acids, the pH is adjusted to 7 with 1 N acetic acid, MgCl$_2$ is added to 0.01 M and deoxyribonuclease (Worthington, electrophoretically purified) is added to 5 μg/ml. This mixture is incubated at 37 C for 15 min and is then extracted with an equal volume of water-saturated, redistilled phenol by stirring vigorously for 15 min. The aqueous layer after centrifugation is treated in the usual way with 1/10 volume of potassium acetate, pH 5, and 2.2 volumes of cold ethanol, and is left at -20 C.

The RNA collected by centrifugation is dissolved in a small volume of water and adsorbed to a 10-ml column of DEAE (diethylaminoethyl cellulose) equilibrated with 0.02 M Tris-HCl in the cold. The column is eluted with a linear gradient of KCl from 0.1 to 1.0 M in 0.02 M Tris, pH 7.8, with a total volume of 200 ml. The sRNA elutes at 0.4–0.5 M salt. The peak tubes are pooled and the RNA precipitated with 2 volumes of ethanol. The RNA is washed once with 80% and once with 95% ethanol and is dried under vacuum over KOH in a desiccator. The final yield from 10 g of cells should be 20 mg.

Assay of Methyl Deficiency

sRNA prepared in this manner is a good acceptor of methyl groups from S-adenosyl-methionine *in vitro*. The assay may be performed using the "S-100" crude supernatant fluid from $100,000 \times g$ centrifugation of a broken-cell preparation from *E. coli* K-12 W-6 grown in the presence of excess methionine. A typical assay contains 10 μmoles of Tris-HCl, pH 7.8, 1.5 μmoles of β-mercaptoethanol, 2.5 μmoles of $MgCl_2$, 0.025 μmoles of S-adenosyl-methionine-methyl-C^{14}, 250 μg of dialyzed S-100 in terms of protein, and 20μg of methyl-deficient sRNA in a total volume of 0.25 ml. The incubations are performed at 30 C and samples are removed at intervals of 15 min to determine the plateau of methyl acceptance for the RNA sample.

The samples are precipitated by rapid addition of 5 ml of cold, 5% TCA. After standing in the cold for 15 min the precipitates are poured onto a millipore filter (pore size, 0.45 μ; disk diameter, 25 mm) and washed 5 times with 5-ml portions of 5% TCA. The filters are mounted on steel planchets with a drop of 2% casein and then heated in an oven at 110 C for 10 min and counted.

The amount of RNA used will accept a maximum of 500 $\mu\mu$moles of methyl groups, if the starvation has been properly carried out. Descriptions of sRNA methylation using more purified enzyme preparations may be found in the literature (8–10).

Properties of the Methyl-Poor sRNA

The sRNA prepared as described is about 50% normal sRNA, contained in the cells before methionine starvation, and 50% an un-methylated species of sRNA. The latter species does, however, contain the normal complement of pseudo-uridine (4). The abnormal component of methyl-poor sRNA appears to be active in amino acid activation and transfer, though it does not behave identically to normal sRNA in certain assays of this type (11,12). In gross physical properties such as sedimentation coefficient, behavior on Sephadex columns, and melting point as determined by loss of hypochromicity, methyl-poor and normal sRNA from *E. coli* appear similar.

REFERENCES

1. BOREK, E., A. RYAN, and J. ROCKENBACH. 1955. J. Bacteriol. *69:* 460.
2. STENT, G., and S. BRENNER. 1961. Proc. Nat. Acad. Sci. U.S. *47:* 2005.
3. MANDEL, L. R., and E. BOREK. 1963. Biochemistry. *2:* 555.
4. MANDEL, L. R., and E. BOREK. 1963. Biochemistry. *2:* 560.
5. GRAY, C. H., and E. L. TATUM. 1944. Proc. Nat. Acad. Sci. U.S. *30:* 404.
6. MEJBAUM, W. 1939. Z. Physiol. Chem. *258:* 117.
7. Adapted from VON EHRENSTEIN, G., and F. LIPMANN. 1961. Proc. Nat. Acad. Sci. U.S. *47:* 941.
8. FLEISSNER, E., and E. BOREK. 1963. Biochemistry. *2:* 1093.
9. HURWITZ, J., M. GOLD, and M. ANDERS. 1964. J. Biol. Chem. *239:* 3462.
10. SVENSSON, I., H. G. BOMAN, K. G. ERIKSSON, and K. KJELLIN. 1963. J. Molecular Biol. *7:* 254.
11. LITTAUER, U. Z., K. MUENCH, P. BERG, W. GILBERT, and P. F. SPAHR. 1963. Cold Spring Harbor Symposia on Quantitative Biology. *28:* 157.
12. PETERKOFSKY, A. 1964. Proc. Nat. Acad. Sci. U.S. *52:* 1233.
13. MAALØE, O. Personal communication.

Methods of Isolation of

Amino Acid Specific sRNA†

KENTARO TANAKA

SHIONOGI RESEARCH LABORATORY

SHIONOGI & CO., LTD.

OSAKA, JAPAN

INTRODUCTION

Since Hoagland, Zamecnik, and their collaborators (1) first observed the essential role of sRNA in protein synthesis, much interest has been paid to this relatively low molecular weight RNA. It soon became established that sRNAs accept amino acids from enzyme-amino acyl adenylate complexes and transfer the amino acid residues to growing polypeptide chains on ribosomes in cell-free systems prepared from a number of different sources (2–4).

The discovery of amino acid specificity for the amino acyl RNA synthetases (2–4) and Crick's "adaptor hypothesis," which postulated the mediation of small polynucleotides in the course of specific protein synthesis (2–5), led to extensive investigations of amino acid specificity of sRNA.

Evidence obtained from a variety of biological experiments (2–4), as well as the observation of partial physical separation of sRNA preparations into fractions with increased acceptor specificity toward particular amino acids (6–7), indicated that sRNA preparations are composed of a population of polynucleotide chains each specific for a particular amino acid.

† sRNA is equivalent to tRNA.

Although much information has been obtained from unfractionated sRNA, isolation of individual specific sRNA molecular species has been desired to elucidate the molecular basis for the unique function and specificity of sRNA. For this purpose, a large number of different techniques have been devised by many investigators. Because several reviews (2–4,8–12) cover most of these studies, in this article an attempt will be made not to cover the bibliography in detail, but to deal primarily with the procedures that are available to obtain amounts of amino acid specific sRNAs sufficient for structural studies. In relation to these studies, some mention will be made of the heterogeneity and species specificity of amino acid specific sRNAs and criteria of the purity of fractionated sRNA preparations.

METHODS UTILIZING DIFFERENCES IN PHYSICAL PROPERTIES OF sRNAs

Countercurrent Distribution and Partition Chromatography

Most of the amino acid specific sRNAs used for structural studies have so far been isolated by methods utilizing the differences in partition coefficients of sRNA molecular species in two-phase solvent systems.

Warner and Vaimberg (13) first reported the effectiveness of the countercurrent distribution technique for separation of RNAs using a solvent system composed of phosphate buffer (pH 8)–formamide–isopropanol. This method was applied to rat liver sRNA with only slight modifications by Holley and Merrill (7,14). They found that the peak of alanine-specific sRNA is significantly displaced from the peak detected by absorbancy at 260 mμ. In later work, they demonstrated almost complete separation of alanine-specific sRNA from tyrosine-specific sRNA (15). The pertinence of the countercurrent distribution for the fractionation of sRNAs was thus clearly indicated, although the recovery of activity was unsatisfactory. To minimize the loss of activity during the operations, the pH of phosphate buffer was changed from 8 to 6, and addition of magnesium chloride was attempted (16–18). Taking precautions to avoid possible causes of degradation of sRNA, Apgar et al. (19) were able to run a countercurrent distribution for 200 transfers with 80% recovery of activity and successive redistributions for a large number of transfers with 60–80% recovery. The initial distribution of yeast sRNAs was carried out by a solvent system composed of 1.25 M phosphate buffer (pH 6)–formamide–isopropanol (10:1:5.2); redistributions of sRNA fractions specific for alanine, valine, histidine, and tyrosine were repeated by use of a solvent system composed of 1.9 M phosphate buffer (pH 6)–formamide–isopropanol (10:1:4.4). The best

fractions of alanine-specific, valine-specific, histidine-specific, and tyrosine-specific sRNAs were estimated to be 66, 60, 23, and 45% pure,
respectively, in regard to their amino acid acceptor activity. In these
estimations absorbance of 23.5 (0.1%, at 260 mμ) was used and a molecular weight of 30,000 was assumed for these sRNAs. Alanine-specific
sRNA was nearly homogeneous, judging from the distribution curve.
Recently Holley et al. (20–21) have reported the complete nucleotide
sequence of this sRNA. Armstrong et al. (22) used essentially the same
method for the isolations of yeast alanine-specific and valine-specific
sRNAs; Hoskinson and Khorana (23) used this method for the isolation of yeast phenylalanine-specific sRNA.

For the countercurrent distribution of other RNAs the two two-
phase solvent systems devised by Kirby (24–25) were employed with
modifications. Since yeast sRNA exhibited a very small partition coefficient in Kirby's original solvent system, which is composed of 2.5 M
phosphate buffer (pH 7.5), 2-ethoxyethanol, 2-butoxyethanol, and N,
N-dibutylaminoethanol, Apgar et al. (26) increased the amount of 2-eth-
oxyethanol and reduced the concentration of phosphate buffer of this
system to obtain a partition coefficient of sRNA close to one. The modified system was composed of 6000 ml of 1.25 M phosphate buffer (pH
7.5), 2400 ml of 2-ethoxyethanol, 800 ml of 2-buthoxyethanol, and 120
ml of N, N-dibutylaminoethanol. The distribution pattern obtained
under these conditions was very similar to that achieved with the phosphate buffer (pH 6)–formamide–isopropanol system (19).

Doctor and Connelly (27) have modified the other Kirby system to
apply it for the fractionation of yeast sRNA as follows: Four milliliters
of formamide and 40 ml of 2-ethoxyethanol were added to a 100 ml of an
aqueous solution of inorganic salts, which contained 30 g of ammonium
sulfate, 0.1 mmole of magnesium chloride, and 1 ml of glacial acetic
acid (pH 4.0, adjusted by ammonium hydroxide). This system also afforded a distribution pattern similar to that obtained by Apgar et al.
(19). Later, Doctor et al. (28) distributed yeast sRNA initially with this
modified Kirby system, then with that of Apgar et al. (19), which was
modified to contain 45 ml of isopropanol/100 ml of 1.85 M phosphate
buffer (pH 6.0). Twice redistributed alanine-specific and tyrosine-specific sRNA fractions were 63 and 66% pure, respectively, in regard to
amino acid acceptor activity, assuming molecular weight of 30,000 and
absorbance of 24.0 for a 0.1% solution at neutral pH. The final distribution curves of each of these sRNAs detected by absorbance of ultraviolet light and by their amino acid acceptor activities were close to
those expected from theory for homogeneous compounds in the solvent
system used. These fractions were submitted to structural studies by
Doctor et al. (28).

Zachau *et al.* (29–30) have demonstrated the separation of several amino acid specific sRNAs with a solvent system composed of *n*-butanol–water–tri-*n*-butylamine–acetic acid–di-*n*-butylether (100:130:10:-2.5:24–31). For the distribution they utilized the tri-*n*-butylamine salt of sRNA, which is readily soluble in the organic phase of this system. In this system, partition coefficients of sRNAs can be controlled by changing the proportion of di-*n*-butylether so that a favorable condition for certain sRNAs may be obtained. At most, 13- and 10-fold enrichments of valine- and serine-acceptor activities, respectively, were achieved. Recently Karau and Zachau (31) isolated 350 mg of highly purified serine-specific sRNA (31 mμmoles serine/mg of RNA) for structural studies.

A solvent system composed of polyethylene glycol and potassium phosphate buffer was also applied by Wiesmeyer *et al.* (32) to the countercurrent distribution of Escherichia coli sRNA and partial fractionation was achieved.

Soon after successful separation was obtained by countercurrent distribution, the first application of partition chromatography for fractionation of yeast sRNAs was carried out by Everett *et al.* (33). They used silicic acid as the supporting medium and employed the solvent system of Holley and Merrill (15) with modifications. The result conclusively indicated that amino acid specific sRNAs can be separated by partition chromatography. Much further attention, however, has not been paid to this method owing to its smaller capacity and the high loss of activity during the process. Some of these disadvantages may be due to the use of silicic acid as a supporting medium.

To overcome these disadvantages Tanaka *et al.* (34) have chosen Sephadex G-25 (Dextran Gel) as a supporting medium and Zachau's system (29) as a solvent system. As Sephadex can hold large volumes of the aqueous phase of the system and the column provides a flow rate sufficient to carry out the chromatography in a large scale, quite large amounts of sRNA can be processed in this manner. Repeated chromatography can be designed to emphasize differences in mobility of the different molecular species of sRNA by changing the proportion of di-*n*-butylether in the solvent system. After one step chromatography they obtained partial separation of several amino acid specific sRNAs with almost quantitative recovery of ultraviolet-absorbing material and only little loss of activity. Serine-specific sRNA obtained after rechromatography was judged to be a highly purified form from the data of chemical and biological studies. This fraction was used for structural studies (35).

Bergquist and Scott (36) have chromatographed yeast and *E. coli* sRNAs in essentially the same procedure utilizing a linear gradient of decreasing di-n-butylether for development. By combining this technique with DEAE-Sephadex column chromatography, they obtained yeast serine- and valine-specific sRNA fractions. The best preparation of serine-specific sRNA was 75% pure with respect to serine acceptor activity and found to be single species. The valine- specific sRNA was 30% pure for valine acceptor activity. In a similar manner, E. coli lysine-specific and phenylalanine-specific sRNAs were partially purified and found to be 50% and 30% pure, respectively. All of these sRNA fractions have been subjected to structural studies.

A solvent system containing aqueous potassium phosphate, ethoxyethanol, butoxyethanol, and triethylamine was employed by Muench and Berg (37) for gradient partition chromatography of E. coli sRNA on Dextran Gel column. Three- to seventeen-fold enrichment of amino acid acceptor activity was obtained for thirteen amino acid specific sRNAs. They also reported 95% recovery of absorbance at 260 mμ and at least 85% recovery of activity.

Quite recently, fractionation of sRNAs by a simple extraction process has been reported by Khym (38). The author showed that sRNAs are quantitatively extractable by a 5.2% solution of tricaprylylmethylammonium chloride in trichlorotrifluoroethane (Freon TF, CCl_2F-$CClF_2$, b.p. 47 C) from 0.25 M NaCl solution and sRNAs are completely re-extracted into 0.4 M NaCl from the Freon layer. Between 0.25 and 0.40 M concentration of NaCl, sRNAs distribute in two phases according to their partition coefficients. Preliminary fractionation with this simple technique may then provide easier separation by other methods.

Ion-Exchange Column Chromatography

Partial separation of tyrosine-specific and leucine-specific sRNAs with column chromatography on Cato-2 (formerly known as Cato-8, an anion exchanger) was the first indication that fractionation of sRNAs with this kind of technique might be possible (6). With more familiar exchangers, such as ECTEOLA-cellulose (39), DEAE-cellulose (40–41), and DEAE-Sephadex (41–43), partial separation of amino acid specific sRNAs was also reported. Kawade et al. (41) indicated that DEAE-Sephadex is somewhat more effective than DEAE-cellulose. They also suggested that the secondary structure of sRNA molecules plays the major role in this fractionation. Cherayil and Bock (44) reported partial resolution of yeast sRNA into individual amino acid specific sRNAs by chromatography on DEAE-cellulose with a salt gradient in the presence of 7 M urea.

Recently Baguley et al. (45), who paid particular attention to the differences in T_m of various sRNA species, fractionated yeast sRNA by chromatography on a DEAE-cellulose column with a linear NaCl gradient at elevated temperature. As the elution temperature was raised to 65 C, the elution profile became broader and a higher salt gradient was required. Assay of the acceptor activity for several amino acids of recovered sRNA fractions indicated fairly good separation and a part of the fractions of rechromatography of lysine-specific sRNA was estimated as more than 81% pure based on an assumed molecular weight of 25,500.

As suggested in these papers, this kind of technique appears to be applicable for large scale fractionation of sRNA prior to other methods of fractionation, since DEAE-cellulose and DEAE-Sephadex are commercially available in standardized grade.

Methylated Serum Albumin Column Chromatography

This procedure has initially been developed by Mandell and Hershey (46) for the fractionation of DNA and introduced for the resolution of *E. coli* amino acyl sRNAs by Sueoka and Yamane (47). They showed that a methylated serum albumin column is capable of separating the amino acyl sRNAs of different amino acids. In several cases, more than one peak of amino acyl sRNA was demonstrated for a single amino acid. As labeled amino acyl sRNA is employed on the column chromatography, a precise elution pattern can easily be obtained from this method. On the other hand, the need of enzymes to prepare the amino acyl sRNAs and the small capacity of the methylated albumin columns are the disadvantages of this method for fractionation on a preparative scale.

To improve the capacity of this column, Okamoto *et al.* (48) have employed as a supporting medium silicic acid, which adsorbs much more serum albumin than kieselguhr does. About 200 mg of free sRNA could be applied on a 4- × 20-cm column and partial fractionation of several amino acid specific sRNAs was achieved.

Filtration on Dextran Gel Columns

Recently, Röschenthaler and Fromageot (49) have fractionated *E. coli* sRNAs into roughly two groups by gel filtration on Sephadex G-100. The sRNAs specific for glutamic acid, leucine, tyrosine, glycine, and serine were found in one group and the sRNAs specific for phenylalanine, lysine, proline, and aspartic acid were detected in the other group. Two proline-specific sRNAs were found only in the second group and two histidine specific sRNAs were found in both groups. The sRNAs belonging to the same group were hardly separated from each other by this method only. Röschenthaler and Fromageot examined elution profiles of sRNAs with several different buffer systems using hemoglobin as a reference standard. The results suggested some kinds of association between the sRNA molecules. This was also indicated by the facts that in the eluted fractions the amino acid acceptor activities for certain amino acids were increased by dialysis or by urea treatment. These results are consistent with the findings of Schleich and Goldstein (50) who studied gel filtration properties of countercurrent distributed sRNAs and observed the aggregation of sRNAs.

Although only rough fractionation of sRNAs can be expected by this method at present, the method will have to be evaluated further from its unique capability, which is possibly due to the molecular sieving ability of Sephadex.

Other Methods

Partial fractionation of sRNAs was also achieved by many other techniques, such as adsorption chromatography on hydroxyapatite (51) or brushite column (11), and electrophoresis in the presence of concentrated urea (11). Since more efficient techniques have been discovered, these methods have not been used in recent works.

At present, only a few species of highly purified sRNAs can be obtained after much patient work. Preliminary rough fractionation of sRNAs with simple techniques may save time and labor in this isolation process. From this point of view, it may be worthwhile to recollect early discoveries, such as the fractional precipitation of sRNAs (6,11,52).

METHODS UTILIZING AMINO ACYL
sRNA SYNTHESIS

Methods Utilizing Chemical Property of Uncharged sRNA

As is known, when a selected amino acid is charged enzymatically on sRNA, the amino acid attaches in ester linkage to the 3'- or 2'-hydroxyl group of the terminal adenosyl residue of corresponding specific sRNA molecule(s) (2–4), while other sRNA molecules remain unaffected and bear free vicinal hydroxyl groups on the terminal adenosyl residue. This structural difference between esterified and unesterified sRNAs has been utilized by many investigators with different techniques.

Monier et al. (53) first observed that 2,4-dinitrophenyl hydrazine can couple with RNA-dialdehyde, which is derived from all unesterified sRNAs by periodate oxidation. Zamecnik et al. (54) later converted oxidized sRNA to a dye-complex by the reaction with 2-hydroxy-3-naphthoic acid hydrazide and successive treatment with tetrazotized o-dianisidine. This blue dye-bound RNA was separated from amino acyl sRNA by fractional precipitation. They obtained fractions of valyl-C^{14} sRNA with a maximum 12-fold enhancement of specific activity. In the case of leucyl-C^{14} sRNA, a ninefold enhancement of the specific activity was indicated. To improve recovery of amino acyl sRNA, they combined this dye-coupling procedure with column chromatography on DEAE-Sephadex. Valyl sRNA emerged from DEAE-Sephadex prior to the bulk of other species of sRNA or the dye-bound RNA (42). They obtained valyl sRNA in mg quantity, which was estimated to be 90% pure assuming a molecular weight of 25,500 (43).

A number of modifications of the method of Zamecnik have been proposed. In place of dye formation, von Portatius et al. (55) have utilized the coupling of dialdehyde RNA with polyacrylic acid hydrazide and successive precipitation of the complex formed with n-butylaldehyde. They obtained a tenfold enhancement of the specific activity of valyl-C^{14} sRNA. Purity of the final solution was calculated to be 28% on the basis of an assumed molecular weight of 25,000.

Zachau et al. (29) have employed solid polyacrylic acid hydrazide (Lewatite 5082S) to remove the oxidized sRNA. By this method partial purification of valyl-C^{14}, leucyl-C^{14}, and seryl-C^{14} sRNAs were achieved. By a combination of this method with their countercurrent distribution procedure, they obtained seryl-C^{14} sRNA in 87% purity, assuming a molecular weight of 30,000. Similar modification was reported by Saponara and Bock (56) who used a phenylhydrazine resin prepared from p-aminobenzylcellulose by diazotization and reduction with Na-BH_4. Zubay (57) separated amino acyl sRNAs by column chromatography on aminoethylcellulose, which binds oxidized sRNA. With this method he obtained leucyl sRNA in 70% purity. By use of aminoethyl-dextran Muench and Berg (37) obtained at least 60% pure valyl sRNA starting from partially purified valine-specific sRNA.

If these methods are utilized as the first step of the fractionation, an inevitable economic disadvantage is that these methods require quantitative degradation by periodate of all the sRNAs other than that charged with single amino acid. Moreover, periodate oxidation may produce chemical modifications of the residue other than the terminal adenosine.

Methods Utilizing Chemical Properties of Amino Acyl sRNAs

Brown et al. (11,58) used polydiazostyrene or diazobenzylcellulose to trap certain amino acyl sRNAs (such as tyrosyl and histidyl sRNA) by diazo-coupling. After removal from unesterified sRNA by washing, the resin or the cellulose was incubated at pH 10.0 to liberate the sRNA. Mehler and Bank (59) have precipitated amino acyl sRNA by growing a polytrifluoroacetyllysine chain on the free amino group of the bound amino acid of amino acyl sRNA with ε-trifluoroacetyllysine N-carboxy anhydride. The precipitate was incubated with mild alkali to hydrolyze the ester linkage between amino acid and sRNA. They reported a threefold enrichment of the valine acceptor activity. The unesterified sRNA recovered from the supernatant liquid of polytri-fluoroacetyllysine formation was charged with leucine and the processes were repeated for leucyl sRNA. Nearly the same degree of purification was achieved for leucine-specific sRNA as found in initial application for valine-specific sRNA. Recovery of amino acid acceptor activity, however, was 16.5% and 35.6% for valine-specific and leucine-specific sRNAs, respectively. More recently, a similar method, which utilized β-benzyl-N-carboxy-L-aspartate anhydride in place of ε-trifluoroacetyl-lysine N-carboxy anhydride was reported by Simon et al. (60). The author obtained polypeptide derivatives of seryl, threonyl, and alanyl sRNAs with a purity of about 60% assuming a molecular weight of 30,000. However, these are indications of technical difficulties in the recovery of biologically active sRNA.

Although these methods are able to evade the economical disadvantage of the periodate oxidation techniques described above, large amounts of purified amino acyl RNA synthetases are required to prepare sufficient amounts of sRNA for structural studies.

Moreover, in the use of the methods utilizing amino acyl RNA synthesis it should be considered that a number of amino acid specific sRNAs have been found to be heterogeneous in regard to molecular species (as mentioned later).

GENERAL REMARKS

Criteria of Purity

Assay of the specific amino acid acceptor activity is used as a measure of the purity of fractionated sRNA preparations.

The ratios of the activity of fractionated material to that of the starting material has often been used to express the degree of purification. However, inasmuch as the absolute activity of the starting material may depend upon the source and method used for its preparation, this type of ratio does not allow direct comparison between the data obtained by different investigators.

The other criterion frequently used is the molar ratio of amino acid charged on sRNA to total sRNA. The calculation of this value usually involves an assumption that molecular weights and absorbances of ultraviolet light of all specific sRNAs are the same as those of the original unfractionated sRNA. Various numbers between 23,000 and 30,000 were assumed for molecular weight of sRNA and different absorbances (for 0.1% solution at 260 mμ) of 20–24 were used for this calculation (19,22,28,43,48,57,61). It can easily be seen that purity estimates may vary 10% or even 20% by use of different numbers for the two values needed, even in the range cited above. Some investigators consider that this criterion of purity may at least represent a minimum value, because of possible degradation of sRNA and the considerable and unknown rate of hydrolysis of amino acyl sRNA during the assay. It has also been found that some of the sRNA chains (and this is true, particularly in yeast sRNA preparations) are terminated predominantly in cytidine; these chains then would have to be repaired by addition of AMP before they could accept amino acids during the assay.

Finally, it has now become quite clear that the assay of amino acid acceptor activity does not assure the purity of sRNA with respect to molecular terms, since the heterogeneity of sRNAs specific for certain amino acids has been well demonstrated (as mentioned below). Chemical analyses, such as analysis of base composition or preferably of enzyme digests, may provide better information for purity of the sRNA preparations in molecular terms.

Heterogeneity of sRNA Specific for a Single Amino Acid

Fractionations of sRNAs by countercurrent distribution (19,23,31, 61–65), with chromatography on methylated albumin column (47,66), and by partition chromatography (33,37,67) have revealed the important fact that a number of amino acid specific sRNAs have more than one component. For instance, after extensive countercurrent distribution of *E. coli* sRNAs, Goldstein *et al.* (64) have detected 29 specific sRNAs by the assay of acceptor activity employing only 16 amino acids. The sRNAs specific for glycine, threonine, methionine, valine, alanine, serine, lysine, and tyrosine were each demonstrated as double peaks. Leucine-specific and proline-specific sRNAs afforded multiple peaks.

In *E. coli* sRNA, at most five leucine-specific sRNAs have been demonstrated by countercurrent distribution (63,65). It has shown that, in synthetic polynucleotide stimulated-polypeptide synthesis, leucine-specific sRNA IA, IB, and IC respond to poly UC, leucine-specific sRNA IIA responds to poly U, and leucine-specific sRNA IIB to poly UG (65,68–69). Further, distinct transfer specificities of leucine-specific sRNA I and IIB have been indicated in hemoglobin synthesis *in vitro* (65).

Several serine-specific sRNAs were separated by countercurrent distribution (61,64) or partition chromatography on Dextran Gel (67). Bennett *et al.* (70) showed that two serine-specific sRNAs of *E. coli* have different responses in synthetic polynucleotide stimulated-polypeptide synthesis. Rushizky *et al.* (61) isolated two components of yeast serine-specific sRNA by countercurrent distribution in 81% purity assuming a molecular weight of 30,000. Five serine-specific sRNAs of yeast have been separated by Bergquist and Robertson (67), with partition chromatography on Sephadex.

At the present time, the list of multiple sRNAs specific for a single amino acid seems to be incomplete even for a single biological species.

Species Specificity of sRNA

In addition to the heterogeneity of specific sRNAs for a given amino acid, species differences of sRNA have also been demonstrated by countercurrent distribution (62,23) by partition chromatography on Sephadex (71), and by methylated albumin column chromatography (66). For example, Apgar *et al.* (62) demonstrated that sRNAs specific for alanine, lysine, tryptophan, and tyrosine of yeast and of rat liver have quite different countercurrent distribution behaviors depending on their biological origin.

It has also been demonstrated by many investigators that there are species differences among the amino acyl RNA synthetases and sRNAs (11,66,72,73). The data thus far obtained indicate that the patterns of cross reactions between sRNAs and the amino acyl RNA synthetases are quite complicated and depend both on the nature of the amino acid and on the biological origin of the enzyme and the sRNA. This situation should be carefully considered when using amino acyl RNA synthetases in the assay of sRNA preparations.

REFERENCES

1. HOAGLAND, M. B., M. L. STEPHENSON, J. F. SCOTT, L. I. HECHT, and P. C. ZAMECNIK. 1958. J. Biol. Chem. *231:* 241.
2. COHEN, G. N., and F. GROS. 1960. Ann. Rev. Biochem. *29:* 525.
3. BERG, P. 1961. Ann. Rev. Biochem. *30:* 293.
4. SIMPSON, M. V. 1962. Ann. Rev. Biochem. *31:* 333.
5. CRICK, F. H. C. 1956. Biochem. Soc. Symp. (Cambridge, England). *14:* 25.
6. SMITH, K. C., E. CORDES, and R. S. SCHWEET. 1959. Biochim. Biophys. Acta. *33:* 286.
7. HOLLEY, R. W., and S. H. MERRILL. 1959. J. Am. Chem. Soc. *81:* 753.
8. HOAGLAND, M. B. 1961. In E. Chargaff and J. N. Davidson, eds., The nucleic acids. Academic Press: New York. Vol. 3, p. 349.

9. STEVENS, A. 1963. Ann. Rev. Biochem. *32:* 15.
10. SCHMIDT, G. 1964. Ann. Rev. Biochem. *33:* 667.
11. BROWN, G. L. 1963. In J. N. Davidson and W. E. Cohn, eds., Progress in nucleic acid research. Academic Press: New York. Vol. 2, p. 259.
12. KIRBY, K. S. 1964. In J. N. Davidson and W. E. Cohn, eds., Progress in nucleic acid research. Academic Press: New York. Vol. 3, p. 1.
13. WARNER, R. C., and P. VAIMBERG. 1958. Fed. Proc. *17:* 331.
14. HOLLEY, R. W., and S. H. MERRILL. 1959. Fed. Proc. *18:* 249.
15. HOLLEY, R. W., B. P. DOCTOR, S. H. MERRILL, and F. M. SAAD. 1959. Biochim. Biophys. Acta. *35:* 272.
16. HOLLEY, R. W., J. APGAR, and B. P. DOCTOR. 1960. Ann. N. Y. Acad. Sci. *88:* 745.
17. HOLLEY, R. W., J. APGAR, B. P. DOCTOR, J. FARROW, M. A. MARINI, and S. H. MERRILL. 1961. J. Biol. Chem. *236:* 200.
18. DOCTOR, B. P., J. APGAR, and R. W. HOLLEY. 1961. J. Biol. Chem. *236:* 1117.
19. APGAR, J., R. W. HOLLEY, and S. H. MERRILL. 1962. J. Biol. Chem. *237:* 796.
20. HOLLEY, R. W., G. A. EVERETT, J. T. MADISON, and A. ZAMIR. 1965. J. Biol. Chem. *240:* 2122.
21. HOLLEY, R. W., J. APGAR, G. A. EVERETT, J. T. MADISON, M. MARQIUSEE, S. H. MERRILL, J. R. PENSWICK, and A. ZAMIR. 1965. Science. *147:* 1462.
22. ARMSTRONG, A., H. HAGOPIAN, V. M. INGRAM, I. SJÖQUIST, and J. SJÖQUIST. 1964. Biochemistry. *3:* 1194.
23. HOSKINSON, R. M., and H. G. KHORANA. 1965. J. Biol. Chem. *240:* 2129.
24. KIRBY, K. S. 1960. Biochim. Biophys. Acta. *41:* 338.
25. KIRBY, K. S. 1960. Biochim. Biophys. Acta. *40:* 193.
26. APGAR, J., R. W. HOLLEY, and S. H. MERRILL. 1961. Biochim. Biophys. Acta. *53:* 220.
27. DOCTOR, B. P., and C. M. CONNELLY. 1961. Biochem. Biophys. Res. Comm. *6:* 201.
28. DOCTOR, B. P., C. M. CONNELLY, G. W. RUSHIZKY, and H. A. SOBER. 1963. J. Biol. Chem. *238:* 3985.
29. ZACHAU, H. G., M. TADA, W. B. LAWSON, and M. SCHWEIGER. 1961. Biochim. Biophys. Acta. *53:* 221.
30. TADA, M., M. SCHWEIGER, and H. G. ZACHAU. 1962. Z. Physiol. Chem. *328:* 85.
31. KARAU, W., and H. G. ZACHAU. 1964. Biochim. Biophys. Acta. *91:* 549.
32. WIESMEYER, H., K. KJELLIN, and H. G. BOMAN. 1962. Biochim. Biophys. Acta. *61:* 625.
33. EVERETT, G. A., S. H. MERRILL, and R. W. HOLLEY. 1960. J. Am. Chem. Soc. *82:* 5757.
34. TANAKA, K., H. H. RICHARDS, and G. L. CANTONI. 1962. Biochim. Biophys. Acta. *61:* 846.
35. CANTONI, G. L., H. ISHIKURA, H. H. RICHARDS, and K. TANAKA. 1963. Cold Spring Harbor Symp. Quant. Biol. *28:* 123.
36. BERGQUIST, P. L., and J. F. SCOTT. 1964. Biochim. Biophys. Acta. *87:* 199.
37. MUENCH, K. H., and P. BERG. 1964. Fed. Proc. *23:* 477.
38. KHYM, J. X. 1965. J. Biol. Chem. *240:* PC1488.
39. OFENGAND, E. J., M. DIECKMANN, and P. BERG. 1961. J. Biol. Chem. *236:* 1741.

40. NISHIYAMA, K., T. OKAMOTO, I. WATANABE, and M. TAKANAMI. 1961. Biochim. Biophys. Acta. *47:* 193.
41. KAWADE, Y., T. OKAMOTO, and Y. YAMAMOTO. 1963. Biochem. Biophys. Res. Comm. *10:* 200.
42. STEPHENSON, M. L., and P. C. ZAMECNIK. 1961. Proc. Nat. Acad. Sci. U.S. *47:* 1627.
43. STEPHENSON, M. L., and P. C. ZAMECNIK. 1962. Biochem. Biophys. Res. Comm. *7:* 91.
44. CHERAYIL, J. D., and R. M. BOCK. 1964. Fed. Proc. *23:* 477.
45. BAGULEY, B. C., P. L. BERGQUIST, and R. K. RALPH. 1965. Biochim. Biophys. Acta. *95:* 510.
46. MANDELL, J. D., and A. D. HERSHEY. 1960. Anal. Biochem. *1:* 66.
47. SUEOKA, N., and T. YAMANE. 1962. Proc. Nat. Acad. Sci. U.S. *48:* 1454.
48. OKAMOTO, T., and Y. KAWADE. 1963. Biochem. Biophys. Res. Comm. *13:* 324.
49. RÖSCHENTHALER, R., and P. FROMAGEOT. 1965. J. Mol. Biol. *11:* 458.
50. SCHLEICH, T., and J. GOLDSTEIN. 1964. Proc. Nat. Acad. Sci. U.S. *52:* 744.
51. HARTMANN, G., and U. COY. 1961. Biochim. Biophys. Acta. *47:* 612.
52. CANTONI, G. L. 1960. Nature. *188:* 300.
53. MONIER, R., M. L. STEPHENSON, and P. C. ZAMECNIK. 1960. Biochim. Biophys. Acta. *43:* 1.
54. ZAMECNIK, P. C., M. L. STEPHENSON, and J. F. SCOTT. 1960. Proc. Nat. Acad. Sci. U.S. *46:* 811.
55. VON PORTATIUS, H., P. DOTY, and M. L. STEPHENSON. 1961. J. Am. Chem. Soc. *83:* 3351.
56. SAPONARA, A., and R. M. BOCK. 1961. Fed. Proc. *20:* 356.
57. ZUBAY, G. 1962. J. Mol. Biol. *4:* 347.
58. BROWN, G. L., A. V. W. BROWN, and J. GORDON. 1961. Brookhaven Symp. Biol. *12:* 47; Chem. *236:* 197.
59. MEHLER, A. H., and A. BANK. 1963. J. Biol. Chem. *238:* PC2888.
60. SIMON, S., U. Z. LITTAUER, and E. KATCHALSKI. 1964. Biochim. Biophys. Acta. *80:* 169.
61. RUSHIZKY, G. W., H. A. SOBER, C. M. CONNELLY, and B. P. DOCTOR. 1965. Biochem. Biophys. Res. Comm. *18:* 489.
62. APGAR, J., and R. W. HOLLEY. 1962. Biochem. Biophys. Res. Comm. *8:* 391.
63. APGAR, J., and R. W. HOLLEY. 1964. Biochem. Biophys. Res. Comm. *16:* 121.
64. GOLDSTEIN, J., T. P. BENNETT, and L. C. CRAIG. 1964. Proc. Nat. Acad. Sci. U.S. *51:* 119.
65. WEISBLUM, B., F. GONANO, G. VON EHRENSTEIN, and S. BENZER. 1965. Proc. Nat. Acad. Sci. U.S. *53:* 328.
66. YAMANE, T., T. CHENG, and N. SUEOKA. 1963. Cold Spring Harbor Sym. Quant. Biol. *28:* 569.
67. BERGQUIST, P. L., and J. M. ROBERTSON. 1965. Biochim. Biophys. Acta. *95:* 357.
68. WEISBLUM, B., S. BENZER, and R. W. HOLLEY. 1962. Proc. Nat. Acad. Sci. U.S. *48:* 1449.
69. VON EHRENSTEIN, G., and D. DAIS. 1963. Proc. Nat. Acad. Sci. U.S. *50:* 81.

70. BENNETT, T. P., J. GOLDSTEIN, and F. LIPMANN. 1965. Proc. Nat. Acad. Sci. U.S. *53:* 385.

71. NATHENSON, S. G., F. C. DOHAN, JR., H. H. RICHARDS, and G. L. CANTONI. 1964. Fed. Proc. *23:* 478.

72. BARNETT, W. E., and K. B. JACOBSON. 1964. Proc. Nat. Acad. Sci. U.S. *51:* 642.

73. YAMANE, T., and N. SUEOKA. 1964. Proc. Nat. Acad. Sci. U.S. *51:* 1178.

3. Viral RNA

Preparation and Testing
of Tobacco Mosaic Virus–RNA

H. FRAENKEL-CONRAT
VIRUS LABORATORY
UNIVERSITY OF CALIFORNIA
BERKELEY, CALIFORNIA

Viral nucleic acids represent the only class of nucleic acids obtainable with relative ease in appreciable amounts and in a state approximating biological and physico-chemical homogeneity. This is because many viruses can be separated in almost pure form from the host tissue with comparatively little effort and that at least the simple viruses contain only one species of nucleic acid, be it RNA or DNA. Thus, with the assumption that a highly purified preparation of a given virus is available, all that is required is a means of dissociating the protein coat without causing damage to the nucleic acid, and separating the two components. With viruses containing DNA, acid must be avoided during the degradation, and other problems reside in the separation methods. For the preparation of single-stranded DNA these and the absence of deoxyribonuclease are the critical factors. For RNA-containing viruses, alkali is more dangerous than acid, but good preparations are obtained only near neutrality. With single-stranded RNA the absence or inhibition of ribonuclease is a very important aspect. The separation of RNA from protein is generally easy, although with all nucleic acids complete freedom from protein is difficult to achieve or assess. Tobacco mosaic virus is one of the most bountiful viruses, and was the first and still is one of the best sources for a biologically active RNA.

ISOLATION OF TOBACCO MOSAIC VIRUS

A dilute solution of tobacco mosaic virus (TMV) (10–100 μg/ml, absorbancy of 100 μg/ml = 0.27 at A_{max} = 260 mμ) or the homogenate of an infected leaf is inoculated onto the bottom leaves of Turkish tobacco plants by rubbing with carborundum. From about 10 plants, with the biggest leaf about 12 cm long, 100–200 mg of virus can be expected. Bigger plants can also be used satisfactorily. After about 1 week the typical symptoms of the mosaic disease begin to appear and the mottled and blistered appearance becomes pronounced, particularly in the young top leaves, during the second week. After 3 weeks the leaves (about 100 g) are harvested and frozen at −30 to −60 C.

If no greenhouse is available for virus-infected plants, then the inoculated leaves can be held in moist chambers (e.g., the stems dipping into petri dishes containing water and placed into baking dishes covered with glass plates, or leaf segments floating on water in petri dishes). When such baking dishes are held under a bank of fluorescent lights for 12–18 hr/day, about 200 mg of virus/100 g of leaf can be obtained after about 10 days.

The frozen leaves are easily powdered in a mortar and triturated with about 150 ml of 0.1 M phosphate, pH 7; the extract is pressed through several layers of cheesecloth to remove the plant tissue debris. The juice is then clarified by centrifugation at 8000 rev/min for 20 min, and the supernatant fluid is centrifuged at 22,500 rev/min (about 60,000 × g) for 1 hr. The pellet is redispersed in 0.1 M phosphate, pH 7, by allowing it to soak overnight. It is subjected twice more to the same cycle of low speed then high-speed centrifugation from 0.1 M phosphate and finally taken up in water. These procedures are carried out at 2–10 C. If the final pellet continues to look green, then it is subjected to one, or if necessary two, additional cycles of centrifugation.

The purpose of obtaining virus in as homogeneous a form as possible has led to many variations in its isolation procedure. The Virus Laboratory of The University of California has tested most of these variations, but none seems to give consistently better preparation in acceptable yields than the simple method in terms of infectivity and homogeneity.

One of the variants designed to give little end to end aggregation of TMV particles avoids phosphate, pH below 7.2, and high ionic strength. The leaf tissue is soaked and ground in 0.05 M EDTA, pH 9.5, and the juice expressed through cheesecloth is immediately adjusted with alkali to pH 7.5. Activated charcoal (5 g/100 g of leaf tissue) is well mixed into the extract, followed by 5 g of celite. The mixture is filtered through celite on a Büchner funnel after about a minute of stirring. The filter cake is washed with 0.05 M EDTA, pH 9. The filtrate is desalted by passage through an 8% granulated agar or Sephadex G25 column, equilibrated with 10^{-3} M EDTA, pH 7.5 (1). Differential centrifugation can then be performed in this medium. If the virus is to be freed thoroughly from fragments, then the high-speed centrifugations (24,000 rev/min in 30 rotor) are performed for only 20 min. Passage through 1% agar has been advocated to further this purpose, but the virus yields are greatly lowered by these procedures (1).

The standard procedure using only phosphate and differential centrifugation yields preparations, which by electron microscopy or ultracentrifugal analysis consist of from 75 to 95% of typical 300-mμ-long rods of about 190 S. The remainder is in part fragments, in part aggregates. The fraction of aggregated material is decreased by one or two sedimentations from water or 10^{-3} M EDTA, for 1 hr at 30,000 rev/min.

Virus prepared under standard conditions shows infectivity roughly proportional to 300-mμ-particle content, although a lesion results from only one out of 75,000 virus particles. (This low efficiency is attributed to physical and biological factors, and not to heterogeneity within the virus population.) Aggregated particles are believed to be less infective and fragments are noninfective. However, some procedures yield virus high in 300-mμ-particle content yet low in infectivity. Although this phenomenon has not been studied in detail, it appears possible that holding the virus at low concentrations for prolonged time periods is a contributing factor.

ISOLATION OF TMV–RNA

TMV, as isolated by differential centrifugation, contains bound nucleases, as well as small molecular phosphorus-containing materials. These and possibly other unidentified contaminants may cause difficulties in the subsequent storage or handling of the RNA. Incubation of the virus in 0.02 M EDTA, pH 7 (37 C, 16 hr), followed by one cycle of differential centrifugation, rids the virus of most of the bound components that were analyzed for.

The most generally used method of splitting of TMV for the purpose of isolating infective RNA is by phenol treatment (2), although equally infective RNA can be obtained after dissociation of the virus by detergents (3) (e.g., sodium dodecyl sulfate), controlled heat-salt treatment, and other methods and combinations thereof.

Phenol Preparation of TMV–RNA

TMV (0.1–2%) in water is brought to 0.005 M with EDTA (pH 7). An equal volume of an approximately 80% solution of pure phenol in water (8 g of phenol, preferably redistilled *in vacuo*, + 2 ml of H_2O, or commercial pure phenol that has been extracted with 0.05 M EDTA and then washed with water) is added and the mixture vigorously stirred or shaken for 5 min at room temperature or in a cold room. The emulsion is centrifuged for 5 min and the upper aqueous phase is pipetted off, carefully avoiding the interphase. The aqueous phase is treated again in the same manner with half as much phenol, and separated with care. The aqueous phase is cooled to 0 C and to it is added with mixing about 2.5 ml of 95% ethanol (cooled to 0 C) and 0.05 ml of 3 M sodium acetate, pH 7, per milliliter of aqueous phase. The precipitated RNA is collected by centrifugation after at least 1 hr at 0 C. The RNA is redissolved in cold H_2O (about 1 ml/5 mg of RNA or 100 mg of virus) and again precipitated with alcohol in the same manner. This process is repeated at least four times, or until the alcohol supernatant liquid no longer shows the characteristic spectrum of phenol (A_{max} at 270 mμ). If a particularly salt-free RNA preparation is desired then the last alcohol precipitation can be performed with much less or no added acetate, allowing about 16 hr at 0 C for the precipitation of the RNA. An alternate technique to repeated alcohol precipitations is repeated ether extraction as a means of phenol removal from the aqueous phase. The ether, in turn, may be removed by bubbling N_2 through the solution.

A micro adaptation of the phenol method permits the isolation of fractions of a milligram of RNA in a 0.2–0.5 ml volume. This is achieved by keeping the aqueous phase in the same small test tube throughout. The virus solution is manually agitated with the phenol (twice) and the latter pipetted out from under the aqueous phase. Subsequent ether washes are similarly pipetted off the top. The RNA recovery by this procedure is similar to that obtained by the standard procedure—about 60–80% of the expected amount of RNA.

The RNA solution containing little or no salts is usually freed from any particulate material by subjecting it to ultracentrifugation at 40,-000 rev/min for 2 hr (40.3 or 40.2 rotor, or 40 rotor with nylon adaptors for 2-ml tubes). The nonsedimented RNA is best stored at or below

—60 C and is usually distributed over several tubes, not because repeated freezing and thawing is harmful, but to minimize the danger of contaminating the entire batch with a trace of a nuclease on a pipet tip, or through contact with a finger or spit.

The RNA concentration is ascertained by spectrophotometry after suitable dilution with water, followed by a second determination of its absorbance after addition of $MgCl_2$ to 10^{-3} M (10 μl of 0.1 M added to 1.0-ml sample). From the second absorbance value at 258 mμ the concentration is derived on the basis of 1 absorbance unit (1 cm light path) = 50 μg of RNA/ml. The first absorbance maximum should be 25% higher, and thereby indicates that the RNA as prepared is fully hyperchromed and the phenol, water, and other solvents used are free of multivalent metals. The plot of the entire spectrum is a good indication of the success of the isolation procedure, since hyperchromed TMV-RNA free of protein shows a low minimum at 228 mμ with an $A_{max}/A_{min} = 3.0$.

The phenol method can also be used in the presence of 0.1 M phosphate or other buffers near neutrality, but alcohol precipitation of the RNA is not advisable if the buffer salt is not soluble in 70% ethanol. The final RNA preparation, after ether extraction, is largely hypochromed and shows little effect upon addition of $MgCl_2$.

Preparation of RNA by Detergent Method

TMV can also be conveniently degraded by treatment for 5 min at 50 C with 1% sodium dodecyl sulfate in 0.002 M EDTA at a starting pH of 7.8. (The pH drops during degradation of the virus.) Addition of half a volume of saturated ammonium sulfate at about 25 C precipitates the protein. If the protein is centrifuged off after 5 min, and the supernatant fluid cooled in an icebath, the RNA precipitates and can be centrifuged off after a few hours in the cold. The RNA is redissolved in water, precipitated with alcohol once or twice, and ultracentrifuged, as described previously.

Use of Bentonite

Nucleases tend to accompany the RNA even though they were diminished by the prior incubation of the virus with chelating agents. Treatment with the acidic clay, bentonite, greatly lowers the nuclease content in TMV-RNA and its use is advocated if the RNA is prepared for purposes where its macromolecular integrity, infectivity, and stability are of importance (4).

Bentonite is prepared for use as follows: Two grams of bentonite, suspended in 40 ml of water, was centrifuged at 2500 rev/min for 15 min and the supernatant fluid was centrifuged at 8500 rev/min for 20 min. The second pellet was resuspended and held for 2 days at room temperature in 0.1 M EDTA, pH 7, and again sedimented at 8500 rev/min. The centrifugation was repeated once more from 0.01 M sodium acetate, pH 6, and the clay finally taken up in the same medium to a concentration of 2–6%, as determined by dry weight.

Bentonite can be added to the virus (5 mg/10 mg of virus) and carried through the phenol procedure. The aqueous phase will then be turbid. It is advantageous to remove most of the bentonite by one ultracentrifugation (40,000 rev/min) prior to the first alcohol precipitation, and the rest by the final ultracentrifugation. The RNA solution can alternatively be treated with bentonite at 0 C for a few hours after its isolation and two alcohol precipitations. About half to equal weights are used, and the bentonite is again removed by a total of two ultracentrifugations. Bentonite adsorbs some RNA and losses can be appreciable if excessive amounts are used. It is advisable to ascertain the minimal amount required for each specific purpose.

TESTS FOR INTEGRITY OF TMV–RNA BY THE ULTRACENTRIFUGE

TMV-RNA can be analyzed at 4 C in 0.05 M phosphate, pH 7, at 50 μg/ml (= 1 absorbance unit/ml) in the Spinco Model E ultracentrifuge equipped with ultraviolet optics. At least 50%, and usually 60%–80%, of the absorbance should settle at a rate of 30 ± 1 S most of the rest representing smaller material, presumably fragments of TMV-RNA.

TESTS FOR INTEGRITY BY BIOASSAY

The infectivity of intact TMV-RNA can easily be determined. However, it is usually only about 2% of that of the undegraded virus on the weight basis (0.1% on the basis of the RNA content), and subject to considerable variations depending on the state of the test plants, the weather, and other factors. Comparative tests of several samples in a group are not hampered by this; but for an absolute assay of an RNA sample, designed to determine its infectivity as compared with that of the virus used as starting material, it is advisable to reconstitute virus from the RNA prior to testing.

Preparation of TMV Protein

TMV protein is prepared by mixing TMV at 0 C with two volumes of undercooled glacial acetic acid. After about 1 hr at 0 C with occasional stirring the suspension is centrifuged. The water-clear supernatant fluid contains the protein. It is dialyzed against several changes of water at 0 C. When the protein reaches the isoelectric region it becomes turbid and can be centrifuged off, preferably in an ultracentrifuge at 30,000 rev/min. It is then redissolved in water at 0 C by trituration with dropwise addition of alkali to pH 7.5–8.5 and freed from any particulate matter by another high-speed centrifugation. Its concentration is determined spectrophotometrically: A_{max} at 280 mμ of 1.0 = 0.77 mg/ml. The complete plot of the spectrum should show a distinct minimum at 248 mμ, and a ratio of A_{max}/A_{min} of 2.4–2.5, which is a good indication of the absence of nucleic acid. The protein is best stored in the frozen state, but undergoes slow partial denaturation upon repeated freezing and thawing or upon prolonged frozen storage. It remains suitable, however, for routine reconstitution tests.

Reconstitution

Definite amounts of the RNA in the 0.005–0.02 mg range (0.125–0.5 A_{260} units, hyperchromed) are mixed with 1.0 mg of TMV protein (0.05 ml of a 2% solution, a 10- to 25-fold excess), water is added to a volume of 0.5 ml, followed by 0.5 ml of 0.2 M sodium pyrophosphate previously adjusted with HCl to pH 7.0. The mixture is held at 30 C for 6 hr, or at 37 C for 3 hr, and is then stored in a refrigerator. Any precipitate represents denatured protein and may be centrifuged off, or disregarded.

Infectivity Assay

A uniform group of plants (*Nicotiana glutinosa*, or *Nicotiana Tabacum* L. var. *Xanthi nc*) is selected. Three to six leaves of each (diameter 5–10 cm) are dusted with carborundum, then one drop (0.05 ml) of the virus freshly diluted with 0.1 M phosphate, pH 7, at 0 C to 0.05 (for *N. glutinosa*) or 0.0025 (for *Xanthi*) μg/ml is applied to one half of the leaf and spread over that half-leaf by means of a conveniently bent glass spatula with roughened underside. Since reconstitution usually proceeds to 35–70%, 2 to 3 times as much reconstituted virus than undegraded virus is applied to a leaf. In terms of the RNA content 5 millimicrogram (mμg) of TMV equals 0.25 mμg of RNA, and is compared with a dilution of the unknown adjusted to contain 0.5 to 1 mμg of RNA.

If only two samples are to be compared (e.g., virus used as starting material versus the reconstituted RNA prepared from it) then application on opposite alternating half-leaves will be most convenient and give the most reliable data. If several samples are to be tested then these should be applied in a manner assuring that each is placed with similar frequency on top, middle, and bottom leaves and on the right- and left-halves of the leaves, with the virus used as standard or reference spaced similarly among them. As a check on the absence of contaminating virus, the water and buffer used for dilution are also applied to leaves both at the beginning and end of a set of test samples.

Direct assay of unreconstituted RNA is performed in the same manner, using 0.2–0.5 μg of RNA/ml. Since it is more labile than the virus, the RNA should be in contact with the phosphate only at 0 C and for as short a time as possible prior to application to the leaves. The addition of bentonite to the solution (5 mg/ml) prior to application to the leaves increases the sensitivity of the test by about one order of magnitude (4).

Necrotic lesions appear 3–4 days after inoculation by virus or RNA and are counted and averaged. If these are in the range of 10–100 per half-leaf they are approximately proportional to virus (or RNA) concentration. The ratio of lesions produced by the unknown to that of the standard virus, divided by the weight ratios of RNA applied, gives the percentage infectivity of the sample. Thus if a sample containing 0.5 mμg of reconstituted RNA/ml gives the same number of lesions as 5 mμg/ml of TMV, containing 0.25 mμg of TMV-RNA, then the reconstituted sample has 50% of the theoretical infectivity.

REFERENCES

1. STEERE, R. L. 1963. Science. *140:* 1089.
2. GIERER, A., and G. SCHRAMM. 1956. Z. Naturforsch. *11b:* 138.
3. FRAENKEL-CONRAT, H., and B. SINGER. 1954. J. Am. Chem. Soc. *76:* 180; Biochim. Biophys. Acta. *24:* 540.
4. SINGER, B., and H. FRAENKEL-CONRAT. 1961. Virology. *14:* 59.

The Isolation and Properties

of High Molecular Weight

RNA from Poliovirus

DONALD F. SUMMERS

ALBERT EINSTEIN COLLEGE OF MEDICINE

YESHIVA UNIVERSITY

BRONX, NEW YORK

INTRODUCTION

In recent years several techniques have made it possible to produce sizable amounts of purified animal viruses with relative ease. Such concentrations of purified virus have permitted studies on large numbers of cells infected at high multiplicities, which in turn allowed extrapolation to the biochemical events occurring during the replicative cycle of the virus in a single cell. From these biochemical studies we have gained considerable insight into the structure and function of the genetic apparatus of animal viruses, and in particular the single-stranded RNA of poliovirus, which can itself initiate the events of the infectious cycle. This RNA of molecular weight 2×10^6 Daltons (1) and known base composition (2,3) acts as the messenger RNA that directs the synthesis of the virus-specific capsid and noncapsid proteins in the infected cell cytoplasm (4).

PRODUCTION OF VIRUS

Growth of large amounts of poliovirus is carried out with greatest ease in suspension cultures of HeLa cells maintained continuously in the logarithmic growth phase ($20-50 \times 10^4$ cells/ml) in Eagle's spinner medium (5) (Table 1) supplemented with 7% horse serum. The cells are thus maintained by diluting the cultures each day with fresh medium. Up to 40 liters of such cells have been grown in one batch in our laboratory for the production of large amounts of virus.

TABLE 1. *Eagle's Medium for Growth of HeLa Cells* (5)

Compound	Concentration (mM)	(mg/liter)	Compound	Concentration (mM)	(mg/liter)
L-*Amino Acids*			$CaCl_2$	1.8 (0)	200 (0)
Arginine	0.6	105	$MgCl_2 \cdot 6H_2O$	1.0	200
Cystine	0.1	24	$NaH_2PO_4 \cdot 2H_2O$	1.1 (11)	150 (1500)
Glutamine	2.0	292	$NaHCO_3$	23.8	2000
Histidine	0.2	31			
Isoleucine	0.4	52	*Vitamins*		
Leucine	0.4	52	Choline		1
Lysine	0.4	58	Folic acid		1
Methionine	0.1	15	Inositol		2
Phenylalanine	0.2	32	Nicotinamide		1
Threonine	0.4	48	Pantothenate		1
Tryptophan	0.05	10	Pyridoxal		1
Tyrosine	0.2	36	Riboflavin		0.1
Valine	0.4	46	Thiamine		1
Carbohydrate			*Serum Protein*		
Glucose	5.5	1000	Whole or dialyzed serum, 5 to 10%		
Salts					
NaCl	116	6800			
KCl	5.4	400			

The poliovirus is grown and purified by a modification (6) of the method of Levintow and Darnell (7). The HeLa cells are first centrifuged out of their growth medium in round-bottomed 250-ml centrifuge bottles in an International PR2 centrifuge at 1500 rev/min for 3 min at 5 C. The cell pellets are gently resuspended by pipetting them up and down in fresh cold medium containing no serum. Several pellets are combined, brought up to 250 ml with cold medium, and centrifuged again.

The cell pellets are now resuspended to one-tenth their original volume (cell concentration $= 2$–5×10^6 cells/ml) in Eagle's spinner medium at 37 C, placed in a suitable vessel equipped with some stirring device to keep the cells in suspension, i.e., a Teflon-coated magnetic stirring bar. This concentrated cell suspension is then infected with a stock solution of poliovirus at an input multiplicity of about 30 plaque forming units (pfu) per cell, and placed at 37 C.

One-half hour following infection horse serum is added to the infected cells to a final concentration of 5%. Infection is then allowed to proceed for 6–6½ hr by which time the infectious cycle is completed, but the cells not yet lysed. The infected cells are centrifuged at 2000 rev/min for 5 min, and Earle's salt solution (116 mM NaCl, 5.4 mM KCl, 1 mM $MgCl_2 \cdot 6H_2O$, 11 mM $NaH_2PO_4 \cdot 2 H_2O$, 23.8 mM $NaHCO_3$) is added to the pellet to bring the volume to one-tenth that of the concentrated cell volume, and the cells are resuspended by pipetting.

The resuspended cells are frozen (in an acetone–Dry Ice bath) and thawed three times to rupture the cells and release the virus. The cell debris is centrifuged down, first by spinning at 2000 rev/min for 10 min at 5 C, and then by spinning the resulting supernatant fluid at 10,000 rev/min for 10 min at 5 C. This clarified supernatant fluid is next centrifuged in a Spinco no. 30 rotor for $2\frac{1}{2}$ hr at 30,000 rev/min at 5 C to sediment the virus.

The resulting gelatinous pellets are resuspended with the aid of a Teflon homogenizer in about 20 ml of 0.02 M sodium phosphate buffer, pH 7.2, and centrifuged at 40,000 rev/min for 2 hr in a Spinco no. 40 rotor. These pellets are once again resuspended in 5–10 ml of phosphate buffer. Some difficulty may be encountered in the resuspension of the gelatinous pellet, but resuspension can be aided by using a probe sonifier set at a low energy level for short periods of sonication. The virus solution can be kept in a small ice bath during sonication to avoid heating and inactivation of the virus.

The resulting opalescent solution is now ready to be chromatographed on a column of ECTEOLA–SF cellulose. (The ECTEOLA–SF, reagent grade, type 20, can be purchased from the Brown Co.) The dry cellulose powder is prepared by suspending in 0.5 N NaOH, stirring well, allowing to settle, and decanting the supernatant liquid and fine particles. The material is then washed repeatedly with distilled water until the supernatant liquid is neutral. The washed ECTEOLA is then resuspended in 0.02 M phosphate buffer for storage at 4 C until used.

A 2- × 20-cm column is packed with ECTEOLA under slight positive pressure. The column is then equilibrated with 0.02 M phosphate buffer, pH 7.2. (A column of these dimensions is adequate to separate the virus from up to about one liter of concentrated cells.) The virus solution is placed on the column and subsequently eluted with the same phosphate buffer and 5-ml fractions are collected until about 20 fractions have been collected. The virus particles are not absorbed to the columns as are the HeLa cell constituents, and appear early in the collection as a fairly sharp peak contained in 5–15 ml. The virus-containing fractions often exhibit a faint bluish opalescence.

Samples of the fractions appropriately diluted are now read for optical density (OD) at 260 and 280 mμ. The 260/280 ratio for the virus peak should optimally be 1.7. The tubes containing the virus are pooled, and the solution concentrated for sedimentation in cesium chloride gradients.

A convenient and rapid means of concentrating the virus is by placing the solution in dialysis tubing, then covering with solid Carbowax 20 M (Union Carbide Chemicals Co.) at 4 C. Examine periodically until the desired volume is obtained.

The concentrated virus solution is now brought to a specific gravity of 1.33 with cesium chloride (0.5 gm of CsCl/ml of virus solution), placed in a Spinco SW39 rotor, and centrifuged at 39,000 rev/min for 20 hr at 5 C.

After centrifugation, the virus will be located as a discreet (usually visible depending on the amount of virus produced) band in the middle of the tube. The virus band is collected by puncturing the bottom of the gradient tube, and collecting fractions of about 0.5 ml each. Samples of these fractions are appropriately diluted with phosphate buffer, and again read at 260 mμ.

Estimation of the amount of poliovirus thus obtained may be obtained from the following data:

$$E_{1cm}^{1\%} = 80 \text{ for whole virus}$$

One optical density unit (a reading of 1.0 at 260 mμ) contains approximately 1.3×10^{13} virus particles, and therefore RNA molecules.

Since the particle-to-plaque-forming-unit ratio for poliovirus is about 200:1, 1 OD unit contains about 6.5×10^{10} pfu/ml.

EXTRACTION OF THE POLIOVIRUS RNA

The desired amount of poliovirus is diluted to 1–2 ml with phosphate buffer to which is added an equal volume of buffer-saturated freshly distilled phenol. This mixture is shaken vigorously in a 60 C water bath for 5 min, and then centrifuged at 2000 rev/min for 5 min at 5 C. The lower phenol phase is carefully removed, and the RNA-containing aqueous phase is extracted twice more with an equal volume of phenol. After the final centrifugation, the aqueous phase is removed. To it are added two volumes of water-saturated ether, the mixture shaken, and the upper ether layer decanted. This ether extraction, to remove excess phenol, is repeated twice more. After the final extraction, nitrogen is bubbled through the solution to blow off residual ether.

CHARACTERIZATION OF THE
POLIOVIRUS RNA

Estimation of Amount

The approximate amount of RNA can be determined by reading a dilution of the freshly extracted RNA at 260 mμ. One OD unit contains approximately 50 μg of RNA. If the above procedure has been carried out with care, a yield of 80 to 90% from whole virus can be expected.

Infectious RNA Assay

The infectious RNA titer may be assayed by the method of Boeyé (8) on monolayers of HeLa cells. Logarithmic dilutions of the poliovirus RNA are made in 1.2 M NaCl buffered with 0.02 M sodium phosphate, pH 7.2. An appropriate number of monolayers (usually 2 or 3 plates per dilution) in petri dishes are washed *carefully* and consecutively with 0.3 and 0.6 M NaCl solutions leaving each solution on the cells for 2 min. The monolayers are then overlaid with 0.5 or 1.0 ml volumes of the RNA dilutions leaving the inocula on the cells for 20 min. The RNA is then aspirated off, and the cell sheets washed once with 0.6 M NaCl solution. After this final wash the monolayers are overlaid at once with the usual agar-media overlay (9). The plates are then examined for plaques in 48 hr. The efficiency of this infectious RNA assay is about 0.1% of the standard plaque assay for whole virus.

Sedimentation Coefficient

The single-stranded RNA molecule of poliovirus has a molecular weight of about 2 million and contains about 6000 nucleotides (1). When this RNA molecule is sedimented in a linear sucrose gradient its sedimentation behavior is affected markedly by the ionic strength in the gradient, which induces configurational changes in the molecule (10). When sedimented through a 15–30% sucrose gradient containing 0.1 M NaCl, 5 mM Tris, pH 7.4, and 0.5% sodium dodecylsulfate its sedimentation coefficient is 35 S, whereas if sedimented through a similar gradient containing 1 mM Tris, 1 mM ethylenediamine tetra-acetic acid, and 0.5% sodium dodecylsulfate the S value of the RNA is approximately 20 S.

REFERENCES

1. SCHAFFER, F. L. 1962. Cold Spring Harbor Symp. Quant. Biol. 27: 89.
2. SCHAFFER, F. L., H. F. MOORE, and C. E. SCHWERDT. 1960. Virology. 10: 530.
3. SUMMERS, D. F., and L. LEVINTOW. 1965. Virology. 27: 44.
4. SUMMERS, D. F., J. V. MAIZEL, and J. E. DARNELL. 1965. Proc. Nat. Acad. Sci. U.S. 54: 505.
5. EAGLE, H. 1959. Science. 130: 432.
6. PENMAN, S., and D. F. SUMMERS. 1965. Virology. In press.
7. LEVINTOW, L., and J. E. DARNELL. 1960. J. Biol. Chem. 235: 70.
8. BOEYÉ, A. 1959. Virology. 9: 691.
9. DARNELL, J. E., and T. K. SAWYER. 1959. Virology. 8: 223.
10. BALTIMORE, D. 1964. Proc. Nat. Acad. Sci. U.S. 51: 450.

Purification of Reovirus 3, Dearing Strain and Extraction of Its RNA

PETER JOHN GOMATOS

INSTITUTE OF VIROLOGY

UNIVERSITY OF GLASGOW

GLASGOW, SCOTLAND

PROCEDURE

Growth of Cells

A continuous cell line derived from mouse fibroblasts is used for growing and assaying reovirus 3, Dearing strain. These cells designated as L cells, strain 929, are grown either in monolayers or in suspension. The cells maintained continuously on monolayers are transferred into suspension only for subsequent infection with reovirus.

When grown in monolayers, the cells are grown in 32-oz prescription bottles at 37 C under 5% CO_2 in air until complete monolayers form. The growth medium for cells is Eagle's minimum essential medium (MEM) (1) supplemented with 5% fetal bovine serum (Microbiological Associates, Inc.). All media contain penicillin (500 units/ml), strepto-

The author is presently affiliated with Sloan-Kettering Institute, New York, New York.

mycin (0.1 mg/ml), mycostatin (25 units/ml), and phenol red (12 or 16 mg/liter).

When complete monolayers form, the medium is discarded and the cells are dispersed with 0.125% trypsin and 0.05% sodium versenate dissolved in phosphate-buffered saline (per liter: 8.0 g of NaCl; 0.2 g of KCl; 0.2 g of KH_2PO_4; 1.15 g of Na_2HPO_4) (2). The cells are harvested, collected by centrifugation at 250 × g for 10 min, and resuspended in spinner medium supplemented with nonessential amino acids, as described by Eagle (1), and with 7% fetal bovine serum. The cells are then suspended at a final concentration of about 2 × 10^5 cells/ml, and the cell suspension is dispensed in 150-ml portions into 200-ml screw-cap centrifuge bottles, Corning Glass Works. The bottles are rotated mechanically at 37 C on a large wheel as described by Siminovitch *et al.* (3), with the wheel modified to accept the large centrifuge bottles.

Growth of Virus

After 36–48 hr, the concentration of cells in suspension is approximately 3–4 × 10^5 cells/ml. The cells are collected by centrifugation at 250 × g for 10 min and the medium discarded. The cells are resuspended in 4.0 ml of reovirus stock solution containing 2–3 × 10^8 plaque forming units/ml. Multiplicity of infection is 15–27. Adsorption occurs at room temperature for 2 hr. During this time, the cells are resuspended every 15 min. At the end of this period about 63–86% of input virus has adsorbed to cells. 150 ml of spinner medium supplemented with 2% fetal bovine serum is then added to each centrifuge bottle and the bottles placed back on the roller drum for 18 or 36 hours, as described below. The contents of each bottle can be used as virus stock or for purification of reovirus.

For preparation of virus stock, the infected cell suspension collected after 18 hr at 37 C is frozen and thawed 3 times and the debris spun out at 1000 × g. The supernatant liquid containing 2–3 × 10^8 pfu/ml of reovirus is then stored in 10-ml aliquots at −55 C until used. Reovirus 3 preparations can be assayed either for infectivity (4) or for hemagglutinating activity (5). One hemagglutinating unit represents about 1.0 × 10^6 pfu of reovirus 3, Dearing strain, when a stabilized suspension of bovine erythrocytes is used. The yield of virus varies from 500 to 1000 pfu/cell. When the virus is grown from cells on monolayers, the yield of virus has varied from 300 to 2600 pfu/cell.

Purification of Reovirus 3

For purification of reovirus, the infected cell suspension is collected after 36 hours at 37 C. The cell suspension is centrifuged at

10,000 × g for 10 min in a Lourdes centrifuge to remove cells and debris. The supernatant liquid containing released virus is then concentrated at 4 C by ultrafiltration under reduced pressure across 24–30 ft of Visking tubing, 8/32 in., coiled in a 4-liter suction flask connected to a vacuum pump or water aspirator. By this method, 6–7 liters of supernatant fluid can be concentrated to a volume of 300 ml in about 24–36 hr. The concentrated virus suspension is then centrifuged in a S30 rotor at 78,000 × g for 3 hr. The pellet is then resuspended in the phosphate-buffered saline described previously, but containing 0.005 M Mg^{2+}.

Ribonuclease and deoxyribonuclease are added at final concentrations of 1 and 15–30 μg/ml respectively and the concentrated virus suspension is incubated 37 C for 45 min. Chymotrypsin is then added at a final concentration of 15–30 μg/ml and the incubation at 37 C continued for a further 30 min. The enzyme-treated suspension is cooled to 0 C and 1/2 volume of the fluorocarbon, genetron 113 (Allied Chemical Company), is added. The mixture is homogenized at 0 C in a Servall homogenizer for 3 min. The homogenate is then centrifuged at 1000 × g for 5 min, and the aqueous layer removed. The aqueous layer is retreated similarly for a second time with the fluorocarbon and recovered by centrifugation. The fluorocarbon is retreated with two volumes of phosphate-buffered saline. After homogenization and centrifugation, the resulting aqueous layer is combined with the first.

To the fluorocarbon-treated suspension is added solid cesium chloride (Harshaw Chemical Company) to an average density of 1.37 g/ml and the suspension is centrifuged at 35,000 rev/min in SW39 rotor for 15–18 hr. A band containing reovirus is visible just below the center of the gradient and is collected from below. The virus has a density in cesium chloride solution of 1.38 g/ml. Upper bands containing cellular membranous components and some virus are either retreated with genetron or discarded.

The virus suspension is dialyzed against 0.15 M KCl–0.015 M potassium citrate for 48 hr with frequent changes of the dialysis fluid. The dialyzed virus suspension can be further concentrated by ultrafiltration under reduced pressure. 3500–7000 μg of purified reovirus 3 can be obtained from 7–10 liters of supernatant fluid containing released virus. The virus is stored at 0 C.

The ratio of viral infectivity to hemagglutinating activity was unchanged by the purification procedure. The infectivity of the virus is unaffected by ether treatment, a fact which suggests that there is no peripheral structural lipid present in the virus particle. Purified preparations of reovirus have been found to contain protein and RNA. Samples from various purified preparations with as much as 473 μg of purified virus containing 73 μg of RNA were found to contain less than 1.5 μg of DNA, a limit set by the sensitivity of the diphenylamine reaction. Purified virus suspensions contain on the average 6.5×10^{10} pfu/mgm protein and no detectable RNA free from the virus particles.

Extraction of Reovirus RNA

The suspension of purified virus is gently rocked for 10 min at room temperature with phenol (Mallinckrodt, analytical reagent) previously equilibrated with 0.15 M KCl–0.015 M potassium citrate. The aqueous layer is collected by centrifugation and extracted two further times with phenol, for 10 and 5 min. The aqueous layer is then extracted five times by gently rocking with diethyl ether. Ether is removed under reduced pressure. The reovirus RNA yield is 500–1000 μg. The ultraviolet absorbancy ratios 230/260 and 260/280 should be less than 0.5 and slightly greater than 2.0, respectively.

PROPERTIES OF REOVIRUS RNA

Reovirus RNA has been shown to be double-stranded RNA (6–8). Reovirus genetic material does not contain deoxyribonucleotide sequences in any detectable amount (6,9). The RNA extracted with phenol from the virus contains two major components with $s_{20,w}^o$ of 11.5 and 13.5 and calculated weight average molecular weights of 0.66×10^6 and 1.5×10^6 Daltons, respectively (8). The smaller component, present in an amount 2.3 times that of the larger component, contains at least one other component as revealed by a secondary peak in the size distribution of RNA extracted from reovirus with phenol. This additional component was not resolved in the sedimentation analysis. The longest free RNA strand measured had a calculated molecular weight of 3.8×10^6 Daltons.

Extensive breakage of the RNA molecules occurs during extraction from reovirus particles. It is not yet known whether the genetic material of reovirus exists in one molecule of minimum molecular weight 10.2×10^6 Daltons or in more than one molecule. In addition to the methods published previously (8), purified preparations of reovirus 3 were treated in the following manner (10): (a) addition of sodium dodecyl sulphate to a final concentration of 0.5% or 1.0%; (b) addition of sodium perchlorate, buffered at pH 7.8, to a final concentration of 2.3 or 4.0 M; (c) dialysis at 4 C against 2.3 or 4.0 M sodium perchlorate, buffered at pH 7.8; (d) dialysis at 4 C against 4.0 M guanidine, buffered at pH 7.0. These procedures release the genetic material from the virus.

When analyzed by the band centrifugation method of Vinograd *et al.* (11), there were at least 3 components absorbing in the ultraviolet. These had S values, uncorrected for the density and viscosity of the medium, of 5.9, 7.3, and 8.4. The percentages of total ultraviolet absorbing material distributed in the various peaks were 26, 31, and 43, respectively. Thus all attempts to isolate reovirus RNA as one molecule of molecular weight, 10.2×10^6 Daltons, and in an infectious form have so far failed.

REFERENCES

1. EAGLE, H. 1959. Science. *130:* 432. SUMMERS, D. F. This volume, p. 488.
2. DULBECCO, R., and M. VOGT. 1954. J. Exp. Med. *99:* 167.
3. SIMINOVITCH, L., A. F. GRAHAM, S. M. LESLEY, and A. NEVILL. 1957. Exp. Cell Res. *12:* 299.
4. GOMATOS, P. J., I. TAMM, S. DALES, and R. M. FRANKLIN. 1962. Virology. *17:* 441.
5. GOMATOS, P. J., and I. TAMM. 1962. Virology. *17:* 455.
6. GOMATOS, P. J., and I. TAMM. 1963. Proc. Nat. Acad. Sci., U.S. *49:* 707.
7. LANGRIDGE, R., and P. J. GOMATOS. 1963. Science. *141:* 694.
8. GOMATOS, P. J., and W. STOECKENIUS. 1964. Proc. Nat. Acad. Sci., U.S. *52:* 1449.
9. GOMATOS, P. J., R. M. KRUG, and I. TAMM. 1964. J. Mol. Biol. *9:* 193.
10. GOMATOS, P. J., and L. V. CRAWFORD. 1965. Unpublished observations.
11. VINOGRAD, J., R. BRUNER, R. KENT, and J. WEIGLE. 1963. Proc. Nat. Acad. Sci., U.S. *49:* 902.

Double-Stranded MS2 RNA
from MS2-Infected
Escherichia coli

MARTIN A. BILLETER AND CHARLES WEISSMANN

DEPARTMENT OF BIOCHEMISTRY

NEW YORK UNIVERSITY SCHOOL OF MEDICINE

NEW YORK, NEW YORK

INTRODUCTION

Cells infected with RNA-containing viruses have been found to contain substantial amounts of virus-specific double-stranded RNA in all instances examined so far (1–5). *Escherichia coli* infected with RNA phages has proved to be a rich source of double-stranded RNA. Besides its interest as a hitherto not readily accessible natural polynucleotide (6,7) the double-stranded RNA has been found to be a useful reagent for the specific assay of viral RNA (18). Two purification procedures will be described—one for the preparation of relatively large batches (20–30 mg) of double-stranded MS2 RNA, the other suitable for preparing unlabeled or radioactive double-stranded RNA on a smaller scale (200–400 μg).

MATERIALS

The RNA phage MS2 and its host, *E. coli* Hfr 3000 (thiamine auxotroph), were originally obtained from Dr. A. J. Clark, University of California. Reagents may be purchased from the following sources:

498

pancreatic ribonuclease A, pancreatic deoxyribonuclease I, and mur-amidase (lysozyme), 2 X crystallized (Worthington Biochemical Corpo-ration); phosphoric acid-P^{32} (carrier-free) (Oak Ridge National Laboratory); Sephadex (Pharmacia Fine Chemicals); Millipore filters (Millipore Company); cesium sulfate, as "G.S. Cesium Sulfate 0.06," (Gallard-Schlesinger) (the 60% w/v solution is taken to dryness prior to use); sodium dodecylsulfate (recrystallized from ethanol prior to use) (Matheson Coleman and Bell Company); serum albumin (Cohn, frac-tion V), (Calbiochem); silicic acid, 100 mesh (Mallinckrodt Chemical Works); phenol (Merck) is distilled in large batches and shaken three times with an equal volume of SSC† immediately prior to use; Super-brite glass beads, type 100-5005 (Minnesota Mining Manufacturing Company); antifoam A (Dow Corning); trypticase (Baltimore Bio-logical Laboratories); yeast extract and bacto-agar (Difco); disposable petri dishes (100 × 15 mm) (Fisher Scientific Company); Liquifluor (Nuclear Chicago); toluene, certified reagent grade (Fisher Scientific Company); dialysis tubing (Visking Company); glass vials (Wheaton Glass and Plastic Manufacturers); Macaloid (purified Hectorite) (Inerto Company) (a 1–2% suspension is prepared by boiling in 0.01 M Tris, pH 7.5, homogenizing with a Waring blendor, centrifuging at 20,000 × g for 30 min and repeating this procedure twice); Saran wrap (Dow Chemical Company).

GENERAL METHODS

Media, Agar Slants, and Plates

TRYPTONE MEDIUM. This contains, in a liter of tap water, 10 g of trypticase, 8 g of sodium chloride, 1 g of yeast extract, 1 g of glucose, and 0.29 g of calcium chloride (anhydrous). The cotton plugged flask (which should not be filled to more than 1/2 or 1/3 its volume) is steri-lized for 30 min at 15 lb/sq in.

TRYPTONE MEDIUM WITHOUT YEAST EXTRACT. This contains all ingredients except the yeast extract. After sterilization, 1 ml of a 1% solution of thiamine hydrochloride in 50% aqueous ethanol is added to each liter of medium.

† Abbreviations: SSC, 0.15 M sodium chloride, 0.015 M sodium citrate, pH 7.0 (a tenfold concentrated stock solution was prepared and the pH adjusted so that on dilution a neutral pH resulted). A_{260} unit, absorbance at λ 260 mμ of 1.0 ml of solu-tion ($l = 1.0$ cm) = 1.0; "plus" strand, RNA strand of the parental type as it is con-tained in the mature virus particle; "minus" strand, RNA strand of complementary base sequence.

AGAR SLANTS AND AGAR PLATES ("HARD AGAR"). Tryptone medium containing 1.5% of agar is sterilized for 40 min at 15 lb/sq. in. and after cooling to 45–50 C is dispensed into either sterile test tubes or sterile petri dishes. Petri dishes are filled to half their height and, after the agar has hardened, inverted and dried at 37 C for 24–48 hr. The plates, wrapped in Saran wrap, may be stored for several weeks at 4 C.

"SOFT AGAR." Tryptone medium containing 0.75% of agar is heated at 100 C until the agar is dissolved completely and dispensed in 2.5-ml portions into cotton plugged tubes. These are sterilized for 40 min at 15 lb/sq. in. and stored at 4 C in beakers sealed with Saran wrap, to avoid loss of moisture.

Growth of Bacteria

DETERMINATION OF CELL DENSITY. It is convenient to estimate the cell density by absorbance measurement. To this purpose a standard curve is prepared, plotting the values obtained by absorbance measurement, for example, at 650 mμ, against the cell counts measured with a Petroff-Hausser counter.

PREPARATION OF CULTURES. *E. coli* Hfr 3000 can be stored on slants for 2–3 months. To prepare submerged cultures, bacteria are transferred with a sterile platinum loop into flasks containing 50 ml of tryptone medium. The flasks are shaken at 37 C until a cell density of about 2–4 $\times$ 10^8/ml is reached. One-ml samples of this culture are transferred to a series of flasks containing 50 ml of medium; these are immediately stored at 4 C and are stable for up to 1 month. When incubated at 37 C with shaking, they are ready for use as inoculum within 2–4 hr. Of each batch of inoculating flasks, one or two are checked for absence of phage.

Growth of Virus†

DETERMINATION OF VIRUS TITER. Serial dilutions of the samples are made immediately before assaying, using 10 ml of a sterile solution of 0.9% sodium chloride and 0.029% calcium chloride (anhydrous) for each dilution step. Tubes containing 2.5 ml of soft agar are held in a boiling water bath until the agar is completely liquified, and are then transferred to a water bath at 46–47 C. A freshly grown culture of *E. coli* Hfr 3000 (0.5 ml) containing about 2 $\times$ 10^8

---

† These methods are based on the techniques described by Adams (8) and Loeb and Zinder (9).

bacteria/ml is pipetted into each soft agar tube, 0.1 ml of the diluted virus sample is added, and the contents of the tube are poured into a petri dish containing a layer of hard agar. Immediately after solidification of the top layer, the plates are inverted and incubated at 37 C for 12–25 hr. The somewhat turbid plaques produced by MS2 and related viruses may vary in size, even on the same plate, but are usually less than 2 mm in diameter and have a somewhat fuzzy border. Plaque size and morphology may depend a good deal on the plating technique and on the moisture content of the hard agar.

VIRUS STOCKS. Flasks containing 1 liter of tryptone medium are inoculated with 20 ml of an *E. coli* inoculum and the flasks are shaken in a gyratory water bath shaker (New Brunswick Scientific Co.) at 37 C and 200 rev/min. When the cell count has reached about 2×10^8 bacteria/ml, about 10^{12} plaque forming units (pfu) of virus are added, and the incubation is continued for 2–3 hr. Spontaneous lysis usually occurs between 1.5 to 2 hr after infection. Chloroform (10 ml) is added to prevent further bacterial growth and to aid lysis. The yields, ranging around 5×10^{11} pfu/ml, may be slightly increased by incubating for further 20 min with 0.01 M EDTA, pH 7.5, and 50 μg/ml of freshly dissolved lysozyme (crystalline muramidase). This treatment liberates intracellular phage. Phage lysates may be stored for several months at 4 C or frozen; however, phage diluted into buffer or salt solution very rapidly loses its viability. Purified phage (**10**) should be stored at 4 C in tryptone medium to preserve its viability (private communication by H. Lodish).

Large Scale Growth of MS2-Infected *E. coli*

150 liters of tryptone medium containing 10 ml of antifoam A are sterilized in a 200-liter vat fermenter for 45 min at 15 lb/sq. in. After cooling to 37 C the medium is inoculated with 2 liters of an overnight growth of *E. coli* Hfr 3000. The contents of the vat are aerated with 2 ft³ of air per minute (filtered through a steam-jacketed charcoal-glasswool filter) and the temperature is maintained at 37 C. When a cell density of about 2×10^8/ml is reached, MS2 phage (10^{15} pfu) is added (this corresponds to about 2 liters of lysate). Aeration is increased to 4 ft³/min. After 30 min, first 300 ml of 1 M MgCl$_2$, then 300 ml of 0.5 M EDTA (sodium salt, pH 7.5) are added. The contents of the vat are cooled by cold water coils and, when the temperature drops to 20 C (this takes about 15 min), centrifugation by means of a refrigerated, continuous flow Sharples open-type super centrifuge, at a rate of 2–3 liter/min, is initiated. The cells are resuspended in 1.5 liters of 0.02 M Tris-HCl, pH 7.2, and centrifuged in the 3RA head of the refrigerated

Lourdes centrifuge at 7500 × g for 20 min. 350–400 g (wet weight) of cells are obtained. The cells are stored at −12 C and can be utilized for at least 6 months for the preparation of RNA synthetase and double-stranded RNA.

Comments

Rooms in which work with RNA phages is being carried out (particularly on a large scale) may become heavily contaminated by airborne virus. For this reason, it is necessary to control frequently the bacterial stock. The contamination subsides spontaneously within 1 or 2 weeks if no further virus work is carried out.

After lysis by MS2 phage, the culture loses the silky sheen (due to birefringence of flow) previously apparent after shaking, and contains dark filaments (bacterial debris) without becoming entirely clear. It is important to infect the bacteria while the culture is still well within the logarithmic growth phase, otherwise lysis may not occur.

It is advisable to remove a sample of the vat contents prior to addition of the phage, in order to check whether the culture was still free of virus at that point. A sample is also removed before harvesting and the virus titer (which at this stage of infection should be about 2×10^{11} pfu/ml) is determined after lysing the bacteria with EDTA and lysozyme, as described previously.

LARGE SCALE PURIFICATION OF DOUBLE-STRANDED MS2 RNA

Purification Procedure

Centrifugations are carried out in a Servall Refrigerated RC-2 centrifuge. g values are given as g maximal. pH values are determined with a precooled Radiometer glass electrode (Type G-7026) and a Beckman pH-meter model G, at 0 C. All operations up to the phenol extraction in Step 2 are carried out at 4 C and in rapid succession.

STEP 1. EXTRACTION OF CELLS. Fifty grams of frozen, MS2-infected *E. coli* is enveloped in Saran wrap and reduced to small pieces by pounding with a mallet, without allowing the cells to thaw. The material is placed in the 400-ml bowl of a Servall Omni-Mixer, together with 20 ml of standard buffer (10 mM Tris-HCl, pH 8; 1 mM EDTA; 3 mM MgCl$_2$; 5 mM mercaptoethylamine); 150 g (dry weight) of Superbrite glass beads (previously washed 10 times with distilled water and twice with standard buffer and not dried) are added. The mixture is homogenized at low speed in an ice bath until the cells are thawed and a smooth paste is obtained. Homogenization is then continued in an ethanol–ice bath at -5 C with the powerstat set at 45 (maximum $= 100$), for a total of 15 min. The contents of the bowl are inspected every 5 min to make sure that the paste is neither freezing near the walls nor warming up above 4 C. 0.1 ml of a solution of 10 mg/ml of deoxyribonuclease and 130 ml of standard buffer are mixed with the homogenate, and the glass beads are allowed to settle for 1 min. The supernatant liquid is decanted and the beads are washed with two further 25-ml portions of standard buffer. The supernatant fluid is combined with the washings and distributed into eight 40-ml tubes. After centrifuging for 30 min at 27,000 × g (15,000 rev/min), the supernatant liquid is carefully decanted and placed in a 500-ml beaker packed in ice. The solution is stirred by a magnetically driven stirring bar and 0.2 M sodium acetate buffer (pH 5.0 at 20 C) is added slowly until pH 6.5 is reached. This requires about 10–15 ml of acetate buffer. The volume of the solution is determined. It contains about 7–10 mg/ml of protein and its absorbance at 260 mμ is about 150/ml.

STEP 2. Mg FRACTIONATION AND FIRST PHENOL EXTRACTION. 1.0 M MgCl$_2$ is added with rapid stirring to the Step 1 preparation, to a final concentration of 0.035 M. The opalescent solution is distributed into eight 40-ml tubes and kept at 0 C. Five minutes after the MgCl$_2$ addition the preparation is centrifuged for 20 min at 30,000 × g (16,000 rev/min). The supernatant fluid is discarded and the precipitate dissolved in 60 ml of 0.02 M Tris-HCl buffer, pH 7.9, containing 0.005 M EDTA and 0.1% sodium dodecyl sulfate, using a hand-operated homogenizer (A. H. Thomas tissue grinder, 55-ml working capacity). At this point, the solution contains about 90 A_{260} units per ml.

The following steps are carried out at room temperature. 2.5 mg of Macaloid and 60 ml of phenol (equilibrated with 0.02 M Tris-HCl buffer, pH 7.9) are added to the solution and the mixture is shaken vigorously for 5 min in a glass-stoppered bottle. Six 50 g batches of infected cells are brought to this stage; the suspensions are then combined and processed together.

The layers are separated by centrifugation in 250-ml plastic bottles (5 min, GSA rotor, maximum speed setting 15,000 × g) and the aqueous phase is drawn off without disturbing the heavy interphase. The aqueous phase is reextracted twice with phenol as above. Sixty milliliters of 0.02 M Tris-HCl buffer, pH 7.9, is used to wash the phenol phases in succession and the combined aqueous layers are then extracted four times with an equal volume of ether. The aqueous phase is freed of residual ether by passing a stream of nitrogen over it. Two volumes of ethanol are added and the resulting suspension is stored overnight at -12 C.

STEP 3. RIBONUCLEASE TREATMENT AND SECOND PHE-NOL EXTRACTION. The precipitate is centrifuged down (30 min at 16,000 $\times$ g and -20 C, GSA rotor), and dissolved in 1800 ml of SSC. The A_{260} of the resulting solution should be not more than about 20–25 units/ml for the following digestion. After adjusting the temperature to 25 C, 50 μg/ml of ribonuclease A is added and the digestion stopped after 30 min by addition of sodium dodecylsulfate to give a final concentration of 0.033%; 2 volumes of ethanol are added with stirring and the temperature of the mixture is lowered and kept at about -15 C with use of an alcohol–water–Dry Ice bath. The precipitate is allowed to settle for 2 hr and the supernatant liquid is syphoned off as completely as possible and discarded. The residual suspension is centrifuged (30 min at 16,000 $\times$ g and -20 C, GSA rotor) and the precipitate suspended in 150 ml of SSC. The solution is extracted four times with 2 volumes of phenol (equilibrated with SSC); 5 mg of Macaloid is added prior to each extraction. The phenol phases are washed in succession with 100 ml of SSC; the aqueous phases are combined and extracted four times with ether. The nucleic acid is precipitated with ethanol as described previously. After 2 hr or longer at -12 C, the precipitate is collected by centrifugation (15 min at 31,000 $\times$ g, -15 C, SS-34 rotor), and dissolved in 10–15 ml of SSC. The opalescent solution contains 1100–1500 A_{260} units/ml, most of which is due to acid-soluble but alcohol-insoluble ribonuclease digestion products.

STEP 4. EXCLUSION CHROMATOGRAPHY ON SEPHADEX G-200. Chromatography is carried out at 2–4 C. The Step 3 solution is placed on a column (2 $\times$ 75 cm) of Sephadex G-200, equilibrated with SSC, and eluted with the same solvent. A small peak, comprising about 4% of the A_{260} units applied to the column is eluted between about 60 and 90 ml and contains double-stranded MS2 RNA. A second, much larger peak corresponds to the ribonuclease digestion products. The fractions corresponding to the first peak are pooled.

STEP 5. DENSITY GRADIENT CENTRIFUGATION IN Cs$_2$SO$_4$. Solid Cs$_2$SO$_4$ is added to the Step 4 solution to give a final density of 1.61 g/cm³ (determined pycnometrically). The solution is then centrifuged in two tubes of the Spinco SW 25.1 rotor for 4 days at 18 C. Two bands are visible after centrifugation—a diffuse band near the top of the gradient containing polysaccharide material and a narrow band near the bottom of the tube (density about 1.68 g/cm³) consisting of a fine precipitate that readily dissolves upon dilution with water; the resulting solution has a spectrum similar to that of nucleic acid. The clear solution *between* the two visible bands is collected in several fractions by means of a fine syphon. The fractions containing the bulk of the ultraviolet-absorbing material are pooled and dialyzed for 24 hr against four 1-liter changes of SSC.

After storage for several months at -12 C the preparation shows no change in its properties. Double-stranded MS2 RNA can be precipitated by layering two volumes of ethanol on the solution and winding up the fibers on a glass rod.

PREPARATION OF THE LITHIUM SALT. A portion of the Step 5 preparation (3 ml) is filtered through a column (1.1 cm $\times$ 30 cm) of Sephadex G-50 (fine) previously equilibrated with 0.1 M LiCl. The RNA-containing fractions are located by absorbance measurements and pooled. The pooled fractions (6 ml) are then filtered through a similar column (2 cm $\times$ 30 cm) equilibrated with glass-distilled water. The RNA-containing fractions are pooled, lyophilized, and dried in high vacuum at room temperature.

Properties of Purified Double-Stranded MS2 RNA (11)

Some analytical data of the Step 5 preparation are given in Table 1. The base composition is that expected of an RNA duplex consisting of an MS2 RNA strand and its complement and is very different from that of the host cell RNA. The molar absorbance $\epsilon(P)$ is lower than that of single-stranded RNA; the absolute and relative (thermal) hypochromicity is higher. The T_m of the helix-coil transition is dependent on the ionic strength and is substantially higher, under comparable conditions, than that of single-stranded RNA and higher than that of native DNA with a similar base composition. As seen in the analytical ultracentrifuge, the preparation is quite homogeneous; the sedimentation coefficient, $s_{20,w}$, of several preparations ranged from 8 to 9.5 S.

Resistance to pancreatic ribonuclease A and B as well as to ribonuclease T_1 is very pronounced at salt concentrations above 0.15 M sodium chloride. After heat denaturation, double-stranded RNA is as susceptible to pancreatic ribonuclease as single-stranded RNA. Reannealing occurs readily at 80–90 C in salt concentrations above 0.15 M NaCl.

The "minus" strand content was determined by annealing techniques. One A_{260} unit of the Step 5 preparation annealed with 0.58 A_{260} units of MS2 RNA ($\epsilon\,{}^{1\%}_{260\,m\mu} = 251$ dl g^{-1} cm^{-1}). Since $\epsilon\,{}^{1\%}_{260\,m\mu}$ of the Step 5 preparation was 210 dl g^{-1} cm^{-1} the preparation contained $\dfrac{(0.58/251)}{(1/210)} = 48.5\%$ "minus" strands and was therefore not less than 97.2% pure double-stranded MS2 RNA.

TABLE 1.   *Comparison of MS2 RNA, Double-Stranded MS2 RNA, and Ribosomal RNA*

Parameter	MS2 RNA or R17 RNA	Double-Stranded MS2 RNA	E. coli Ribosomal RNA
Phosphorus (%)	—	9.58 (calc; 9.46)	—
Orcinol test (A_{665}-units per μmole of purine)	—	11.8	11.8
Cysteine test	—	less than 2% DNA	—
ϵ (P)$_{260m\mu}$	8600 (10)[a]	6670	7450 (13)
Base composition (%)	A 23.7 (10) U 24.4 (10) G 27.1 (10) C 24.8 (10)	24.6 (calc. 24.05) 23.7 (calc. 24.05) 25.9 (calc. 25.95) 25.8 (calc. 25.95)	25.1 20.4 32.6 21.9
Buoyant density in Cs_2SO_4	1.626	1.609	1.646 (13)
$s_{20,w}$ (high ionic strength)	26 S (0.2 M NaCl) (12)	8.45 S (SSC)	24 S, 18 S (0.1 M KCl, 0.05 M Tris) (13)
$s_{20,w}$ (low ionic strength)	20.4 S (0.02 M NaCl) (12)	8.1 S (0.01 SSC)	19 S, 15 S (0.005 M KCl, 0.0025 M Tris) (13)
T_m (high ionic strength)	47 C (SSC)	103 C (SSC)	54 C (0.1 M sodium phosphate buffer) (12)
T_m (low ionic strength)	—	87 C (0.1 × SSC)	
Hypochromicity	18%	26.5%	21.9%
X-ray diffraction pattern	not oriented	highly oriented (19)	not oriented

[a] Numbers in parentheses refer to bibliography at end of chapter.

Table 2 summarizes the purification and yields, based on "minus" strand content. The Step 4 preparation, which is still contaminated with some polysaccharides and some nucleotide material of nonviral nature, is quite satisfactory for most annealing experiments.

Purification procedures have been described by Montagnier and

TABLE 2. *Purification of Double-Stranded MS2 RNA*
(300 g of infected cells)

Purification step	Volume (ml)	Total A_{260} units	mg^a	OD_{260} Units^b	Purity^c (%)	Yield (%)
					Double-Stranded MS2 RNA	
1. Crude extract	1,500	316,500	147	3,090	0.98	100
2. MgCl$_2$ precipitation	726	32,500	57	1,200	3.6	39
3. Ribonuclease treatment	222	16,400	49	1,030	6.3	33
4. Exclusion chromatography	50.6	820	39.4	828	101	27
5. Final preparation	40.4	443	21.3	447	101	14.4

^{a} Determined by the specific annealing test (11,3).

^{b} Calculated using $\varepsilon_{260}^{1\%}$ for purified double-stranded MS2 RNA of 210 dl g^{-1}cm^{-1}.

^{c} Calculated on the basis of absorbance.

Sanders (1), Kaerner and Hoffman-Berling (14), and Ammann, Delius, and Hofschneider (15) for the double-stranded RNAs of encephalomyocarditis virus, phage fr and phage M 12, respectively.

LABELED DOUBLE–STRANDED MS2 RNA

Determination of Acid-Insoluble and Ribonuclease-Resistant Radioactivity

DETERMINATION OF ACID-INSOLUBLE RADIOACTIVITY. To the radioactive sample in 2 ml of SSC, 0.1 ml of 0.1% bovine serum albumin is added. The sample is chilled in ice and 0.2 ml of 60% trichloroacetic acid is added. After standing for 10–30 min at 0 C the precipitate is collected on a Millipore filter (pore size 0.45 μ, disc diameter 25 mm) using a Millipore Pyrex Filter Holder. The filter is washed with three 10-ml portions of chilled 6% trichloroacetic acid. If the radioactivity is to be determined on an end window or gas-flow counter, the filter is placed in an aluminum planchet and dried under an infrared lamp. For scintillation counting, the filters are pierced through the edge by a glass needle and inserted in an upright position into a glass vial. After drying overnight at 55–60 C, Liquifluor [10% diphenyloxazole and 0.125% 1, 4-bis-2-(5-phenyloxazolyl) benzene in toluene] diluted 1:25 with toluene, is added as scintillator.

DETERMINATION OF RIBONUCLEASE-RESISTANT RADIO-
ACTIVITY. The radioactive sample, in 2 ml of SSC, is brought to
25 C in a water bath. 0.02 ml of a solution of ribonuclease A (5 mg/ml)
is thoroughly mixed with the sample using a Vortex mixer and the
solution is incubated for 30 min at 25 C. The samples are chilled,
bovine serum albumin and trichloroacetic acid are added, and the acid-
insoluble radioactivity is determined as described above.

DETERMINATION OF RIBONUCLEASE RESISTANCE AFTER
HEAT DENATURATION. Partially purified preparations of P^{32}-
labeled double-stranded RNA contain considerable amounts of radioactivity due to compounds other than RNA (polyglycerol phosphate,
phospholipids). They are most easily detected by heating the sample
under conditions where double-stranded RNA becomes susceptible to
ribonuclease and then determining the ribonuclease-resistant radioactivity. To this purpose, samples are diluted to 1.8 ml with 0.01 mM
EDTA. The final salt concentration should be 0.1 × SSC or less and
no Mg^{2+} should be present in the sample. [The tubes used for this experiment should be rinsed with hot EDTA solution (0.1 M) and glass-
distilled water.] The sample is heated at 100 C for 5 min and rapidly
chilled in ice. 0.2 ml of 10 × SSC is added and the ribonuclease-resistant
radioactivity is determined as described previously.

Preparation of Radioactive MS2-Infected *E. coli*

Two 2-liter flasks, each containing 1 liter of tryptone medium without yeast extract (but supplemented with thiamine), are inoculated
with 20 ml of a culture of *E. coli* Hfr 3000. The cultures are grown at
37 C, on a gyratory shaker at 200 rev/min. When a density of 2×10^8
bacteria/ml is reached, about 10^{12} pfu of MS2 phage are added to each
flask. Two minutes after infection 4 mc of carrier-free phosphoric
acid-P^{32} or 50 μc of C^{14}-labeled uracil and enough cold uracil to give
a final concentration of 15 μg/ml are added. Forty minutes after infection the flasks are cooled in ice, and the cells are harvested by centrifugation (15 min at about 8000 × g). The radioactive supernatant
liquid is poured off carefully and the remaining liquid removed as completely as possible with a Pasteur pipet. The cells are resuspended in
200 ml of chilled 0.05 M potassium phosphate buffer, pH 7. This is accomplished most conveniently by adding 10–20 ml of the buffer to each
flask, stirring up the precipitate, and then, using a large rubber bulb,
repeatedly drawing the suspension in and out of a 10-ml short-tipped
pipet with a wide opening (about 1 mm). A smooth suspension can
rapidly be obtained in this way with a minimum of handling of the

radioactive material. The cells are recentrifuged as above and the supernatant liquid is discarded. The cells may be stored at −12 C. These cells contain homogeneously labeled viral RNA.

Purification Procedure

STEP 1. LYSIS AND DEPROTEINIZATION. The bacteria are evenly resuspended in 35 ml of TNE buffer (0.05 M Tris-HCl buffer, pH 8, containing 0.1 M NaCl and 0.005 M EDTA) by the technique outlined in the previous section. The suspension is transferred to a 120-ml glass-stoppered centrifuge tube (International centrifuge), and sodium dodecylsulfate (25% solution) is added to a final concentration of 1%. The suspension is kept at 30 C until a clear, very viscous solution is obtained. This occurs within a few minutes with the strain of E. coli used. One volume of phenol, equilibrated just prior to use with TNE buffer, is added and the mixture is vigorously shaken by hand for 5 min. After centrifugation (5 min at 1000 × g), the top aqueous layer is slowly drawn off with a Pasteur pipet, without disturbing the interphase. The aqueous phase is transferred to a second glass-stoppered centrifuge tube and the phenol extraction repeated twice. Each of the three phenol phases is washed in succession with one and the same 30-ml portion of TNE buffer. The aqueous phases are combined and extracted five times in the cold in a glass-stoppered centrifuge tube with 1 volume of peroxide-free ether. Centrifugation at low speed may be necessary to separate the phases following the first two ether extractions. The ether phase is drawn off by suction and residual ether is finally evaporated by blowing a stream of nitrogen over the surface of the solution. Two volumes of ethanol are added and, after mixing thoroughly, the suspension is transferred to 40-ml plastic centrifuge tubes (Servall). After at least 2 hr at −12 C the precipitate is collected by centrifugation (10 min at 10,000 × g) and dissolved in 36 ml of 0.02 M Tris-HCl buffer, pH 7.2, containing 0.005 M MgCl₂. It is important to make sure that the solution does not contain any sodium dodecylsulfate, otherwise the following digestion by nucleases is incomplete. If traces of foaming are apparent upon shaking, the alcohol precipitation should be repeated.

STEP 2. DEOXYRIBONUCLEASE AND RIBONUCLEASE TREATMENT. The Step 1 preparation is incubated with 20 μg/ml of deoxyribonuclease (stock solution, 5–10 mg/ml) for 30 min at 25 C. Four milliliters of 10 × SSC and pancreatic ribonuclease A (stock solution, 5–10 mg/ml) to a final concentration of 50 μg/ml are added and the incubation at 25 C is continued for a further 30 min. After adding sodium dodecylsulfate to a final concentration of 0.03%, the

nucleic acid is precipitated with 2 volumes of ethanol and the precipitate is collected by centrifugation (10 min at 10,000 × g) after standing for 2 or more hours at −12 C. The precipitate is dissolved in 3 ml
of SSC; 0.1 mg of Macaloid is added; and the solution is shaken vigorously for 5 min with 2 volumes of phenol equilibrated with SSC in a
12-ml glass-stoppered centrifuge tube. The layers are separated by
low-speed centrifugation and the aqueous layer is drawn off and
transferred to a fresh centrifuge tube. Care is taken not to transfer
any of the phenol phase. 0.5 ml of SSC is layered on top of the phenol
and the tube is gently rotated to mix the remaining aqueous layer
with the SSC. The wash is added to the aqueous layer, along with
0.1 mg of Macaloid, and the phenol extraction is repeated. A total of
four phenol extractions are carried out in this fashion. The combined
aqueous layers are finally extracted four times with ether, as described
above. The residual ether is removed in a stream of nitrogen, and 2
volumes of ethanol are added. After standing at −12 C, for 2 or more
hours, the precipitate is centrifuged for 20 min at 30,000 × g. The
pellet should be compact and contain as little ethanol as possible. It is
dissolved in 0.5 ml of SSC.

STEP 3. EXCLUSION CHROMATOGRAPHY ON SEPHADEX
G-200. A column of Sephadex G-200 (1.2 cm × 25 cm) is prepared
and equilibrated with SSC. The Step 2 preparation is chromatographed
on this column at a flow rate of 3–4 ml/hr. Fractions of about 0.5–1 ml
are collected. The radioactive fractions are located by assaying small
portions for acid-insoluble radioactivity. The double-stranded RNA
emerges from the column in a sharp peak after about 11–12 ml of
solvent have passed through. The pooled fractions contain about 6 A_{260}
units. The RNA- and DNA-breakdown products are eluted in the
fractions beyond 25 ml of eluate and are discarded. In the case of the
C^{14}-labeled uracil preparation, the first peak contains all of the radioactivity in double-stranded MS2 RNA. However, when P^{32} is used much
of the label is in compounds other than RNA, as evidenced by the fact
that 80% of the radioactivity is ribonuclease resistant after heat denaturation (cf. pp. 507–508, "Determination of Acid-Insoluble and
Ribonuclease-Resistant Radioactivity"). This material is removed completely by the following step.

STEP 4. CHROMATOGRAPHY ON METHYLATED ALBUMIN-
SILICIC ACID. The pooled fractions corresponding to the first peak
obtained by Sephadex chromatography are adjusted to 0.5 M NaCl,
0.05 M potassium phosphate buffer, pH 6.8, and filtered by gravity
through a methylated albumin–silicic acid column (1.2 cm × 5 cm)
prepared according to Okamoto and Kawade (16). Practically all radio-

activity remains adsorbed. Fifteen milliliters of a buffer containing 0.5 M NaCl, 0.05 M potassium phosphate, pH 6.8, is passed through the column and then a 1.0 M NaCl solution in 0.05 M potassium phosphate buffer, pH 6.8, is used to elute the double-stranded RNA. Fractions (1.0 ml) are collected and the RNA is located by determining acid-precipitable radioactivity on small samples. The material is usually completely eluted with the first 3 ml of buffer. The pooled fractions are dialyzed overnight against 2 liters of SSC. The final preparation contains 5 A_{260} units (about 240 μg) of double-stranded RNA. Its specific radioactivity is about 6000 dpm/μg in the case of P[32] and 4000 dpm/μg in the case of uracil-C[14].

COMMENTS. If higher specific activities are desired, P[32]-labeling of the bacteria may be carried out in a medium (17) with limiting phosphate and 40 mc of P[32]/liter. In the case of uracil-C[14], a higher specific radioactivity may be used. However, the final 15 μg/ml concentration of uracil should be maintained; otherwise the viral RNA may not be labeled homogeneously.

Properties of the Radioactive Double-Stranded RNA

Under the conditions of the standard ribonuclease assay the radioactive RNA is 95% resistant. After heat denaturation, only 1.2% of the radioactivity remains ribonuclease resistant. Under appropriate conditions, 85% of the denatured double-stranded MS2 RNA can be annealed to reconstitute an ribonuclease-resistant duplex. As determined by the specific dilution test (11), 50% of the radioactivity is in "plus" strands, i.e., in strands of the parental type.

REFERENCES

1. MONTAGNIER, L., and F. K. SANDERS. 1962. Nature. 199: 664.
2. BALTIMORE, D., Y. BECKER, and J. E. DARNELL. 1964. Science. 143: 1034.
3. WEISSMANN, C., P. BORST, R. H. BURDON, M. A. BILLETER, and S. OCHOA. 1964. Proc. Nat. Acad. Sci. U.S. 51: 682.
4. FENWICK, M. L., R. L. ERIKSON, and R. M. FRANKLIN. 1964. Science. 146: 527.
5. RALPH, R. K., R. E. F. MATTHEWS, A. I. MATUS, and H. G. MANDEL. 1965. J. Mol. Biol. 11: 202.
6. GOMATOS, P. J., and I. TAMM. 1963. Proc. Nat. Acad. Sci. U.S. 49: 707.
7. GOMATOS, P. J., and I. TAMM. 1963. Proc. Nat. Acad. Sci. U.S. 50: 878.
8. ADAMS, M. H. 1950. Methods in Med. Res. 2: 1.
9. LOEB, T., and N. D. ZINDER. 1961. Proc. Nat. Acad. Sci. U.S. 47: 282.
10. STRAUSS, J. H., JR., and R. L. SINSHEIMER. 1963. J. Mol. Biol. 7: 43.
11. BILLETER, M. A., C. WEISSMANN, and R. C. WARNER. J. Mol. Biol. In press.

12. GESTELAND, R., and H. BOEDTKER. 1964. J. Mol. Biol. *8:* 496.
13. STANLEY, W. M., JR. 1963. *Thesis.* University of Wisconsin. BOLTON, E. W. This volume, p. 442.
14. KAERNER, H. C., and H. HOFFMANN-BERLING. 1964. Z. Naturforsch. *19B:* 593.
15. AMMANN, J., H. DELIUS, and P. H. HOFSCHNEIDER. 1964. J. Mol. Biol. *10:* 557.
16. OKAMOTO, T., and Y. KAWADE. 1963. Biochem. Biophys. Res. Commun. *13:* 324.
17. GAREN, A., and O. SIDDIQI. 1962. Proc. Nat. Acad. Sci. U.S. *48:* 1121.
18. WEISSMANN, C. 1965. Proc. Nat. Acad. Sci. U.S. *54:* 202.
19. LANGRIDGE, R., M. A. BILLETER, P. BORST, R. H. BURDON, and C. WEISSMANN. 1964. Proc. Nat. Acad. Sci. U.S. *52:* 114.

5. Synthetic RNA

rAU Copolymer

MICHAEL J. CHAMBERLIN
VIRUS LABORATORY
UNIVERSITY OF CALIFORNIA
BERKELEY, CALIFORNIA

PRINCIPLE

Alternating rAU† copolymer is synthesized enzymatically from ATP and UTP using purified RNA polymerase with alternating dAT copolymer as template (2).

Materials

Fraction IV RNA polymerase from *Escherichia coli* is prepared as described by Chamberlin and Berg (3). The alternating dAT copolymer is prepared enzymatically according to Schachman *et al.* (4). Protein is removed from dAT by phenol extraction followed by passage of the polymer through Amberlite XE-64 resin (see below) and the final product is dialyzed against 0.01 M Tris buffer at pH 8. Sodium citrate buffer, pH 5.4, contains 1 mole of trisodium citrate to 1.3 moles of citric acid. Sodium citrate buffer, pH 7.5, contains 2 moles of sodium chloride

This investigation was supported by Public Health Service Research Grant, GM 12010, from the National Institute of General Medical Sciences.

† The nomenclature used is essentially that of Inman and Baldwin (1). In addition the alternating copolymer of riboadenylic acid and deoxyuridylic acid is designated rA(d)U.

to 1 mole of trisodium citrate. Concentrations of citrate buffers are given in terms of the sodium ion concentration. Cesium sulfate is "optical grade" material obtained from the S. H. Cohen Co. (Yonkers, New York).

Procedure

LARGE SCALE SYNTHESIS OF rAU COPOLYMER. The reaction mixture in a final volume of 39 ml contains 1.4 mmoles of Tris buffer, pH 8.0, 40 μmoles of $MnCl_2$, 200 μmoles of $MgCl_7$ 430 μmoles of 2-mercaptoethanol, 45μmoles of ATP, 45 μmoles of UTP, 100 μg of pyruvate kinase, 30 μmoles of PEP, 400 μmoles of KCl, 1.1 μmoles of dAT, and 9.2 mg of Fraction IV RNA polymerase (50,000–60,000 units). After incubation at 37 C for 2 hr, 3.5 ml of 5% sodium lauryl sulfate are added and the mixture is incubated for 3 min at 37 C, then chilled at 0 C for 2 hr. The resulting precipitate is removed by centrifugation and discarded and 1.9 ml of 1 M sodium citrate, pH 5.4, are added to the supernatant fluid. The mixture is warmed to 25 C and extracted three times with an equal volume of buffer-saturated phenol. The pooled phenol layers are then extracted with two 15-ml portions of 0.05 M sodium citrate, pH 5.4. The pooled aqueous layers are filtered through an Amberlite XE-64 column as described below, and the rAU is precipitated from the effluent by the addition of 5 M NaCl solution to 0.5 M and two volumes of cold ethanol. The precipitate is collected by centrifugation and dissolved in 10 ml of 0.05 M sodium citrate, pH 5.4, and dialyzed for 48 hr against 2 changes of 500 ml each of 0.5 M sodium citrate buffer, 0.01 M EDTA pH 7.5, then for 48 hr against 2 changes of 500 ml each of 0.5 M sodium citrate buffer, 0.001 M EDTA pH 7.5, and finally for 48 hr against 2 changes of 500 ml each of 0.05 M sodium citrate buffer, 0.001 M EDTA, pH 7.5. The resulting preparation is stored at −15 C or, if possible, at −196 C in a liquid nitrogen refrigerator.

The yield of rAU copolymer obtained from the reaction is about 50% of the triphosphates added. The reaction has been scaled down to 1 ml with no appreciable change in yield.

UTP can be replaced with $\overline{BU}$TP (2), dUTP (Chamberlin, unpublished observations), or dTTP (5) although in the latter case both the rate and the extent of the reaction are considerably reduced.

HANDLING OF rAU COPOLYMER PREPARATIONS. Early preparations of rAU copolymer were unstable, becoming nonsedimentable and acid soluble when heated to 70 C or when stored for several months at −15 C. A similar instability of other high molecular weight RNA preparations has been noted previously (6–9). The degradation may be due to ribonuclease present in the enzyme preparations, introduced by handling (9), or released by trace bacterial contaminants. The following precautions should therefore be taken during the isolation and use of rAU preparations:

1. Sterile glassware, reagents, and techniques are used in all experiments in which the physical integrity of the polymer is required.
2. Dialysis tubing is handled with sterile gloves; it is prepared by heating to 80 C for 30 min in 0.01 M EDTA, pH 7.5, soaked overnight in fresh 0.01 M EDTA, pH 7.5, and stored in 0.001 M EDTA, pH 7.5.
3. Polymer preparations that cannot be sterilized—such as the dAT copolymer used to direct rAU synthesis—are passed through a 5- × 1-cm column of Amberlite XE-64, which has been equilibrated with 0.05 M sodium citrate buffer, pH 5.4.
4. Sterile, quartz distilled water is used.

The stability of rAU preparations obtained and handled using these techniques has been investigated by determining the effect of heating at 70 C in 0.05 M sodium citrate buffer, pH 7.5, on the mean sedimentation coefficient determined in that buffer at 25 C (2). The unheated preparation had a sedimentation coefficient of 8.5 ± 0.3 S; heating for 15 min reduced this to 8.1 S, and after 6 hr the sedimentation coefficient had fallen to 7.2 S. The sedimentation coefficient of this same unheated preparation decreased to 7.8 S on storage for 5 months at -15 C (the preparation was frozen and thawed, and samples were withdrawn frequently during this period).

Preparations of rAU that have not been dialyzed against high levels of EDTA, or that have been dialyzed against buffers not containing EDTA even after prior dialysis against EDTA, show striking changes in hydrodynamic properties and in thermal melting in high and low salts, which are consistent with an appreciable content of bound polyvalent metal ions. The viscosity observed for such preparations in 1 M salt is time dependent, increasing rapidly due to aggregation of the polymer. Thermal melting of such preparations in 10^{-3} M sodium ion does not show the usual, characteristic, sharp optical density transition, but shows a broadened transition with melting occurring over a 10° range. The melting profile is no longer symmetrical, but becomes increasingly gradual at the higher temperatures. In 1 M sodium ion there is the sharp transition characteristic of EDTA dialyzed preparations, but the curve is not reversible; the optical density transition on cooling is broadened, and the final optical density after cooling is from

10 to 15% higher than before melting, indicating that considerable degradation of the rAU has occurred. Degradation of RNA by polyvalent metal ions at high temperatures has been observed in other studies (10,11).

Properties

CHEMICAL COMPOSITION OF rAU. The rAU copolymer prepared as described above contains less than 0.5% protein as determined by the Lowry method (12). The amount of dAT template remaining in the preparation has not been determined but represents a maximum contamination of 2%. The nucleotide sequence of the rAU copolymer is strictly alternating (2,13) as would be expected from the alternating nature of the dAT added as template (4).

The spectra of the helix and coil forms of rAU are shown in Fig. 1. For the helix a value of ϵ_P^{260} of 6100 has been found ($\lambda_{max} = 261$ mμ), for the coil $\epsilon_P^{260} = 10,400$ ($\lambda_{max} = 259$ mμ). Degradation of the polymer to mononucleotides using 0.3 N KOH gave an ϵ_P^{260} of 12,400 for the neutralized digest.

PHYSICAL PROPERTIES OF rAU COPOLYMER. The mean sedimentation coefficient, $s_{20,w}$, of the rAU copolymer preparation described above was 7.8 in 0.05 M sodium citrate buffer, pH 7.5. No significant dependence of S on polymer concentration was observed in the concentration range tested (less than 5% variation in the range of 65–380 mμmoles per ml). The intrinsic viscosity of this preparation was 1.89 dl/g, giving a molecular weight of about 318,000 g/mole by the Scheraga-Mandelkern equation (14) assuming values of $\beta = 2.5 \times 10^6$ and $\bar{v} = 0.5$ (15,16). Neither the sedimentation coefficient nor the reduced viscosity of rAU copolymer changed appreciably on varying the concentration of sodium ion in the solution from 10^{-3} to 1 M.

The dAT copolymer used as template in the above preparation had an average molecular weight estimated from sedimentation and viscosity measurements of 8×10^6, whereas the rAU product was about $\frac{1}{25}$ this size. Thus the size of the rAU product does not seem to bear any simple relationship to the size of the primer. This suggests that either the enzyme produces a considerable range of product sizes, or that the product is degraded during synthesis or isolation.

Solutions of rAU and other alternating copolymers show a sharp optical density transition when they are heated (Table 1). The midpoint of this helix-coil transition (T_m) is characteristic of the copolymer and of the salt concentration at which the experiment is carried out. RNA-containing copolymers are always more stable than their DNA-

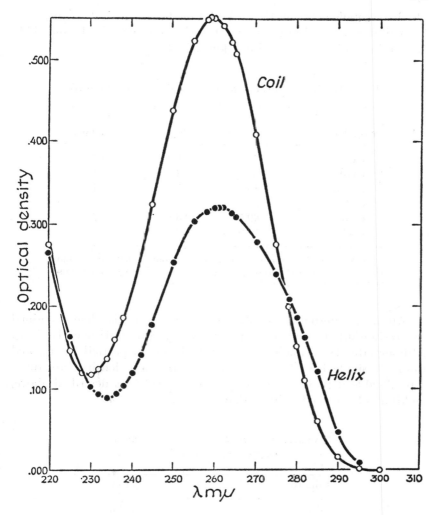

Fig. 1. Spectrum of rAU copolymer in the helix and coil forms. The spectra were determined in 0.01 M sodium citrate buffer, pH 7.5, at a nucleic acid concentration of 5.3×10^{-5} M. The helix spectrum was measured at 25 C, the coil spectrum at 56 C.

analogues, whereas the mixed, alternating copolymer rA(d)U has a very low thermal stability. Copolymers containing 5-BU are markedly more stable than their U-containing analogues. The breadth of the melting transitions are quite similar in each case, but the increase in optical density at 260 mμ (hyperchromicity) observed upon melting rAU and rABU (65–70%) is considerably greater than that found with comparable deoxycopolymers (40–45%). A plot of the T_m against the negative logarithm of the sodium ion concentration for rAU, dAT, and dAU gives a linear relationship, with a slope of −17.5 C.

TABLE 1.   *Melting of Alternating Copolymers in 0.01 M Na^{+a}*

Copolymer	T_m	δT_m	% Increase at 260 mμ
rAU	47.5	3.5	67
rA$\overline{\text{BU}}$	67.3	2.8	64
rA(d)U	18.4	2.5	44
dAU	37.2	4.0	44
dA$\overline{\text{BU}}$	49.5	2.6	47
dAT	39.9	2.9	42

a Melting determinations were carried out in 0.01 M sodium citrate buffer at pH 7.5. δT_m is the temperature range over which 90% of the total optical density change occurs.

All of the alternating copolymers give sharp bands when examined in a cesium sulfate gradient in the analytical ultracentrifuge (Table 2). Although the RNA copolymers generally band in a partially aggregated form (2), single bands are obtained and buoyant densities are quite reproducible if preparations are stored in EDTA as described above, and if highly purified cesium sulfate is used.

TABLE 2.   *Buoyant Densities of Alternating Copolymers in Cesium Sulfate at pH 8^a*

Copolymer	ρ 25 C
dAT	1.426
dA$\overline{\text{BU}}$	1.540
rAU	1.614
rA$\overline{\text{BU}}$	1.695
rA(d)U	1.500

a Densities given for the DNA copolymers are taken from Inman and Baldwin, 1964 (17). Densities given for the rAU and rA(d)U copolymers were determined in 44.5% cesium sulfate containing 0.01 M Tris buffer, pH 8.0, with dAT copolymer as a density reference. The value for rA$\overline{\text{BU}}$ was determined in 49.0% cesium sulfate with dA$\overline{\text{BU}}$ as a density reference.

REFERENCES

1. INMAN, R. B., and R. L. BALDWIN. 1962. J. Mol. Biol. *5:* 172.
2. CHAMBERLIN, M., R. L. BALDWIN, and P. BERG. 1963. J. Mol. Biol. *7:* 334.
3. CHAMBERLIN, M., and P. BERG. 1962. Proc. Nat. Acad. Sci. U.S. *48:* 81.
4. SCHACHMAN, H. K., J. ADLER, C. M. RADDING, I. R. LEHMAN, and A. KORNBERG. 1960. J. Biol. Chem. *235:* 3242.
5. CHENG, T. Y., and P. O. TSO. 1965. Fed. Proc. *24:* 602.
6. ARONSON, A. I., and B. J. MCCARTHY. 1961. Biophys. J. *1:* 215.
7. FRAENKEL-CONRAT, H., and B. SINGER. 1958. Bull. Soc. Chem. Biol. *40:* 1717.
8. FRAENKEL-CONRAT, H., B. SINGER, and A. TSUGITA. 1958. Virology. *14:* 54.
9. HOLLEY, R. W., J. APGAR, and S. H. MERRILL. 1961. J. Biol. Chem. *236:* PC 42.
10. MATSUSHITA, S., and F. IBUKI. 1960. Mem. Res. Inst. Food Sci., Kyoto Univ. No. 22: 32, 38.
11. MILLIGAN, J. O., and P. BERG. 1963. Unpublished results.
12. LOWRY, O., J. S. ROSEBROUGH, A. L. FARR, and R. J. RANDALL. 1951. J. Biol. Chem. *193:* 265.
13. FURTH, J. J., J. HURWITZ, and M. GOLDMAN. 1961. Biochem. Biophys. Res. Comm. *4:* 362.
14. SCHERAGA, H. A., and L. MANDELKERN. 1953. Am. Chem. Soc. *75:* 179.
15. EIGNER, J. 1960. Ph.D. thesis, Harvard University.
16. LUBORSKY, S. W., and G. L. CANTONI. 1962. Biochim. Biophys. Acta. *61:* 481.
17. INMAN, R. B., and R. L. BALDWIN. 1964. J. Mol. Biol. *8:* 452.

Enzymatic Synthesis
of Oligoribonucleotides
# of Defined Sequence

ROBERT E. THACH

HARVARD UNIVERSITY

CAMBRIDGE, MASSACHUSETTS

BLOCK COPOLYNUCLEOTIDES

Principle

The following method for the synthesis of block copolynucleotides derives from the finding of Singer *et al.* (1) that highly purified preparations of polynucleotide phosphorylase from *Micrococcus lysodeikticus* have a nearly absolute requirement for oligonucleotide primer in the polymerization of nucleoside diphosphates (NDP). These primers serve as obligatory initiators of chain growth: the enzyme is incapable of initiating polymer synthesis *de novo,* as it cannot condense two NDP molecules to form a dinucleotide (2). The reaction mechanism may therefore be written as

$$NDP + NDP \rightarrow \text{No reaction} \tag{1}$$

$$(pN')_n + NDP \rightleftharpoons (pN')_n pN + P_i \tag{2}$$

$$\vdots \qquad \vdots \qquad \vdots \qquad \vdots$$

$$(pN')_n(pN)_m + NDP \rightleftharpoons (pN')_n(pN)_{m+1} + P_i \tag{3}$$

where $(pN')_n$ is an oligonucleotide primer, $(pN')_n(pN)_m$ is a block copolynucleotide, and P_i is inorganic orthophosphate.† The chain length of the polymer product obtained from this reaction may be controlled by the inclusion of an appropriate concentration of NaCl in the reaction mixture (3).

Reaction Conditions

0.04 M NDP
0.2 M Tris buffer, pH 8.2
1 mM Mg(OAc)$_2$
[1 mM CuSO$_4$]‡
0.1–0.6 mM oligonucleotide primer (preferably labeled with C^{14} or H^3)
0.3–1.5 M NaCl
Enzyme [polynucleotide phosphorylase from *Micrococcus lysodeikticus*, purified according to Singer and O'Brien (4)]
Incubation at 34 C or 37 C

Assay

The course of a polymerization reaction may be followed by removing samples from a reaction mixture at various times and applying them to Whatman 3MM chromatography paper. Chromatograms are then developed in a solvent in which unincorporated primer migrates away from the origin, while longer chains remain immobile (see "Chromatography of Oligonucleotides" for details of the chromatography procedure).

After the developed chromatograms are dried, origin spots are eluted in 1–3 ml of buffer (0.01 M Tris, pH 8.2, 1 mM EDTA) overnight at room temperature. The amount of polynucleotide present may be determined by radioactivity measurement. (Alternatively, if the primer is not radioactive, the amount incorporated can be calculated as the difference between the amount remaining unincorporated and that initially present.) The ratio of these two quantities (total nucleotide

---

† Abbreviations: N, (pN), and NDP represent, respectively, the nucleoside, nucleotide residue, and nucleoside diphosphate of any base. Specific bases are abbreviated in the usual way: adenosine, A; uridine, U; cytidine, C; guanosine, G; inosine, I, and xanthosine, X. Oligonucleotide chain sequences are written with the 5′ hydroxyl end on the left and the 3′ hydroxyl end on the right. If a block copolymer is heterogeneous with regard to the chain length of one component a number average chain length is given, this being indicated by a bar over the numerical subscript, e.g., A(pA)$_2$(pU)$_{\bar{1}}$.

‡ The inclusion of CuSO$_4$ is optional. It has proven useful as an inhibitor of nucleases which often contaminate partially purified preparations of polynucleotide phosphorylase (5). However, it has recently been observed that nuclease activity may be more effectively inhibited by prolonged dialysis of enzyme preparations to remove all traces of NH$_4^+$ and K$^+$ cations (7).

residues): (incorporated primer residues), is the number average chain length of the product.

Procedure

In the synthesis of block oligonucleotides it is desirable (a) that a high proportion of the primer molecules be incorporated into polymer, (b) that these incorporated primer residues be unaltered with regard to their original chain length and base sequence, and (c) that the growth of the 3′ block component be controlled so as to yield a homogeneous oligonucleotide preparation of a predetermined average chain length. These requirements can be met by selecting appropriate reaction conditions. Most important is the NaCl concentration, which determines both the chain length of the product (Fig. 1) and the over-all rate of the reaction (Table 1). Once the NaCl concentration has been chosen, other reaction conditions may be selected accordingly. The concentration of primer must be low enough so that less than 10% of the NDP initially present will be polymerized, thereby insuring a high NDP : Pi ratio throughout the course of the reaction. Finally, a sufficient amount of time must be allowed for the complete incorporation of primer. In cases where this reaction time is longer than 2 hr, it is advisable to conduct the incubation at 34 C since polynucleotide phosphorylase is more stable at lower temperatures. (It should be noted that there is a slight inverse correlation between incubation temperature and chain length of product (7): this tendency can be corrected by an appropriate change in NaCl concentration.)

After suitable conditions for the synthesis of the desired block oligonucleotide have been determined through trial experiments, a large scale reaction may be carried out. The product obtained from this reaction may be purified in a variety of ways, the most convenient being dictated by individual circumstances. Oligonucleotides of over-all chain length greater than about 20 may be purified as follows. The reaction mixture is diluted to a convenient volume (usually about 2–10 ml) with water and made 10 mM in EDTA. This solution is extracted twice with an equal volume of redistilled water-saturated phenol, after which the aqueous layer is dialyzed against 0.1 M ammonium bicarbonate for 12 hr, and then against two changes of deionized water for 12 hr each. The solution containing pure polynucleotide is then lyophilyzed or stored frozen.

Oligonucleotides that are too small to be dialyzed may be purified either by column or paper chromatography, depending on the amount synthesized. A very convenient method for purifying up to 10 mg of material is to apply the undiluted reaction mixture to Whatman 3 MM

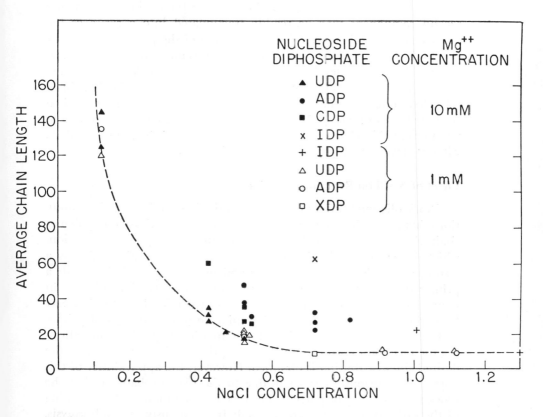

Fig. 1. Dependence of average chain length on the concentration of NaCl and Mg²⁺. Each chain length value corresponds to a point in the reaction at which 90% of the primer was incorporated. All points obtained from reactions containing 1 mM Mg²⁺ lie on or near the broken line, with the exception of reactions containing IDP. (Reproduced by permission, from Science, Ref. 3.)

chromatography paper, by streaking the solution along the origin line and drying with a stream of warm air. The chromatogram may then be developed in one of a series of solvents described below. In this way a product that is heterogeneous with regard to the chain length of the second component may be readily fractionated into a series of homologous block oligonucleotides. Resolution of the pure fractions may be obtained up to the 11-mer with little difficulty. After the chromatograms have been developed and dried, they are soaked in absolute ethanol for 1 hr to remove ammonium acetate, and then for 10 min in ether to remove the ethanol. The oligonucleotide components may then be eluted with water, or, for longer chains, a buffer composed of 0.01 M ammonium bicarbonate-carbonate, pH 8.5, and 0.01 mM EDTA. Eluates may then be lyophilized or stored frozen.

Effect of NaCl on Reaction Kinetics

Block oligonucleotides cannot be synthesized under reaction conditions that are optimal for the polymerization of NDP into long polymer chains.† This is due to the kinetics of the polymerization reaction, which favor the production of very long polymer chains (3,5); as a result, only unincorporated primer and long polymer chains (with a primer residue at the 5′ end) are present in the reaction mixture in appreciable quantities at any time (6). In principle, this situation may be avoided by using in the reaction mixture concentrations of primer and NDP corresponding to the ratio desired in the product, and allowing the reaction to proceed until all the primer is incorporated and the desired size distribution is obtained. However, the applicability of this approach is seriously restricted, due to the high probability that the block sequence may be partially destroyed or randomized. A scrambling of the order of the bases would result from extensive phosphorolysis, which proceeds at a rapid rate at or near equilibrium: The danger then arises that oligonucleotide primer will be phosphorolyzed to produce the corresponding NDP, which in turn may be reincorporated as a contaminant in the second block component. Thus, this approach may be used with confidence only when the primer is a dinucleotide, since the latter are resistant to phosphorolysis (2). (The application of this method to the synthesis of tri-, tetra-, and pentanucleotides of defined sequence is discussed below.)

The difficulties that arise from unfavorable polymerization kinetics may be overcome by the inclusion of a high concentration of NaCl in the reaction mixture (3): this has the effect of inhibiting chain growth

---

† Conditions which are optimal for polymer synthesis are: 0.04 M NDP, 0.01 M Mg(OAc)₂, 0.2 M glycine buffer, pH 9.3, and 0.1 mM primer.

beyond a certain length, thus preventing the synthesis of long polymers and allowing short block oligonucleotides to accumulate. Since chain growth occurs at only a very slow rate after the oligonucleotides have reached a certain size, the reaction is effectively terminated at that point even though a large excess of unreacted NDP may remain. This feature insures that a high ratio of NDP to P_i will prevail throughout the course of the reaction, thus preventing extensive phosphorolysis of either unreacted primer or block oligonucleotide product. The average chain length of oligonucleotides produced in this reaction is inversely proportional to the NaCl concentration in the reaction mixture (Fig. 1). It is therefore possible to obtain a product of any desired chain length by conducting the reaction at a suitable concentration of NaCl.

Several other factors besides NaCl concentration influence the chain length of the product. For example, the product size may be altered to varying degrees by changes in Mg^{2+} concentration or incubation temperature, or by the inclusion of urea in the reaction mixture (3). Moreover, different NDPs behave differently under a given set of reaction conditions, as is evident in Fig. 1. Thus whereas the extent of polymerization of ADP depends markedly on the Mg^{2+} concentration, this effect is not observed when UDP is polymerized. Also, the inhibition of IDP polymerization requires 2–3 times more NaCl than is necessary for any other NDP. In view of these and other differences in the behavior of the various NDPs it is essential that preparations requiring unfamiliar reaction conditions be preceded by small scale trial experiments.

Reaction Time

The amount of time required for complete incorporation of oligonucleotide primer varies widely, depending upon the reaction conditions, the type of primer used, and the NDP being polymerized. The relationship between reaction time and NaCl concentration for a given system is complex. A typical example is shown in Table 1, from which it is evident that the rate of primer incorporation may pass through a maximum at an intermediate salt concentration. The variation of reaction time with Mg^{2+} concentration is also shown.

Both the chain length and the base composition of the primer influence the rate at which it will be incorporated into longer oligonucleotides. A sharp increase in priming ability with increasing chain length has been observed in the size range from two to ten residues (4,7). Moreover, the rate of incorporation of a specific size of primer increases in proportion to its purine content (7).

Thus, a wide variety of factors are involved in determining the

TABLE 1. *Effect of Reaction Conditions on Polymerization Kinetics*

Reaction: $C(pC)_5 + nADP \longrightarrow C(pC)_5(pA)_n + nP_1$			
Reaction[a] Conditions	Time (min)	Fraction of Primer Incorporated	Average Chain Length of Oligonucleotide[b]
0.12 M NaCl	60	0.23	67
1 mM Mg²⁺	90	0.28	95
	120	0.34	110
0.52 M NaCl	60	0.27	9
1 mM Mg²⁺	90	0.46	14
	120	0.56	17
	180	0.76	18
0.92 M NaCl	90	0.12	9
1 mM Mg²⁺	120	0.14	10
	180	0.22	11
0.52 M NaCl	40	0.78	25
10 mM Mg²⁺	60	0.92	33
	80	0.97	36
	100	1.00	40

[a] All reaction mixtures contain the following ingredients in addition to those listed: 0.04 M ADP, 0.2 M Tris buffer, pH 8.2, 0.1 mM CuSO₄, 0.1 mM C(pC)₅ (labeled with C¹⁴), and enzyme. Incubation at 37 C.

[b] This average does not include unincorporated primer.

reaction rate of a given system, and it is important to determine the kinetics of a reaction in advance, before large scale preparations are attempted. The error most frequently incurred is to allow an insufficient time for complete incorporation of primer; incubation for overlong periods does little harm, since most reactions are essentially self-terminating.

TRI-, TETRA-, AND PENTANUCLEOTIDES OF DEFINED SEQUENCE

Principle

The chain length distribution of polynucleotides synthesized by purified polynucleotide phosphorylase (*M. lysodeikticus*) is determined by the ratio of NDP to primer originally present in the reaction mixture, provided that the reaction is allowed to proceed to a state of thermodynamic equilibrium (8,9). Under normal reaction conditions this state is not achieved until long after the incorporation of NDP has ceased. Thus it is possible to obtain oligonucleotide preparations rich in trimer, tetramer, and longer chain homologues of known sequence by incubating a reaction mixture containing appropriate concentrations of NDP and dinucleotide (or dinucleoside monophosphate) primer for a sufficiently long time. (Note: oligonucleotides longer than two residues may not be used as primers, since these may suffer phosphorolytic cleavage during the course of the reaction.)

Reaction Conditions

0.01 to 0.03 M NDP
0.01 M Mg(OAc)$_2$
[0.1 mM CuSO$_4$]†
0.2 M glycine buffer, pH 9.3
0.4 M NaCl‡
7.5 mM dinucleotide or dinucleoside monophosphate primer
Enzyme
Incubation at 34 C

Assay

The course of this reaction may be followed by essentially the same procedure as employed in assaying block polynucleotide synthesis. In this case, however, a chromatography solvent that provides adequate resolution of di-, tri-, tetra-, and pentanucleotides (see below) should be used. Any of the following criteria may be used to determine the extent of reaction: (a) concentration of unincorporated primer, which declines to a minimum value at equilibrium, and (b) concentration of tri-, tetra-, or pentanucleotides, all of which rise to maximum values at equilibrium. The course of a typical reaction is shown in Fig. 2.

Procedure

The rates of reaction of both primer and substrate vary somewhat, depending on base composition. In particular, longer incubation times are required when the primer is a dipyrimidine or when the NDP is a purine (7). Therefore trial experiments should be conducted to deter-

† The inclusion of CuSO$_4$ is optional. It has proven useful as an inhibitor of nucleases which often contaminate partially purified preparations of polynucleotide phosphorylase (5). However, it has recently been observed that nuclease activity may be more effectively inhibited by prolonged dialysis of enzyme preparations to remove all traces of NH$_4$+ and K+ cations (7).

‡ NaCl is included specifically for the purpose of inhibiting the endogenous polymerization reaction, which normally proceeds slowly in the absence of primer and NaCl. The extent to which this concentration of salt inhibits the formation of long polymer chains under the conditions employed is not significant.

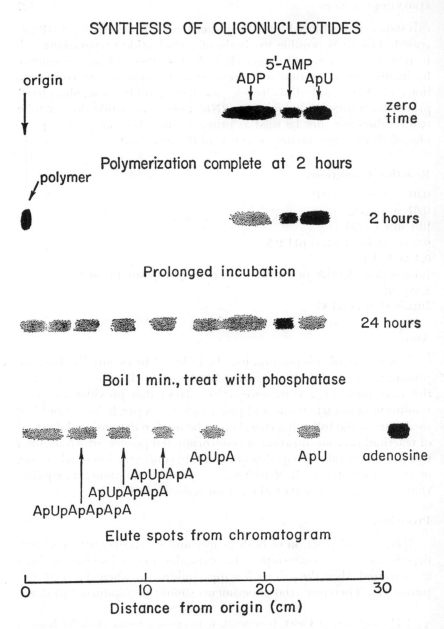

Fig. 2. Sequence of stages in an oligonucleotide synthesis reaction. Samples were withdrawn from a reaction mixture and applied to chromatography paper, which was developed in a solvent composed of equal parts of 1 M ammonium acetate and 95% ethanol. The distribution of ultraviolet-absorbing spots is reproduced here. (Reproduced, by permission, from Science, Ref. **8.**)

mine the incubation time required for equilibrium to be achieved, before large scale preparations are undertaken.

Oligonucleotide products may be purified by paper chromatography as described previously. However, before submitting samples to chromatography it is often desirable to remove unreacted NDP, which otherwise may contaminate the tri- and tetranucleotide species. This may be done as follows. At the end of the incubation, the reaction vessel is placed in a boiling water bath for 2 min to inactivate polynucleotide phosphorylase. Alkaline phosphatase (the enzyme preparation used must be free of nuclease activity) is then added and the mixture is incubated at 37 C until the release of P_i is complete, indicating quantitative conversion of NDP to nucleoside. The entire mixture may now be applied to chromatography paper, and developed in a solvent suitable for fractionation of the components. (This procedure cannot be used, of course, when 5'-phosphorylated oligonucleotides are desired.)

Variation of Chain Length Distribution with Time

One limitation of the preparative procedure described in "Block Copolynucleotides" arises from the failure of dinucleotides (pN'pN' or N'pN') to prime polymerization at high NaCl concentrations; consequently, it is not possible to prepare tri- and tetranucleotides of specified sequence by this technique. Moreover, reaction conditions that are optimal for the synthesis of long polynucleotide chains† cannot be used for this purpose, since the desired oligonucleotides [pN'pN'pN', pN'pN'(pN)₂, etc., or N'pN'pN, N'pN'(pN)₂, etc.] are not present in significant amounts at any time during the course of the reaction (5,6); instead only long polymer chains (more than 100 residues) and unincorporated primer molecules are found.

A solution to this problem became apparent with the realization that the very skewed chain length distribution of the polymer product is an artifact of kinetics (8) and thermodynamically unstable (9); rather, the equilibrium chain length distribution should instead be of the "most probable" type, in which entropy is at a maximum. In this state the average chain length of the polynucleotide product should be proportional to the ratio of NDP to primer that was originally present in the reaction mixture. This feature suggests that oligonucleotides of any desired chain length can be synthesized, provided that appropriate concentrations of primer and NDP are used, and that the true state of thermodynamic equilibrium can be achieved in a practical time span.

In practice the equilibrium chain length distribution is attained only after a prolonged period of incubation. During this time, the primer that remains unincorporated after net polymer synthesis has

---

† Conditions which are optimal for polymer synthesis are: 0.04 M NDP, 0.01 M Mg(OAc)₂, 0.2 M glycine buffer, pH 9.3, and 0.1 mM primer.

ceased is gradually incorporated into short oligonucleotide chains. Concomitant with this slow synthesis reaction is a phosphorolysis of the very long chains originally formed. The net result is simply a redistribution of nucleotide residues, since the over-all concentrations of NDP and P_i remain constant. The oligonucleotide product resulting from this process is of intermediate size, the average chain length being proportional to the mole ratio of NDP to primer originally present in the reaction mixture.

The progress of a typical synthetic reaction is shown in Fig. 2. The concentration of substrates was chosen so as to provide a product with an average chain length of four residues. The net synthesis of polynucleotide is essentially complete in 2 hr, whereas the redistribution of chain lengths continues throughout a subsequent 22-hr incubation period.

Product Yields

The yield of any single oligonucleotide species depends primarily on the relative concentrations of NDP and primer originally present in the reaction mixture. The range of reaction conditions described above generally provides yields of 20–35% for the trimer (yield is calculated as the ratio of μmoles of oligonucleotide recovered to μmoles of primer originally present). The amounts of tetra- and pentanucleotides recovered are somewhat lower, usually falling between 10 and 20%.

The yield of oligonucleotides is independent of the base composition of both primer and NDP, with the following exceptions. Poor results are sometimes obtained when a dipyrimidine is used to prime the polymerization of a purine NDP. In this case primer is incorporated into polynucleotide at a very slow rate; hence large amounts of enzyme and very long incubation times may be required in order to obtain high yields. A second type of difficulty is frequently encountered when GDP is polymerized. In this case only small amounts of oligonucleotides are recovered, the major product being poly G. However, trinucleotides ending in 3'-G may be obtained in greater than 80% yield if T_1 ribonuclease is included in the reaction mixture during incubation. The initial product is a trinucleotide phosphorylated at the 3' hydroxyl, which may be subsequently dephosphorylated to the trinucleoside diphosphate by the addition of alkaline phosphatase.

A similar method for the synthesis trinucleotides has been developed by Leder et al. (10). Conditions have been found which favor the synthesis of appreciable amounts of oligonucleotides during the course of the polymerization; consequently the reaction may be terminated before the equilibrium distribution has been achieved. The yields of trinucleotides obtained by this procedure are generally lower than those described above.

CHROMATOGRAPHY OF OLIGONUCLEOTIDES

Principle

A series of chromatography solvents is described in which the mobility of oligonucleotides depends on chain length and base composition. The proportion of the two solvent components (1 M ammonium acetate and 95% ethanol) may be varied in order to achieve maximum mobility and resolution of oligonucleotide species of chain lengths as high as 20 residues.

Reagents

1 M ammonium acetate, pH 7.0–7.3 (referred to as the aqueous component, or A)
95% ethanol (referred to as the ethanolic component, or E)

Procedure

Samples to be chromatographed are applied to the origin of a strip of Whatman 3MM paper at least 40 cm long. The amount of oligonucleotide should not exceed 10 mg in a 15-cm streak, otherwise artifacts due to overloading may occur. Large amounts of NaCl (over 0.1 mmole/15 cm) should also be avoided. Chromatograms are then developed in a suitable solvent, usually for from 16 to 24 hr at room temperature. The migration of oligonucleotide components may be monitored during development with an ultraviolet light source: if the desired mobility or resolution is not obtained, the solvent in the trough may be changed and development continued. Oligonucleotides may be recovered from chromatograms by eluting with water or buffer as described in "Block Copolynucleotides."

Large quantities of NaCl and NDP (such as are present in the synthesis of short block oligonucleotides) may be removed from samples by using initially a solvent containing a high proportion of ethanol, in which the mobility of oligonucleotides is minimal. When the NDP band has migrated well away from the oligonucleotide components, the latter may be recovered and then rechromatographed in a solvent providing high resolution. Alternatively, if the oligonucleotides have remained at the origin during the preliminary chromatography step, the solvent may simply be changed and development continued in order to effect resolution.

Effect of Solvent Composition on Chromatographic Mobility

Four factors determine the distance an oligonucleotide will migrate in this chromatographic system: chain length, base composition, time of development, and composition of the solvent. As the first two factors are defined by the nature of the oligonucleotide product to be analyzed, the second two must be adjusted to provide the desired mobility and resolution. The relationship between solvent composition and mobility is shown in Table 2. In general, an increase in the proportion of the aqueous component (i.e., 1 M ammonium acetate) results in a striking increase in the rate of migration of oligonucleotides. This effect is more

TABLE 2. *Effect of Solvent Composition on Chromatographic Mobility of Oligonucleotides*

Oligonucleotide	Distance Migrated (cm)	
	45A:55E Solvent (20 hr)	70A:30E Solvent (16 hr)
UpU	31.2	37.7[a]
U(pU)$_3$	23.0	35.0[a]
U(pU)$_5$	16.3	31.8[a]
U(pU)$_7$	9.2[a]	27.6[a]
U(pU)$_9$	5.5[a]	25.0[a]
UDP	25.5	—
CpC	29.4	35.0[a]
C(pC)$_3$	18.5	30.2[a]
C(pC)$_5$	9.9	25.8[a]
C(pC)$_7$	5.1[a]	21.6[a]
C(pC)$_9$	2.4[a]	—
CDP	22.2	36.7
ApA	23.0	25.3
A(pA)$_2$	—	19.6
A(pA)$_3$	8.6	13.4
A(pA)$_4$	4.2	8.3
A(pA)$_5$	1.6[a]	5.0[a]
A(pA)$_6$	0.8[a]	2.5[a]
ADP	20.0	—

[a] Oligonucleotides are incompletely resolved from shorter or longer chains.

pronounced with pyrimidines than with purines. Moreover, the effect is relatively greater for longer chains; thus resolution is diminished as mobility is increased. However, the resolution obtained in any solvent may always be increased by prolonging the development time.

The choice of solvent and development time will be dictated by the particular nature of each experiment. Several general applications of this chromatography technique to problems commonly arising in oligonucleotide synthesis are listed below:

ASSAY OF PRIMER INCORPORATION IN BLOCK OLIGO-NUCLEOTIDE SYNTHESIS. For this type of experiment a solvent is desired in which unincorporated primer migrates a short distance from the origin, while longer chains remain immobile. The optimum solvent composition will vary from 30A:70E in the case of $C(pC)_2$ or $U(pU)_3$ primer, to 70A:30E with $A(pA)_6$ or $U(pU)_{16}$ primer. The migration of unincorporated primer may be easily followed during development with an ultraviolet light source.

ASSAY OF TRI-, TETRA-, AND PENTANUCLEOTIDE SYN-THESIS. In this case only 2 basic solvents are needed: one for fractionating chains on the basis of the number of purine residues (50A:50E, as in Fig. 2), the other for chains differing in the number of pyrimidines (40A:60E). A development time of about 16 hr is required.

FRACTIONATION OF OLIGONUCLEOTIDES INTO HOMOL-OGOUS SERIES. The optimum solvent composition is determined by the base composition and chain length of species to be separated, and the degree of resolution required. In general, solvents that give low mobility but high resolution are used; consequently, development times are longer than usual. For example, good resolution of short pyrimidine oligonucleotides (up to about the 7-mer) is easily achieved in 48 hr in the 40A:60E solvent; however, if resolution of longer chains is desired (up to the 11-mer), a solvent of lower mobility, such as 30A:70E, and a longer development time will be required. The same general rules apply for purine oligonucleotides, although in this case solvents richer in the aqueous component may be used. When oligonucleotides contain both purines and pyrimidines, the solvent is chosen with regard to the type of base that varies in number. For example, fractionation of $A(pA)_2(pU)_4^-$ requires a low mobility solvent (35A:65E) and long time (72 hr or more), since separation is made on the basis of a difference in the number of pyrimidine residues. On the other hand, $U(pU)_7(pA)_3^-$ may be fractionated far more rapidly (24 hr) in a solvent richer in the aqueous component (60A:40E). When high resolution of components is not required, high mobility solvents and shorter times may be used.

REFERENCES

1. SINGER, M. F., L. A. HEPPEL and R. J. HILMOE. 1960. J. Biol. Chem. *235:* 738.
2. GRUNBERG-MANAGO, M. 1963. Polynucleotide phosphorylase. *In* J. N. Davidson and W. E. Cohn, editors, Progress in nucleic acid research, Academic
   Press, New York. Vol. I.
3. THACH, R. E., and P. DOTY. 1965. Science. *147:* No. 3663, 1310.
4. SINGER, M. F., and B. M. O'BRIEN. 1963. J. Biol. Chem. *238:* 328.
5. THACH, R. E. Thesis, Harvard University.
6. HEPPEL, L. A. 1963. J. Biol. Chem. *238:* 357.
7. THACH, R. E. Unpublished results.
8. THACH, R. E., and P. DOTY. 1965. Science. *148:* No. 3670, 632.
9. PELLER, L., and L. BARNETT. 1965. J. Phys. Chem. *66:* 680.
10. LEDER, P., M. F. SINGER, and R. L. C. BRIMACOMBE. 1965. Biochemistry. *4:* 1561.

Section B. Deoxyribonucleic Acid

1. Bacterial DNA

Isolation of High Molecular Weight DNA from Bacteria and Cell Nuclei

C. A. THOMAS, JR., K. I. BERNS, AND T. J. KELLY, JR.
DEPARTMENT OF BIOPHYSICS
THE JOHNS HOPKINS UNIVERSITY
BALTIMORE, MARYLAND

DNA FROM BACTERIA

Growth and Harvesting of Cells

There is a wide latitude in the growth medium and the stage of growth at which the cells are collected. *Escherichia coli, Serratia, Hemophilus,* and *Salmonella* can be grown in broth or synthetic media (including label if desired) to early or late log phase, at which time they are collected by centrifugation and washed two or more times with standard saline-citrate (SSC: 0.15 M NaCl, 0.015 M Na Citrate, pH 7). The cells are resuspended in 27% sucrose in SSC (27 g of sucrose + SSC to make 100-ml solution) at a concentration not higher than 10^{10}/ml. The suspension may be frozen at −86 C; this step is convenient for storage and aids subsequent lysis but is not necessary. The sucrose can be omitted unless DNA of the very highest molecular weight is desired. We are uncertain what effect freezing has on the final molecular weight of the product.

Lysis and Pronase Digestion

Preliminary to lysis the bacteria are diluted to the desired concentration in SSC (which contains 27% sucrose, if desired) in 50-ml screw-capped (Neoprene cap liners) tubes. The best yields are obtained with 10^9 cells/ml. The enormous viscosity of bacterial DNA solutions precludes working with more concentrated suspensions, unless one resorts to vigorous shaking with phenol, a treatment that results in extensive shear damage to the DNA.

Solid pronase powder (1) is added to a final concentration of 1–2 mg/ml. Pronase is a highly active proteolytic enzyme of broad specificity, which reduces many proteins to amino acids (1). It appears to contain no nuclease activity. Previously purified *Hemophilus* DNA molecules or purified T2 DNA molecules survive digestion with the enzyme without further fragmentation implying the absence of active deoxyribonuclease (2). Pronase digestion does not inactivate the amino-acid accepting ability of sRNA; it actually enhances it, perhaps by removing the terminal amino acid (3). It contains no active ribonuclease by this test.

After the pronase is dissolved, the smallest amount of sodium lauryl sulfate (SLS) that will effectively lyse the cells as evidenced by loss of turbidity and increased viscosity is added. *Hemophilus* requires about 0.2% SLS, *E. coli* and *Serratia* may require 1%. Incubation at 37 C is begun promptly and continued for 7 hr. This step is of critical importance if good yields of DNA are to be obtained.

Phenol Extraction

The purification and preparation of water-saturated phenol is described on page 557. An equal volume of this phenol is added to the digest and the mixture "rolled" at 60 rev/min for 30 min at room temperature (4). The mixture is chilled to 0 C to condense the water-saturated phenol and centrifuged at 5000 rev/min by floating the glass tubes in the centrifuge buckets with water to prevent breaking them. The phenol layer (on top when the aqueous layer contains 27% sucrose) is carefully removed by pipetting, more phenol is added, and the extraction is repeated. In general, there is very little precipitate left at the interface between the phenol and aqueous layers if the pronase digestion has been effective. If the pronase digestion step is omitted, all but a small fraction of the DNA is in the interfacial precipitate. The aqueous layer is then repeatedly dialyzed against the desired buffer to remove the phenol. If RNA is to be removed by hydroxyapatite, it is mandatory that the final preparation contain no citrate or other chelating agent.

Note: DNA is extremely sensitive to shear breakage and if the very highest molecular weights are desired, the solutions must be poured, not pipetted.

RNA Elimination

For some purposes the presence of RNA is not important; for others it is. Since even the gentlest manipulations cause shear breakage, we have not yet found a way of removing RNA without lowering the molecular weight to 200 million. However, if this can be tolerated, the following procedure suggested by Bernardi (5) is useful.

HYDROXYAPATITE DECANTATION. The DNA–RNA preparation is dialyzed (or otherwise adjusted) to 0.20 M phosphate buffer (equal moles of NaH_2PO_4 and Na_2HPO_4, pH 6.8), and 2 ml (packed volume) of hydroxyapatite [prepared by the method of Tiselius, Hjerten, and Levin (6) as modified by Miyazawa and Thomas (7)] is added for each 50 ml of preparation. The mixture is gently agitated intermittently for 15 min at room temperature. The DNA binds to the crystals, which subsequently fall to the bottom leaving the RNA in the supernatant liquid to be decanted. The DNA is recovered from the crystals by washing with 0.50 M phosphate buffer. This can be diluted to 0.20 M and the decantation step repeated. The RNA can be recovered from the supernatant liquid by diluting to 0.05 M phosphate buffer and adding more hydroxyapatite. The RNA binds to the crystals at this phosphate concentration. It may be recovered by washing with 0.20 M phosphate buffer.

RIBONUCLEASE DIGESTION. Treatment of the preparation with 20 μg/ml of Pancreatic ribonuclease (boiled 10 min to inactivate deoxyribonucleases) may be employed prior to dialysis or hydroxyapatite decantation. All the RNA is not rendered dialyzable by this treatment. It is possible that a combination of pancreatic ribonuclease and takadiastase digestion would effect complete degradation of the RNA.

Physical Characterization of Product

ZONE SEDIMENTATION. Sedimentation through linear sucrose gradients in the presence of labeled marker DNA molecules of known molecular weight allows the estimation of the molecular weight of the bacterial DNA (2,8,9). By this criterion Hemophilus DNA of 400 million Daltons has been isolated by the above procedure (2). Boundary sedimentation may be used to obtain a qualitative estimation of sedimentation coefficient, but it should be remembered that DNAs of very high molecular weight show unusual convection and concentration effects (8,10).

CHROMATOGRAPHIC CHARACTERIZATION. The chromatography of DNA on MAK or hydroxyapatite columns is not only useful for further purification, but allows fractionation with respect to molecular weight and state of denaturation.

SEDIMENTATION EQUILIBRIUM. Equilibrium sedimentation in CsCl may be used to check the characteristic densities of bacterial DNAs (11).

ELECTRON MICROSCOPY. The lengths of purified bacterial DNA molecules can be determined by electron microscopy (9) using the method of Kleinschmidt and Zahn (12). There is accumulating evidence that the observed molecular length is proportional to molecular weight.

Chemical Characterization

IDENTIFICATION. Ultimately DNA is identified by the fact that it contains deoxynucleotides. Quantitative enzymatic hydrolysis and chromatographic or electrophoretic separations should be employed for this purpose.

YIELD. The yield of bacterial DNA may be determined by measuring the recovery of tritiated thymidine from the original lysate. Measured volumes of solution are dried on squares of filter paper and counted in a liquid scintillation counter. In a specific case 78, 71, and 90% of the DNA in *H. influenzae, E. coli,* and *Serratia marcescens,* respectively, were recovered in the final aqueous phase (13). RNA is also recovered with equal or higher efficiencies.

DNA–RNA DETERMINATIONS. After the addition of bovine serum albumin as carrier (0.1 mg/ml of sample), a sample of P^{32}-labeled DNA–RNA preparation is made 0.30 M in trichloracetic acid (TCA) and chilled for 15 min. The resulting precipitate is collected on a Millipore filter and counted in a geiger counter. The radioactivity of the precipitate is a measure of the total nucleic acid content (DNA + RNA) of the sample. A similar sample is incubated in 0.50 M NaOH at 37 C for 2 hr to hydrolyze RNA. Carrier protein is added, the NaOH is neutralized, and acid precipitation is carried out as above. The radioactivity of this precipitate is a measure of the DNA content. Assuming both RNA and DNA have the same specific activity (which is expected if the cells are uniformly labeled), one finds that there is about as much RNA as DNA in samples prepared according to the preceding procedure.

PROTEIN DETERMINATION. A sample of the final product containing about 500 μg of DNA and an equal amount of RNA is chilled and adjusted to 0.30 M TCA. The precipitate is collected by centrifugation and redissolved in 0.50 M NaOH. It is then incubated at 37 C for 2 hr, reprecipitated with TCA, and centrifuged. The pellet is redissolved in 0.60 ml of 0.20 M NaOH. Of this 0.10 ml is diluted $\frac{1}{50}$ in water to measure A_{260} for DNA content and the remaining 0.50 ml is put directly into the Lowry protein determination (14). Samples containing known amounts of bovine serum albumin are treated similarly. Samples prepared according to the above procedure contain less than 10% as much protein as DNA on a weight basis (2). More severe phenol extractions will lower the protein content substantially at the expense of breaking the DNA.

DNA FROM THYMUS NUCLEI

The above procedure with modifications may be applied to the isolation of high molecular weight DNA in high yield from calf thymus nuclei.

Procedure

Fresh thymus glands are obtained from the local abattoir, cut into (150 g) pieces, and frozen in individual packages at −60 C. Following the procedure of Allfrey, Mirsky, and Osawa (15), 50 g of freshly-thawed tissue is minced and mixed with 50 ml of 0.50 M sucrose + 400 ml of 0.25 M sucrose–0.0033 M $CaCl_2$ solution. The mixture is homogenized in a Waring Blendor at 1000 rev/min (or less, if effective) for 5 min at 4 C. The homogenate is filtered twice through a double layer of cheesecloth, then twice through a double layer of single-ply flannelette. The nuclei are recovered from the filtrate by centrifugation at 1000 rev/min for 10 min (or less). The number of nuclei in the pellet and supernatant fluid can be counted in a Petroff-Hauser bacterial counting chamber. The nuclei are resuspended in 100 ml of 0.25 M sucrose–0.0033 M $CaCl_2$ and filtered again through a double layer of single-ply flannelette. They are then collected by centrifugation and resuspended in 60 ml of 0.25 M sucrose–0.0033 M $CaCl_2$. There should be at least 10^8 nuclei/ml in such a preparation. The DNA content per nucleus is

7.15×10^{-9} mg/nucleus (16). The nuclei are lysed by adjusting the suspension to 0.5% SLS, and 200 mg of pronase powder predissolved in 2 ml of 0.25 M sucrose–0.0033 M $CaCl_2$ is added. To this solution 3 ml of 2 M Tris buffer, pH 8.6 is added and the mixture is incubated for 8–12 hr at 37 C with gentle agitation. Phenol extraction is carried out in the same manner as for bacteria (see "Phenol Extraction"). After three phenol extractions, the phenol is removed from the aqueous layer by dialysis.

Product

The physical and chemical characterization of the product can be accomplished in the same way as with bacterial DNAs (see "Physical Characterization of Product" and "Chemical Characterization"). The product contains less than 5% RNA and less than 2% protein. Boundary sedimentation gives S = 45 corresponding to about 60 million molecular weight.

REFERENCES

1. NOMOTO, M., Y. NARAHASHI, and M. MURAKAMI. 1960. J. Biochem. (Japan). *48:* 453, 593, 906.
2. BERNS, K. I., and C. A. THOMAS. 1965. J. Mol. Biol. *11:* 476.
3. LITTAUER, U. Z. 1965. Personal communication.
4. FRANKEL, F. R. 1963. Proc. Nat. Acad. Sci. U.S. *49:* 366.
5. BERNARDI, G. 1962. Biochem. J. *83:* 32.
6. TISELIUS, A., S. HJERTEN, and O. LEVIN. 1956. Arch. Biochem. Biophys. *65:* 132.
7. MIYAZAWA, Y., and C. A. THOMAS. 1965. J. Mol. Biol. *11:* 223.
8. BURGI, E., and A. D. HERSHEY. 1963. Biophys. J. *3:* 309.
9. MACHATTIE, L. A., K. I. BERNS, and C. A. THOMAS. 1965. J. Mol. Biol. *11:* 648.
10. THOMAS, C. A., and T. C. PINKERTON. 1962. J. Mol. Biol. *5:* 356.
11. SCHILDKRAUT, C. L., J. MARMUR, and P. DOTY. 1962. J. Mol. Biol. *4:* 430.
12. KLEINSCHMIDT, A., and R. K. ZAHN. 1959. Z. Naturforsch. *14b:* 770.
13. BERNS, K. I. 1965. Ph.D. thesis, Johns Hopkins University, Baltimore, Maryland.
14. LAYNE, E. 1957. *In* S. P. Colowick and N. O. Kaplan, editors, Methods in enzymology. Academic Press, New York. Vol. III, p. 448.
15. ALLFREY, V. G., A. E. MIRSKY, and S. OSAWA. 1957. J. Gen. Physiol. *40:* 451.
16. MIRSKY, A. E., and S. OSAWA. 1961. *In* J. Brachet and A. E. Mirsky, editors, The cell. Academic Press, New York. Vol. II, p. 700.

Transforming DNA

from Pneumococcus

ROLLIN D. HOTCHKISS
THE ROCKEFELLER UNIVERSITY
NEW YORK, NEW YORK

ASSAY

$$\begin{matrix} \text{Competent} + \text{DNA} \\ \text{cells} \end{matrix} \longrightarrow \begin{matrix} \text{Transformed} \\ \text{cells} \end{matrix} + \begin{matrix} \text{Untransformed} \\ \text{cells} \end{matrix}$$

A known number of treated cells, or a known volume of treated culture, is diluted into selective medium. The cells transformed for a selective trait (e.g., drug resistance) grow in the selective medium (e.g., drug containing) and are counted.

Materials

High molecular weight DNA; final concentration in cell suspension, 10^{-5} to 10^{0} μg/ml. Preparation described below.

COMPETENT CELLS. Bacteria of a "competent" strain (e.g., derived from R36A of Pneumococcus) grown to a receptive state in suitable competence media, usually about 5 to 50×10^6 cells/ml and used either fresh, or frozen and maintained in a freezer after adding 10% glycerol by volume. Final cell suspension obtained by diluting or concentrating such fresh or thawed cultures.†

---

† With reference to production of competent cells, it has recently become feasible to produce them from incompetent pneumococcal cells by treatment with extracts of competent cells (19,20).

TRANSFORMATION ENVIRONMENT. Usually a growth medium (but not for *Bacillus subtilis* transformation), having a pH 7.6 or higher, also calcium ion concentration higher (approximately 10^{-3} M) than necessary for growth, plus serum albumin (Armour and Co. bovine plasma fraction V, 0.12–0.4%).

SELECTION MEDIA. As suitable for the marker or markers being transferred; neopeptone-meat infusion media plus streptomycin, sulfanilamide, aminopterin, etc., for the corresponding resistances; casein hydrolysate plus vitamin media (1) lacking certain pyrimidines, etc., or provided with specific sugars as energy source, for biochemical traits.

Various media are described in references 1–3. For *Bacillus subtilis* see (4), for *Hemophilus influenzae* see (5).

Procedure

An inoculum of competent pneumococci (R36A or derivative strain) is allowed to pass through at least four and preferably ten or more divisions in competence medium at 37 C to give a previously confirmed receptive state, usually about 10^7 colonies per ml. Yield is increased by "phasing" the cell division state by cooling to 25 C for 15 min. Cells may be either used immediately or frozen with 10% sterile glycerol addition, stored at −20 to −40 C, and thawed at 0 C on the day of use.

Competent cells in transformation medium are preincubated at 30 C for 15 min if coming from a frozen culture, and treated with desired concentration of genetically marked donor DNA, incubating at 30 C for a known time, of the order of 2–30 min. The reaction is terminated by the addition of deoxyribonuclease (e.g., Worthington Co. crystalline pancreatic deoxyribonuclease, final concentration 1–5 μg/ml). The time of contact must be precisely known if kinetics are being measured, and should preferably be brief if the marker used has a long "expression time" (e.g., 90 min for streptomycin resistance) during which multiplication may commence. The total number of cells exposed to DNA is measured by the appropriate cell assay at this point.

For the convenient high streptomycin resistance marker, the treated cells are "expressed" by incubation at 37 C in a suitable growth medium for 90 min. The number of streptomycin-resistant colonies increases from zero to some value, perhaps 10% of the exposed colony number during this time, but the transformant colonies do not increase by

replication during 90 min or perhaps slightly longer, 120 min, for somewhat deficient media. (This time course should best be confirmed under
the specific conditions of medium, marker, and strain used.) If desired,
a delayed selection can be applied after the cells are separated by dilution (6) or immobilized on agar (7,8) so that replication during the
expression period does not interfere with quantitation.

Selection and scoring of the number of transformants is made by
usual bacterial counting techniques in the appropriate selective media
(in presence of 100 to 500 μg of streptomycin/ml for high resistance to
this drug). In general, agar plates can be used; but in the special case
of pneumococcal assay in the author's laboratory, colonies are produced
and measured in liquid media. A low quantity of anti-R agglutinin
(globulin fraction from anti-pneumococcal serum) is added to liquid
media: The cells grow at a concentration of about 5–75 colony-forming
units per ml in small test tubes containing 0.6–1 ml. The cells are
immobilized as agglutinated growing clones, which fall through the
medium and are counted at the bottom of the tube after 15–20 hr incubation. With this special assay, numerous duplicate and serial dilutions
are made in each of the selective media desired.

The proportion of transformed to total cells is most properly assessed by relating the numbers:

$$\frac{\text{transformed colonies at expression time}}{\text{total colonies at time of DNA contact}}$$

For selective media that do not kill but merely starve the untrans-
formed cells, the expression time can be short, so that there is even less
danger of replication of the transformants in such cases.

Applications and Principles Involved

YIELD OF TRANSFORMED CELLS.   The yield at expression
time, divided by the total colonies at DNA time as above, is measured
at the plateau or at a known concentration of DNA, with a constant
short time of exposure. To correct for n cells per colony-forming unit,
multiply by $1/n$ if division of transformants has not occurred.

STANDARDIZATION OF RECIPIENT CULTURE (INCLUD-
ING TEST OF GROWTH MEDIA).   Compare the percent cells transformed for a chosen marker at the plateau concentration of DNA with
the yield in the standard culture.

TEST OF TRANSFORMATION ENVIRONMENT OR MEDIUM.
Compare the yield in percent or per ml with the active culture at

DNA Concentration vs Response

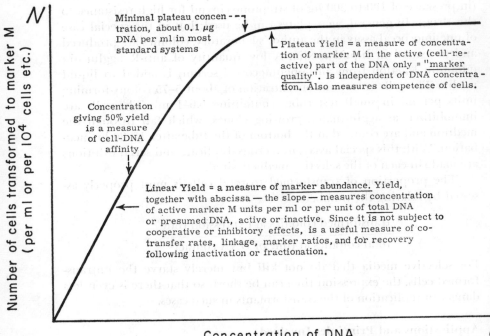

Fig. 1. Concentration-response relation for genetic transformation of bacteria by DNA. Number of cells transformed, N, as affected by DNA concentration, C, for a fixed exposure time. Linked transformations follow a similar course, at lower yield. Unlinked double transformations fall off quadratically below plateau levels.

plateau concentration of DNA at constant short exposure, in the environments which are of interest.

ACTIVITY OF A DNA PREPARATION—QUALITY. Compare the yield in percent or per ml for the same marker in the unknown preparation and standard DNA on the same culture, both at plateau concentration (appreciably above 0.2 μg/ml). This measures *quality* (i.e., marker activity in that part of the DNA with the highest affinity for cells), a good measure of the physical state of the DNA, and it is well to keep a running comparison of all DNA preparations made in a laboratory. This criterion is not affected by most impurities.

ACTIVITY OF A DNA PREPARATION—PURITY. This may be measured in the same manner as the quality measure just preceding except that it is made at the linear region (concentration 0.05 μg/ml or below). This measures marker activity in relation to *total* weight of DNA, or optical density ($\lambda = 260$), or acid insoluble phosphorus, etc. It is affected by impurities; therefore, it is a measure of purity, in terms of weight, OD, or P, etc.

APPLICATION OF ACTIVITY MEASUREMENTS. To measure the effect of denaturation, inactivation, hydrolytic or enzymatic degradation, or radioactive decay, one can use either the plateau or the linear assay. To judge the yield in purification, fractionation, or recovery, use the linear assay. The standardized culture may be dispensed with if one measures the yield against the amount of DNA actually taken up by the cells, as P^{32} or other labeled DNA—this, like the plateau assay measures the fraction of the DNA with highest cell affinity, but can be measured at any DNA concentration. Affinity can still vary with the strain of the recipient cells.

These features are represented schematically in Fig. 1. Also indicated is the fact that the concentration giving half-maximal yield is a measure of average affinity of the cells for the particular DNA.

ACTIVITY OF GENETICALLY HETEROLOGOUS OR MODIFIED DNA. The cell reactivity, or "quality" of any DNA, heterologous or modified experimentally, may be measured by mixing it with active DNA in known proportions and measuring the reduction in percent transformants at plateau concentrations of DNA. DNA preparations have generally been found equal, weight for weight, to pneumococcal DNA in their ability to saturate the cell sites, especially when the concentrations are judged by the hyperchromic increment (9).

RELATION BETWEEN INDEPENDENT MARKERS.   Markers are incorporated without apparent interference, thus P_{MA}/P_M, the proportion of double transformants at plateau for markers M and A (unlinked) to those acquiring only M, approximates P_A/N, the fraction of total cells transformed to A. The first ratio can be estimated independently of the size of the colony-forming unit (chains of cells or multiply nucleated cells, size n), but P_A/N is dependent, since a unit containing only one transformed cell can survive selection. If truly unselective growth is allowed until all units are homogeneous (in excess of $\log_2 n$ divisions) then,

$$P_{MA}/P_M \cong P_A/N \text{ (latter measured after further growth)}$$

Or if the nuclei per average unit, n, can be estimated (e.g., an average chain of pneumococci has about four cells):

$$P_{MA}/P_M \cong P_A/nN_0 \text{ (}N_0 \text{ measured at DNA time)}$$

where P yields are measured at minimal expression time. It will be seen that P_{MA}, the yield of MA doubles, is approximately equal to the apparent yield P_M, multiplied by the frequency of A transformations. In such calculations P_M and P_A naturally include all units transformed to M or A, e.g., including any MA units.

The same relations hold for the linear region of DNA concentration, e.g.,

$$L_{MA}/L_M \cong L_A/nN_0$$

but it will be recognized that at low DNA concentrations these ratios become smaller as yields of both A and M transformants decrease, so that the absolute yield of MA,

$$L_{MA} \cong L_M \times L_A/nN_0$$

becomes very low, falling with the square of the DNA concentration (10).

On a log-log plot of transformants *vs.* DNA concentration the single (and linked) marker transformations increase with slope 1 in the linear region—the unlinked double transfers increase with slope 2. The kinetic way of recognizing unlinked cotransformations will be given below.

RELATIONS BETWEEN LINKED MARKERS.   In estimating or testing for linkage between two markers, A and B, the principal expectation is that

$$P_{AB}/P_A > P_B/N$$

and the difference between the frequency of AB among total A's and the frequency of all B's in the population is the simplest measure of linkage. Strictly, N should represent only the competent fraction of the population; in our work with Pneumococcus this is usually the total population, as indicated by the frequency of unlinked pairs. Since the AB linked transformations will decrease only linearly at lowered DNA concentrations, the ratio

$$P_{AB}/P_A \cong L_{AB}/L_A$$

stays relatively constant and does not fall off as the DNA and the over-all yield is lowered. The use of shortened exposures to DNA—the kinetic method—to be discussed next also lowers the bimolecular transformations and helps reveal linkages. Ephrussi-Taylor has proposed the use of competing DNA to dilute out the double transformations (11) and the use of reference unlinked markers to judge the proportion of competent cells (12).

The measures of linkage indicated above relate double transformations to the transformation rate for one of the component markers. One may also use the cotransfer index (13) of Lederberg, which relates doubles to all (detected) transformations in the region:

$$\frac{L_{AB}}{L_{AB} + L_{A\,only} + L_{B\,only}} = \frac{L_{AB}}{L_A + L_B - L_{AB}}$$

KINETIC PARAMETERS—CONSTANT CONCENTRATION, VARYING TIME. Fully competent cells exposed to DNA at 30 C become transformed linearly with increasing time of exposure (1). This has been made the basis of methods (10,14) for judging the molecularity of a transformation. Preincubated cells are exposed to DNA and samples are treated with deoxyribonuclease at exactly known times ranging from 2 to 30 min. Single and linked markers become incorporated linearly (see Fig. 2), at rates that now become a sensitive measure of linkage frequency. Even low linkages become demonstrable (14).

On the other hand, unlinked markers enter by a bimolecular process and accumulate quadratically (proportional to square of the time of contact). This behavior is shown also by marker pairs coming from different donors in mixed DNA (14).

MEASUREMENT OF LOCALIZED DAMAGE TO DNA. Linked markers show the behavior of single markers after localized damage; this can be demonstrated by a study of either the concentration or time dependence of transformation rate, as described above (14).

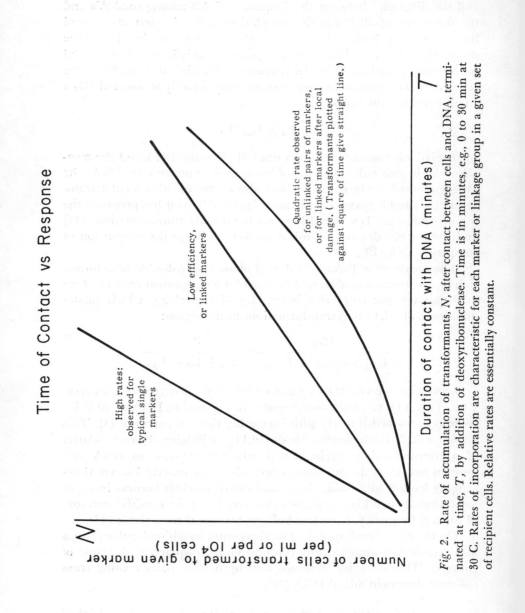

Time of Contact vs Response

High rates: observed for typical single markers

Low efficiency, or linked markers

Quadratic rate observed for unlinked pairs of markers, or for linked markers after local damage. (Transformants plotted against square of time give straight line.)

Number of cells transformed to given marker (per ml or per 10^4 cells)

N

Duration of contact with DNA (minutes) *T*

Fig. 2. Rate of accumulation of transformants, N, after contact between cells and DNA, terminated at time, T, by addition of deoxyribonuclease. Time is in minutes, e.g., 0 to 30 min at 30 C. Rates of incorporation are characteristic for each marker or linkage group in a given set of recipient cells. Relative rates are essentially constant.

PREPARATION OF PNEUMOCOCCAL
TRANSFORMING DNA

Principle

Pneumococci are "bile soluble," i.e., sodium deoxycholate and other bile salts initiate a rapid autolysis. If this lysis occurs in the presence of deoxyribonuclease inhibitors such as sodium citrate, high molecular DNA is released into solution. Proteins are removed by forming a chloroform-gel of surface denatured protein, and RNA by the action of purified ribonuclease. Alcohol precipitates the DNA as a fibrous precipitate, hastens the denaturation of the ribonuclease and protein for removal with chloroform, and is used to sterilize the DNA. This is essentially the procedure of McCarty and Avery (15) modified in certain practical ways (9).

Most of these steps are used in the procedure of Marmur (16), generalized for a variety of bacteria by the use of detergent or lysozyme lysis. The general procedure can give biologically active pneumococcal DNA; for other organisms the product has generally only been tested by physical means.

Substitution of phenol extraction to remove protein from DNA has also been made; it is generally supposed that this can involve less hydrodynamic shear of the DNA particles, but there is no evidence that biological activity or genetic linkage is better preserved.†

Procedure

Cultures of donor pneumococci having appropriate markers are grown in meat infusion neopeptone broth with maintenance of pH above 7, to approximate maximal growth, then centrifuged promptly in the cold. Selective media are used if back mutation is a danger; with semisynthetic media, it is particularly important to harvest the cells before growth saturation leads to stagnation and lysis. Growth can be to some extent forced with excess glucose and periodic adjustment of the pH by addition of alkali.

Packed wet cells are quickly resuspended in citrate-saline (0.1 M trisodium citrate, 0.15 M sodium chloride). Description for handling of the cells from 1 liter of culture ($1-3 \times 10^{11}$ cells) follows. Cells, re-

---

† Relatively high genetic linkage and generally good biological activity have been reported for phenol-extracted DNA preparations of *Hemophilus influenzae* (21) and of *Bacillus subtilis* (22).

suspended in 7–8 ml of citrate saline at 25–28 C, are quickly treated with sodium desoxycholate (about 20 mg in 0.3 ml). The suspension becomes quickly ropy, then somewhat translucent, increasing greatly in viscosity. After 3–15 min, when no further change is apparent, 2 to 3 volumes of chloroform are added, and 0.5 ml of isoamyl alcohol. The mixture is shaken mechanically at a gentle rate sufficient to drive drops of chloroform continually through the aqueous layer. (This process is conducted quickly to remove the bulk of the proteins and enzymes. It should be followed immediately by an alcohol precipitation, which if done before some protein is removed would give a rubbery precipitate that would dissolve only with difficulty.)

After 15 min shaking, the mixture is centrifuged at moderate speed at room temperature or in the cold. The turbid upper aqueous layer is removed from the cake of protein emulsion and lower chloroform layer and precipitated with an equal volume of ethyl alcohol. If coherent, the more or less fibrous precipitate is wound on a glass rod moistened with the solution—if somewhat fragmented, it is collected in the centrifuge. Rubbing of the alcohol precipitate against the glass degrades the DNA and long standing in alcohol somewhat hardens the precipitate and so should be avoided. The collected precipitate is dissolved in saline (without citrate unless long standing or high deoxyribonuclease activity is anticipated) at the same (7 ml) or appropriate volume and again treated with chloroform, now about equal volume, and isoamyl alcohol. After shaking and centrifuging as before, the aqueous layer is ready for one more chloroform treatment, if protein content is considerable, or for ribonuclease treatment.

RNA is depolymerized by treating the aqueous solution with 100 μg of ribonuclease (Worthington pancreatic ribonuclease, either known to be free of deoxyribonuclease, or heated at 100 C for 5 min at acid pH). After incubation at 37 C for 30 min, the DNA is precipitated by overlayering with 1.2 volumes of ethanol. A glass rod is used to stir the two layers together and the precipitate, now less bulky, should easily gather upon the rod. If fibrous fragments or flocculent precipitates are obtained, the solution is probably too dilute and the DNA precipitate should be concentrated and handled in a smaller volume of saline.

After the alcohol precipitation at least one more chloroform treatment, as above, is given. The final saline solution should give no more than a slight scum of emulsion at the chloroform interface when it is adequately deproteinized. A final alcohol precipitation can be used to remove chloroform and sterilize the preparation for bacteriological work. In this case, the precipitate is left in 60–70% alcohol for about 1 hr before removal to sterile saline, and allowed ample time for redissolving before analysis or use.

DNA can be preserved at 4 C for many months in solutions of 200 μg/ml or more in neutral saline, but slowly loses activity and linkage integrity. Optimal preservation seems to be afforded by leaving an alcohol precipitate under fresh 70–90% concentrations of alcohol in well stoppered vials at 4 C.

Besides phenol extraction to remove proteins, other modified procedural steps include magnesium salt precipitation (17) and charcoal adsorption (7,18) to remove RNA.

Hyperchromic Assay of DNA Solutions

A spectrophotometric assay of double-stranded DNA has been described in detail elsewhere (9). Briefly, it depends upon the hyperchromic increase of optical density (about 33%) occasioned by denaturation with alkali, or better, by deoxyribonuclease hydrolysis. The hyperchromic increment, corrected for dilution and blank is calculated to denaturable DNA on the basis that an optical density increase of 1.0 at $\lambda = 260$ mμ corresponds to 135 μg of DNA/ml (as free acid).

REFERENCES

1. FOX, M. S., and R. D. HOTCHKISS. 1957. Nature. *179:* 1322.
2. LACKS, S., and R. D. HOTCHKISS. 1960. Biochem. Biophys. Acta. *39:* 508.
3. MINDICH, L., and R. D. HOTCHKISS. 1964. Biochem. Biophys. Acta. *80:* 73.
4. YOUNG, F. E., and J. SPIZIZEN. 1961. J. Bacteriol. *81:* 823.
5. GOODGAL, S. H., and R. M. HERRIOTT. 1961. J. Gen. Physiol. *44:* 1201.
6. HOTCHKISS, R. D. 1957. *In* W. D. McElroy and B. Glass, editors, The Chemical basis of heredity. The Johns Hopkins Press. Baltimore. p. 321.
7. LERMAN, L. S., and L. J. TOLMACH. 1957. Biochem. Biophys. Acta. *26:* 68.
8. EPHRUSSI-TAYLOR, H. 1958. *In* Almquist and Wiksell, editors, Recent progress in microbiology. 7th Intern. Congress. Microbiol., Stockholm, p. 51.
9. HOTCHKISS, R. D. 1957. *In* S. P. Colowick and N. O. Kaplan, editors, Methods in enzymology. Academic Press, New York. Vol. 3, p. 692; p. 708.
10. GOODGAL, S. H. 1961. J. Gen. Physiol. *45:* 205.
11. EPHRUSSI-TAYLOR, H. 1957. *In* W. D. McElroy and B. Glass, editors, The chemical basis of heredity. The Johns Hopkins Press. Baltimore. P. 299.
12. MICHEL, J. F., A. M. SICARD, and H. EPHRUSSI-TAYLOR. 1964. Exptl. Cell Res. *36:* 368.
13. NESTER, E. W., and J. LEDERBERG. 1961. Proc. Natl. Acad. Sci. U.S. *47:* 52.
14. KENT, J. L., and R. D. HOTCHKISS. 1964. J. Mol. Biol. *9:* 308.
15. MCCARTY, M., and O. T. AVERY. 1946. J. Exptl. Med. *83:* 97.
16. MARMUR, J. 1961. J. Mol. Biol. *3:* 208.
17. EPHRUSSI-TAYLOR, H. 1951. Exptl. Cell Res. *2:* 549.

18. ZAMENHOF, S., and E. CHARGAFF. 1951. Nature. *168:* 604.
19. TOMASZ, A., and R. D. HOTCHKISS. 1964. Proc. Natl. Acad. Sci. U.S. *51:* 480.
20. TOMASZ, A., and J. MOSSER. 1966. Proc. Natl. Acad. Sci. U.S. In press.
21. BERNS, K. I., and C. A. THOMAS, JR. 1965. J. Mol. Biol. *11:* 476.
22. KELLY, M. S., and R. H. PRITCHARD. 1965. J. Bacteriol. *89:* 1314.

2. Viral DNA

The Isolation and

Characterization of DNA

from Bacteriophage

C. A. THOMAS, JR., AND JOHN ABELSON

DEPARTMENT OF BIOPHYSICS

THE JOHNS HOPKINS UNIVERSITY

BALTIMORE, MARYLAND

PHAGE GROWTH

Growth in Liquid Media

Table 1 decribes the growth conditions for several bacteriophage types. A saturated broth culture of the bacteria is diluted 100-fold into sterile growth medium and aerated at 37 C by bubbler tubes or coarse fritted sporringers. The culture should be growing logarithmically at the time of infection. The bacteria may be conveniently counted in a Petroff-Hausser counter (Arthur H. Thomas Co., Philadelphia). When the desired bacterial concentration is reached, the culture is infected with phage from a stock derived from a single plaque and aeration is continued. Ofter the turbid culture will clear as the result of spontaneous lysis. To complete lysis or to induce lysis where it does not occur spontaneously, the culture is aerated for several minutes with 1/50 volume $CHCl_3$. If the lysate is particularly viscous, deoxyribonuclease and ribonuclease (Worthington Biochemical Corp., Freehold,

TABLE 1. *Growth Conditions for Various Types of Bacteriophage*

Phage	Host Cell	Medium	Bacterial Concentration at Infection (cells/ml)	Multiplicity of Infection (phage/cell)	Length of Time for Lysis (hr)	Optical Cross Section × 10^{+11} cm²/PFU	S for[a] Whole Molecules Boundary	S for[a] Whole Molecules Zone	Molecular Weight of DNA × 10^{-6}
$T_{2,4,6}$	*E. coli* BB	TCG[b]	2×10^8	0.1	3	0.7–1.0 (19)[c]	63 (15,19)	63.5 (17,22)	130 (11)
T*2	*E. coli* B/4$_o$ (29)	TCG	5×10^8	5.0	1				128 (30)
T5st	*E. coli* H	TCG + Ca^{2+}	1×10^8	0.1	3	0.62 (19)	49 (19)	52.5 (22)	78 (22)
T7	*E. coli* BB	TCG	5×10^8	0.25	1	0.30 (31)	32.2 (32)[d]	32.0 (17)	25 (17,22)
λ	*E. coli* W3110	Peptone (26) Tris	5×10^8	5.0	3	0.31 (6)	31 (15)	35.1 (17)	32 (21)
P22	*Salmonella* LT2	TCG	1×10^8	0.001	2	0.40 (19)	30–35 (19)	35.4 (22)	30 (22)
P1kc	*E. coli* K$_{12}$ (λ)	Z agar	5×10^8	0.5	5	–	–	–	60 (23)

a The boundary sedimentation coefficients are not corrected to $s_{20, w}$ but they are the measured rates under the conditions of Burgi and Hershey (15). The zone sedimentation coefficients are corrected to $s_{20, w}$; see Studier (17).

b This is a modification of the tris-casamino acid medium of Kozinski and Szybalski (27).

c Numbers in parentheses refer to bibliography at end of chapter.

d Corrected to $s_{20, w}$.

H$_2$O	450 ml
0.10 M Na$_2$SO$_4$	0.8 ml
1.0 M MgSO$_4$	0.5 ml
25% NaCl	1.0 ml
0.5 M CaCl$_2$	0.10 ml, 1.1 ml for T$_5$ growth (sterilized separately)
0.001 M FeCl$_3$	1.50 ml
0.10 M KH$_2$PO$_4$	3.20 ml
1.0 M Tris, pH 7.4	50.0 ml
10% glucose	5.0 ml (sterilized separately)
5% casamino acid	5.0 ml

N.J.) can be added to 10 μg/ml and incubation continued for 30–60 min.

Growth on Solid Media

P_1 is an example of a phage that does not grow well in liquid media (1). Good yields can be obtained by the confluent lysis technique (2). To 3 ml of liquid agar (0.66%, containing 0.002 M Ca^{2+}, held at 45 C) are added 10^8 log-phase bacteria (in 0.2 ml) and 5×10^7 phage particles (in 0.02 ml). The mixture is poured onto a Z agar plate (containing per liter of H_2O, 10 g of tryptone, 5 g of yeast extract, 10 g of NaCl, and 2×10^{-3} M $CaCl_2$). After the top layer has solidified, the plate is incubated for 5 hr at 37 C. Two milliters of broth is pipetted onto the agar surface and allowed to stand for 10 min. The entire top layer is then scraped off, homogenized with a glass rod, and centrifuged for 10 min at 5000 rev/min. The supernatant fluid is removed and filtered through celite. Purification can then proceed as described below.

Incorporation of Radioisotopes into Phage DNA

Phage DNA can be labeled with C^{14}, H^3, or P^{32}. P^{32}-labeled phage are prepared by adding aqueous orthophosphate-P^{32} to the growth medium about 30 min prior to infection. TCG contains 20 μg/ml of phosphorous; if 10 μc/ml of P^{32} is added to the medium the DNA will have a specific activity of about 0.5 μc/μg of phosphorous (10^5 dpm/μg of DNA).

C^{14} can be incorporated into phage DNA in the form of thymidine-C^{14} or uniformly labeled glucose-C^{14}. In the case of glucose, high specific activities are obtained by centrifuging the bacteria just prior to phage infection and washing and resuspending them in growth medium containing only labeled glucose. Thymidine-C^{14} and -H^3 are best incorporated into the DNA by infecting the bacteria with a multiplicity of 5 phage/cell when the bacterial concentration is 5×10^8 cells/ml and adding the thymidine 10 min after infection (3).

P^{32}-labeled P_1 can be prepared by adding P^{32} to the Z agar when the plate is poured. Acceptable results have been obtained by adding 100 μc to each 30-ml plate.

PHAGE PURIFICATION

Differential Centrifugation

There are a number of ways to purify phage, but the simplest and most reliable method for large bacteriophage is differential centrifugation. The lysate is centrifuged twice at low speed (5000 × g for 10 min) and once at high speed (55,000 × g for 25 min, 35,000 × g is enough for T_2). The supernatant liquid from the high-speed spin is discarded and the phage pellet is resuspended by shaking for several hours in about 1/50 of the original volume of T_2 buffer (4). The phage may be given another cycle of low- and high-speed centrifugations if a pure preparation of phage is required.

Filtration

The initial low-speed spins may be replaced by filtration of the crude lysate through a layer of celite (Hyflo, Supercel, Johns-Manville, New York) on a Büchner funnel followed by filtration through a Millipore filter (HA type, 0.45-μ pore size, Millipore Filter Corp., Bedford, Mass.) on which is deposited a 5-mm layer of celite. Phage are occasionally lost during the Millipore filtration.

Hydroxyapatite

By using a suggestion of G. Bernardi (5), a method has been perfected for the purification of λ bacteriophage (6) by chromatography on hydroxyapatite. Lysates purified by filtration through a Millipore filter are adjusted to 0.01 M PO_4, pH 6.8, by dilution from a stock solution containing per liter of solution 0.50 mole of Na_2HPO_4, 0.50 mole of NaH_2PO_4, 10 ml of 1.0 M Tris, pH 7.4, 10 ml of 0.10 M $MgSO_4$, and 20 ml of 5% NaCl. To each 100 ml of lysate, 2.0 ml (packed volume) of hydroxyapatite is added and the mixture agitated intermittently for 15 min at room temperature. The hydroxyapatite is allowed to settle and the supernatant fluid is decanted. More than 95% of the phage become adsorbed to the hydroxyapatite crystals, which are then resuspended in 0.02 M PO_4 buffer. The suspension is then loaded into a glass fritted column and washed with the same solvent until the eluate shows no ultraviolet absorption at 260 mμ. At this point the column is washed with 0.10 M PO_4 buffer to elute the phage particles. This procedure may prove useful for other types of bacteriophage.

Centrifugation in CsCl

A rapid method for obtaining a pure phage preparation is to sediment the phage in a preformed CsCl gradient (34). Solutions of CsCl are prepared having densities of 1.3, 1.5, and 1.7 g/cc. A convenient formula for the preparation of CsCl solutions is

$$\text{Weight percent} = 137.48 - 138.11(\frac{1}{\rho}) \quad (7).$$

The density of the solution may be checked by reading its refractive index and applying the relationship

$$\rho(25\ C) = 10.8601\eta\,_D^{25} - 13.4974 \quad (8).$$

A volume of 1.3 ml each of the three CsCl solutions (1.3, 1.5, and 1.7 g/cc, in that order) are pipetted sequentially into the bottom of a 5-ml centrifuge tube with a Pasteur pipet. Then 1.0 ml of concentrated phage suspension is layered onto the top of the gradient. The tubes are centrifuged for 1 hr at 35,000 rev/min in a Spinco SW39 swinging bucket rotor. During this time a roughly linear gradient of CsCl is formed in the tube. After centrifugation, the phage are visible as a thin blue band in the lower half of the tube. They are collected by puncturing the bottom of the tube and collecting fractions. The CsCl is removed by dialysis.

Titration of the Phage

A fraction of the purified phage suspension is diluted and its absorbancy measured at 260 mμ. Further dilutions are made and the bacteriophage are titered by the soft agar technique (2). This enables one to measure the optical cross section of the phage (A_{260}/titer) (9). The optical cross section obtained for a phage suspension is a relative measure of the extent to which the phage have been purified, lower values indicating greater purity. The values obtained for several bacteriophage are listed in Table 1.

EXTRACTION OF DNA

Analytical reagent grade liquefied phenol (Mallinckrodt Chemical Co.) is freshly distilled over metallic zinc into water with constant flushing of the distillation system by nitrogen gas. The phenol is stored in the dark at 4 C under nitrogen. Before use, the phenol is neutralized by adding 1/50 volume 1.0 M PO$_4$ buffer, pH 6.8. Phenol that shows any color contains undesirable contaminants and should be redistilled before use.

After purification the phage are adjusted to a concentration having an absorbance at 260 mμ of 5–15 cm^{-1} and are placed in a pointed screw-capped tube. An equal volume of water-saturated phenol is added and the tube is rolled (10) in a horizontal position at 60 rev/min for 30 min at room temperature. The tube is chilled to 0 C and centrifuged for 5 min at 3000 rev/min in a clinical centrifuge to separate the two phases. The phenol layer (the bottom one) is removed with a Pasteur pipet. The extraction is repeated twice more with briefer periods of rolling. The aqueous layer is then transferred to a Visking No. 20 dialysis bag (Union Carbide Co., Chicago). Just prior to use the dialysis tubing is boiled in 5% sodium bicarbonate for 20 min and washed extensively with distilled water. The DNA is dialyzed exhaustively against a suitable buffer to remove the phenol and stored at 4 C with a drop of chloroform.

Alternatively, the phenol may be extracted with cold aqueous ether (not anhydrous ether + water), but dialysis is preferred.

CHARACTERIZATION OF THE DNA

Recovery

P^{32}-labeled phage preparations show that nearly all of the label is recovered in the aqueous layer.

Spectrophotometry

The product should show the absorption spectrum characteristic of DNA. The absorbancy at 260 mμ should be 1.6–2.0 times that at 280 mμ and 1.8–2.2 times that at 230 mμ. The specific absorbancy of T_2 DNA at 260 mμ is 0.0181 cm^2/μg (11). For nonglucosylated DNAs, the specific absorbancy is 0.020 cm^2/μg (12).

RNA

The product should be completely resistant to digestion in 0.4 N NaOH at 37 C for 1 hr (RNA is rendered acid soluble by this treatment), and should be completely precipitated in cold 0.6 N trichloroacetic acid following the NaOH digestion.

Protein

Folin tests for protein (13) on phenol-extracted phage DNAs using internal standards give 0.5–1% protein. All phenol must be removed to make this test meaningful.

Chromatographic Characterization

Phage DNAs chromatograph well on MAK (14) and hydroxyapatite columns (5, 6). The former fractionates largely with respect to molecular weight, whereas the latter fractionates with respect to state of denaturation. Phage DNA preparations extracted by this procedure have very little broken material and contain no detectable denatured material. These columns are useful for further purifying DNA molecules.

Sedimentation of Native DNA

Sedimentation coefficients can be measured in the Spinco Model E analytical centrifuge under the "standard conditions" of Burgi and Hershey (15) or by the zone sedimentation procedure of Vinograd et al. (16, 17). The sedimentation coefficients of unbroken DNA molecules from a number of phage are listed in Table 1. It should be realized that boundary sedimentation coefficients of high molecular weight DNA are influenced by the following variables: salt concentration (18), DNA concentration (19), rotor speed (20), and choice of cell centerpiece (15). In general, these effects are more pronounced on higher molecular weight DNAs such as T_2 DNA.

One may obtain a reliable measure of the sedimentation coefficient of an unknown DNA by a double-label sucrose density gradient centrifugation using T_2, T_5, or T_7 DNA as a standard. The molecular weights of these DNAs are known, and assuming that the unknown molecule is a linear duplex, the molecular weight of the unknown DNA may be calculated using the empirical relationship derived by Burgi and Hershey (21):

$$\frac{D_2}{D_1} = \left(\frac{M_2}{M_1}\right)^{0.35},$$

where D_2/D_1 is the ratio of the distances sedimented.

Sedimentation of Denatured DNA

All but one of the bacteriophage listed in Table 1 contain a single duplex DNA molecule composed of two continuous polynucleotide chains (19, 17, 22, 33). The exception is T_5, which contains a single duplex DNA molecule with at least four natural interruptions located at specific places (22).

One may examine the state of the single strands in a DNA molecule by sedimenting the DNA in 5–20% sucrose gradients containing 0.9 M NaCl and 0.1 N NaOH, or by zone centrifugation in the analytical centrifuge as described by Studier (17). If there are no interruptions in the strands, the polynucleotide chains will sediment as a sharp unimodal band.

Sedimentation in alkaline sucrose reveals that DNA molecules are remarkably sensitive to indirect radiation damage (23,35). We have obtained good results by growing the phage at a specific activity of 0.05 μc P^{32}/μg of phosphorus or in thymidine-C^{14} and glucose-C^{14}. Preparations labeled with thymidine-H^3 are rapidly damaged and we no longer use this isotope for studies on the single strands of DNA.

To minimize radiation damage, labeled preparations are used as soon as possible after growth. Labeled DNA prepared according to the method described above and stored at 10^5 dpm/ml is visibly damaged within 1 week. Work is in progress to find ways of minimizing radiation damage.

Electron Microscopy

The lengths of DNA molecules may be measured from electron-micrographs of grids prepared by the protein monolayer technique of Kleinschmidt and Zahn (24). Phage DNA molecules extracted as above and purified on the MAK column show a monodisperse population of lengths. The molecular weights calculated from these lengths agree well with the values obtained by zone sedimentation (25). Once the intricacies of this technique are mastered, a reliable value for the length of a given DNA molecule may be obtained in 2 weeks. The additional advantage of being able to visualize interesting topological features of a molecule, such as circularity, makes this an extremely valuable technique.

REFERENCES

1. LENNOX, E. S. 1955. Virology. *1:* 190. GARRICK, L., and P. HARTMAN. Personal communication.
2. ADAMS, M. H. 1959. Bacteriophages. Interscience: New York.
3. HERSHEY, A. D., E. GOLDBERG, E. BURGI, and L. INGRAHAM. 1963. J. Mol. Biol. *6:* 230.
4. HERSHEY, A. D., and M. CHASE. 1952. J. Gen. Physiol. *36:* 39.
5. BERNARDI, G. 1961. Biochem. Biophys. Res. Comm. *6:* 54.
6. MIYAZAWA, Y., and C. A. THOMAS, JR. 1965. J. Mol. Biol. *11:* 223.
7. VINOGRAD, J., and J. HEARST. 1964. *In* Progress in the Chemistry of Organic Natural Products. Springer Verlag: Vienna. Vol. 20, p. 372.
8. THOMAS, C. A., JR., and K. I. BERNS. 1961. J. Mol. Biol. *3:* 277.
9. HERSHEY, A. D. 1955. Virology. *1:* 108.
10. FRAENKEL, F. 1963. Proc. Nat. Acad. Sci. U.S. *49:* 366.
11. RUBENSTEIN, I., C. A. THOMAS, JR., and A. D. HERSHEY. 1961. Proc. Nat. Acad. Sci. U.S. *47:* 1113.
12. CHARGAFF, E. 1955. *In* E. CHARGAFF and J. N. DAVIDSON, Editors, *The Nucleic Acids*. Academic Press: New York. Vol. 1, p. 336.
13. LAYNE, E. 1957. *In* S. COLOWICK and N. KAPLAN, Editors, *Methods in Enzymology*. Academic Press: New York. Vol. III, p. 448.
14. MANDELL, J. D., and A. D. HERSHEY. 1960. Anal. Biochem. *1:* 66.
15. BURGI, E., and A. D. HERSHEY. 1961. J. Mol. Biol. *3:* 458.
16. VINOGRAD, J., R. BRUNNER, R. KENT, and J. WEIGLE. 1963. Proc. Nat. Acad. Sci. U.S. *49:* 902.

17. STUDIER, F. W. 1965. J. Mol. Biol. *11:* 373.
18. EIGNER, J., and P. DOTY. 1965. J. Mol. Biol. *12:* 549.
19. THOMAS, C. A., JR., and T. PINKERTON. 1962. J. Mol. Biol. *5:* 356.
20. ROSENBLOOM, J., and V. SCHUMAKER. 1963. Biochemistry. *2:* 1206.
21. BURGI, E., and A. D. HERSHEY. 1963. Biophys. J. *3:* 309.
22. ABELSON, J., and C. A. THOMAS, JR. 1965. J. Mol. Biol. In press.
23. TOMIZAWA, J., and N. ANRAKU. 1965. J. Mol. Biol. *11:* 509.
24. KLEINSCHMIDT, A. K., and R. K. ZAHN. 1959. Z. Naturforsch. *14b:* 770.
25. MAC HATTIE, L. A., and C. A. THOMAS, JR. 1964. Science. *144:* 1142.
26. BURGI, E. 1963. Proc. Nat. Acad. Sci. U.S. *49:* 151.
27. KOZINSKI, A. W., and W. SZYBALSKI. 1959. Virology. *9:* 260.
28. HERSHEY, A. D., E. BURGI, and L. INGRAHAM. 1962. Biophys. J. *2:* 423.
29. HATTMAN, S., and T. FUKASAWA. 1963. Proc. Nat. Acad. Sci. U.S. *50:* 297.
30. DAVISON, P. F., and D. FREIFELDER. 1965. Biopolymers. *2:* 15.
31. DAVISON, P. F., and D. FREIFELDER. 1962. J. Mol. Biol. *5:* 635.
32. DAVISON, P. F., and D. FREIFELDER. 1962. J. Mol. Biol. *5:* 643.
33. BERNS, K. I., and C. A. THOMAS, JR. 1961. J. Mol. Biol. *3:* 289.
34. MATTHEWS, R. E. F. 1960. Virology. *12:* 521.
35. RHOADES, M. M., and C. A. THOMAS, JR., manuscript in preparation.

α Phage DNA

S. AURISICCHIO
INTERNATIONAL LABORATORY OF GENETICS
AND BIOPHYSICS
NAPLES, ITALY

INTRODUCTION

At the Institute of Microbiology of the University of Rome a temperate bacteriophage of *Bacillus megatherium,* which has been called α, has been isolated. This bacteriophage comes from the waters of the Tiber, whereas its host, *Bacillus megatherium* (Paris strain), is an old strain of the collection of the Institute of Microbiology obtained more than thirty years ago from the Institut Pasteur.

For the large scale preparation of phage for chemical studies and for the purification of DNA, the "clear mutant" α_{c3} is used.

TECHNIQUE FOR THE LARGE SCALE PREPARATION OF PHAGE α (1)

Materials

1. Square dishes 50 cm × 3 cm in depth, of perspex 9 mm thick, with covers
2. Agar broth, 2% and 1%
3. Nutrient broth
4. Chemical products:

   "Tris" [(Hydroxy Methyl) Amino Methane from L. Light & Co., Ltd.]

Deoxyribonuclease (Worthington Biochemical Corp.)
Ribonuclease (Sigma Chemical Corp.)
Tripsin (Sigma Chemical Corp.)

Technique†

1200 ml of 2% agar at 60 C are poured into a dish placed on a level surface to provide a smooth and uniform layer of agar. When the agar has solidified, the dish (partly uncovered) is placed in a thermostat at 37 C for 1 hr. Then pour 120 ml of a 24-hr broth culture of *B. megatherium* containing approximately 2×10^6 particles of phage α into the dish. The dish is kept at 27 C for 12–14 hr. 200 ml of broth are then added, followed by a further incubation at 27 C for 45 min. The liquid is then removed with a pipette (taking care not to touch the agar with the tip) and is collected in a flask. This procedure is repeated three times. The liquid is then centrifuged at $1064 \times g$ for 90 min to remove the bacteria; 600 ml of a phage suspension are thus obtained with a titer of about 10^{11} phage particles/ml.

The phage is subsequently concentrated and purified by the following procedure:

1. Centrifugation at $40,000 \times g$ for 2 hr in the No. 20 rotor of the Spinco centrifuge Model L.
2. Resuspension of the pellet with 15 ml of 0.2 M NaCl.
3. Centrifugation at $17,033 \times g$ for 90 min in an International Centrifuge Model PR-2.
4. Resuspension of the pellet in 2 ml of 0.2 M NaCl plus 0.02 M Tris-HCl buffer at pH 7.4. To this suspension 10 μg/ml of deoxyribonuclease and 10 μg/ml of ribonuclease are added; these enzymes are allowed to act for 2 hr at 22 C. Trypsin, 10 μg/ml, is then added and incubation is continued for another 2 hr at the same temperature. The suspension is then brought up to 15 ml with the same buffered saline.
5. Centrifugation at $1064 \times g$ for 15 min.
6. Centrifugation of the supernatant fluid at $17,033 \times g$ for 90 min.
7. Resuspension of the pellet with 15 ml of the buffered saline.
8. Centrifugation at $1064 \times g$ for 15 min.
9. Centrifugation of the supernatant fluid at $17,033 \times g$ for 90 min.
10. Resuspension of the pellet with 3 ml of 0.2 M NaCl.
11. Determination of the protein concentration of the suspension according to the method of Lowry *et al.* (2) (reference curve prepared with serum albumin).

† Quantities refer to 1 dish.

PHYSICOCHEMICAL STUDIES OF PHAGE α AND ITS DNA

Description of the Phage

From electron micrographs (3) it can be seen that phage α has a head of regular icosahedral form. The dimensions of the phage have been determined from measurements performed on about one hundred particles (3). From these data the volume of the whole particle can be deduced, which is $(69 \pm 6) \times 10^{-18}$ cm³ (taking into account the error of the magnification).

If the value found for the sedimentation coefficient of the phage (470 S) is compared with those reported in the literature for other phages (4) it can be seen that the molecular weight of phage α can be estimated to be about 7×10^7, assuming that the particles compared have similar hydrodynamic properties.

The CsCl density gradient technique (5) allows more complete results by furnishing two independent measurements: the density and the molecular weight of the dehydrated particles. The latter result gives $(68 \pm 6) \times 10^6$, whereas the value obtained for the density $(1.521 \pm 0.002$ g/cm³) combined with that of the volume determined by electron microscopy, yields $M = V\rho = (70 \pm 10) \times 10^6$ (6).

The agreement between the two values of the molecular weight determined from the width of the band and from the product $V\rho$ indicates that there is no detectable density heterogeneity among the phages.

α PHAGE PHYSICOCHEMICAL CONSTANTS

Shape: regular icosahedral form

ρ_{CsCl} 1.521 ± 0.002 g/cm³

Molecular weight $70 \pm 10 \times 10^6$

$\dfrac{\text{P atoms}}{\text{Phage particles}}$ (by autoradiography) $= 1.19 \times 10^5$

$\dfrac{\text{P atoms in DNA}}{\text{P atoms in whole phage}}$ $= 0.87$, that is, there is phosphorus in the phage in addition to that associated with the DNA

Preparation of DNA from the phage (7)

The phage suspension containing about 10^{13} particles per ml is centrifuged at 2.7×10^4 g for 30 min and resuspended in a saturated solution of sodium tetraborate at 4 C, to which is added an equal volume of phenol saturated with tetraborate. The emulsion is shaken for 5 min and centrifuged at low speed to separate the fractions: The lower fraction is phenolic and the upper one contains the DNA. When the phenolic fraction has been removed by pipetting, the aqueous fraction is centrifuged at 1.5×10^4 g to separate the precipitated protein. The clear aqueous fraction is then treated twice with the tetraborate saturated phenol.

The pooled phenolic fractions are extracted with a volume of tetraborate half that which was used to suspend the phage. The fraction acquired by this emulsion is added to the original aqueous fraction. The solution is dialyzed after eliminating the ether in a nitrogen current with two changes of potassium phosphate buffer, 1.3 M at pH 7.5 (8). All operations up to the evaporation of the ether and following the dialysis with phosphate are carried out at 4 C. The removal of any residual protein is assured by shaking with half a volume of N-N dimethylformamide. The organic fraction containing the DNA is then separated by centrifugation and prolonged dialysis is carried out using three changes of SSC (saline citrate solution): 0.15 M NaCl plus 0.015 M sodium citrate at pH 7.0 (7).

Physicochemical Study of Purified DNA

In order to obtain the maximum amount of high molecular weight DNA, it is necessary to reduce to a minimum the mechanical treatment of DNA. A preparation of phage α, purified and suspended in a standard saline citrate solution (0.15 M NaCl and 0.015 M Na-citrate), is heated for about 30 min at 60 C. The DNA thus obtained can be studied by the analytical ultracentrifuge. Introduction with a syringe must be avoided (9); this can be done by depositing one drop of a concentrated solution of DNA in the center of the disassembled cell. The drop is very viscous and will not be displaced if the cell is reassembled with care. The solvent is then introduced very slowly with a syringe and its concentration in the cell is determined from the photographs done during ultracentrifugation with ultraviolet optics, or by examining the same solution spectrophotometrically. A value of the sedimentation coefficient is then found (extrapolated for zero concentration) amounting to 41 ± 1 S. This value is considerably beyond the range in which the relation of Doty, McGill, and Rice (10) was found to be valid; therefore the value of 40×10^6, which is obtained for the molecular weight corresponding to 41 S, is only indicative. A value of $(30-40) \times 10^6$ for the molecular weight of α DNA is made plausible from these measurements and from those obtained by autoradiography (11). Base composition of α DNA has been carried out following the paper chromatography method (12) that gives a GC content of 0.43 ± 0.01.

α PHAGE DNA PHYSICOCHEMICAL CONSTANTS

$s_{20,w}$ 41 ± 1

Molecular weight	by autoradiography	3.4×10^7
	by Doty, McGill, and Rice formula	4.0×10^7

ρ_{native} 1.704 ± 0.002 g/cm^3

$\rho_{denatured}$ $\begin{cases} \alpha_L & 1.714 \\ \alpha_H & 1.724 \end{cases}$

Melting point (SSC)   85 C

Base composition in (G + C)%

    from density ρ 46.0 ± 0.002

    from melting point 42.0

    from chromatography 43.0 ± 0.01

HEAT DENATURATION OF DNA

A good indication of the double-stranded structure of the phage α DNA was provided by the values of the density of DNA and of its relative content in G + C ($\rho = 1.705$ g/cm^3; %(G + C) = 0.425) (13, 14). These values allow the determination of a point in the graph of ρ as a function of the G + C content, a point which falls on the line found (15) for native double-stranded DNA, whereas the single-stranded DNA should have a higher density by an additive factor of 0.015 g/cm^3.

The behavior of α DNA when subjected to heat denaturation at 100 C followed by fast cooling shows (16) that the two complementary strands of this DNA are different. Denatured bacterial or phage DNA, when put in CsCl density gradient, form a single band of a higher density than that of the native DNA. The density difference is ∼0.015 g/cm^3.

However, in the case of the DNA of phage α, after heating at 100 C and fast cooling, there appear in the density gradient two bands with densities higher than that of native DNA by 0.010 g/cm^3 and 0.020 g/cm^3. The two bands are of equal height and width.

SEPARATION OF THE STRANDS

The densitometric profile of the heat-denatured α DNA shows two bands that occupy equivalent areas with a difference in relative density of ∼0.010 g/cm^3 [we shall refer to α_L and α_H as the materials showing a buoyant density of 1.714 and 1.724, respectively (17)]. This difference in density (and therefore in base composition) makes it possible to separate the strands of heat-denatured material on methylated albumin columns. Separation is carried out thus: First the kieselguhr covered with methylated albumin is prepared according to the directions of Mandell and Hershey (18) and is packed in columns of 3-cm diameter, 1.5 cm high (19). The column is washed with about 300 ml of a 0.2 M NaCl solution buffered with phosphate, 0.25 M at pH 7.9. The DNA is diluted in SSC to a concentration of 20 μg/ml and is denatured by heating at 95 C for 10 min. The solution is then rapidly cooled passing in 1 min from 95 to 2 C. The cold liquid is then carefully poured into the column and washed with 0.2 M NaCl plus 0.25 M phosphate at pH 7.9. Step elution is effected by use of solutions in which the NaCl molarity increases progressively by 0.05 (17). The material eluted at the lowest molarities (0.35–0.4 M) contains the α_L strand in its purest state (see table 1); at higher molarities the eluent contains increasing quantities of α_H. The method gives a high variability insofar as the yield of α_L is concerned. The purity of the α_L fraction is tested by heating in a sealed ampoule at 60 C for 4 hr; then a standard DNA of known density is added and the solution is ultracentrifuged in a CsCl gradient. Pure α_L treated in this manner gives densities of 1.713–1.714 (17).

TABLE 1. *Base Composition of the Complementary Strands of α DNA and of a Specific RNA* (20)

DNA	RNA	G	A	C	T or U
α_L		24.1	30.1	21.3	24.5
α_H		19.9	24.0	24.2	32.1
	α_{RNA}	25.5	31.0	20.5	23.0

REFERENCES

1. AURISICCHIO, S., A. COPPO, P. DONINI, C. FRONTALI, F. GRAZIOSI, and G. TOSCHI. 1961. Rapporti dei Lab. di Fisica dell'Ist. Superiore di Sanità, ISS 61/33. (1961).

2. LOWRY, O., J. S. ROSEBROUGH, A. L. FARR, and R. J. RANDALL. 1951. J. Biol. Chem. *193:* 265.

3. CHIOZZOTTO, A., A. COPPO, P. DONINI, and F. GRAZIOSI. 1960. Proc. Eur. Reg. Conf. on Electron Microscopy. Delft. Vol. II.

4. PUTNAM, F. W. 1951. J. Biol. Chem. *190:* 61.

5. MESELSON, M., F. W. STAHL, and J. VINOGRAD. 1957. Proc. Acad. Sci. U.S. *43:* 581.

6. AURISICCHIO, S., A. CHIOZZOTTO, A. COPPO, P. DONINI, C. FRONTALI, and F. GRAZIOSI. 1960. Nuovo Cimento. *18:* Suppl. No. 2.

7. SINSHEIMER, R. L. 1959. J. Mol. Biol. *1:* 43–53.
8. KIRBY, K. S. 1957. Biochem. J. *66:* 495–503.
9. DAVISON, P. F. 1959. Proc. Nat. Acad. Sci. U.S. *45:* 1560.
10. DOTY, P., B. B. MCGILL, and S. A. RICE. 1958. Proc. Nat. Acad. Sci. U.S. *44:* 432.
11. AURISICCHIO, S., G. CORTINI, V. EMMA, and F. GRAZIOSI. 1959. Intern. J. Rad. Biol. *1:* No. 1, 86.
12. BENDICH, A. 1957. *In* S. P. COLOWICK and N. O. KAPLAN, editors, Methods in Enzymology. Academic Press, New York. Vol. III, pp. 715–723.
13. AURISICCHIO, S., C. FRONTALI, F. GRAZIOSI, and G. TOSCHI. 1962. Nuovo Cimento. *25:* Suppl. No. 1, 35–40.
14. CORDES, S., H. T. EPSTEIN, and J. MARMUR. 1961. Nature. *191:* 1097–1098.
15. SUEOKA, N., J. MARMUR, and P. DOTY. 1959. Nature. *183:* 1429.
16. DOTY, P., J. MARMUR, J. EIGNER, and C. SCHILDKRAUT. 1960. Proc. Nat. Acad. Sci. U.S. *46:* 461.
17. AURISICCHIO, S., E. DORE, C. FRONTALI, F. GAETA, and G. TOSCHI. 1964. Biochim. Biophys. Acta. *80:* 514–516.
18. MANDELL, J. D., and A. D. HERSHEY. 1960. Anal. Biochem. *1:* 66.
19. SUEOKA, N., and T. Y. CHENG. 1962. J. Mol. Biol. *4:* 161.
20. TOCCHINI-VALENTINI, G. P., M. STODOLSKY, A. AURISICCHIO, M. SARNAT, F. GRAZIOSI, S. B. WEISS, and E. P. GEIDUSCHEK. 1963. Proc. Nat. Acad. Sci. U.S. *50:* 935–942.

3. Single-Stranded DNA

φX174 DNA

ROBERT L. SINSHEIMER
DIVISION OF BIOLOGY
CALIFORNIA INSTITUTE OF TECHNOLOGY
PASADENA, CALIFORNIA

CULTURE AND PURIFICATION OF BACTERIOPHAGE φX174

φX174–wild type†

Inoculate two liters of TPG3A medium (in a 10-liter flask to contain foaming) with 100 ml of an *Escherichia coli* C406 culture grown from a slant to 4–5×10^8/ml (all cultures at 37 C, with vigorous aeration). When the cell concentration reaches 2–3×10^8/ml inoculate with wild-type φX (**6**) at a multiplicity of 3 phage/cell. Thirty minutes later, add 10 ml 0.1 M disodium versenate, adjusted to pH 7. Foaming will begin about 10 min later. Allow lysis to continue until the culture clears (5–7 hr). The lysate titer should be 4–12×10^{11}/ml.

TPG3A MEDIUM (2 LITERS)

Dissolve in 1000 ml of H_2O, 5.4 g of a mixture of the 20 natural l-amino acids (Nutritional Biochemical Corp.).

† All phage types and bacterial strains are available from the author.

569

Dissolve in 500 ml of H_2O: NaCl   1.0 g

                                         KCl   16.0 g

                                         NH_4Cl 2.2 g

                                         Tris   24.2 g

                                         KH_2PO_4 2.0 g

                                         Sodium pyruvate   1.6 g

Mix these solutions. Add: 2.0 ml of 20% (w/v) $MgCl_2 \cdot 6H_2O$

                                         0.2 ml of 1 M $CaCl_2 \cdot 2H_2O$

                                         100 ml of adenine (50 mg/100 ml)

                                         2.0 ml of 0.16 M Na_2SO_4

Adjust pH to 7.4 Make up to 2 liters. Autoclave.

After autoclaving, add: 2.0 ml of $FeCl_3 \cdot 6H_2O$ (1 mg/10 ml of sterile

                                     water)

                                     20.0 ml of 20% (w/v) sterile dextrose

Transfer the lysate to a separatory funnel and add 126 ml of 20% (w/w) sodium dextran sulfate 500 and 400 ml of 40% (w/w) polyethylene glycol (Carbowax 6000). Shake very well. Let stand 48 hr in cold room to allow the phases to separate. Separate the top phase, the interface (plus some unavoidable liquid), and the bottom phase. 90% of the lysate titer will be in the interface, 5% in the top phase, 1–2% in the bottom phase. Top and bottom phases are discarded.

The interface material is spun down (10–15 min at 10,000 × g) and the supernatant liquid is removed and discarded. The interface material is then resuspended in 10 ml 0.01 M Tris-acetate, pH 8.0, and sedimented again. The supernatant fluid, which will contain 1–2% of the lysate titer, is discarded.

The pellet is suspended in 15 ml of saturated (at 4 C) sodium borate and stirred overnight at 4 C. The suspension is sedimented as before. This borate supernatant liquid will contain 50–55% of the lysate titer.

The pellet is resuspended in 5-ml saturated borate, stirred well, and resedimented. The borate supernatant liquid will contain an additional 5–10% of the lysate titer. The two borate supernatant liquids are pooled.

To the pooled borate supernatant fluid is added 1/10 volume of 5X Tryptone (Tryptone, Difco, 5 g/100 ml). CsCl (Harshaw) is added (0.625 g of CsCl/g of solution) to raise the density to 1.41. The virus suspension is then centrifuged in the Spinco Model L centrifuge in the 40 rotor at 37,000 rev/min for 24 hr at 6 C. The visible virus band in each tube is removed by withdrawing liquid above the band with a Pasteur pipet and then similarly taking up the band. The recovery of virus titer in the band is usually 40–50% of the titer before addition of CsCl.

The ultraviolet-absorption spectrum and the plaque-forming titer of the virus preparation are obtained. The percentage of particles able to form a plaque is calculated as

$$\% \text{ viable particle} = \frac{\text{Titer/ml}}{A_{260} \times 1.3 \times 10^{13}} \times 100$$

Usually 50–60% of the particles are viable.

The over-all yield of this procedure is 5–10 mg of purified ϕX174 of 50–60% viability. The purified virus is usually dialyzed against sodium borate and stored in the borate solution.

ϕX174–ρ^- or am3 Mutants

The discovery of lysis-defective mutants of bacteriophage ϕX174 has considerably simplified the preparation of larger quantities of this virus. ϕX174ρ^- lyses poorly in concentrated cell cultures. It can be assayed on the usual host, *E. coli* C, but forms small, irregular plaques. ϕX174 am3 is an amber-type mutant. It will not lyse *E. coli* C in which it is "restricted." It may be assayed on the "permissive" strain CR34/C416 on which it forms normal plaques.

The same culture and purification procedures are used with either phage. If ϕX174 am3 is to be grown, it is important that the virus inoculum used to infect the bacterial culture contain less than 0.1% of revertants to wild-type virus (assayable on *E. coli* C).

Inoculate 2 liters of Fraser 3XD medium (in a 10-liter flask) (3) with 100 ml of an *E. coli* C culture grown from a slant to about 4–5×10^8/ml (all cultures at 37 C, with vigorous aeration). When the cell concentration reaches 2–3×10^9/ml inoculate with the ϕX mutant at a multiplicity of 3 phage/cell. Continue aeration for 3 hr.

FRASER 3XD MEDIUM (2 LITERS)

KH_2PO_4	9.0 g
NH_4Cl	6.0 g
$CaCl_2$ (1 M)	0.6 ml
Na_2HPO_4	21 g
$MgSO_4 \cdot 7H_2O$	0.6 g
Glycerin	48 ml
Casamino acids	30 g
Gelatin (1% solution)	6 ml
H_2O	To two liters

(Dissolve components in sequence. Autoclave.)

The infected *cells* are sedimented (14,000 × g for 25 min) and the supernatant liquid is discarded. The cells are then resuspended in 100 ml of 0.25 M Tris buffer, pH 8.1 (at room temperature). To lyse the cells, 4 ml of lysozyme (10 mg/ml in 0.25 M Tris buffer, pH 8.1) are added, followed by 20 ml of 8% disodium versenate. After thorough mixing, the suspension is set in an ice bath for 10–15 min. It is then placed overnight in a −20 C freezer. After thawing, refreezing, and thawing again, the phage will be released from the cells to provide a titer of 2–5 × 10^{13}/ml.

The phage suspension is now dialyzed against 2 liters of D medium.

D MEDIUM (2 LITERS)

NaCl	1 g
KCl	16 g
NH_4Cl	2.2 g
Tris	24.2 g
KH_2PO_4	2.0 g
$MgCl_2 \cdot 6H_2O$ (20% w/v)	2 ml
$Na_2SO_4 \cdot 10H_2O$ (0.16 M)	2 ml
Amino acid mixture	
(20 natural 1-amino acids,	
Nutritional Biochemical	
Corp.)	0.45 g

Dissolve. Adjust to pH 7.4. Make up to 2 liters. Autoclave. After autoclaving add 20 ml of sterile 20% (w/v) dextrose.

After dialysis the volume is measured (approximately 120 ml) and the suspension is transferred to a separatory funnel. Add, per 100 ml of phage suspension, 6.3 ml of 20% (w/w) sodium dextran sulfate 500 and 20 ml of 44% (w/w) polyethylene glycol (Carbowax 6000). Mix well and then allow to stand 48 hr in the cold room. Recover the interface fraction and continue purification as in the procedure for ϕX–wild type.

EXTRACTION OF ϕX174 DNA

Hot Phenol Extraction

Phenol (Mallinckrodt, Liquefied, Analytical Reagent, without preservative) is distilled and stored frozen. Shortly before use a sample is thawed and equilibrated, by shaking at room temperature, with a solution of saturated sodium borate.

For extraction of ϕX174 DNA, one volume of such phenol is brought to 70 C. An equal volume of virus (usually in saturated borate) is then brought to 70 C. The two volumes are immediately combined and alternately shaken and reheated in the 70 C bath for 3 min. The mixture is cooled to room temperature and centrifuged at 1000 × g for 5 min to separate the phases. Two additional phenol extractions, at room temperature, are performed on the aqueous layer and the three phenol layers are then serially extracted with one-half volume of saturated borate. The two aqueous layers are combined.

Phenol may be removed either by repeated (4–5X) extraction with ether (which can in turn be removed by bubbling N_2 through the solution) or by dialysis.

With virus suspensions containing 500 γ/ml or more of ϕX174, the recovery of DNA by this procedure is 70–90%. Such extractions can be successfully performed on solutions containing as little as 0.1 γ virus/ml (10^{10} particles) if 1 mg of bovine serum albumin per ml of virus is added before extraction.

The DNA content of the final preparation can be determined from the ultraviolet absorption. A solution for which A_{260} is 1.0 (at 25 C, in 0.2 M NaCl) contains 1.3×10^{13} molecules/ml or 36 μg/ml.

Cold Phenol Extraction

With certain temperature-sensitive mutants of ϕX174, hot phenol extraction has, for unknown reasons, been unsatisfactory, and it has been necessary to employ the same procedure at 4 C, with reduced recovery of DNA.

It is desirable to perform the purification of the ϕX virus and extraction of the DNA as rapidly as is feasible. DNA preparations made in this way have been found to consist of over 95% single-stranded rings (2). Such preparations may be stored at −20 C for many months without change in physical properties or biological activity.

PREPARATION OF ϕX174 REPLICATIVE FORM (RF) DNA

Inoculate 1 liter of CAS medium with *E. coli*, strain C (all cultures at 37 C, with vigorous aeration). When the cell concentration reaches 2–5 × 10^8/ml, add 20 mg of chloramphenicol (Parke-Davis & Co.) (dissolved in 10 ml of distilled water). Ten minutes later inoculate with wild-type ϕX at a multiplicity of 3 phage/cell. Continue aeration for 45 min and then harvest the cells, in the cold, by centrifugation.

CAS MEDIUM (2 LITERS)

KH_2PO_4	9.0 g
K_2HPO_4	23.2 g
Na_2HPO_4	2.0 g
NH_4Cl	6.0 g
$CaCl_2$ (1 M)	0.2 ml
$MgSO_4 \cdot 7H_2O$	0.6 g
Glycerol	48 ml
Casamino acids	30 g
Gelatin (1% solution)	6 ml

Make up to two liters. Autoclave.

The pellet of cells is resuspended in 25 ml of 1.5 M sucrose. To these are added 1.5 ml of BSA (Armour & Co., 30% sterile solution bovine serum albumin), 1.5 ml of lysozyme (2 mg/ml in distilled water, Worthington Biochemical Co., crystalline egg white lysozyme), and 3.0 ml of 4% disodium versenate. The suspension is incubated at room temperature for 20 min, during which time the cells are converted to protoplasts. To lyse the protoplasts, the suspension is alternately frozen and thawed four times. The viscous solution is deproteinized by addition of 10 ml of saturated sodium tetraborate and 30 ml of phenol, previously equilibrated against the borate solution, thorough mixing, and then incubation at 45 C, with occasional shaking, for 1 hr. After chilling, the layers are separated by centrifugation (the phenol layer is, in this instance, the upper layer). Phenol extraction of the aqueous layer is repeated. The two phenol layers are combined and extracted twice with 40-ml portions of the borate solution. The three aqueous extracts are then combined.

The nucleic acids are precipitated by addition of 0.1 volume of 3 M sodium acetate and 2 volumes of cold isopropanol. The mixture is allowed to stand in the cold overnight and then centrifuged. The precipitate is redissolved in 200 ml of 0.1 M NaCl after which the precipitation is repeated. The precipitate is redissolved in 150 ml of 0.1 M NaCl, the molarity of NaCl is adjusted to 1 M, and the solution is allowed to stand in the cold overnight. The ribosomal RNA that precipitates is centrifuged down in 30 min at 13,000 rev/min in the Servall SS-1 centrifuge.

To the supernatant liquid (150 ml), 2.5 g of cetyltrimethylammonium bromide is added and the mixture is warmed to room temperature. Upon slow addition, with stirring, of 110 ml of distilled water (dilution to 0.57 M NaCl), threads of DNA form, which are removed from solution on a glass stirring rod. The remaining solution is allowed to stand at room temperature for 4 hr. The flocculent precipitate that forms (and which contains most of the replicative form) is collected by centrifugation, and redissolved in 1 M NaCl (35 ml). Distilled water (27 ml) is again added slowly, with stirring; usually no additional threads form. After standing at room temperature for 4 hr, the flocculent precipitate that forms is collected by centrifugation, and again dissolved in 1 M NaCl.

The cetyltrimethylammonium bromide is then removed from this nucleic acid solution. Isopropanol (2 volumes) is added and, after standing 4 hr at room temperature, the DNA precipitate is collected by centrifugation and redissolved in 0.1 M NaCl (10 ml). Precipitation with isopropanol is repeated twice (all operations are now carried out at 4 C).

After the last precipitation, the DNA, which contains infectivity equivalent to about 4×10^{11} single-strand ϕX-DNA molecules, is dissolved in 0.1 M NaCl (10 ml), and then diluted to 100 ml with 0.4 M NaCl. This solution is applied to a methylated albumin column, prepared in the manner described by Mandell and Hershey (5). A flow rate of approximately 30 ml/hr is maintained during addition of the DNA to the column and its subsequent elution. After washing the column with 100 ml of 0.4 M NaCl, a linear salt gradient is applied from 0.6 to 0.8 M NaCl. (The replicative form is eluted between 0.65 and 0.7 M NaCl; single-stranded DNA is eluted at molarities greater than 0.85 M.) Fractions (7 ml) are collected, and assayed for biological activity (4); the ten fractions containing the highest biological activity are combined, diluted to 0.4 M NaCl, applied to a second column, and eluted in the manner described previously. The peak fractions are combined (150 ml), dialyzed against two changes 0.05 M sodium phosphate buffer, pH 6.7, and concentrated to 50 ml, using a rotary evaporator. This solution is exhaustively dialyzed against 0.005 M sodium phosphate buffer, and then concentrated to a volume of 5 ml.

A replicative form preparation made in this way contained infectivity equivalent to that of 6.8×10^{10} single-strand ϕX-DNA molecules/ml. The absorbance of the solution was 0.85 at 260 mμ. With the assumption that the specific infectivity of the ϕX-RF DNA is 1/20 that of single-strand ϕX-DNA (7), the solution contained 1.36×10^{12} infective replicative form molecules. By assuming that an absorbance of 0.85 is equivalent to 38 γ RF-DNA/ml or 7×10^{12} RF-DNA molecules, approximately 20% of the RF-DNA molecules were infective.

Control experiments, in which P^{32}-labeled *E. coli* DNA has been added to the RF-containing nucleic acid preparation before fractionation (1) indicate that such a replicative form preparation contains 0.5–1% of *E. coli* DNA.

REFERENCES

1. BURTON, A., and R. L. SINSHEIMER. 1965. J. Mol. Biol. *14*. In press.
2. FIERS, W., and R. L. SINSHEIMER. 1962. J. Mol. Biol. *5:* 424.
3. FRASER, D., and E. A. JERREL. 1953. J. Biol. Chem. *205:* 291.
4. GUTHRIE, G., and R. L. SINSHEIMER. 1963. Biochim. Biophys. Acta. *72:* 290.
5. MANDELL, J. D., and A. D. HERSHEY. 1960. Anal. Biochem. *1:* 66.
6. SINSHEIMER, R. L. 1959. J. Mol. Biol. *1:* 37.
7. SINSHEIMER, R. L., M. LAWRENCE, and C. NAGLER. 1965. J. Mol. Biol. *14*. In press.

4. Synthetic DNAs

Biosynthetic

Polydeoxynucleotides

F. J. BOLLUM
BIOLOGY DIVISION
OAK RIDGE NATIONAL LABORATORY
OAK RIDGE, TENNESSEE

SINGLE–CHAIN POLYDEOXYNUCLEOTIDES

Terminal deoxynucleotidyl transferase, isolated from calf thymus gland (1), may be used to prepare a series of single-chain polydeoxynucleotides according to the following reaction:

$$d(pX)_m + n \ dYTP \xrightarrow{\quad Mg^{2+} \quad} d(pX)_m(pY)_n + nPP_i ,$$

Initiator   Monomer   Polymer

where $m \geqq 3$ and $n \geqq 50$ and X and Y may be any nucleic acid base or certain derivatives thereof. The reaction requires an oligodeoxynucleotide initiator that has at least three phosphate groups and a free 3'-OH group. The monomer must be a deoxynucleoside triphosphate. The polydeoxynucleotides produced are graft polymers containing the initiator molecule at the 5'-phosphate terminus.

Research sponsored by the U.S. Atomic Energy Commission under contract with the Union Carbide Corporation.

Reagents

Terminal deoxynucleotidyl transferase, 20,000 units per ml (usually 1 mg/ml) in 0.05 M potassium cacodylate buffer, pH 6.8.

0.20 M Potassium cacodylate, pH 6.8

0.20 M MgCl$_2$

0.1 mM Oligodeoxynucleotide in H$_2$O

10 mM 2-mercaptoethanol

10 mM Deoxynucleoside triphosphate in H$_2$O

5 M NaCl

0.5 M NaCl, 20 mM in sodium acetate buffer, pH 4.5–4.7

10 μg/ml of yeast inorganic pyrophosphatase (having 400–800 units per mg, 1 unit = 1 μmole phosphate liberated per minute at 25 C)

Sephadex G-50 (coarse beads) in a 2.5- × 40-cm Pharmacia laboratory column equilibrated with 10 mM NaCl

Procedure

Reaction mixtures contain

40 mM Potassium cacodylate, pH 6.8

1 mM 2-mercaptoethanol

8 mM MgCl$_2$

10 μM Oligodeoxynucleotide initiator

1–3 mM Deoxynucleoside triphosphate

20–40 μg/ml of terminal deoxynucleotidyl transferase

0.1 μg/ml of yeast inorganic pyrophosphatase

The reaction is started by addition of terminal transferase to the polymerization mixture incubating at 35 C. A 50-μliter sample (zero time sample) is diluted into 3 ml of 0.5 M NaCl diluent (pH 4.7) and further samples are taken over the period required for polymerization. The absorbancy of diluted samples is measured at a wavelength chosen for the particular polymerization. The approximate hypochromicity expected for each polymer may be calculated from the polymer extinction coefficients in Table 1 and the published values for deoxynucleoside triphosphates (5). Precise values for absorbance changes are not presented here because of variations that may result from different salt concentration, pH, and the presence of divalent ions in the reaction mixture. The hypochromicity of poly dT is not large enough to be useful for analytical purposes.

When a suitable degree of polymerization has been achieved, the reaction is stopped by addition of 1 mole of Versene per mole of divalent metal. Reaction volumes up to 30 ml are then passed directly through 2.54- × 40-cm Pharmacia laboratory columns packed

TABLE 1. *Extinction Coefficients of Homopolymers[a]*

Description	A_{260}^{P} [b]	250/260	280/260
Polydeoxyadenylate	9.65	0.91	0.29
Polydeoxyinosinate	5.35	1.64	0.36
Polydeoxyguanylate	8.99	1.15	0.54
Polydeoxyxanthylate	6.99	1.08	0.61
Polydeoxycytidylate	5.30	0.77	1.27
Polydeoxythymidylate	8.14	0.67	0.62

[a] All extinction coefficients reported here should be considered tentative. The value for poly dA in Table 1 seems more reasonable than earlier values reported from this laboratory (3).

[b] 0.001 M Tris-Cl, pH 8.0. A_{260}^{P} is the absorbance of a solution milli-molar in phosphate.

with Sephadex G-50 coarse beads and equilibrated with 10 mM NaCl. The polymer formed is not retarded by G-50 and is completely separated from orthophosphate and unused monomer. The polydeoxynucleotide, still contaminated with enzyme protein, is precipitated by adding one-tenth volume of 5 M NaCl to the pooled polymer fractions and then 2 volumes of 95% ETOH. The precipitate is harvested and dissolved in 1 mM Tris-Cl, pH 8.0. Any turbidity resulting from denatured protein is removed by centrifugation. Larger reaction volumes may be precipitated directly with ETOH, as described, harvested, and dissolved in up to 30 ml before final gel filtration. Dialysis against 0.1 M NaCl may also be used to remove residual monomer, if desired.

Table 2 presents data on the rate of polymerization and the yields to be expected under the conditions described. The low yield of poly

TABLE 2. *Formation of Polydeoxynucleotides*

Monomer	Initial Concentration	Polymerization Rate[a]	% Yield[b]
dATP	3 mM	12.5	90
dITP	3 mM	26.2	96
dGTP	1 mM	1.85	30
dXTP	1 mM	3.90	52
dCTP	1 mM	3.60	51
dTTP	1 mM	2.57	51

[a] Rate measured by pyrophosphate liberation = μmoles of PP_i released/hr/mg protein.

[b] Yield of polymer after 24-hr incubation.

dG is probably due to aggregation and precipitation of polymer. Poly dC also aggregates at the pH used (cf. 2) and better yield (but lower polymerization rate) may be achieved at pH 7.5 in Tris-Cl buffer. Poly dI aggregates extensively in the presence of Mg^{2+}, but the yield does not seem to be affected. The total amount of poly dI and poly dA (and also the chain length of the product) can be increased by adding a second and third portion of substrate as it is used up in the polymerization (cf. 3).

DOUBLE–CHAIN POLYMERS

Replicative deoxynucleotidyl transferase (DNA polymerase), isolated from calf thymus gland (1), may be used to prepare a series of double-chain polydeoxynucleotides according to the following reaction:

$$d(pX)_n + n \text{ dYTP} \xrightarrow{\text{Mg}^{2+}} d(pX)_n : d(pY)_n + n\text{PP}_i,$$

$$\underset{\text{Template}}{} \quad \underset{\text{Monomer}}{} \qquad \qquad \underset{\substack{\text{Homopolymer} \\ \text{complex}}}{}$$

where n is generally greater than 100 and Y is a deoxyribonucleoside triphosphate complementary to the bases in the template molecule, X. The polydeoxynucleotides produced are homopolymer complexes containing equivalent amounts of the two complementary bases. The initial rate of synthesis of the complementary chain is enhanced by the presence of a complementary initiator oligodeoxynucleotide [for example, $d(pT_6)$ for the synthesis of dA : dT on a polydeoxyadenylate template]. This type of polymer synthesis is said to be initiated synthesis on a template. Polymers are also produced in uninitiated synthesis, presumably by a slow reaction involving terminal addition of the complementary monomer to the polydeoxynucleotide template, followed by the rapid phase of synthesis when a complementary chain long enough to initiate synthesis on a template has been formed. In the initiated case, strand-separable polymers are produced. In the uninitiated case, polymers incapable of strand separation are the product (4).

Reagents

DNA polymerase
0.40 M Potassium phosphate, pH 7.0
10 mM 2-mercaptoethanol
0.20 M $MgCl_2$
10 mM Deoxynucleoside triphosphate in H_2O

5 mM Solution of polydeoxynucleotide template

5 M NaCl

0.50 M NaCl, 20 mM in sodium acetate buffer, pH 4.5–4.7

Procedure

Reaction mixtures contain

40 mM Potassium phosphate, pH 7.0
1 mM 2-mercaptoethanol
8 mM MgCl$_2$
1 mM Template polydeoxynucleotide
1–1.5 mM Deoxynucleoside triphosphate
50–100 μg/ml of DNA polymerase

The reaction is started by addition of the DNA polymerase to the polymerization mixture incubating at 35 C. A 50-μliter zero time sample is diluted into 3 ml of 0.5 M NaCl diluent (pH 4.7) and further samples are taken over the period required for polymerization to occur. The absorbancy of the diluted samples is measured at a suitable wavelength for the particular polymerization. The hypochromicity expected for each homopolymer complex may be calculated from the homopolymer complex extinction coefficients in Table 3, the published values for deoxynucleoside triphosphates (5), and the single-chain polydeoxynucleotide extinction coefficients listed in Table 1.

When the polymerization is complete, the reaction is stopped by the addition of 1 mole of Versene per mole of divalent metal present in the reaction mix and the reaction is applied directly to the Pharmacia laboratory column. The homopolymer complex is not retarded and is completely separated from nonpolymeric constituents of the

TABLE 3. *Properties of Homopolymer Complexes*[a]

Description	Polymer Composition[b]	A_{260}^{P} [c]	250/260	280/260	Melting Temperature[d] SSC	SSC/10
dA:dT	50:50	6.97	0.83	0.58	69.5	51
dI:dC	50:50	6.34	1.20	0.62	47.5	33
dG:dC	50:50	7.95	0.99	0.58		78[e]

[a] All extinction coefficients reported here should be considered tentative.

[b] By formic acid hydrolysis and chromatography of bases.

[c] 0.001 M Tris-Cl, pH 8.0. A_{260}^{P} defined as in Table 1.

[d] SSC is 0.15 M NaCl containing 15 mM Na$_3$ citrate. SSC/10 is the above diluted tenfold.

[e] 0.01 M potassium phosphate, pH 7.5.

reaction mixture. The homopolymer complex may be concentrated by precipitation with alcohol as described for the single-chain polymers or may be used directly as desired.

It is apparent that homopolymer complexes are also available by simple mixing of the complementary polydeoxynucleotides synthesized separately by the terminal deoxynucleotidyl transferase. The DNA polymerase step may be superfluous in many instances. It should be emphasized, however, that the structural detail of the polymers formed by physical mixing and those formed by DNA polymerase are not necessarily the same. In any event, the combination of enzymes provides a versatile procedure for making a variety of polymers by independent methods.

Specific Examples

PREPARATION OF HOMOPOLY dA:dT. A 200-ml reaction mixture containing 124 μmoles of homopoly dA, 155 μmoles of dTTP, 15 mg of calf thymus DNA polymerase, 8 mM MgCl$_2$, 40 mM potassium phosphate, pH 7.0, and 1 mM 2-mercaptoethanol was incubated and the optical density at 260 mμ was followed. After 10 hr of incubation the optical density of the mixture was 74% of the starting value, and further incubation for 12 hr resulted in no further decrease. At this time the solution was turbid due to precipitation of magnesium pyrophosphate, and this crystalline precipitate was removed by filtration through a Millipore filter (Type HA, 0.45 μ). One-tenth volume of 5 M NaCl and 500 ml of 95% ETOH was added. The copious precipitate that formed was allowed to settle out and was then harvested by centrifugation. The translucent precipitate was dissolved in 30 ml of 20 mM Tris-Cl, pH 8.1, and reprecipitated with ethanol as described above. The second precipitate was dissolved in 40 ml of 20 mM Tris-Cl, pH 8.1, and dialyzed against three 1-liter changes of 0.2 M NaCl. The dialyzed preparation was precipitated directly with 2 volumes of 95% alcohol and the final yield of product was about 1000 A_{260} units, equivalent to about 146 μmoles of polymer phosphate. In this preparation the yield is about 60% of the theoretical yield and is low because some A_{260} was lost on the Millipore filter during removal of magnesium pyrophosphate. It would be preferable to solubilize the magnesium pyrophosphate by degradation to orthophosphate with yeast inorganic pyrophosphatase. Base analysis by hydrolysis in 98% formic acid and chromatography in isopropanol : HCl demonstrates that the poly dA : dT contains equal amounts of adenine and thymine.

PREPARATION OF dG:dC. A 20-ml reaction mixture containing 25 μmoles of poly dC, 50 μmoles of dGTP, 3 mg of DNA polymerase, 40 mM potassium phosphate, pH 7.5, 1 mM 2-mercaptoethanol, and 8 mM $MgCl_2$ was incubated for 90 hr at 35 C. The reaction mixture was passed directly through the Sephadex G-50 column and produced a breakthrough peak having 262 optical density units. The final product was concentrated by evaporation and precipitated with alcohol. The final product, 262 optical density units, contained equal parts of guanine and cytosine by hydrolysis and chromatography in isopropanol : HCl. The final yield in this synthesis was again about 60%. This polymer aggregates and losses are incurred at any filtration or centrifugation step. Correction of these losses will depend on finding an adequate solvent for the polymer.

PREPARATION OF POLY dI:dC. A 10-ml reaction mixture contained 10 μmoles of polydeoxyinosinate, 18 μmoles of deoxy CTP, 40 mM potassium phosphate, 1mM 2-mercaptoethanol, 2mM $MgCl_2$, and 0.75 mg of DNA polymerase. The reaction mixture was incubated for 48 hr at 35 C and was then passed directly through the Sephadex G-50 column. The polymer product contained 112 A_{250} units and a residual of 62 optical density units of monomer remained. This polymer was precipitated directly with 0.1 volume of 5 M NaCl and 2 volumes of ethanol to produce a final yield of 112 A_{250} units. The yield in this synthesis was approximately 95%. Base analysis indicated that the polymer contained equal parts of hypoxanthine and cytosine.

Properties of the Homopolymer Complexes

Spectral properties of the homopolymer complexes, synthesized as described above, are shown in Table 3. It may be seen that these polymers have a high degree of hypochromicity and that their absorbancy ratios indicate the presence of the constituent bases. Melting temperatures are listed for SSC and SSC/10. Each of the polymers melts with a single, sharp transition. The molecular weights of these polymers range from 100,000 to 300,000.

REFERENCES

1. BOLLUM, F. J. This volume, p. 284.
2. INMAN, R. B. 1964. J. Mol. Biol. 9: 624.
3. BOLLUM, F. J., E. GROENIGER, and M. YONEDA. 1964. Proc. Natl. Acad. Sci. U.S. 51: 853.
4. BOLLUM, F. J. 1964. Science. 144: 560.
5. Specifications and criteria for biochemical compounds, NAS-NRC Publication 719, 1960.

Synthesis of dA:dT

SYLVIA LEE-HUANG AND LIEBE F. CAVALIERI
DIVISION OF BIOLOGICAL CHEMISTRY
SLOAN-KETTERING INSTITUTE
NEW YORK, NEW YORK

THE REACTION

dA:dT is a high molecular weight polymer composed of polydeoxy-adenylate and polythymidylate chains. It is synthesized *in vitro* by *Escherichia coli* DNA polymerase, using poly (A + U) as a template and dATP and dTTP as substrates (1). The synthetic reaction may be represented by the following equation:

$$n \ (dATP + dTTP) \ \underset{\xleftarrow{\hspace{3cm}}}{\overset{\text{Poly (A + U)} \atop \text{DNA Polymerase} \atop \xrightarrow{\hspace{3cm}}}{}} \ (dA:dT)n + nPPI$$

In an analogous manner, the polyribonucleotide poly (C + I) may also serve as a template in this system to yield poly dG:dC.

The enzyme assay is described in "Synthesis of dA:dT" (page 588). A unit of enzyme activity is defined as that amount of enzyme which catalyzes the incorporation of 1 mμmole of substrates into an acid-insoluble product in 20 min at 37 C.

PREPARATION OF ENZYME (11)

Crude Extract

DNA polymerase is isolated from *E. coli* B extracts made from late log phase bacteria purchased from the Grain Processing Corporation,

The authors are also affiliated with the Sloan-Kettering Division, Graduate School of Medical Sciences, Cornell University, New York, New York.

Muscatine, Iowa. Bacteria stored at -20 C for as long as a year produced active polymerase, though no systematic study of the quality or yield of the enzyme has been made.

All operations are carried out at 4 C unless otherwise stated. Five hundred grams of frozen cells are divided into five equal portions. To each portion is added 100 ml of extracting buffer (0.01 M Tris buffer, pH 7.5, containing 0.01 M $MgCl_2$, 0.005 M CH_3CH_2SH, 0.001 M EDTA). One hundred grams of cold Alcoa Alumina powder (A 305, special bacterial grade) are also added to each portion. The mixture is then homogenized by hand for 15 min with a mortar and pestle. The resulting thick slurry is centrifuged at $7000 \times g$ for 10 min to remove the alumina and debris. The pellets are combined and rehomogenized twice with the mortar and pestle, each time with 100 ml of extracting buffer. The turbid supernatant liquid from each tube is decanted, combined (a total of 700 ml) and centrifuged for 3 hr at $78,000 \times g$ (rotor 30) in a Spinco Model L Ultracentrifuge. The hard pellet primarily contains ribosomes. The lower part of the supernatant liquid is usually turbid and the upper clear. (The proportions of turbid to clear in the supernatant fluid depends on the protein concentration; the higher the concentration the greater the turbid fraction.) The entire supernatant liquid is decanted from each tube, collected, and transferred into clean centrifuge tubes. The centrifugation is repeated for an additional 4–6 hr to form a "soft" pellet, which contains a large proportion of RNA polymerase. The clear supernatant liquid that contains the DNA polymerase is withdrawn with the aid of a pipette. This is the crude extract.

Protamine Sulfate Precipitation

The crude extract, 500 ml, is diluted with extracting buffer to 750 ml and 250 ml of a 0.5% solution (pH 5) of protamine sulfate (Gallard-Schlesinger) added. After 10 min, the stringy precipitate is collected by centrifugation at $7000 \times g$ for 10 min. The liquid is decanted and the protamine sulfate precipitate is washed twice by suspending it in 100 ml of extracting buffer. The washings contain negligible amounts of enzyme activity and are discarded.

$\beta\beta'$-Dimethylglutarate Elution

DNA polymerase is eluted from the washed protamine sulfate precipitate by suspending it in 200 ml of a solution of 0.1 M $\beta\beta'$-dimethylglutarate (grade C, Calbiochem.), pH 6.4, containing 0.01 M $MgCl_2$, 0.01 M CH_3CH_2SH, and 0.005 M EDTA and homogenizing it by hand with a mortar and pestle for 10 min. After waiting for an additional 15 min, the $\beta\beta'$-dimethylglutarate eluate is collected by centrifugation at $7000 \times g$ for 10 min.

Ammonium Sulfate Fractionation

To 200 ml of the $\beta\beta'$-dimethylglutarate are added 56.5 g of solid ammonium sulfate (Mann, special enzyme grade) over a period of 45 min. After an additional 30 min the precipitate is removed by centrifugation at 78,000 $\times$ g for 1½ hr. The pellet contains hybrid polymerase (2), whereas DNA polymerase remains in the supernatant solution. DNA polymerase is then precipitated by the slow addition (ca. ¾ of an hour) of 28.2 g of solid ammonium sulfate. After an additional 30 min, the precipitate is collected by centrifugation at 78,000 $\times$ g for 1½ hr. This precipitate, containing most of the DNA polymerase activity, is dissolved in 25 ml of 0.05 M Tris buffer, pH 7.7, containing 0.01 M MgCl$_2$, 0.01 M CH$_3$CH$_2$SH, and 0.001 M EDTA and dialyzed against 2 liters of buffer for 45 min; the dialysis is repeated twice, each time with fresh buffer. The ratio, 280/260 mμ, of this dialyzed enzyme solution is usually 1.5 or greater. Lower ratios indicate improper fractionation or unsuccessful extraction or both. The protein concentration in the final solution is usually 4 to 5 mg/ml.

DEAE-Cellulose Column Fractionation

A column of DEAE-cellulose (20 cm $\times$ 3 cm) is prepared and washed with two liters of a solution containing 0.05 M Tris buffer, pH 7.7, 0.01 M MgCl$_2$, 0.01 M CH$_3$CH$_2$SH, and 0.001 M EDTA. The dialyzed enzyme solution is diluted with this buffer solution to 40 ml and applied to the column at the flow rate of 0.5 ml/min. The absorbant is washed three times with 10 ml of buffer solution each time. The column is then washed with 80 ml of 0.1 M Tris buffer, pH 7.7, containing 0.1 M CH$_3$CH$_2$SH and 0.001 M EDTA. The enzyme is eluted with 0.5 M Tris, pH 7.5, 0.01 M MgCl$_2$, 0.01 M CH$_3$CH$_2$SH, and 0.001 M EDTA. The eluate is collected in 3-ml fractions, the protein being monitored and recorded continuously at 280 mμ. Of the protein applied to the column, up to 70% is eluted in a single, sharp peak between the 44th and 48th fractions. The specific activity of the polymerase is constant across the peak. The fractions of the entire peak, 15 ml, are pooled and precipitated with 6.3 g of solid ammonium sulfate. After 30 min, the precipitate is collected by centrifuging at 125,000 $\times$ g for 1 hr. This purified pellet is dissolved in 0.0025 M Tris, pH 7.7, and 0.001 M CH$_3$CH$_2$SH and dialyzed against the same buffer until free of (NH$_4$)$_2$-SO$_4$. The dialyzed enzyme solution is lypholized and stored at -20 C.

The amino acid composition of the purified DNA polymerase has been determined and is given in Table 1. These values are similar to those reported by Richardson, et al. (3), and to those of the total protein of E. coli reported by Sueoka (4). The DEAE-purified DNA poly-

TABLE 1. *Amino Acid Composition of DNA Polymerase and Total Protein of* E. coli B

Amino Acid	Mole % DNA Polymerase This Paper	Richardson et al. (3)	Total Protein Suekoa (4)
Aspartic acid	10.5	9.1	10.3
Threonine	5.7	5.2	5.5
Serine	4.8	3.9	4.6
Glutamic acid	12.2	13.5	11.2
Proline	4.3	6.0	4.2
Glycine	8.6	6.4	9.2
Alanine	10.2	10.8	10.4
Valine	6.4	6.0	7.2
Methionine	2.8	2.7	2.9
Isoleucine	5.2	5.6	5.4
Leucine	9.2	11.6	8.7
Tyrosine	2.4	3.5	2.7
Phenylalanine	3.5	2.7	3.5
Lysine	5.7	6.1	6.4
Histidine	2.2	1.8	2.0
Arginine	6.1	5.0	5.3

merase was further examined for purity by electrophoresis in 5% acrylamide gel. The conditions were: 300 v, 2½ hr, 0.076 M Tris-citrate buffer, pH 8.8. One main band about 1 cm wide appeared at 6.5 in. from the origin. There were several faint bands flanking the main band. DNA polymerase activity was principally in the main band.

The DNA polymerase shows marked instability at stages prior to the DEAE column fractionation. Purified enzyme fractions, over a 7-month period, were found to be gradually converted to other polymerase activities with a concomitant decrease in DNA polymerase activity (5). Freezing and thawing, urea, glycial acetic acid, acridine orange, or simply KOH accelerates these interversions (6).

The yield and purification of the enzyme is shown in Table 2.

TABLE 2. *Purification of DNA Polymerase*

Fraction	Total Units	Protein (mg/ml)	Specific Activity
Crude extract	21,000	56.44	1.07
DEAE-cellulose fraction	5,000	0.205	2,500

SYNTHESIS OF dA:dT

Reagents

0.5 M Tris buffer, pH 7.7, measured at 25 C
0.05 M MgCl$_2$
0.05 M CH$_3$CH$_2$SH
5×10^{-4} M C^{14}-8-dATP (1×10^5 cpm)
5×10^{-4} M dTTP
2×10^{-4} M poly (A + U)
Enzyme

Poly A and poly U were purchased from Miles Laboratories, New Jersey. Poly (A + U) primer is prepared by mixing equimolar amounts of poly A and poly U in the presence of 5×10^{-4} M Mg^{2+} (7). The sedimentation constants of poly A, poly U, and poly (A + U) in 0.2 M NaCl are 11.3, 8.4, and 31, respectively. C^{14}-labeled deoxynucleoside-5'-triphosphate were obtained from Schwarz BioResearch, Inc., Orangeburg, New York. Unlabeled substrates were purchased from P-L Biochemicals, Inc., Milwaukee, Wisconsin.

The course of dA:dT synthesis may be followed by either of two methods:

a. Incorporation of C^{14} or α-P^{32}-labeled deoxynucleoside-5'-triphosphates into an acid-insoluble product. The reaction mixture, 0.5 ml, contains 0.05 ml of 0.5 M Tris, pH 7.7, 0.05 ml of 0.05 M MgCl$_2$; 0.05 ml of 0.05 M CH$_3$CH$_2$SH; 0.05 ml of 5×10^{-4} M dATP-8-C^{14} (1×10^5 cpm); 0.05 ml of 5×10^{-4} M dTTP; 0.1 ml of poly (A + U) OD$_{260}$ = 1.49 (1.49 is equivalent to 2×10^{-4} M based on phosphate), 0.1 ml (ca. 12 μg) of purified DNA polymerase and 0.05 ml of water. The incubation period is 20 min at 37 C after which the assay tube is placed in an ice bath and 0.1 ml of a cold solution of 5% bovine albumin is added as carrier. The product is precipitated by the immediate addition of 1 ml of 1 N HClO$_4$. After 10 min at 0 C the precipitate is dispersed by the addition of 3.0 ml of ice-cold distilled water and 15 min later the mixture is centrifuged at 10,000 $\times$ g for 20 min. The supernatant solution is discarded and the precipitate is dissolved in 0.5 ml of 0.2 N NaOH. dA:dT is reprecipitated by the addition of 1.0 ml of ice-cold 1 N HClO$_4$, the precipitate is again thoroughly dispersed by ice-cold distilled water. After centrifugation this precipitate is again dissolved, reprecipitated and recentrifuged. Finally, the precipitate of dA:dT is dissolved in 2.0 ml of 0.1 N NH$_4$OH and incubated at 37 C until it is completely dissolved. The solution is pipetted into a metal planchet and the assay tube washed twice with 2 ml of 0.1 N NH$_4$OH each time.

b. The hypochromism that accompanies the conversion of substrates into an ordered polymer. This procedure is used for large scale synthesis and isolation of the product. The assay reaction mixture is scaled up about 500-fold by increasing the concentrations of substrates 50-fold and increasing the volume of the reaction mixture 10-fold. Greater increases in concentration result in a much lower yield of high molecular weight product. Optical density readings are taken at 2-min intervals, after dilution of the reaction mixture with ice-cold 0.2 M NaCl. To remove unused substrate and low molecular weight polymers the reaction mixture is dialyzed successively against: 0.2 M NaCl; 0.01 M EDTA, pH 7.5; distilled water and finally 0.02 M NaCl. The optical density of this solution is about 15. A dry powder convenient for storage may be obtained by lyophylization.

Under the experimental condition described here, the absorbancy drops 30% in 15 min, which corresponds to about 70% utilization of equimolar quantities of dATP and dTTP. Usually there is a 10–15 fold net synthesis over the template used. The time required for the maximum decrease in absorbancy varies and must be determined for each polymerase preparation. The yield of product decreases if a longer period of time elapses. The product may be concentrated with Sephadex G-25 or Bio-gel P-10 and then lyophylized.

PROPERTIES OF dA:dT

Light Scattering

Turbidity measurements were made with a Brice-Phoenix light-scattering photometer, according to the procedure described elsewhere (8). A typical average molecular weight was ca. 2×10^6 with a radius of gyration of 2000 A. The observed sedimentation constant of such material was about 21.

Sedimentation

Although the sedimenting boundary is quite sharp, indicating a narrow distribution of sedimenting species, the sedimentation constants nevertheless vary from one preparation to another. The values are a function of the purity of the DNA polymerase, the level of enzyme and substrate concentrations and the isolation procedure of the product. High enzyme and substrates concentrations tend to give smaller polymers. A number of attempts at concentrating solutions of dA:dT with Sephadex G-25 resulted in an apparent decrease in molecular weight, presumably because of preferential absorption of the high molecular weight polymer.

Helix-Coil Transitions

dA:dT melts sharply at 41.2 C in 0.01 M NaCl, 58 C in 0.1 M NaCl and 60 C in 0.2 M NaCl with an increase of 35–40% in absorbancy at 260 mμ. On fast cooling, the optical density returns to its original value, indicating a reversible helix-coil transition.

Nearest-Neighbor Analysis

The enzymatic hydrolysis of the product to 3′-deoxyribonucleotides by micrococcal deoxyribonuclease and spleen phosphodiesterase was carried out according to the method of Josse, Kaiser, and Kornberg (9). The nucleotide analyses were carried out on Dowex-1 formate columns (10). The results are given in Table 3. Two reaction mixtures were

TABLE 3. *Determination of Nucleotide Sequence in Poly dA:dT*

Experiment	Substrates for Synthesis	3′-deoxyadenylate		3′-thymidylate	
		(cpm)	% P^{32} Recovery	(cpm)	% P^{32} Recovery
1	dAPPP + TP^{32}PP	—	—	20,000	100
2	dAP^{32}PP + TPPP	19,500	100	—	—

analyzed, one contained dATP and dTP^{32}PP and the other dAP^{32}PP and dTTP. The results show that each deoxyadenylate is followed by a deoxyadenylate in one chain of the dA:dT and each thymidylate by a thymidylate in the second chain.

Priming Activity

dA:dT homopolymer, prepared as described above, served as a primer for dA:dT synthesis by DNA polymerase.

REFERENCES

1. LEE-HUANG, S., and L. F. CAVALIERI. 1963. Proc. Natl. Acad. Sci., U.S. *50:* 1116.
2. LEE-HUANG, S., and L. F. CAVALIERI. 1964. Proc. Natl. Acad. Sci., U.S. *51:* 1022.
3. RICHARDSON, C. C., C. L. SCHILDKRANT, H. W. APOSHIAN, and A. KORNBERG. 1964. J. Biol. Chem. *239:* 222.
4. SUEOKA, N. 1961. Proc. Natl. Acad. Sci., U.S. *47:* 1141.

5. LEE-HUANG, S., and L. F. CAVALIERI. 1965. Science. *148:* 1474.

6. CAVALIERI, L. F., and S. LEE-HUANG. Unpublished Data.

7. FELSENFELD, G., and S. LEE-HUANG. 1959. Biochim. Biophys. Acta. *34:* 242.

8. CAVALIERI, L. F., B. H. ROSENBERG, and J. DEUTSCH. 1961. Biophys, J. *1:* 301.

9. JOSSE, J., D. KAISER, and A. KORNBERG. 1961. J. Biol. Chem. *236:* 864.

10. HURLBERT, R. B., H. SCHWITZ, A. F. BRUMM, and V. R. POTTER. 1954. J. Biol. Chem. *209:* 23.

11. Editor's note: An alternative method for the isolation of *E. coli* DNA polymerase is given in this volume, p. 263.

Preparation of
Oligodeoxynucleotides

F. J. BOLLUM

BIOLOGY DIVISION

OAK RIDGE NATIONAL LABORATORY

OAK RIDGE, TENNESSEE

The availability of procedures for the synthesis of single-chain poly-deoxynucleotides by terminal deoxynucleotidyl transferase and double-chain polymers by calf thymus DNA polymerase (1) or *Escherichia coli* DNA polymerase (cf. 2) provides material for the degradative synthesis of oligodeoxynucleotides. The structure of the oligodeoxynucleotide that may be prepared in this manner is a function of the mode of degradation used and several enzymes (3) are available for these purposes. The obvious method of procedure is to obtain the desired polydeoxynucleotide, obtain the endonuclease having the required specificity (3'- or 5'-phosphate former), degrade the polymer, and separate the oligodeoxynucleotide products by DEAE chromatography. Some difficulties may be encountered in each specific instance (4), however, and this chapter is intended to provide some guidance to the preparation of deoxyribonuclease I oligodeoxynucleotides, with the thought that the type of problems encountered while using this enzyme might occur in other endonuclease degradations (cf. 5).

Degradation of Single-Chain Polydeoxynucleotides

OLIGO dA. Oligodeoxyadenylates are prepared from polydeoxy-adenylate as follows: 1000 A_{260} units (about 103 μmoles) of polymer

Research sponsored by the U.S. Atomic Energy Commission under contract with the Union Carbide Corporation.

phosphate was digested for 16 hr with 5 mg of deoxyribonuclease I (Worthington Biochemical Corporation) in the presence of 10 mM $MgCl_2$. The reaction mixture, 10 ml, was buffered with 50 mM potassium phosphate buffer at pH 7.0. After incubation the reaction mixture was diluted to 50 ml with H_2O and loaded directly onto a 1- × 25-cm DEAE-Cl column. The column was washed with H_2O and then eluted with a linear gradient of 0.02 M sodium acetate, pH 4.8 (1 liter) to 0.4 M sodium chloride, 0.02 M sodium acetate, pH 4.8 (1 liter). The elution diagram is shown in Fig 1.

The chain length of the oligoadenylates formed in this digestion was assigned on the basis of ability to initiate terminal-addition polymerization (6). Peak one was inactive; peak two and all subsequent peaks were active. Therefore, peak one is a dinucleotide, peak two is tri-, three is tetra-, etc. The digest thus contains oligodeoxyadenylates ranging in chain length from 2 to 11. Peak one was recovered by acidification, adsorption to charcoal, and elution with ammoniacal ethanol. Each of the peaks, two through ten, was diluted threefold with water, adjusted to pH 8 at the pH meter, and reabsorbed onto a 1 × 4 DEAE column (7). The column was washed with 0.02 M NH_4HCO_3 until the effluent was negative for chloride and then the oligomer was eluted with 0.5 to 1.0 M NH_4HCO_3 (8). The oligomer fractions, now in completely volatile buffer, were recovered by evaporation. The total A_{260} recovered in peaks 1–10 was 1223 units. Peaks 1–10 contained, respectively, 13.5, 19.2, 16.9, 17.1, 16.1, 9.3, 4.0, 2.2, 0.7, and 0.6% of the A_{260} recovered. Each of the recovered peaks gave a single spot upon chromatography in 70% isopropanol (ammonia vapor phase) on Whatman No. 1 paper.

OLIGO dC AND OLIGO dI.   Polydeoxycytidylate and polydeoxyinosinate were not hydrolyzed by deoxyribonuclease I at pH 7.0 or pH 7.5 in the presence of 10 mM $MgCl_2$. Polydeoxyinosinate and polydeoxycytidylate (separate chains) are hydrolyzed at pH 7.5 in the presence of 8 mM $MgCl_2$ with 2 mM $CaCl_2$. In these degradations a relatively large amount of deoxyribonuclease I (1 mg for 5 mg of polymer) was used. After overnight digestion, the elution diagram showed largely mono-, di-, tri-, and only small amounts of tetra- and pentanucleotides. The conditions used here should probably be modified by reducing the proportion of deoxyribonuclease I if one desires a broader spectrum of oligodeoxynucleotides.

Degradation of Copolymers

As mentioned in the paragraph above, large amounts of deoxyribonuclease I used in the presence of Mg^{2+} and Ca^{2+} led to a rather low average molecular weight for the fragments produced. It is some-

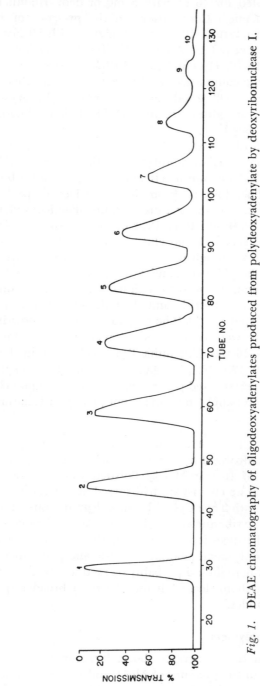

Fig. 1. DEAE chromatography of oligodeoxyadenylates produced from polydeoxyadenylate by deoxyribonuclease I. (See text for conditions.)

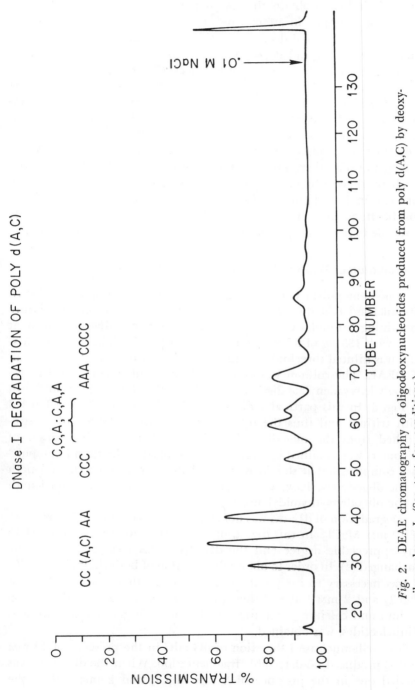

Fig. 2. DEAE chromatography of oligodeoxynucleotides produced from poly d(A,C) by deoxy-ribonuclease I. (See text for conditions.)

times desirable to obtain the lowest possible molecular weight fragment. For example, in attempting to decide whether copolymers produced by the terminal deoxynucleotidyl transferase were true random copolymers, we degraded poly d(A,C) with a large amount of deoxyribonuclease I in the presence of 8 mM $MgCl_2$ and 2 mM $CaCl_2$. The digest produced, shown in Fig. 2, was largely dinucleotides. The first was identified as dideoxycytidylate, mixed deoxyadenylate–deoxycytidylate dinucleotides are in peak two, and peak three is dideoxyadenylate. Thus, the copolymer structure does not contain (on the average) long runs of A and C, but instead contains a fair proportion of A and C next to each other. The conditions for degrading a polymer should be changed according to the nature of the experiment at hand. Thus, for some analytical purposes it is often necessary to produce the smallest possible fragment; whereas for general preparative purposes it is usually desirable to have a larger spread of separable oligodeoxynucleotides.

Degradation of Double-Chain Polydeoxynucleotides

The homopolymer complex dA : dT was readily attacked by deoxyribonuclease I in the presence of 10 mM $MgCl_2$. A reaction mixture containing 5 μmoles of nucleotide phosphorus was digested 16 hr at 35 C with 139 μg of deoxyribonuclease I at pH 7.0. The reaction mixture was diluted threefold and adsorbed directly onto a 1×20 column of DEAE. The column was eluted with the gradient described above for polydeoxyadenylate digest and produced the elution diagram shown in Fig. 3. In this particular digest the thymidylate chain was labeled with tritium and thus the oligodeoxyadenylates were readily distinguished from the oligodeoxythymidylates. A useful distribution of oligomers was obtained by degradation of this double-chain homopolymer complex, but it should be noticed that the average chain length of the oligodeoxyadenylates was greater than the average chain length of the oligodeoxythymidylates.

Degradation of dI : dC was not completely successful in the presence of 10 mM $MgCl_2$. In this digest, only the dI chain was hydrolyzed to any appreciable degree and the dC chain was recovered practically unchanged (4). In order to obtain degradation of both chains of dI : dC, it was necessary to carry out the digestion in the presence of 8 mM $MgCl_2$ and 2 mM $CaCl_2$. When the digestion was activated by magnesium and calcium, a mixture of oligomers, largely mono-, di-, and trinucleotides, was obtained.

Deoxyribonuclease I digestion of dG : dC in the presence of 10 mM $MgCl_2$ produced no detectable fragmentation. When the digestion was carried out in the presence of 8 mM $MgCl_2$ and 2 mM $CaCl_2$, the homopolymer complex was completely degraded to a mixture of mono-,

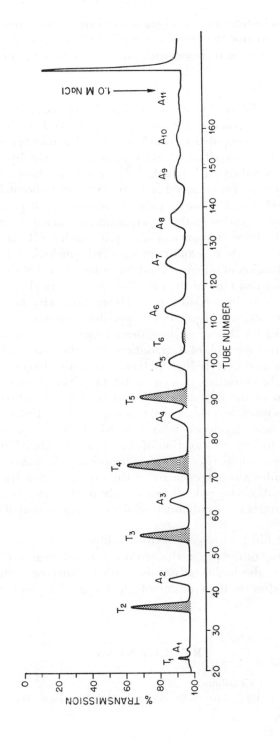

Fig. 3. DEAE chromatography of oligodeoxynucleotides produced from dA:dT(^{3}H) by deoxyribonuclease I. (See text for details.) Shaded areas denote radioactivity.

di-, and trinucleotides (4). In digests containing oligodeoxyguanylates it is desirable to run the chromatography in 7 M urea (7) at 51 C to avoid the aggregation common with guanine-containing fragments.

General Comments

As indicated in the introduction, this chapter is intended only to present some experience as a form of guidance. We have been able to split all of the homopolydeoxynucleotides and a number of random copolymers with deoxyribonuclease I, even though the hydrolysis did not always proceed as anticipated. It is clear from these experiments that Wiberg's study (9) on metal activation of deoxyribonuclease I can be put to good practical use in polydeoxynucleotide degradations. In order to obtain digestion in the experiments conducted so far, we have used relatively large amounts of deoxyribonuclease I. It would be preferable to use lower amounts of deoxyribonuclease I to obtain a broader distribution of oligomers and for easier control of the digestion. In carrying out this kind of degradation, the analytical monitoring of the digestion is an important aspect. Hyperchromicity measurements, automatic titration, or phosphatase-suspectible phosphate are analytical methods useful for following these degradations. For a qualitative or semiquantitative measure of degradation, it is often convenient to run the digestions at relatively high polymer concentrations so that small portions may be chromatographed on DEAE paper (6) to see the average migration of the degradation products. Thus, 50-μliter fractions (containing as much as 5 A_{260} units) of a digest are applied to Whatman DEAE paper and developed with 1 M NH_4HCO_3 containing 1 mM Versene for 2 to 4 hr. Observation of the ultraviolet-absorbing areas on the paper and comparison with appropriate oligodeoxynucleotide markers provides a rough estimate of the average chain length of the products. If radioactive polynucleotides are used, a quantitative distribution of products can be obtained with an actigraph scan of the DEAE strip.

The availability of oligodeoxynucleotides permits further analysis and cataloguing of the properties of these rare substances. Oligodeoxynucleotides are also useful for certain synthetic purposes (10) and for a variety of studies on their immunological and other biological properties.

REFERENCES

1. BOLLUM, F. J. This volume, p. 284.
2. KORNBERG, A. 1962. Enzymatic synthesis of DNA. John Wiley and Sons, New York.

3. See DE WAARD, A., and I. R. LEHMAN, p. 122; HEINS, J. N., H. TANIUCHI and C. B. ANFINSEN, p. 79; and LASKOWSKI, M., SR., p. 85, this volume.

4. BOLLUM, F. J. 1965. J. Biol. Chem. *240:* 2599.

5. LINN, S., and I. R. LEHMAN. 1965. J. Biol. Chem. *240:* 1294.

6. BOLLUM, F. J. 1962. J. Biol. Chem. *237:* 1945.

7. RUSHIZKY, G. W., and H. A. SOBER. 1962. Biochim. Biophys. Acta. *55:* 217.

8. TOMLINSON, R. V., and G. M. TENER. 1963. Biochemistry. *2:* 697.

9. WIBERG, J. S. 1958. Arch. Biochem. Biophys. *73:* 337.

10. BOLLUM, F. J., E. GROENIGER, and M. YONEDA. 1964. Proc. Natl. Acad. Sci. U.S. *51:* 853.

5. Nucleohistone

Isolation of Nucleohistone

BETH P. SONNENBERG AND GEOFFREY ZUBAY
DEPARTMENT OF ZOOLOGY
COLUMBIA UNIVERSITY
NEW YORK, NEW YORK

INTRODUCTION

Nomenclature

We define histones as a complex mixture of basic proteins found in the nucleus in combination with DNA. The complex between DNA and histone is called nucleohistone or deoxyribonucleoprotein (DNP). Nucleohistone, containing about equal weights of DNA and histone, is a major component of the chromosomes in most cells of multicellular organisms. The over-all composition of histones shows considerable variation in different organisms, but total histone generally contains about 25% basic amino acid residues. Within a given cell type, such as the calf thymus lymphocyte, fractionation of the histones attests to the presence of a mixture of several proteins with widely differing properties. In some cells, such as the mature spermatozoa of certain fishes, histone is replaced by a much more basic, lower molecular weight group of proteins called protamines.

Scope

We deal exclusively with the isolation of nucleohistones and of nucleohistone-related complexes. It is our intention to provide a detailed description of the preparation of nucleohistone from calf thymus gland (1,2), which is the most convenient source known. Preparation of nucleohistone from other animal tissues will be discussed in less detail with the emphasis, wherever possible, on the rationale of the investigators in their choice of preparative technique for a particular starting material. Among plant tissues, techniques for extracting nucleohistone from wheat germ and from pea embryos have been studied extensively. *In situ* cytochemical localization of histone and DNA in the chromosomes (3) is strong evidence that the nucleohistone preparations from animal and plant tissues do have some valid relationship to the *in vivo* system. "DNP complexes" have also been isolated from bacterial systems, although the protein moieties do not appear closely related to the histone of higher organisms. Furthermore, there are serious doubts as to whether these complexes are present *in vivo* in bacteria.

The material presented here can be supplemented by reference to other recent review articles. Commerford, Hunter, and Oncley (4) provide a source up to 1963 of references to DNP preparations from calf thymus and liver and also compare some of the properties of several major preparations from these sources. A more recent review by K. Murray (5) deals with the basic proteins of the cell nucleus.

PREPARATION OF NUCLEOHISTONE

Generalities

There are some general considerations involved in preparing nucleohistone from any source. An obvious one is the condition of the starting material. With some organisms (such as laboratory animals, plants, and bacteria) fresh material is obtainable within minutes of starting the extraction procedure. Other tissues (such as calf thymus or liver) must be brought into the laboratory some time after the death of the animal. Materials such as calf tissues should therefore be quickly and efficiently frozen (for example, in Dry Ice or preferably in liquid nitrogen) within minutes of the death of the animal and stored at subzero temperatures (usually −70 C) until used. It is usually convenient to carry out most of the preparative operations in a cold room at 2–5 C.

Keeping the preparation cold and working rapidly (particularly in the initial operation) are simple procedures aimed at diminishing the action of degradative enzymes. It is therefore desirable, if possible, to choose the preparatory method that is fastest; however, some tissues pose special problems necessitating additional steps in order to eliminate gross contaminants from the nucleohistone preparation. For example, with most tissues it is advisable, and sometimes necessary, to isolate the nuclei as a preliminary step. The degree of difficulty involved in preparing a clean nuclear fraction is very dependent on the tissue used (6,7). Thus, the characteristics of the starting material frequently dictate that yields and speed be secondary considerations.

A very important factor is the selection of appropriate buffer solutions for the various preparative steps. Media used for nuclear isolation are generally considered good if they preserve the *in vivo* structure of the nuclei as observed with the microscope. In developing techniques for isolating nuclei, therefore, most investigators have used microscopic examination as a guide after each preparative step (8). Homogenizing, extracting, and washing media must have the ionic strength, composition, and pH controlled so that the nucleohistone is neither denatured nor dissociated into its histone and DNA components. In addition, the properties of these media should be adjusted to inactivate any enzymes that degrade DNA or histone; if this condition is not easily satisfied then the properties should be such as to avoid the range of optimal activity of these enzymes.

Calf Thymus Nucleohistone

Calf thymus nucleohistone is considered first, and at length, for several reasons. Calf thymus glands are exceptionally good starting material for nucleohistone extraction. They contain a relatively low proportion of cytoplasm, making prior nuclear isolation unnecessary (6).

EARLY METHODS FOR EXTRACTING NUCLEOHISTONE FROM THYMUS. In general, the procedures for isolating DNP from mammalian cells depend on the fact that DNP is insoluble in dilute salt solutions, whereas ribonucleoproteins are soluble and can be removed by repeated washing of the DNP sediment (9). Some of the early methods involved extraction with 1.0 M NaCl, which yields a DNP preparation largely dissociated into DNA and histone (10). At the time of publication of the Zubay–Doty procedure (1,2), the most widely used method was that described by Chargaff (11,12) based on contributions made by several investigators (10,13–17).

In this preparation: (a) Chilled fresh calf thymus gland (50 g of tissue) is homogenized in a blender for 30 sec at high speed; the solvent used is 50 ml of an ice-cold mixture of aqueous 0.10 M NaCl and 0.05 M sodium citrate at pH 7. The homogenate is centrifuged at $2000 \times g$ for 30 min. (b) The sediment is suspended in 100 ml of the saline-citrate solvent and centrifuged again. (c) In order to remove electrolytes, the sediment is then washed three times by suspension in 50 ml of distilled water (which has been brought to pH 7 with about 0.4 mM $NaHCO_3$) followed by centrifugation. During the washing the sediment swells and becomes gelatinous. (d) This gelatinous sediment is blended and shaken with water to produce a very viscous solution containing 5–10 mg/ml of nucleophotein. (e) The nucleohistone is then usually precipitated with 0.15 M NaCl, washed with water and partially dried or lyophilized.

ZUBAY–DOTY PROCEDURE   [See Figure 1 (2).] Several refinements of the basic preparative procedure of Chargaff were introduced in this study, based on careful analyses of the effects of altering each step of the earlier procedures. Certain conditions were found to encourage either the partial separation of histone from the DNP complex or the interaction between histones leading to gelation. These conditions are (a) relatively high DNP concentrations (greater than about 0.8 g/dl), (b) salt precipitation and permitting salt-washed DNP to stand before homogenizing in water, (c) insufficient rapidity in carrying out the water homogenization, and (d) high ionic strength.

Two special precautions were introduced into the homogenization steps: (a) A powerstat (variable transformer) was used in series with the Waring Blendor for precise speed control. (b) Capryl alcohol was blended with the "saline-versene" standard solvent (which is 0.075 M NaCl and 0.024 M sodium ethylenediamine tetra-acetate, adjusted to pH 8 with NaOH) just before the tissue or the DNP-containing sediments were added. In the initial homogenization (Fig. 1) 1 ml of alcohol was used and subsequently 0.5 ml was added in each saline-versene homogenization. Dispersal of the alcohol greatly improves its suppression of surface denaturation. The saline-versene solvent minimizes enzyme action in two ways: (a) The EDTA inhibits deoxyribonuclease I by chelating divalent cations. (b) The pH of 8 suppresses the action of cathepsins on histones (18) and exceeds the pH at which deoxyribonuclease II is active.

The result of this study was the development of a method for isolating DNP in high yield, free of gel structure:

1. Calf thymus glands, obtained about 10 min after slaughter, are quickly frozen in liquid nitrogen; the frozen tissue is broken into small pieces and stored in plastic bags in dry ice until used. All operations are performed in a cold room (3–5 C).

2. About 20 g of frozen thymus glands are homogenized in a Waring Blendor with 200 ml of saline-versene for 1 min with the powerstat set at 80 v, followed by four minutes at 50 v.

3. For removal of connective tissue the homogenate is strained

20 G OF QUICKLY FROZEN CALF THYMUS
HOMOGENIZED IN 200 CC OF STANDARD SOLVENT
Standard solvent is 0.075 M NaCl plus
0.024 M sodium ethylenediamine tetraacetate
with pH adjusted to 8

↓

Centrifuged

↓

SEDIMENT

↓

Suspended in 200 cc of standard solvent
Carefully homogenized
Centrifuged
Cycle repeated six times

↓

SEDIMENT
(chromosomes)

↓

Homogenized with 1 liter of H₂O
Stirred rapidly

↓

VISCOUS SOLUTION

↓

Dialyzed against 0.7 mM phosphate buffer
Centrifuged 30 min at 29,000 rev/min

↓

SUPERNATANT
DNP SOLUTION
About 600 mg in 1 liter

Fig. 1. Outline of preparative procedure for deoxyribonucleoprotein particles.

through twelve thicknesses of cheesecloth (which has been prewashed in the saline-versene solvent) and the filtrate is centrifuged in the International Centrifuge at 2000 rev/min (about $400 \times g$) for 10 min.

4. The resulting sediment is homogenized in the same volume of saline-versene for 5 sec at 80 v and 30 sec at 45 v and the homogenate is centrifuged as before.

5. This same homogenization–centrifugation cycle is repeated six more times.

6a. This final salt-washed sediment consists mainly of DNP. It may be dispersed in water to produce a gel. This is accomplished by homogenizing the sediment in the Waring Blendor with 50 ml of water and adding water as the DNP expands to the final desired volume. At 5 C or below this gel should be stable for 2 weeks or more. The main problem is bacterial contamination. In case a true solution of DNP molecules is desired, step 6a should be skipped.

6b. The final (eighth) sediment from step 5 is dispersed in water, which has been doubly distilled to ensure that there is no metal ion contamination. No capryl alcohol is added in this step. Dispersion is accomplished by rapid mixing (60 v) in the Blendor, starting with 50 ml of water and increasing this to 1000 ml in 5 sec. The mixture is then quickly transferred to a 2-liter beaker and stirred rapidly with a glass propeller-type stirrer for 1 hr; the optimum diameter of the stirrer blades is two-thirds the diameter of the beaker. The stirring speed should be as high as possible without foaming and must therefore be continually reduced because of the progressive decrease, during stirring, in the viscosity of the DNP solution. It is clear that the shearing forces resulting from the use of the Waring Blendor and subsequent stirring operations are capable of degrading the nucleohistone. These operations are used in spite of this because it is the most convenient and least destructive manner of producing solutions of reproducible character.

7. The DNP solution is then dialyzed against 0.7 m$\textsc{m}$ potassium phosphate buffer, pH 8; this solvent is generally employed in all physical measurements on DNP.

8. DNP solutions prepared in this way should contain no more than 15% of the DNP in the form of gel particles. These are removed by centrifuging for 30 min at $70,000 \times g$.

About 0.6 g of DNP are obtained from 20 g of wet tissue, or about two-thirds of the DNP originally present. A low yield usually results from insufficient homogenization in the initial step.

CHARACTERISTICS OF PROPERLY PREPARED THYMUS NUCLEOHISTONE. A properly prepared specimen of nucleohistone should make a solution of nucleohistone molecules that is stable for several days at 5 C. The extinction coefficient, $E^{1\%}_{259 m\mu}$, is 106 ± 5, the DNA content is $47 \pm 2\%$, and the nitrogen/phosphorus ratio is 3.7 ± 0.3. A summary of some physicochemical properties of DNP and DNA from calf thymus is presented in Table 1.

TABLE 1. *Some Physicochemical Properties of Calf Thymus DNP and DNA*

	Mol. Wt. (Light Scattering)	$[\eta]$, dl/g (Intrinsic Viscosity)	$s_{20, w}$ (Sedimentation Coefficient)
DNP			
Zubay and Doty (1,2)	19×10^6	35	50
Bayley, Preston, and Peacocke (19)	20.5×10^6	30	—
Lloyd and Peacocke (20)	—	—	—
			50 for 70% of the material
DNA			
Zubay and Doty (1,2)	8×10^6	70	22

Any degradation of the DNA component of DNP would have a marked effect on the rigidity of the molecule and would result in a substantial decrease in the intrinsic viscosity. On the other hand, DNP is very susceptible to aggregation, which would also cause a viscosity decrease. Aggregation is encouraged by salts in general and by small amounts of multivalent cations in particular, and the utmost care must be taken to prevent such contaminants when making physical measurements. DNA is less sensitive to aggregation, and the absence of degradation in the DNA component of DNP can alternately be tested for by making comparable measurements on DNA prepared from the DNP. The absence of DNA degradation is good evidence that the preparation is free of degrading enzymes. Tests for histone degradation, which are more difficult and less sensitive, need not be made if the DNA passes inspection.

Nucleohistone from Other Animal Tissues

Where the choice exists, direct extraction of nucleohistone is preferable to nuclear isolation followed by extraction. This is because of the greater speed and greater ease in handling large quantities of tissue with a direct extraction procedure. With many tissues amenable to direct DNP extraction but having proportionally more cytoplasm than calf thymus the DNP of the preparative sediments can be separated from the cell debris that forms the lower layer of the sediment (11). An important consideration is the extent to which the isolated nuclei, regardless of the extent of preservation of nuclear morphology, have lost intranuclear material to other cell fractions in the course of isolation and washing (6). Even freshly prepared nuclei contain an appreciable amount of low molecular weight DNA derivatives, indicating that there is probably considerable DNP degradation during nuclear isolation (21).

DIRECT TISSUE EXTRACTION. In a comparative study by Crampton et al. (22), DNP from calf liver and kidney and from guinea pig testis was prepared by a method similar to the one applied to calf thymus by Chargaff (11,12). Hnilica and Busch (23) have prepared "crude deoxyribonucleoprotein" from rat Walker 256 carcinosarcoma by direct extraction. The tumors were used after 6–7 days of growth. The tissue was placed in cold 0.9% sodium chloride solution; in the cold room, connective and necrotic tissue was dissected away and the remaining tissue was cut into small pieces and blended (with capryl alcohol) in 0.14 M NaCl and 0.01 M trisodium citrate solution. The homogenate was strained through cheesecloth and centrifuged, and the sediment was resuspended in saline-citrate; the homogenate was then made 0.1 mM for diisopropyl fluorophosphate, to prevent enzymatic hydrolysis of nuclear proteins, and centrifuged. After at least four washes the final sediment was collected.

METHODS USING PRIOR NUCLEAR ISOLATION. Rotherham et al. (21) have made an extensive study of the location and properties of rat liver deoxyribonuclease and have used their findings as a guide in the nuclear isolation step as well as in the DNP extraction. After perfusion in situ with 0.15 M NaCl followed by 0.25 M sucrose–1.8 M $CaCl_2$, the livers were homogenized and centrifugally fractionated in the sucrose–$CaCl_2$ medium. Cell fractions were assayed for deoxyribonuclease activity by measuring the amount of acid-soluble phosphorus released from highly polymerized DNA by each fraction. Deoxyribonuclease activity was concentrated in the mitochondrial fraction, perhaps within the lysosomes. Disruption of the particles in this fraction leads to the release of more deoxyribonuclease, and therefore to increased degradation.

Rat liver was found to have two deoxyribonucleases. The "acid" deoxyribonuclease (optimal pH of 5) is independent of the magnesium ion concentration, whereas in the optimal range for "neutral" deoxyribonuclease (pH 6.8–7.3) enzymatic activity is stimulated by 10^{-3} M Mg^{2+} and inhibited by chelating agents (such as EDTA or citrate). The acid deoxyribonuclease of rat liver is inactivated at low ionic strength, the extent of inactivation depending on the buffer solution used. The deoxyribonucleases of several other mammalian tissues, which of course differ to some extent from the rat liver enzymes, are also discussed briefly in this paper; this makes it an important reference for those attempting to prepare DNP from animal tissues, whether by direct extraction or by nuclear isolation.

Because most of the catheptic activity, as well as the deoxyribonuclease activity, is in the mitochondrial fraction, the most critical steps in the DNP preparation are those prior to separation of the nuclei from the cytoplasmic fractions. The homogenization must be carried out with minimal damage to nuclear and mitochondrial (and/ or lysosomal) membranes, and the nuclei must be washed several times to remove residual mitochondria. In addition, the pH, ionic strength, and other considerations are equally applicable to nuclear isolation methods as to direct extractions.

Commerford et al. (4) used the saline-versene solvent described for calf thymus for extracting DNP from calf liver nuclei. Large blood vessels were removed and the liver was minced by pressing it through a perforated steel disk (with the aid of a hydraulic press) and then through successively finer-meshed stainless steel screens. This mince was suspended in a phosphate buffer solution (8 mM K_2HPO_4, 2 mM KH_2PO_4, 0.12 M NaCl, 0.2 mM $CaCl_2$; pH 7.4) and allowed to stand for 30 min, during which time the coarse connective tissue fragments settled out. The supernatant fluid (nuclear fraction) was siphoned off and centrifuged (3000 × g). The nuclear pellet was resuspended in saline-versene buffer; the suspension was stirred for 30 min, centrifuged, resuspended, and centrifuged again. The washing operation was repeated twice with a bicarbonate buffer (0.05 M $NaHCO_3$, 0.10 M NaCl, pH 8.0) to facilitate some of the analyses performed on the DNP preparation. The final sediment was dispersed by blending with distilled water. One drawback to this preparation is the use of large volumes of solvent (10 liters of suspension per 500 g of wet liver throughout the washings), which necessitates lengthy continuous-flow centrifugations, during which extensive degradation may occur.

Rat thymus nuclei have been prepared in a sucrose medium (0.25 M sucrose and 3.3 mM $CaCl_2$ in 5.0 mM Tris-HCl buffer, pH 7.3) (24). Creasey and Stocken (25) have isolated nuclear fractions from rat liver, brain, spleen, lymph node, intestinal mucosa, thymus, pancreas, bone marrow, and kidney using sucrose and other media. Sporn *et al.* (7) found that rat brain nuclei prepared by simple differential centrifugation (including washing of the nuclear pellet) are very often contaminated with other cell components; one major source of contamination is the large amount of myelin in the brain, which makes it difficult to wash the nuclei free of other contaminating particles. In addition, brain nuclei are relatively easily ruptured and are very heterogeneous in size and density because they come from different types of neurons and glia. However, Sporn was able to obtain very small yields of highly pure nuclei by means of gentle homogenization and thorough washing by several cycles of differential centrifugation. Brains were rapidly removed from decapitated rats, cleaned of meninges and blotted with filter paper to remove blood. The tissue was minced with a scissors and homogenized briefly in a Dounce homogenizer with a loose pestle; the solvent was 0.32 M sucrose, 1.0 mM $MgCl_2$, 0.4 mM KH_2PO_4, 0.4 mM K_2HPO_4, pH 6.7–6.8. The homogenate was centrifuged for 10 min at $850 \times g$, the supernatant fluid aspirated off, and the nuclear sediment washed twice by resuspension in fresh homogenizing solution and centrifugation. There were three more washes in the sucrose medium, with centrifugation for 8 min at $600 \times g$. The crude nuclear sediment was resuspended in homogenizing solution and a hypertonic sucrose solution (2.39 M sucrose, 1.0 mM $MgCl_2$, 3.5 mM K_2HPO_4, 0.7 mM disodium salt of ATP to help preserve nuclear morphology, pH 6.7–6.8) was added to give a final sucrose concentration of 2.05–2.15 M. This was followed by vigorous mixing and by centrifugation for 2 hr at $50,000 \times g$. Contaminants float on the hypertonic sucrose and were thus easily discarded.

Among nonmammalian animal tissues, some noteworthy DNP preparations have been made from fish erythrocytes and spermatozoa (26), from various embryonic and adult chicken tissues (27,28), and from sea urchin sperm (27,29). These procedures will now be described.

In a comparative study of nucleohistones and nucleoprotamines in the nuclei of three species of fish (26), blood was collected in a bowl containing cold physiological saline solution with citrate and heparin (to prevent clotting); mature spermatozoa were obtained by gentle pressing of the abdomen. Erythrocytes were collected by centrifuging the blood and were resuspended in fresh medium. They were then hemolyzed with saponine. Hemoglobin passed into the solvent, leaving the nuclei surrounded by ghostlike membranes; these were centrifuged down and washed two or three times in physiological saline solution. The spermatozoa were suspended in distilled water and shaken with glass beads to remove tail and intermediate pieces. The DNP was extracted with 1.0 M NaCl only because no other method was applicable to the erythrocyte nuclei and to the sperm heads; the 1 M NaCl treatment results in the loss of a great deal of protein from the DNP.

Sporn and Dingman (27) isolated brain and liver nuclei from 1-yr-old chickens by essentially the same procedure used for rat brain nuclei (7). Chicken blood was collected in cold 0.1 mM KHCO$_3$, allowed to hemolyze, and centrifuged at 1000 × g for 10 min. Homogenization of erythrocytes was performed with a very tight pestle, in order to remove the stroma adherent to the nuclei, in the same sucrose medium used for the other tissues. The homogenate was processed in the same way as the brain and liver homogenates. In a later study (28) they extracted DNP from isolated nuclei of several embryonic and adult chicken tissues, adapting the solvents and techniques to the particular tissue being processed.

Sea urchin sperm heads are usually first treated with citrate or versene and the DNP particles are then dissolved in water (29).

Nucleohistone from Plant Tissues

Because plant cells are surrounded by cellulose cell walls, plant material does not lend itself to nuclear isolation by the methods that have been applied to animal tissues (30). Both plant preparations to be discussed utilize direct extraction of tissue homogenates.

WHEAT–GERM NUCLEOHISTONE. Stedman and Stedman (30) studied the composition of the nuclear material of wheat germ in order to demonstrate that basic proteins occur in association with the DNA of plant as well as animal nuclei. Wheat-germ nucleohistone was prepared as follows:

1. The wheat germ (600 g) was ground in a mortar and suspended in two liters of physiological saline.

2. The suspension was stirred for 15 min and then centrifuged for 20 min at 2000 rev/min.

3. The turbid supernatant fluid (containing some of the nonnuclear material) was discarded and extraction was repeated on the sediment.

4. The second sediment (produced by re-extraction and centrifugation of the first sediment) was stirred with 1 liter of 10% NaCl and this suspension was allowed to stand, with occasional stirring, for 6 hr.

5. The suspension was centrifuged at 2500 rev/min for 20 min and the viscous, yellow supernatant fluid was strained through muslin to remove some of the coarser contaminating particles. The residue of this (third) centrifugation was extracted in the same manner.

6. The two extracts (from 5) were combined and clarified in a Sharples' centrifuge, for removal of additional cytoplasmic contaminants.

7. The nucleoprotein was then precipitated from the clarified extract by slow dilution of the extract with 3 volumes of water. The nucleoprotein rises to the surface as a viscous, coherent mass and was removed from the liquid by collecting it on muslin.

8. Nucleoprotein was purified by redissolving it in 10% NaCl followed by clarification and reprecipitation of the solution. This purification procedure was generally repeated two or three times. If more reprecipitations were performed, the nucleoprotein became gradually more difficult to collect and eventually failed to precipitate at all, due to a protein loss, which occurred at each precipitation step.

PEA EMBRYO NUCLEOHISTONE. Nucleohistone from pea embryos has been actively studied in recent years. The general preparative procedure of Bonner is as follows (31,32):

1. First the pea seeds are germinated by soaking them for 5 hours in running water (20 C) and then spraying them with water for 35 hr longer.

2. The embryonic axes (about 1 cm long) are separated from the cotyledons ("in a semiautomatic three-stage disassembly line") and are chilled and sterilized with diluted clorox.

3. Next the embryos are blended for 1 min with an equal weight of "grinding medium" (0.025 M sucrose, 0.05 M Tris, pH 8.0, 0.01 M β-mercaptoethanol, 1.0 mM $MgCl_2$) and filtered through cheesecloth and miracloth to remove cell wall fragments.

4. Starch and chromatin are sedimented at $4000 \times g$ for 30 min and the gelatinous chromatin (top) layer is scraped from the firm starch layer.

5. The chromatin is washed several times by resuspension and recentrifugation ($10,000 \times g$) in the grinding medium minus $MgCl_2$.

6. The final pellet is resuspended in 0.05 M Tris buffer (pH 8.0) yielding a solution of "crude chromatin," which contains about 95% of the DNA of the starting material.

7. Gradient centrifugation in 2 M sucrose containing 0.01 M β-mercaptoethanol is performed in order to remove contaminating "nonchromosomal protein" from the DNP. This yields "purified chromatin."

8. The DNP preparation is then dispersed in distilled water to a final concentration of less than 100 mg/ml, blended for 2 min at 115 v and stirred vigorously for 1 hour with a propeller-type stirrer.

9. This suspension is centrifuged for 1 hr at 10,000 × g; the clear supernatant fluid (DNP fraction) contains about 65% of the chromosomal DNA. Bonner and Huang (32) report a histone-to-DNA ratio of 1.3 to 1.0 in this supernatant liquid, whereas in the "crude chromatin" the ratio was 1.0 to 1.1 (31).

NUCLEOPROTEIN EXTRACTS FROM BACTERIA

Recently, Bhagavan and Atchley (33) have found basic proteins in extracts of *Bacillus subtilis*. The DNA-protein complex studied was precipitated from a protoplast extract by addition of 0.01 M $MgCl_2$; the complex was more soluble at higher and at lower $MgCl_2$ concentrations. Butler and Godson (34), working with the closely related organism *Bacillus megaterium*, also used a medium containing 0.01 M $MgCl_2$ in preparing the nuclear material. Because of its dependence on a narrow range of $MgCl_2$ concentration, it is doubtful whether the DNA-protein complex exists in the intact *Bacillus* cells. Magnesium-free (saline-versene) extracts of *Escherichia coli* (35) yielded a DNA-protein extract whose protein component was nonbasic and of the same over-all amino acid composition as total *E. coli* protein.

SUMMARY

We have attempted to make the methods of preparing nucleo-histones from animal and plant sources, and nucleoprotein extracts from bacteria, available to a broad group of investigators. We have concentrated on the isolation of material that is biochemically pure, and that is neither degraded nor denatured. In general, such material is most useful for physicochemical and biochemical studies and for subsequent isolation of histone. The literature on nucleohistone isolation from animal sources is much more extensive than the literature on plant preparations. Deoxynucleoproteins that have thus far been isolated from bacterial sources are of questionable significance. In this survey, the isolation of nucleohistone from calf thymus has been discussed in detail, as this tissue is a most convenient and reliable source. Isolation of nucleohistone from other sources has only been presented in summary form here; the investigator will therefore have to refer to the original article cited in order to use these other methods. It must be understood, in referring to most of the methods cited, that the established criteria for judging calf thymus nucleohistone have not always been applied to preparations from other sources. Although we are not, therefore, in a position to give unqualified approval to the use of these other methods, we feel that any general survey of the literature on nucleohistone isolation should include references to preparations from many sources.

REFERENCES

1. DOTY, P., and G. ZUBAY. 1956. J. Am. Chem. Soc. *78:* 6207.
2. ZUBAY, G., and P. DOTY. 1959. J. Mol. Biol. *1:* 1.
3. SWIFT, H. 1964. *In* J. Bonner and P. Ts'o, editors, The nucleohistones. Holden-Day, San Francisco. P. 169.
4. COMMERFORD, S. L., M. J. HUNTER, and J. L. ONCLEY. 1963. J. Biol. Chem. *238:* 2123.
5. MURRAY, K. 1965. Ann. Rev. Biochem. *34:* 209.
6. PHILLIPS, D. M. P. 1962. Prog. Biophys. Biophys. Chem. *12:* 211.
7. SPORN, M. B., T. WANKO, and W. DINGMAN. 1962. J. Cell. Biol. *15:* 109.
8. MAGGIO, R., P. SIEKEVITZ, and G. E. PALADE. 1963. J. Cell Biol. *18:* 267.
9. BUTLER, J. A. V., and P. F. DAVISON. 1957. Adv. Enzymol. *18:* 161.
10. SHOOTER, K. V., P. F. DAVISON, and J. A. V. BUTLER. 1954. Biochim. Biophys. Acta. *13:* 192.
11. CRAMPTON, C. F., R. LIPSHITZ, and E. CHARGAFF. 1954. J. Biol. Chem. *206:* 499.
12. CHARGAFF, E. 1956. *In* The nucleic acids. Academic Press, New York. Vol. II, p. 313.
13. HAMMARSTEN, E. 1924. Biochem. Z. *144:* 383.
14. MIRSKY, A. E., and A. W. POLLISTER. 1942. Proc. Nat. Acad. Sci. U.S. *28:* 344.
15. GAJDUSEK, D. C. 1950. Biochim. Biophys. Acta. *5:* 397.
16. STERN, K. G., G. GOLDSTEIN, and G. G. ALBAUM. 1951. J. Biol. Chem. *188:* 273.
17. BERNSTEIN, M. H., and D. MAZIA. 1953. Biochim. Biophys. Acta. *10:* 600.
18. MAVER, M. E., and A. E. GRECO. 1949. J. Biol. Chem. *181:* 853.
19. BAYLEY, P. M., B. N. PRESTON, and A. R. PEACOCKE. 1962. Biochim. Biophys. Acta. *55:* 943.
20. LLOYD, P. H., and A. R. PEACOCKE. 1963. Nature. *200:* 428.
21. ROTHERHAM, J., D. D. SCHOTTELIUS, J. L. IRVIN, and E. M. IRVIN. 1956. J. Biol. Chem. *223:* 817.
22. CRAMPTON, C. F., W. H. STEIN, and S. MOORE. 1957. J. Biol. Chem. *225:* 263.
23. HNILICA, L. S., and H. BUSCH. 1963. J. Biol. Chem. *238:* 918.
24. SMIT, J. A., and L. A. STOCKEN. 1964. Biochem. J. *91:* 155.
25. CREASEY, W. A., and L. A. STOCKEN. 1959. Biochem. J. *72:* 519.
26. VENDRELY, R., A. KNOBLOCH-MAZEN, and C. VENDRELY. 1960. *In* The cell nucleus. Faraday Society, Butterworths, London. P. 200.
27. SPORN, M. B., and C. W. DINGMAN. 1963. Science. *140:* 316.
28. DINGMAN, C. W., and M. B. SPORN. 1964. J. Biol. Chem. *239:* 3843.
29. MAZIA, D. 1954. Proc. Nat. Acad. Sci., Wash. *40:* 521.

30. STEDMAN, E., and E. STEDMAN. 1951. Phil. Trans. Royal Soc. London, Ser. B. *235:* 565.

31. HUANG, RU-CHIH C., and J. BONNER. 1962. Proc. Nat. Acad. Sci. U.S. *48:* 1216.

32. BONNER, J., and RU-CHIH C. HUANG. 1963. J. Mol. Biol. *6:* 169.

33. BHAGAVAN, N. V., and W. A. ATCHLEY. 1965. Biochemistry. *4:* 234.

34. BUTLER, J. A. V., and G. N. GODSON. 1963. Biochem. J. *88:* 176.

35. ZUBAY, G., and M. R. WATSON. 1959. J. Biophys. Biochem. Cytol. *5:* 51.

APPENDIX

Preparation and Properties

of sRNA† from Rabbit Liver

G. L. CANTONI AND H. H. RICHARDS

NATIONAL INSTITUTE OF MENTAL HEALTH

NATIONAL INSTITUTES OF HEALTH

BETHESDA, MARYLAND

sRNA has been prepared by phenol extraction of intact cells (1,14), by phenol extraction of the fraction of tissue homogenates not sedimentable after 1 hr at 100,000 $\times$ g, or of the "pH-5" fraction prepared therefrom (2,3), and by extraction of *Escherichia coli* with hot detergent (4). The sRNA obtained by the phenol-extraction procedures is partially and variably charged with amino acids, and additional treatment is usually required to remove them (1,5). Moreover, with mammalian tissues, phenol-extraction methods are not particularly suitable for large-scale operation.

Treatment with NaCl at 80 C. was used by Pain and Butler (6) and by Mihalyi *et al.* (7) to prepare RNA from rat liver and myosin.

We have developed a modification of this procedure for the preparation of sRNA from the pH-5 fraction of rabbit liver as detailed below.

White male rabbits were anesthetized with sodium nembutal (60 mg/kg/intraperitoneally) and killed by exsanguination. The livers were excised immediately and dropped in ice-cold Medium A (see ref. 8). The livers of two or three animals were homogenized in a Waring Blendor for 10 sec at top speed and then for 2 min at half-speed with three volumes of Medium A. Intact cells, cellular debris, and nuclei were removed by centrifugation at 2 C for 30 min at 19,000 rev/min in a Model-L Spinco centrifuge, using rotor No. 21.

† sRNA is equivalent to tRNA.

617

The supernatant fluid was carefully decanted through a glass-wool plug to remove floating fatty material and then centrifuged again for 120 min at 105,000 × g using rotor No. 30. The supernatant fluid was collected as above and diluted with two volumes of cold Medium B (see ref. 8). The pH of this solution was lowered to 5.2 by addition of ice-cold 1 N acetic acid. The pH was determined with external electrodes on a Beckman Model-G pH meter, standardized to pH 7.0 with ice-cold buffer, and with the temperature control turned all the way toward the lower temperatures.

After a few minutes at pH 5.2, the mixture was centrifuged at 4000 × g at 2 C. The supernatant fluid was discarded and the precipitate washed with approximately 50 ml of Medium B. After centrifugation at 15,000 × g in the cold, the precipitate was dissolved in 0.025 M NaCl in 0.025 M potassium phosphate buffer (pH 7.6) using approximately 25 ml/g of liver. This is the pH-5 enzyme fraction. To extract the sRNA from this preparation, two volumes of 15% NaCl in 0.025 M potassium phosphate buffer (pH 7.6) were added, the mixture was warmed with constant stirring to 90 C and kept at this temperature for 3 min. This step is conveniently performed on 200–400 ml of material, which may be accumulated by keeping the "pH-5 precipitate" at −20 C. Stainless steel beakers are advantageous in this step, as it is important to reach the specified temperature rapidly, i.e., within 3 min. The mixture was then cooled rapidly in ice to 10 C or lower and centrifuged for 10 min at 12,000 × g in the cold. Two volumes of ethanol, previously cooled at −20 C, were then added slowly, and with stirring, to the clear supernatant fluid, and the mixture was allowed to stand overnight in the cold room. The precipitate was collected by centrifugation, and suspended in 0.025 M NaCl in 0.025 M potassium phosphate buffer (pH 7.6) using 1 ml of this solution for each 6 ml of the "pH-5 enzyme" fraction. The resulting suspension was dialyzed 4 hr against NaCl in potassium phosphate buffer (pH 7.6) (each 0.025 M) and centrifuged for 1 hr at 105,000 × g to remove insoluble impurities.

After addition of 0.1 volume of 1.0 M potassium phosphate buffer (pH 7.6), saturated ammonium sulfate was added, with stirring, to 35% saturation. After 1 hr at 2 C, the solution was centrifuged (30 min at 19,000 × g) and the precipitate was collected by centrifugation and dissolved in a small volume of the NaCl-phosphate buffer described above. The resulting solution was dialyzed overnight against the same salt-buffer mixture. To remove traces of residual protein, including nucleases, the sRNA can be treated, without loss of activity, with phenol as described by Kirby (9).

The RNA solution thus obtained may be stored at −60 C and is stable for an indefinite period. The yield of sRNA is 50 mg/kg of liver.

CHEMICAL PROPERTIES OF
RABBIT-LIVER sRNA

The base composition of rabbit-liver sRNA is given in Table 1, together with data from the analysis of rabbit-liver microsomal RNA and sRNA from *E. coli* and yeast. It is noteworthy that with $(NH_4)_2SO_4$-purified rabbit-liver sRNA, the major, and sometimes the only, component of the nucleoside fraction is adenosine. With yeast sRNA, on the other hand, the amount of adenosine is variable and appears to bear a relation to the source of the yeast used for the sRNA preparation.

TABLE 1. *Nucleotide Composition of sRNA*

| | Rabbit Liver | | *E. coli* | Yeast |
	sRNA	Microsomal RNA	sRNA	sRNA[a]
		µmoles/73	µmoles total[b]	
Adenosine	0.71	0.18	0.71	0.46
Cytidine	0.04	0.07	0.11	0.44
Guanosine	<0.01	0.1	<0.05	<0.01
MeCMP	0.34	<0.01	0.48	0.24
CMP	19.62	22.41	21.48	17.80
AMP	11.73	12.29	12.36	13.78
MeAMP	0.44	<0.05	0.16	0.34
MeGMP	1.66	0.15	0.86	1.61
ΨUMP	3.06	1.06	1.72	3.28
GMP	22.01	23.38	21.60	18.86
UMP	11.21	11.85	11.35	14.31
pGMP	1.13	0.44	1.01	0.86
TMP	1.01	—	0.96	1.03

a Commercial baker's yeast.

b Yeast and *E. coli* sRNA (and presumably also mammalian sRNA) contain dihydro UMP, IMP and thio UMP. These components are not included in the total µmoles listed in this table.

Alkaline hydrolysis of sRNA from yeast grown in the laboratory and harvested during the logarithmic growth phase yields adenosine and cytidine in approximately equivalent amounts, whereas sRNA obtained from commercial baker's yeast often yields a considerable excess of cytidine (see page 624, this volume). The four major components appear in about the same amounts in the sRNA from *E. coli*, rabbit liver, or yeast. However, rabbit-liver sRNA and yeast sRNA contain a considerably larger fraction of the minor or "unusual" nucleotides than *E. coli* sRNA. This is thought to reflect the fact that both of these preparations are more homogeneous with respect to sRNA content than the sRNA obtained from *E. coli*. A comparison of the base composition of rabbit-liver sRNA, before and after the $(NH_4)_2SO_4$-purification step (18), supports this interpretation, since, as indicated by ultracentrifugation studies (10), the preparation before $(NH_4)_2SO_4$ fractionation contains an appreciable fraction of RNA with sedimentation properties different from those of sRNA.

EXTINCTION COEFFICIENT OF sRNA

The average of duplicate determinations is 23.0 ± 0.2 ml/mg/cm. From the known (11,12) nucleotide composition of this sRNA, the equivalent weight of the average nucleotide in the chain (Na salt) is found to be 345 g/mole (equivalent to 9.0% phosphorus in "Na sRNA"). Combining this figure with that for the specific absorbance, and assuming an average of one sRNA phosphorus per nucleotide, one predicts the absorbance per mole of phosphorus, ε_p, to be 7.9 ml/μmole/cm. Our experimentally determined value is 7.7 ± 0.2, which is in excellent agreement with this prediction and indicates that we are dealing with an essentially pure RNA preparation. In addition to normal experimental variation, the small difference between these values could also be due to some uncertainty in the magnitude of the Donnan-equilibrium effect.†

MOLECULAR WEIGHT

The molecular weight, or chain length, of the sRNA has been determined by a variety of techniques. The ultracentrifugal measurements yielded a value for the weight-average s/D of $(4.9 \pm 0.2) \cdot 10^{-7} sec^2/cm^2$.

† No analyses were performed to determine the amount of NaCl in the sRNA residue. The only information available on the salt distribution to be expected after dialysis concerns the Donnan equilibrium observed with polyphosphate solutions (13). From these results, the effective degree of ionization of the phosphates is only about 20%. Using this value to estimate the amount of salt inside the dialysis bags, one finds that the method of calculation used leads to about a 1% underestimation in the absorbancy. Because of the uncertainties in this estimation, it was not thought worthwhile to correct for such a small error. The agreement of the ε_p values, in fact, places a limit on this error.

If the $s_{20,w}$ for this concentration, obtained in a separate measurement is combined with this s/D value, D is found to be $(7.6 \pm 0.4) \cdot 10^{-7} cm^2/sec$, a result in excellent agreement with that of Tissieres (15). In agreement, then, with the results of other physical measurements (14–16) the weight-average molecular weight, calculated according to the Svedberg equation (17), is $23,000 \pm 1300$, which corresponds to a chain length of 68 ± 4 nucleotides. This value is also consistent with those estimated by chemical means.

Attempts have been made in this laboratory to verify this chain length by independent means (18) such as determination of end groups by measurements of the nucleoside liberated upon alkaline digestion, and determination of inorganic phosphate released on treatment with alkaline phosphatase from *E. coli* (19). In spite of the technical limitations which exist in the use of alkaline phosphatase for determining chain lengths, the calculated chain length determined (18) after 3 hr of incubation agrees quite closely with the results of the physical studies.

AMINO ACID-ACCEPTOR ACTIVITY

The amino acid-acceptor activity was determined as follows: Reaction mixtures contain 0.02 M potassium phosphate buffer, pH 7.6, 0.02 M in NaCl, 0.005 M ATP (sodium salt, neutralized), 0.013 M $MgCl_2$, 0.004 M reduced glutathione, 0.066 μmole/ml C^{12} amino acids (each of 19 other amino acids except the one being assayed), 0.066 μmole/ml C^{14} amino acid (specific activity, 4 μc/μmole), and 10 OD_{260} units/ml sRNA in a final volume of 0.38 ml. Assay tubes are incubated for 30 min at 37 C with suitable amounts of aminoacyl RNA synthetases, as contained in "pH-5 enzyme" from beef liver (18). Incubations are terminated by addition of 0.05 ml of 0.02 M C^{12} amino acid to each tube. Portions of the reaction mixture (0.1 ml) are spotted on paper discs, and the aminoacyl sRNA is precipitated with cold 10% trichloroacetic acid. The paper discs are then washed successively in 3% perchloric acid (3 times), ethanol (2 times), and ether (once), and then air-dried. The paper discs are then counted in a liquid scintillation counter using 5 ml of 0.4% PPO, 0.01% POPOP in toluene.

SPECTRUM OF ACCEPTOR ACTIVITY

The ability of sRNA to act as acceptor of 15 different activated amino acids was tested using "pH-5 beef-liver enzymes" (18) as a source of the aminoacyl RNA synthetases. The enzyme preparation was simultaneously assayed for aminoacyl RNA synthetases by means of the pyrophosphate-exchange assay. Results are summarized in Table 2.

It can be seen that the rabbit-liver sRNA exhibited acceptor activity for all of the 15 amino acids tested. By assuming that all 15 amino acids are independently bound (2,20) to separate amino acid-acceptor chains, and that all amino acid-acceptor chains have the same molecular weight (21), it may be calculated that the acceptor chains for the 15 amino acids account for 35% of the total RNA present. These calculations, however, are subject to some uncertainty. Thus, control experiments showed that between 0.1 and 0.15 μmole of free amino acids was formed under the condition of the experiment, probably through proteolysis. Each of the radioactive amino acids may therefore have been diluted during the experiment by unlabeled amino acid. This amount could be as high as 100%. This uncertainty about dilution makes precise determination of the distribution of amino acid specific sRNAs impossible.

Addition of CTP was without effect on the acceptor activity of sRNA, using either partially purified proline or valine sRNA syn-

TABLE 2.   *Spectrum of Amino Acid-Acceptor Activity of Rabbit-Liver sRNA*

	mμmoles of amino acid/535 OD native sRNA[a, b]
Proline	25.8
Methionine	16.3
Tryptophane	7.0
Glycine	21.5
Lysine	19.3
Glutamine	12.0
Isoleucine	59.6
Valine	29.0
Tyrosine	8.0
Alanine	34.3
Leucine	54.2
Histidine	9.0
Threonine	13.0
Phenylalanine	17.6
Serine	43.2
Total	369.8

a 1.0 OD (absorbancy unit) native sRNA = 1.19 OD hydrolyzed sRNA.

b 535 OD is the absorption of 1 μmole of sRNA, i.e., 68 μmoles of nucleotides and 1 μmole of end group.

thetases or the crude pH-5 fraction, and [^{14}C] proline, [^{14}C] valine, or a mixture of ^{14}C-labeled amino acids from Chlorella protein hydrolyzate. As discussed above, the base-analysis studies indicate that adenosine accounts for 60–90% of the nucleoside end of our sRNA preparations and that the remainder is cytidine.

REFERENCES

1. MONIER, R., M. L. STEPHENSON, and P. C. ZAMECNIK. 1959. Biochim. Biophys. Acta. *43:* 1.

2. HOAGLAND, M. B., M. L. STEPHENSON, J. F. SCOTT, L. I. HECHT, and P. C. ZAMECNIK. 1958. J. Biol. Chem. *231:* 241.

3. ALLEN, E. H., E. GLASSMAN, E. CORDES, and R. S. SCHWEET. 1960. J. Biol. Chem. *235:* 1068.

4. OFENGAND, E. J., M. DIECKMANN, and P. BERG. 1961. J. Biol. Chem. *236:* 1741.

5. LIPMANN, F., W. C. HÜLSMANN, G. HARTMANN, H. G. BOMAN, and G. ACS. 1959. J. Cell Comp. Physiol. *54:* 75.

6. PAIN, R. H., and J. A. BUTLER. 1957. Biochem. J. *66:* 298.

7. MIHALYI, E., D. F. BRADLEY, and M. I. KNOLLER. 1957. J. Am. Chem. Soc. *79:* 6387.

8. KELLER, E. B., and P. C. ZAMECNIK. 1956. J. Biol. Chem. *221:* 45.

9. KIRBY, K. S. 1956. Biochem. J. 405.

10. LUBORSKY, S. W., and G. L. CANTONI. 1962. Biochim. Biophys. Acta. *61:* 481.

11. CANTONI, G. L. 1962. Acides Ribonucleiques et Polyphosphates. Editions DU Centre National De La Recherche Scientifique, Paris, France, No. 106, pp. 201–216.

12. ARCHIBALD, W. J. 1947. J. Phys. Chem. *51:* 1204.

13. STRAUSS, U. P., and P. ANDER. 1958. J. Am. Chem. Soc. *80:* 6494.

14. ZUBAY, G. This volume, p. 455.

15. TISSIERES, A. 1959. J. Mol. Biol. *1:* 365.

16. OSAWA, S. 1960. Biochim. Biophys. Acta. *43:* 110.

17. SVEDBERG, T., and K. O. PEDERSEN. 1940. The Ultracentrifuge, Part I. The Clarendon Press, Oxford, Chap. B.

18. CANTONI, G. L., H. V. GELBOIN, S. W. LUBORSKY, H. H. RICHARDS, and M. F. SINGER. 1962. Biochim. Biophys. Acta. *61:* 354.

19. GAREN, A., and C. LEVINTHAL. 1960. Biochim. Biophys. Acta. *38:* 470.

20. BERG, P., and E. J. OFENGAND. 1958. Proc. Natl. Acad. Sci. U.S. *44:* 78.

21. KLEE, W. A., and G. L. CANTONI. 1960. Proc. Natl. Acad. Sci. U.S. *46:* 322.

Preparation of sRNA†

from Yeast

G. L. CANTONI AND H. H. RICHARDS
NATIONAL INSTITUTE OF MENTAL HEALTH
NATIONAL INSTITUTES OF HEALTH
BETHESDA, MARYLAND

The principal function of sRNA is to transfer activated amino acid from the cell cytoplasm to the growing peptide chains in the ribosomes. At least two steps can be recognized in the transfer function. The first step, amino acid activation, takes place in the soluble portion of the cell; whereas the second step, transfer of the activated amino acid to the growing polypeptide chain, is ribosomal-bound.

It is well established that there are as many different molecular species of sRNA as there are amino acids, and in fact, there is increasing evidence that there are multiple species of sRNA for a single amino acid just as there are multiple code words for the same amino acid.

The basis of the biological specificity of the different amino acid specific species of sRNA resides in their nucleotide sequence and in the secondary structure which is generated by this sequence. While the elucidation of the primary sequence of alanine sRNA from yeast (1) is a landmark in nucleic acid research, it will also serve to stimulate further interest in the detailed study of the sequence and structure of other amino acid specific sRNAs from yeast and other organisms.

At the present time, yeast is the most convenient source from which to prepare average sRNA‡ in quantities large enough to serve as start-

---

† sRNA is equivalent to tRNA.

‡ Average sRNA denotes a preparation of sRNA containing all or most amino acid specific sRNAs.

TABLE 1. *Spectrum of Amino Acid-Acceptor Activity of Yeast sRNA*

	mμmoles incorporated	
	per OD	per 535 OD
Alanine	.011	5.7
Aspartic	.041	21.9
Arginine	.067	35.8
Glycine	.009	4.8
Glutamic	.020	10.7
Histidine	.019	10.2
Isoleucine	.041	21.7
Leucine	.076	40.7
Lysine	.055	29.4
Methionine	.035	18.7
Phenylalanine	.035	18.7
Proline	.013	6.8
Serine	.083	44.4
Threonine	.065	34.8
Tyrosine	.033	17.7
Valine	.065	34.8
Total	0.668	356.8

ing material for the preparation of amino acid specific sRNAs in gram quantities. Average sRNA obtained from yeast compares with similar materials prepared from *Escherichia coli* or rabbit liver as far as the amino acid-acceptor function is concerned when such function is assayed with relatively crude homologous amino acid sRNA synthetases (Table 1). However, a large (but variable) fraction of the total yeast sRNA lacks the terminal adenosine, so that yeast sRNA cannot be fully charged by highly purified amino acid sRNA synthetases from which the sRNA CTP, ATP pyrophosphorylase has been removed during purification (2).

The procedure to be described for the preparation of sRNA from yeast is based upon the procedure of Monier, Stephenson, and Zamecnik (3) as modified by Holley *et al.* (4). In this procedure DNA and the bulk of cellular RNA and DNA are removed together with non-nucleic acid material in the first step (phenol extraction). Amino acids and small oligopeptides attached to sRNA are removed in the alkali treatment.† Chromatography on DEAE effectively removes contaminating

---

† All peptides may not be removed by this step as the ester linkage between sRNA and the COOH group of a peptide is considerably more stable than the corresponding linkage with a single amino acid.

polysaccharides, which may interfere with subsequent fractionation of amino acid specific sRNAs. Treatment with EDTA is necessary to remove divalent cation contaminants.

ISOLATION PROCEDURE

Brewer's yeast cream harvested during the logarithmic growth phase and thoroughly washed free of molasses can be obtained through commercial sources. (Fresh pressed baker's yeast can also be used and may be obtained from local bakeries.)

30 liters of yeast cream are mixed with 45 liters of 90% liquid phenol (U.S. Pharmacopea) in a large stainless steel vat mounted on wheels and supplied with an outflow valve at the bottom; the mixture is gently stirred at room temperature for 2–3 hr. The vat is rolled into a cold room and kept there overnight. Next day, approximately $1/5$ of the mixture is removed from the bottom through the outflow valve and discarded. This fraction contains the heavier portion of the sediment consisting of unbroken cell, cell debris, etc. The remaining $4/5$ of the phenol-water mixture is centrifuged in the cold in an International centrifuge #3, at top speed for 15 min, to separate the phenol from the aqueous phase. Glass or preferably polyethylene bottles are used. The upper phase is removed by means of a syphon and collected. A large interphase material is collected separately in a large separatory funnel, and additional quantities of upper phase can be recovered from it.

0.1 volume of 1 M potassium acetate buffer, pH 5.0, and $2\frac{1}{2}$ volumes of precooled 95% ethanol are added to the aqueous phase. The mixture is stirred to insure complete mixing and left overnight in the cold room. The clear supernatant ($9/10$ of the volume) may then be siphoned off and the precipitate collected from the remainder of the mixture by centrifugation.

The precipitate is resuspended in 0.1 M Tris buffer, pH 7.5, using approximately 1 liter per 30 liters of yeast cream. After two extractions with an equal volume of anaesthesia ether the sRNA is reprecipitated by addition of 3 volumes of ethanol plus 0.1 volume of 1 M potassium acetate, buffer pH 5.0. The precipitate is collected by centrifugation in the cold.

The paste is suspended in cold distilled H_2O (1200 ml are used for 150 g of paste). The mixture is stirred mechanically for 15–30 min and clarified by centrifugation at 2000 rev/min. Difficulties may be experienced in solubilizing the sRNA at this step if the ethanol content is too high. This may be remedied by use of larger volumes of distilled water or by brief dialysis.

The pH of the solution is adjusted to 10 by careful addition of 3 N KOH (ca 14–16 ml) at room temperature with efficient mechanical stirring. Next, the solution is incubated 30 min at 37 C, then centrifuged to remove the precipitate formed during the pH adjustment. The pH is then brought to 7.6 by slow addition of 1 N HCl. Both of these pH adjustments are carried out with the aid of glass electrodes.

Acid-washed Norite[†] is added to the solution, 1 mg/10.0 OD_{260} units calculated in Step 1, and the mixture is stirred 20 min, then filtered through double sheets of Whatman #5. From the filtrate, which should be clear and almost colorless, sRNA is precipitated as above by addition of 2.5 volumes of ETOH and 0.1 volume of K acetate, pH 5.

The precipitate from the Norite step is dissolved in 0.1 M Tris buffer, pH 7.5, containing 0.0015 M $MgCl_2$ and dialyzed 14 hours against 100 volumes of the same buffer with several changes. A 90% solution is made from distilled phenol and an equal volume is added to the sRNA. The mixture is shaken gently for 30 min at room temperature, then centrifuged for 15 min at 2500 rev/min in an International centrifuge. The upper phase containing the sRNA is siphoned off and shaken twice with an equal volume of anaesthesia ether. The sRNA is precipitated with 2.5 volumes of ethyl alcohol and $\frac{1}{10}$ volume of 20% potassium acetate, pH 5. The collected precipitate is dissolved in 0.1 M Tris buffer, pH 7.5, containing 0.0015 M $MgCl_2$ and dialyzed as above. All operations are carried out at 3–4 C except where specified.

A fraction of the dialyzed sRNA containing 1.0 million OD_{260} units is applied to an 11- × 85-cm column of DEAE previously equilibrated with 0.1 M Tris buffer, pH 7.5, containing 0.0015 M $MgCl_2$. The column is washed with 20 liters of 0.1 M Tris buffer, pH 7.5, containing 0.0015 M $MgCl_2$ and 0.25 M NaCl, and then eluted with 14 liters of a linear gradient 0.1 M Tris buffer, pH 7.5, 0.0015 M $MgCl_2$, and NaCl concentration from 0.25 M to 1.0 M. The flow rate is approximately 800 ml/hr and the eluate is collected in 500 ml fractions. The $OD_{280/260}$ ratio of each fraction is checked, and those fractions where the ratio is 0.49 are pooled and precipitated as before with ethanol and potassium acetate. The collected precipitate is dissolved in 0.1 M Tris buffer, pH 7.5, containing 0.0015 M $MgCl_2$. The recovery should be approximately 80%.

A fraction of sRNA containing 1 million OD_{260} units is dialyzed 4 hr at room temperature against 32 liters of 0.2 M EDTA, neutralized with Tris. The dialysis is continued at 4 C against 0.001 M EDTA in 0.05 M Tris buffer, pH 7.0, also containing 0.01 M NaCl, and 0.001 M $MgCl_2$. The sRNA is stored frozen and is stable indefinitely.

---

† Add 5 volumes of concentrated HCl to Fischer Norite-A, stir, and allow to stand overnight. Decant and wash twice with H_2O, once with concentrated NH_4OH until neutral, and finally ethanol. Air dry.

Amino Acid-Acceptor Activity

The amino acid-acceptor activity of yeast sRNA can be determined exactly as described for rabbit liver sRNA except that crude yeast amino acid synthetases are used. The enzyme preparation is obtained as follows:

A 100-g portion of pressed baker's yeast (Fleischmann's) is homogenized with 300 g of glass beads, 160 mg of reduced glutathione, 0.4 ml of n-octyl alcohol, and 100 ml of buffer containing 0.016 M K_2HPO_4, 0.004 M KH_2PO_4, and 0.002 M mg SO_4 (3). Homogenization is carried out in a Waring Blendor cooled with ice at the speed obtained by connection to a powerstat set at 90 v. In order to keep the temperature below 15 C during the procedure, homogenization is carried out for five intervals of 3 min each separated by periods of additional cooling on ice (2). After homogenization an additional 200 ml of buffer is added, and the suspension is mixed, allowed to settle, and decanted. The extract is centrifuged for 60 min at 78,000 × g in a Spinco Model L ultracentrifuge, and the supernatant is dialyzed several hours against 30 volumes of buffer containing 0.016 M K_2HPO_4, 0.004 M K_2HPO_4, 0.0001 M EDTA, and 0.0002 glutathione. The final protein concentration is approximately 20 mg/ml and the yield 4.0 g.

Spectrum of Amino Acid-Acceptor Activity

The ability of yeast sRNA to act as acceptor was tested as described for rabbit-liver sRNA (see page 621, this volume). The results are summarized in Table 1, which may be compared with Table 2, this volume, page 622.

REFERENCES

1. HOLLEY, R. W., J. APGAR, G. A. EVERETT, J. T. MADISON, M. MARQUISEE, S. H. MERRILL, J. R. PENSWICK, and A. ZAMIR. 1965. Science. *147:* 1462.
2. MAKMAN, M. H., and G. L. CANTONI. 1965. Biochemistry. *4:* 1434.
3. MONIER, R., M. L. STEPHENSON, and P. C. ZAMECNIK. 1960. Biochim. Biophys. Acta. *43:* 1.
4. HOLLEY, R. W., J. APGAR, B. P. DOCTOR, J. FARROW, M. A. MARINI, and S. H. MERRILL. 1961. J. Biol. Chem. *236:* 200.

INDEXES